CONTENTS

Introduction

Exotic spices have been used for centuries to liven up the daily staples of rice, noodles and bread with sauce dishes known as curries. Pungent spices and scented flavourings contribute magical tastes to curry dishes all over the world, and this makes preparing and eating sensational curries an exciting experience. Carefully prepared blends of such exotic spices as cardamom and coriander, saffron and turmeric, provide the most mouthwatering tastes, flavours and aromas. Discover just how easy it is to make authentic dishes in this guide to the great curries of the world.

The key to a successful curry lies in the art of blending spices and herbs, rather than sophisticated cooking techniques. Recipes have traditionally been handed down from one generation to another. Far from being a disadvantage, this has actually helped to fire the imagination of the creative cook, and many dishes that first started out as experiments in spice blends and flavour combinations have now become world classics.

India has long been known as the spice bowl of the world, and South-east Asia, too, occupies its own important place in the history of the spice trade. The use of premium quality spices in these sun-drenched, monsoon-fed lands was an established way of life long before traders and merchants, among them Arabs, English, Dutch, Portuguese and Spanish, came to the area, lured by the value of these exotic ingredients.

In India, the word curry refers to a sauce or gravy used as an accompaniment to moisten grains of *chawal* (rice) or to make *rotis* (bread) more enjoyable. The word curry is generally believed to be an anglicized version of the south Indian word *kaari*, a Tamil word meaning sauce. It is thought that when the British were active in this area, the spelling was somehow changed to curry. Other theories suggest that the word *cury* has existed in English in the context of cooking since the 14th century, and that it was originally derived from the French verb *cuire* (to cook).

Besides offering fabulous flavours, cooking curry style is extremely healthy. The emphasis is firmly on freshness, with a wide range of meats, fish and shellfish, vegetables and salads, together with wheat or rice as the staple dish. Meat and fish are served in small quantities, surrounded by inviting little side dishes, such as pickles, chutneys, salads and sambals, flavoured with fresh herbs and chillies, yogurt or soy sauce, and used as seasonings. Rice or breads such as naan, chapatis and parathas in India and rice or noodles in South-east Asia form the staple diet and are eaten daily.

Many of the ingredients used in these dishes are known for their medicinal properties. For example, there is strong evidence that garlic and fresh root ginger, two of the most essential ingredients in curries, contain properties that can help to combat heart diseases and stomach ulcers respectively.

Herbs are added to a curry dish during the cooking time to add flavour and aroma, but spices, including those used mainly for taste or for aroma, perform a more complex role. The exquisite flavour of cardamom pods, the warmth of cumin, the sweet, mellow taste of coriander, the woody aroma of ginger and fiery chillies are characteristic flavours, adding zest and flavour to countless curries. The flavour of a dish will vary according to the sequence in which the spices are added and the length of time each spice is cooked.

The striking resemblance in many cooking and serving styles in India and South-east Asia is reflected in their ingredients. The coconut-based curries of south India strongly resemble those of South-east Asia in taste, aroma and flavour; curries from these regions are distinguished by the curry leaves used in south Indian curries and the kaffir lime leaves used in South-east Asia.

The Indian commercial community, who emigrated to South-east Asia, added their own identity to local cuisines and customs, and this has helped to merge culinary practices. The Indian influence is strongest in Malaysia, while the cuisines of Vietnam and the islands of the Philippines have profound French and Spanish legacies. Only Thailand has remained free from colonial rule.

In India, too, foreign powers have introduced cooking styles that are still in practice today. The north continues to be dominated by Mogul cuisine, while the east has tribal and Anglo-Indian styles. In the south, Syrian Jews and French traders contributed techniques, and western India came under the influence of the Portuguese and the Persians (Parsis). The result is a multi-dimensional, colourful cuisine of richness and depth, with a repertoire of recipes that is virtually unmatched anywhere else in the world.

Culinary skills and expertise from around the world have their basis in the traditional cooking of India and South-east Asia, and the best of the resulting dishes are featured in this wonderful collection. The aim of this volume is to offer traditional curry recipes with authentic flavours and uncomplicated preparation and cooking methods, encouraging even novice cooks to get to know the delights of cooking hot and spicy curries.

INDEX

PLANNING a CURRY MEAL

When planning your menu, always bear in mind that an everyday curry meal features only three items: the main dish, a side dish and a staple, which would be rice or bread. Chutneys, salads and raitas can also be served to add a tangy taste.

Planning the menu

When deciding which foods to serve, consider the main dish. Is it going to be highly spiced, such as a vindaloo or a bhuna? Or will it have subtle flavours, such as a korma or a pasanda? A little careful planning will ensure that the flavours of the dishes complement, rather than compete with, each other. Choose the side dish according to the strength of the main one. A lightly spiced

Below: There is no rigid structure to a curry meal, but there should always be a good balance of dry and moist dishes.

side dish is more enjoyable when the main dish is spicier. This does not apply in reverse, however, and a side dish with complex spicing is not the ideal accompaniment to a mild main dish.

Dishes with a drier consistency are generally accompanied by a vegetable curry or a lentil dish. Biryanis, pilaus and pulaos are traditionally served with a simple raita, although they are more usually served with a vegetable curry in restaurants in the West.

How to serve

A curry meal is not served as separate courses, with an appetizer, followed by a main dish and one or two side dishes. Although the meal will usually consist of several dishes, all complement each other and are brought to the table at the same time, with diners helping themselves to each dish in any order.

USEFUL STANDBYS

• Use bottled ginger and garlic purées (paste) rather than peeling and chopping the fresh spices.
• Canned chopped tomatoes can be used instead of fresh tomatoes, although you may need to increase the quantities of souring agent, salt and chilli to compensate for the depleted flavour.
• Canned or packet creamed coconut is a convenient replacement for fresh coconut. Use according to the manufacturer's instructions.

For entertaining and more lavish occasions, you can add other dishes to the standard three-dish menu. One or two dry meat dishes, such as a kabab or tandoori chicken, in addition

NOODLES with CHICKEN, PRAWNS and HAM

The cuisine of the Philippines is a harmonious blend of Malay, Chinese and Spanish influences. This recipe has Chinese origins, and is known in Malaysia as pansit guisado. Any kind of meat can be cooked with the prawns.

SERVES 4–6

285g/10oz dried egg noodles
15ml/1 tbsp vegetable oil
1 onion, chopped
1 garlic clove, crushed
2.5cm/1 in piece fresh root ginger, grated
50g/2oz canned water chestnuts, drained
   and sliced
15ml/1 tbsp light soy sauce
30ml/2 tbsp fish sauce or chicken stock
175g/6oz cooked chicken breast, sliced
150g/5oz cooked ham, thickly sliced, cut
   into short fingers
225g/8oz peeled, cooked prawn
   (shrimp) tails
175g/6oz/¾ cup beansprouts
200g/7oz canned baby corn, drained
2 limes, cut into wedges, and 1 small
   bunch fresh coriander (cilantro),
   shredded, to garnish

1 Soak the egg noodles in a large bowl of water, and cook them according to the instructions on the packet. Drain the noodles and set aside.

2 Meanwhile, in a wok or large pan, fry the onion, garlic and ginger until soft. Add the water chestnuts, soy sauce and fish sauce or chicken stock, and the chicken and ham and prawn tails.

3 Add the noodles, beansprouts and corn. Stir-fry for 6–8 minutes. Garnish with the lime wedges and shredded coriander. Serve immediately.

COOK'S TIP
Egg noodles can be prepared in advance. Cook them up to 24 hours before they are needed, and keep them in a large bowl of cold water.

to some chutneys, pickles, raitas and poppadums, with a dessert to follow, can turn an ordinary family meal into dinner-party fare.

Desserts

A meal will usually end with fresh fruit, rather than elaborate or cooked desserts. Fruits can be served with real flair, however, and are often combined with other ingredients to create imaginative and exciting flavours. Choose one or two exotic fruits, such as papaya, pomegranate or star fruit, and combine them with everyday fruits in a fruit salad. Serve with Greek (US strained plain) yogurt flavoured with rose water and a little ground cardamom.

Sweets (candies) are quite heavy and are served as a snack with tea and coffee, in the same way as cakes and biscuits (cookies) are eaten in the West.

COOKING FOR A PARTY

It is a good idea to cook the curry dishes a day ahead of the party, storing them in the refrigerator until you are ready to reheat them. Accompanying dhal dishes can also be prepared 24 hours in advance, although the seasonings should not be added until just before serving. You can prepare vegetables in advance, but do not cook them more than a few hours ahead. Likewise, you can prepare ingredients for raitas a day ahead, but do not assemble them until a few hours before they are needed; the yogurt for raitas should always be fresh. Pickles and chutneys will benefit from advance preparation, but follow individual recipes for timing guides, as some will deteriorate more quickly than others. The bread dough for rotis can be made the day before. The rotis can be made 2 hours before you plan to serve them. Spread them with butter and wrap in foil to keep warm, then set them aside; reheat in the oven before serving.

Freezing curries

In today's busy world, it is not always possible to serve a meal while it is still sizzling in the pan. If you are entertaining, you may prefer to cook the curry in advance to save yourself time on the day, or you may like to cook a larger quantity than you will need and freeze some for another meal; you may even have leftovers.

Spicy food is ideal for freezing as the flavours seem to improve when the food is thawed and reheated. Most of the spices used in cooking curries have natural preservative qualities, as does the acid in souring agents. However, you should bear in mind the following factors if cooking specifically for the freezer:
• Leave the food slightly underdone.
• Cool the food rapidly. The best way to do this is to tip it into a large tray (a large roasting pan is ideal) and leave it in a cool place.
• Once the food has cooled completely, spoon it into plastic containers, then label and chill it in the refrigerator for a couple of hours, before transferring it to the freezer. The food will keep in the freezer for 6–8 months, depending on the star rating of your freezer.

Food that you did not plan to freeze, such as leftovers, should not be kept in the freezer for longer than 2–3 months, again, depending on the efficiency of your freezer. Meat and poultry curries freeze very successfully, as do curries made from vegetables, lentils and pulses. Fish curries can be frozen, but they are generally less successful as changes in the water balance may damage the more delicate texture of cooked fish.

Thawing and reheating

It is important to thaw frozen food thoroughly and slowly. Leave it in the refrigerator for 18–24 hours before reheating. After reheating, always make sure the food is piping hot before serving. These steps are crucial in order to ensure that any potentially harmful bacteria are destroyed. If you have a temperature probe, check that the reheated food is at least 85°C/185°F right the way through before serving.

REHEATING LEFTOVERS

This method will make leftover food that has been frozen taste really fresh. The method can also be used to reheat food that has been stored for a day or two in the refrigerator.

Heat about 10ml/2 tsp vegetable oil in a wok, karahi or large pan over a medium heat. Add up to 1.5ml/¼ tsp garam masala (depending on the quantity of food), and allow to bubble gently for 10–15 seconds. Add the thawed food to the pan and increase the heat to high. Let the food bubble or sizzle in the pan until it is heated through, stirring from time to time to make sure the heat is well distributed. Add a little water if the food looks particularly dry. Stir in 15ml/1 tbsp chopped fresh coriander (cilantro). Remove from the heat, transfer to a warmed platter and serve immediately.

A certain amount of water separation is to be expected as a defrosted dish thaws out. The dish will return to its normal consistency when it is reheated, as the water will be reabsorbed by the meat or vegetables.

Thawed food can be reheated in the microwave or in a covered casserole on the stove top. If using a microwave, cover the food with microwave cling film (plastic wrap). Stir the food from time to time as it is heated, to ensure the heat passes right the way through. You may need to add a small amount of water when reheating, to ensure that the dish does not dry out.

COURGETTES with NOODLES

Any vegetable from the same family as courgette or squash can be used in this Indonesian recipe, which is known as oseng oseng. *It is very similar to a dish enjoyed in Malaysia, and there are strong links between the cuisines of these two neighbouring countries.*

SERVES 4–6

450g/1lb courgettes (zucchini)
1 onion, finely sliced
1 garlic clove, finely chopped
30ml/2 tbsp vegetable oil
2.5ml/½ tsp ground turmeric
2 tomatoes, chopped
45ml/3 tbsp water
115g/4oz peeled, cooked prawns (shrimp)
25g/1oz cellophane noodles
salt

COOK'S TIP
Keep an eye on the time as cellophane noodles soften very quickly.

1 Use a potato peeler to cut thin strips from the outside of each courgette. Cut the courgettes into neat slices, then set aside. Fry the onion and garlic in hot oil in a pan; do not allow to brown.

2 Add the turmeric, courgette slices, chopped tomatoes, water and the cooked prawns.

3 Put the noodles in a large pan and pour over enough boiling water to cover. Leave the noodles to soak for a minute and then drain. Cut the noodles into 5cm/2in lengths and then add them to the vegetables.

4 Cover the pan with a lid and allow everything to cook in its own steam for 2–3 minutes. Toss well together. Season the noodles with salt to taste, and transfer to a warmed serving bowl.

NORTH INDIA

The cuisine of northern India has been heavily influenced by a great

many foreign settlers, traders and pilgrims. The most notable of these

were the Moguls, who added Mughlai food and a selection of exotic

fruit and nuts to the established traditions of Kashmir and Punjab.

CRISPY FRIED RICE VERMICELLI

Mee krob is usually served at celebration meals. It is a crisp tangle of fried rice vermicelli, with minced pork, prawns, dried shrimp and beansprouts, tossed in a piquant sweet-and-sour sauce and garnished with strips of omelette.

SERVES 4–6

vegetable oil, for frying
175g/6oz rice vermicelli
15ml/1 tbsp chopped garlic
4–6 dried chillies, seeded and chopped
30ml/2 tbsp chopped shallot
15ml/1 tbsp dried shrimps, rinsed
115g/4oz minced (ground) pork
115g/4oz peeled, raw prawns (shrimp),
   chopped
30ml/2 tbsp brown bean sauce
30ml/2 tbsp rice wine vinegar
45ml/3 tbsp fish sauce
75g/3oz palm sugar or light brown sugar
30ml/2 tbsp tamarind or lime juice
115g/4oz/½ cup beansprouts
salt and ground black pepper

For the garnish
2 spring onions (scallions), shredded
30ml/2 tbsp fresh coriander (cilantro)
   sprigs
2 heads pickled garlic (optional)
2-egg omelette, rolled and sliced
2 fresh red chillies, chopped

4 To the same pan, add the brown bean sauce, vinegar, fish sauce and palm sugar or brown sugar. Bring to a gentle boil, stir to dissolve the sugar and cook until thick and syrupy.

5 Add the tamarind or lime juice and adjust the seasoning. It should be sweet, sour and salty.

6 Reduce the heat. Add the pork and prawn mixture and the beansprouts to the sauce; stir to mix.

7 Add the rice noodles and toss gently to coat them with the sauce. Transfer the noodles to a platter. Garnish with spring onions, coriander leaves, pickled garlic, omelette strips and red chillies.

1 Heat the oil in a wok or large pan. Cut the vermicelli into handfuls about 7.5cm/3in long, and deep-fry until they puff up. Remove. Drain on kitchen paper.

2 Leave 30ml/2 tbsp of the hot oil in the pan. Add the garlic, chillies, shallot and shrimps and fry for 2–3 minutes.

3 Add the pork and stir-fry for about 3–4 minutes, until it is no longer pink. Add the prawns and fry for 2 minutes. Remove the mixture and set aside.

KASHMIRI CHICKEN CURRY

Surrounded by the snow-capped Himalayas, Kashmir is popularly known as the "Switzerland of the East". The state is also renowned for its rich culinary heritage, and this aromatic dish is one of the simplest among the region's repertoire.

2 Rub the chicken pieces with the marinade and allow to rest in a cool place for a further 2 hours, or in the refrigerator overnight. Bring to room temperature before cooking.

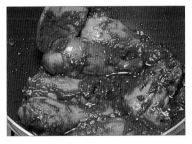

3 Heat the oil in a wok, karahi or large pan and fry half the ginger and all the garlic until golden. Add the chicken and fry until both sides are sealed. Cover and cook until the chicken is tender, and the oil has separated from the sauce.

SERVES 4–6

20ml/4 tsp Kashmiri masala paste
60ml/4 tbsp tomato ketchup
5ml/1 tsp Worcestershire sauce
5ml/1 tsp five-spice powder
5ml/1 tsp granulated sugar
8 chicken joints, skinned
45ml/3 tbsp vegetable oil
5cm/2in piece fresh root ginger, finely
    shredded
4 garlic cloves, crushed
juice of 1 lemon
15ml/1 tbsp coriander (cilantro) leaves,
    finely chopped
salt

1 To make the marinade, mix the masala paste, tomato ketchup, Worcestershire sauce, five-spice powder, salt and sugar. Allow the mixture to rest in a warm place until the sugar has dissolved.

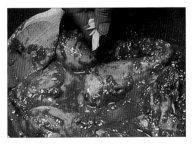

4 Sprinkle the chicken with the lemon juice, remaining ginger and chopped coriander leaves, and mix in well. Serve hot. Plain boiled rice would make a good accompaniment.

MIXED MEAT FRIED NOODLES with PRAWNS

This fried noodle dish, known as bamie goreng, *is wonderfully accommodating. To the basic recipe you can add other vegetables, such as mushrooms, tiny pieces of chayote, broccoli, leeks or beansprouts. As with fried rice, you can use whatever you have to hand.*

SERVES 6–8

450g/1lb dried egg noodles
115g/4oz chicken breast fillets, skinned
115g/4oz pork fillet
115g/4oz calf's liver (optional)
2 eggs, beaten
90ml/6 tbsp vegetable oil
25g/1oz butter or margarine
2 garlic cloves, crushed
115g/4oz peeled, cooked prawns
    (shrimp)
115g/4oz spinach or Chinese leaves
    (Chinese cabbage)
2 celery sticks, finely sliced
4 spring onions (scallions), shredded
about 60ml/4 tbsp chicken stock
dark soy sauce and light soy sauce
salt and ground black pepper
deep-fried onions and celery leaves,
    to garnish (optional)

1 Cook the noodles in salted, boiling water for 3–4 minutes. Drain, rinse with cold water and drain again. Set aside until required.

2 Finely slice the chicken, pork fillet and calf's liver, if using.

3 Season the eggs. Heat 5ml/1 tsp oil with the butter or margarine in a small pan until melted and then stir in the eggs and keep stirring until scrambled. Set them aside.

4 Heat the remaining oil in a wok or large pan and fry the garlic with the chicken, pork and liver, if using, for 2–3 minutes, until they change colour. Add the prawns, spinach or Chinese leaves, celery and spring onions, tossing well.

5 Add the cooked, drained noodles and toss well again so that all the ingredients are well mixed. Add enough stock just to moisten, and dark and light soy sauce to taste. Stir in the scrambled eggs. Garnish the dish with deep-fried onions and celery leaves.

COOK'S TIP
When choosing ingredients for this dish, bear in mind the need to achieve a balance of colour, flavour and texture.

TANDOORI CHICKEN

Punjab, in northern India, is the home of tandoori food. The tandoor, or clay oven, originated in Egypt and found its way into India with the Moguls. It is probably the most versatile oven in the world, capable of roasting, grilling and baking all at the same time.

SERVES 4–6

1.3kg/3lb oven-ready chicken
250ml/8fl oz/1 cup natural (plain)
   yogurt, beaten
60ml/4 tbsp tandoori masala paste
75g/3oz/2 tbsp ghee or vegetable oil
salt
lemon slice and onion rings, to garnish
lettuce, to serve

1 Using a small, sharp knife or scissors, remove the skin from the chicken and trim off any excess fat. Using a fork, prick the flesh at random.

2 Cut the chicken in half down the centre and through the breast. Cut each piece in half again. Make a few deep gashes diagonally into the flesh.

3 Mix the yogurt with the masala paste and season with salt. Spread the chicken with the yogurt mixture, spreading some into the gashes. Leave to marinate in a cool place for at least 2 hours, or in the refrigerator overnight.

4 Preheat the oven to 240°C/475°F/ Gas 9. Place the chicken quarters on a wire rack in a deep baking tray. Spread the chicken with any excess marinade, reserving a little for basting halfway through the cooking time.

COOK'S TIP
If the chicken is left overnight in the refrigerator, remove it a hour or two before you want to start cooking to allow it to return to room temperature.

5 Melt the ghee and pour over the chicken pieces to seal the surface. This helps to keep the centre moist during roasting. Roast the chicken for about 10 minutes, then remove from the oven, leaving the oven on.

6 Baste the chicken with the remaining marinade. Return to the oven and switch off the heat. Leave the chicken in the oven for 15–20 minutes without opening the door. Serve on a bed of lettuce and garnish with the lemon and onion rings.

THAI FRIED NOODLES

Phat Thai, as this dish is known, has a fascinating flavour and texture. It is made with rice noodles, combined with shellfish and beancurd, a range of vegetables and ground peanuts, and is considered one of the national dishes of Thailand.

SERVES 4–6

350g/12oz rice noodles
45ml/3 tbsp vegetable oil
15ml/1 tbsp chopped garlic
16 raw king prawns (jumbo shrimp),
    peeled, tails left intact and deveined
2 eggs, lightly beaten
15ml/1 tbsp dried shrimps, rinsed
30ml/2 tbsp pickled white radish
50g/2oz fried beancurd or tofu, chopped
2.5ml/½ tsp dried chilli flakes
115g/4oz garlic chives, cut into 5cm/
    2in lengths
225g/8oz/1 cup beansprouts
50g/2oz/⅓ cup roasted peanuts,
    coarsely ground
5ml/1 tsp granulated sugar
15ml/1 tbsp dark soy sauce
30ml/2 tbsp fish sauce
30ml/2 tbsp tamarind juice or 5ml/1 tsp
    concentrated tamarind pulp
30ml/2 tbsp fresh coriander (cilantro)
    leaves and 1 kaffir lime, to garnish

1 Soak the noodles in a bowl of warm water for 20–30 minutes, then drain.

2 Heat 15ml/1 tbsp of the oil in a wok or large pan. Add the garlic and fry until golden. Stir in the prawns and cook for 1–2 minutes until pink, tossing from time to time. Remove and set aside.

3 Heat another 15ml/1 tbsp of oil in the pan. Add the eggs and tilt the wok to spread them into a thin sheet. Stir to scramble and break the egg into small pieces. Remove from the pan and set aside with the prawns.

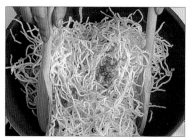

4 Heat the remaining oil in the same pan. Add the dried shrimps, pickled radish, beancurd or tofu and dried chillies. Stir-fry briefly. Add the soaked noodles and stir-fry for 5 minutes.

5 Add the garlic chives, half the beansprouts and half the peanuts. Season with the granulated sugar, soy sauce, fish sauce and tamarind juice or pulp. Mix well and cook until the noodles are completely heated through.

6 Return the prawn and egg mixture to the pan and mix with the noodles. Serve garnished with the rest of the beansprouts, peanuts, coriander leaves and kaffir lime wedges, if using.

COOK'S TIP
Pickled white radish is available in jars from Asian food stores and markets.

KARAHI CHICKEN with MINT

A karahi is similar to a Chinese wok, and its use is most widespread in northern India, which is closest to the border with China. A traditional karahi is made of heavy cast iron, which is excellent for heat distribution and retention, and it is used extensively for cooking all types of meat, poultry and vegetable dishes. Because of its shape, it is also ideal for deep-frying and is used for this purpose all over India.

2 Heat the oil in a large pan, add the chopped spring onions and stir-fry for about 2 minutes until soft.

3 Add the boiled chicken strips to the pan and stir-fry briskly over a medium heat for about 3 minutes, or until the chicken is browned.

SERVES 4

450g/1lb chicken breast fillets, skinned and
   cut into strips
300ml/½ pint/1¼ cups water
30ml/2 tbsp vegetable oil
2 small bunches spring onions
   (scallions), roughly chopped
5ml/1 tsp grated fresh root ginger
5ml/1 tsp crushed dried red chilli
30ml/2 tbsp lemon juice
30ml/2 tbsp chopped fresh coriander
   (cilantro), plus extra sprigs to garnish
30ml/2 tbsp chopped fresh mint, plus extra
   sprigs to garnish
3 tomatoes, seeded and roughly chopped
5ml/1 tsp salt

1 Put the chicken and water into a large pan, bring to the boil and lower the heat to medium. Cook for about 10 minutes or until the water has evaporated and the chicken is cooked. Remove the pan from the heat and set aside.

4 Add the grated fresh root ginger, chilli, lemon juice, chopped coriander and mint, tomatoes and salt, and stir gently to blend the flavours.

5 Transfer the curry to a warmed serving platter and garnish with fresh coriander and mint sprigs before serving. Plain boiled rice would make a good accompaniment to this dish.

VARIATION
Use strips of turkey breast meat or pork tenderloin instead of chicken. If using pork tenderloin, flatten the meat with a steak mallet first to tenderize it, then cut into strips and use as directed.

PINEAPPLE FRIED RICE

When buying a pineapple, look for a sweet-smelling fruit with an even brownish/yellow skin. To test for ripeness, tap the base – a dull sound indicates that the fruit is ripe. The flesh should also give slightly when pressed.

SERVES 4–6

1 pineapple
30ml/2 tbsp vegetable oil
1 small onion, finely chopped
2 fresh green chillies, seeded and chopped
225g/8oz lean pork, cut into strips
115g/4oz cooked, peeled prawns (shrimp)
675–900g/1½–2lb/3–4 cups plain boiled
   rice, cooked and completely cold
50g/2oz/⅓ cup roasted cashew nuts
2 spring onions (scallions), chopped
30ml/2 tbsp fish sauce
15ml/1 tbsp soy sauce
2 fresh red chillies, sliced, and 10–12 fresh
   mint leaves (optional), to garnish

1 Using a sharp knife, cut the pineapple into quarters. Remove the flesh from both halves by cutting around inside the skin. Reserve the pineapple skin shells for serving the rice.

2 Slice the pineapple flesh and chop it into small even-size cubes. You will need about 115g/4oz of pineapple in total. Any remaining fruit can be reserved for use in a dessert.

3 Heat the oil in a wok or large pan. Add the onion and chillies and fry for about 3–5 minutes until softened. Add the strips of pork and cook until they have browned on all sides.

4 Stir in the prawns and rice and toss well together. Continue to stir-fry until the rice is thoroughly heated.

5 Add the chopped pineapple, cashew nuts and spring onions. Season to taste with fish sauce and soy sauce.

6 Spoon into the pineapple skin shells. Garnish with sliced red chillies, and with shredded mint leaves, if you like.

COOK'S TIP
This dish is ideal to prepare for a special occasion meal. Served in the pineapple skin shells, it is sure to be the talking point of the dinner.

KARAHI CHICKEN with FRESH FENUGREEK

This karahi chicken was the dish that inspired a style of cooking known as karahi cuisine in northern India, where fenugreek is a typical flavouring agent. In the West, dried fenugreek leaves can be used for convenience, as fresh fenugreek is generally more difficult to find. The dried leaves are sold in Indian and Pakistani food stores throughout the year, and will keep well in an airtight jar.

SERVES 4

225g/8oz chicken thigh meat, skinned
    and cut into strips
225g/8oz chicken breast fillets, skinned
    and cut into strips
2.5ml/½ tsp crushed garlic
5ml/1 tsp chilli powder
2.5ml/½ tsp salt
10ml/2 tsp tomato purée (paste)
30ml/2 tbsp vegetable oil
1 bunch fresh fenugreek leaves or
    15ml/1 tbsp dried
15ml/1 tbsp chopped fresh coriander
    (cilantro)

1 Bring a large pan of water to the boil, add the chicken strips and cook for 5–7 minutes. Drain and set aside.

2 In a bowl, combine the garlic, chilli powder and salt with the tomato purée.

COOK'S TIP
Discard the stems of fresh fenugreek, as they will impart a bitter flavour to the dish.

3 Heat the oil in a wok, karahi or large pan. Lower the heat and add the tomato purée and spice mixture.

4 Add the chicken pieces and stir-fry for 5–7 minutes. Lower the heat further.

5 Add the fenugreek leaves and the chopped fresh coriander to the pan. Continue to stir-fry for 5–7 minutes, then pour in 300ml/½ pint/1¼ cups water, cover and cook for a further 5 minutes. Serve hot.

INDONESIAN FRIED RICE

One of the most familiar and well-known Indonesian dishes, Nasi Goreng is a marvellous way to use up leftover rice, chicken and meats such as pork. It is important that the rice is quite cold and the grains are separate before adding the other ingredients.

SERVES 4–6

350g/12oz/3/4 cups dry weight long grain
    rice, such as basmati, cooked and
    allowed to become completely cold
2 eggs
30ml/2 tbsp water
105ml/7 tbsp vegetable oil
225g/8oz pork fillet or fillet of beef
115g/4oz peeled, cooked prawns (shrimp)
175–225g/6–8oz cooked chicken, chopped
2–3 fresh red chillies, seeded and sliced
1cm/1/2 in cube shrimp paste
2 garlic cloves, crushed
1 onion, sliced
30ml/2 tbsp dark soy sauce or
    45–60ml/3–4 tbsp tomato ketchup
salt and ground black pepper
celery leaves, fresh coriander (cilantro)
    sprigs, to garnish

1 Once the rice is cooked and cooled, fork it through to separate the grains and keep it in a covered pan or dish until required.

2 Beat the eggs with seasoning and the water and make two or three omelettes in a frying pan, with a minimum of oil. Roll up each omelette and cut into strips when cold. Set aside.

3 Cut the pork or beef into neat strips and put the meat, prawns and chicken pieces in separate bowls. Shred one of the chillies and reserve it.

COOK'S TIP
Always store cooked and cooled rice in the refrigerator.

4 Put the shrimp paste, with the remaining chilli, garlic and onion, in a food processor and grind to a paste, or pound using a pestle and mortar.

5 Fry the paste in the remaining hot oil, without browning, until it gives off a rich, spicy aroma. Add the strips of pork or beef and fry over a high heat to seal in the juices. Stir constantly to prevent the meat sticking to the bottom of the pan.

6 Add the prawns, cook for 2 minutes and then stir in the chicken, cold rice, dark soy sauce or ketchup and seasoning to taste. Stir constantly to keep the rice light and fluffy and prevent it from sticking to the base of the pan.

7 Turn on to a hot platter and garnish with the omelette strips, celery leaves, reserved shredded fresh chilli and coriander sprigs.

CHICKEN TIKKA MASALA

Though chicken tikka is a traditional dish from northern India, the word masala *is pure invention. The word refers to the sauce in which the cooked tikka is simmered and which is a western adaptation. However, it is not dissimilar to another traditional Indian dish known as butter chicken, in which cooked tandoori chicken is simmered in a creamy sauce.*

SERVES 4

675g/1½lb chicken breast fillets, skinned
90ml/6 tbsp tikka paste
60ml/4 tbsp natural (plain) yogurt
30ml/2 tbsp vegetable oil
1 onion, chopped
1 garlic clove, crushed
1 fresh green chilli, seeded and chopped
2.5cm/1in piece fresh root ginger, grated
15ml/1 tbsp tomato purée (paste)
15ml/1 tbsp ground almonds
250ml/8fl oz/1 cup water
45ml/3 tbsp ghee or butter, melted
50ml/2fl oz/¼ cup double (heavy) cream
15ml/1 tbsp lemon juice
fresh coriander (cilantro) sprigs, natural
    (plain) yogurt and toasted cumin seeds
    to garnish
naan bread, to serve

1 Cut the chicken into 2.5cm/1in cubes. Put half of the tikka paste and the yogurt into a bowl, then stir in the chicken. Leave to marinate for 20 minutes.

COOK'S TIP
Soak wooden kebab skewers in water before use to prevent them from burning while under the grill (broiler).

2 For the tikka sauce, heat the oil and fry the onion, garlic, chilli and ginger for 5 minutes. Add the remaining tikka paste and fry for 2 minutes. Add the tomato purée, almonds and water, and simmer for 15 minutes.

3 Thread the chicken on to wooden kebab skewers. Preheat the grill (broiler).

4 Brush the chicken pieces with the melted butter and grill (broil) under a medium heat for about 15 minutes. Occasionally, turn and brush the chicken pieces with more butter.

5 Put the tikka sauce in a blender or food processor and process until smooth. Return the sauce to the pan and stir in the cream and lemon juice.

6 Remove the chicken from the grill, slide the cubes off the wooden skewers and add them to the pan. Simmer gently for 5 minutes more. Garnish with fresh coriander, yogurt and cumin seeds, and serve with warm naan bread.

MALACCA FRIED RICE

Using leftover rice to make up a new dish is a common practice all over the East. In most Eastern countries, rice is equivalent to wealth and it is never thrown away. It is believed that if you throw away wealth it will never return to you.

SERVES 4–6

2 eggs
45ml/3 tbsp vegetable oil
4 shallots or 1 onion, finely chopped
5ml/1 tsp grated fresh root ginger
1 garlic clove, crushed
225g/8oz peeled prawn (shrimp) tails, raw or cooked
5–10ml/1–2 tsp chilli sauce (optional)
3 spring onions (scallions), green part only, roughly chopped
225g/8oz/2 cups frozen peas, thawed
225g/8oz thickly sliced roast pork, diced
45ml/3 tbsp light soy sauce
350g/12oz long grain rice, cooked and allowed to become completely cold
salt and ground black pepper

1 In a bowl, beat the eggs well, and season to taste with salt and ground black pepper.

2 Heat 15ml/1 tbsp of the vegetable oil in a wok or large pan, pour in the eggs and allow them to set, without stirring, for less than a minute.

3 Roll up the pancake with your hands, then cut it into thin strips and set aside. The pancake can be allowed to cool down to room temperature, although it can also be served hot, if you like.

COOK'S TIP
Store cooked, cooled rice in an airtight container in the refrigerator. Heat the rice thoroughly, and make sure the grains are piping hot when using precooked and cooled rice in any recipe.

4 Heat the remaining vegetable oil in the wok, add the shallots or onions, chopped ginger, garlic and prawn tails and cook gently for 1–2 minutes. Keep stirring the contents of the wok to ensure that the garlic doesn't burn.

5 Add the chilli sauce, if using, spring onions, peas, pork and soy sauce. Stir to heat through, then add the rice. Fry the rice over a moderate heat for 6–8 minutes. Turn into a warmed serving dish and decorate with the pancake.

CHICKEN TIKKA

The word tikka refers to the use of boneless, skinless cubes of chicken breast. Strictly speaking, the term cannot be applied to other types of meat, even if they are prepared and cooked in a similar way. Traditionally cooked in the tandoor (Indian clay oven), chicken tikka is enduringly popular in the West as well as in India.

SERVES 6

450g/1lb chicken breast fillets, skinned, and cubed
5ml/1 tsp grated fresh root ginger
5ml/1 tsp crushed garlic
5ml/1 tsp chilli powder
1.5ml/¼ tsp ground turmeric
5ml/1 tsp salt
150ml/¼ pint/⅔ cup natural (plain) yogurt
60ml/4 tbsp lemon juice
15ml/1 tbsp chopped fresh coriander (cilantro)
15ml/1 tbsp vegetable oil

To serve (optional)
lettuce
1 small onion, cut into rings
lime wedges
fresh coriander (cilantro)

1 In a large bowl, mix the chicken cubes, ginger, garlic, chilli powder, turmeric, salt, yogurt, lemon juice and coriander. Leave to marinate in a cool place for at least 2 hours, or in the refrigerator overnight.

COOK'S TIP
Thread the meat on to oiled skewers, and turn and baste it during cooking.

2 Place the chicken on a grill (broiler) tray, or in a flameproof dish lined with foil, and baste with the oil.

3 Preheat the grill to medium. Grill (broil) the chicken for 15–20 minutes until cooked, turning and basting two or three times. Serve with lettuce, onion rings, lime wedges and fresh coriander.

COCONUT RICE

This is a very popular way of cooking rice throughout the whole of South-east Asia. Nasi uduk, as it is known in Indonesia, makes a wonderful accompaniment to any meat dish, and goes particularly well with fish, chicken and pork.

SERVES 4–6

350g/12oz Thai fragrant rice
400g/14oz can coconut milk
300ml/½ pint/1¼ cups water
2.5ml/½ tsp ground coriander
2.5cm/1in piece cinnamon stick
1 lemon grass stalk, bruised
1 pandan (screwpine) or bay leaf or
  2–3 drops screwpine essence
salt
fresh coriander (cilantro) sprigs and
  deep-fried onions, to garnish

1 Wash the rice in several changes of water and then put in a large pan with the coconut milk, water, coriander, cinnamon stick, lemon grass and pandan, bay leaf or screwpine essence, if using, and salt. Bring to the boil, stirring constantly to prevent the rice from settling on the base of the pan. Cover with a lid and cook over a very low heat for 12–15 minutes, or until the coconut milk has been absorbed.

2 Fork through and remove the lemon grass, cinnamon, and pandan or bay leaf. Cover and cook for 3 minutes more.

3 Cover the pan with a tight-fitting lid and continue to cook over the lowest possible heat for 3–5 minutes more.

4 When the rice is ready, pile on to a warm serving dish and garnish with the coriander sprigs and crisp deep fried onions. Serve immediately.

COOK'S TIP

If you wish to use fresh coconut milk, crack open the coconut and remove the clear water (this makes an excellent cooling drink). Using a small, sharp knife, remove the flesh in sections, then peel off the brown skin. Process the flesh in a food processor, and squeeze out the milk through a muslin (cheesecloth) cloth.

CHICKEN SAAG

The word saag *means greens and, traditionally, spinach is the usual choice for adding to meat and poultry, although other greens also work well. Chicken saag is one of the best-known dishes to have originated in the state of Punjab.*

SERVES 4

225g/8oz fresh spinach leaves, washed
2.5cm/1in piece fresh root ginger, grated
2 garlic cloves, crushed
1 fresh green chilli, roughly chopped
200ml/7fl oz/scant 1 cup water
30ml/2 tbsp vegetable oil
2 bay leaves
1.5ml/¼ tsp black peppercorns
1 onion, finely chopped
4 tomatoes, skinned and
    finely chopped
10ml/2 tsp curry powder
5ml/1 tsp salt
5ml/1 tsp chilli powder
45ml/3 tbsp natural (plain) yogurt,
    plus extra to serve
8 chicken thighs, skinned
naan bread, to serve

1 Cook the spinach, without water, in a tightly covered pan for 5 minutes. Put the spinach, ginger, garlic and chilli with 50ml/2fl oz/¼ cup of the water into a food processor and process to a purée.

2 Heat the oil, add the bay leaves and peppercorns and fry for 2 minutes. Add the onion and fry for 6–8 minutes more.

3 Add the chopped tomatoes to the pan and simmer for a further 5 minutes. Add the curry powder, salt and chilli powder and stir well to mix. Allow to cook for 2 minutes.

4 Add the spinach purée and the remaining water to the pan, and leave to simmer for 5 minutes.

5 Stir in the yogurt, about 15ml/1 tbsp at a time, and simmer for 5 minutes.

6 Add the chicken. Cover and cook for 25–30 minutes or until the chicken is tender. Serve with warm naan, drizzle over some natural yogurt and dust lightly with the chilli powder.

FESTIVE RICE

Rice is the staple food throughout South-east Asia. There are numerous varieties, but the two commonly used ones are polished white long grain and glutinous rice. Generally, any long grain rice will produce good results, but Thai fragrant rice is particularly delicious.

SERVES 8

450g/1lb/2⅓ cups Thai fragrant rice
   or other long grain rice
60ml/4 tbsp vegetable oil
2 garlic cloves, crushed
2 onions, finely sliced
5cm/2in piece fresh turmeric, crushed
750ml/1¼ pints/3 cups water
400g/14oz can coconut milk
1–2 lemon grass stalks, bruised
1–2 pandan (screwpine) leaves
   (optional)
salt

For the accompaniments
omelette strips
2 fresh red chillies, shredded
cucumber chunks
tomato wedges
deep-fried onions
Coconut and Peanut Relish
prawn (shrimp) crackers

1 Wash the rice thoroughly in several changes of water. Drain well.

2 Heat the vegetable oil in a wok or frying pan and gently fry the crushed garlic, finely sliced onions and crushed fresh turmeric for a few minutes until soft but not browned.

3 Add the rice and stir well so that each grain is coated in oil, and the rice mixes with the garlic, onion and turmeric. Pour in the water and coconut milk and add the bruised lemon grass, pandan leaves, if using, and add salt to taste.

4 Bring to the boil, stirring well. Cover the pan and cook gently for about 15–20 minutes, until all of the liquid has been absorbed.

5 Remove the pan from the heat. Cover with a clean dishtowel, put on the lid and leave the pan to stand in a warm place for 15 minutes. Remove the lemon grass and pandan leaves, if used.

6 Turn out the rice on to a warmed serving platter and garnish with the accompaniments before serving.

COOK'S TIP
It is the custom to shape the rice into a cone (to represent a volcano) and then surround it with the accompaniments. Shape the rice with oiled hands or use a conical sieve.

CHICKEN in GREEN MASALA SAUCE

The use of green spice mixes is popular all over India. Although in southern India the mixes are generally used to cook vegetables and fish, in the north, where most people are meat-eaters, they are more often used to prepare meat and poultry dishes.

SERVES 4

1 crisp green eating apple, peeled, cored and cubed
60ml/4 tbsp fresh coriander (cilantro) leaves
30ml/2 tbsp fresh mint leaves
150ml/¼ pint/⅔ cup natural (plain) yogurt
45ml/3 tbsp fromage frais or ricotta cheese
2 fresh green chillies, seeded and chopped
1 bunch spring onions (scallions), chopped
5ml/1 tsp salt
5ml/1 tsp granulated sugar
5ml/1 tsp crushed garlic
5ml/1 tsp grated fresh root ginger
15ml/1 tbsp vegetable oil
225g/8oz chicken breast fillets, skinned and cubed
25g/1oz sultanas (golden raisins)

1 Place the apple, 45ml/3 tbsp of the coriander, the mint, yogurt, fromage frais or ricotta, chillies, spring onions, salt, sugar, garlic and ginger in a food processor and process for 1 minute. Scrape around the outside of the bowl and process for a few seconds more.

2 Heat the oil in a wok, karahi or large pan, pour in the yogurt mixture and cook gently over a low heat for about 2 minutes.

COOK'S TIP
This dish makes a good dinner-party main course. Nut Pulao would make a good accompaniment.

3 Add the chicken pieces and stir well to blend everything together. Cook over a medium-low heat for 12–15 minutes or until the chicken is fully cooked.

4 Sprinkle the sultanas and the remaining coriander over the chicken (do not mix in, but leave as a garnish). Serve with Nut Pulao, if you like.

SOUTH-EAST ASIAN RICE AND NOODLES

The unassertive flavours of rice and noodles make them perfect partners for the fragrant, aromatic foods of South-east Asia. Rice grows in abundance throughout the region. Like noodles, it is a staple food, and is eaten with every meal on a daily basis.

SPICY GRILLED CHICKEN

This dish is inspired by the tandoori style of cooking, in which the meat and poultry are marinated before being grilled or roasted in a clay oven. Serve it with rice and a salad, or, for a real treat, with a mushroom curry.

SERVES 6

12 chicken thighs
90ml/6 tbsp lemon juice
5ml/1 tsp grated fresh root ginger
5ml/1 tsp crushed garlic
5ml/1 tsp crushed dried red chillies
5ml/1 tsp salt
5ml/1 tsp soft light brown sugar
30ml/2 tbsp clear honey
30ml/2 tbsp chopped fresh coriander
    (cilantro), plus extra sprigs
    to garnish
1 fresh green chilli, finely chopped
30ml/2 tbsp vegetable oil
Saffron Rice and a mixed salad,
    to serve (optional)

1 Prick the chicken thighs with a fork, rinse under running water, pat dry with kitchen paper and set aside.

2 In a bowl, mix the lemon juice, ginger, garlic, red chillies, salt, sugar and honey.

3 Transfer the chicken thighs to the spice mixture in the bowl and coat well. Leave to marinate for 45 minutes.

4 Preheat the grill (broiler) to medium. Add the fresh coriander and chopped green chilli to the chicken and mix well, then transfer the marinated chicken thighs to a flameproof dish.

5 Pour any remaining marinade over the chicken and baste with the oil, using a pastry brush.

6 Grill (broil) the chicken thighs for 15–20 minutes, turning and basting the meat occasionally, until cooked through and browned.

7 Transfer the chicken to a warmed serving dish and garnish with the fresh coriander sprigs. Serve with Saffron Rice and a salad, if you like.

COOK'S TIP
If you prefer, you can cook the chicken on a barbecue for a wonderful smoky flavour. Baste with the oil only when the chicken is almost cooked.

COCONUT AND PEANUT RELISH and HOT CHILLI AND GARLIC DIPPING SAUCE

These flavoursome accompaniments can be served with many Indonesian dishes.

COCONUT AND PEANUT RELISH

MAKES 120ML/4FL OZ/½ CUP

115g/4oz fresh coconut, grated,
    or desiccated (dry, unsweetened,
    shredded) coconut
175g/6oz/1 cup salted peanuts
5mm/¼in cube shrimp paste
1 small onion, quartered
2–3 garlic cloves, crushed
45ml/3 tbsp vegetable oil
2.5ml/½ tsp tamarind pulp, soaked in
    30ml/2 tbsp warm water
5ml/1 tsp coriander seeds, roasted
    and ground
2.5ml/½ tsp cumin seeds, roasted
    and ground
5ml/1 tsp dark brown sugar

1 Dry-fry the coconut in a wok or large pan over a medium heat, stirring the coconut constantly until crisp and golden colour. Allow to cool and add half to the peanuts in a bowl. Toss together to mix.

2 Process the shrimp paste, the onion and garlic in a food processor or with a pestle and mortar to form a paste. Fry the paste in hot oil, without browning.

3 Strain the tamarind and reserve the juice. Add the coriander, cumin, tamarind juice and brown sugar to the fried paste in the pan. Cook for 3 minutes, stirring.

4 Stir in the remaining toasted coconut and leave to cool. When cold, mix with the peanut and coconut mixture. Leave to stand for 30 minutes before serving.

HOT CHILLI AND GARLIC DIPPING SAUCE

MAKES 120ML/4FL OZ/½ CUP

1 garlic clove
2 fresh Thai red chillies, seeded and
    roughly chopped
10ml/2 tsp granulated sugar
5ml/1 tsp tamarind juice
60ml/4 tbsp soy sauce
juice of ½ lime

1 Process the garlic, chillies and sugar in a food processor or with a pestle and mortar to create a smooth paste.

2 Add the tamarind juice, soy sauce and lime juice, and mix together. Leave to stand for 30 minutes before serving.

CHICKEN in a CASHEW NUT SAUCE

Nut pastes were introduced into north Indian cooking by the Moguls, the travellers who provided what was probably the most important outside influence on Indian cuisine. Mughlai food, as this style of cooking is known, is famed for its rich yet delicate flavours.

SERVES 4

2 onions
30ml/2 tbsp tomato purée (paste)
50g/2oz/⅓ cup cashew nuts
7.5ml/1½ tsp garam masala
5ml/1 tsp crushed garlic
5ml/1 tsp chilli powder
15ml/1 tbsp lemon juice
1.5ml/¼ tsp ground turmeric
5ml/1 tsp salt
15ml/1 tbsp natural (plain) yogurt
30ml/2 tbsp vegetable oil
15ml/1 tbsp chopped fresh coriander
    (cilantro), plus extra
    to garnish
15ml/1 tbsp sultanas (golden raisins)
450g/1lb chicken breast fillets, skinned
    and cubed
175g/6oz button (white) mushrooms
300ml/½ pint/1¼ cups water

1 Cut the onions into quarters, then place in a food processor or blender. Process for 1 minute.

2 Add the tomato purée, cashew nuts, garam masala, crushed garlic, chilli powder, lemon juice, turmeric, salt and yogurt to the onions and process for a further 1–1½ minutes.

3 In a wok, karahi or large pan, heat the oil, lower the heat to medium and pour in the onion and spice mixture from the food processor or blender. Fry gently, stirring frequently, for about 2 minutes, lowering the heat if necessary.

4 Add the fresh coriander, sultanas and cubed chicken to the pan and continue to stir-fry for a further minute.

5 Add the mushrooms, pour in the measured water and bring to a simmer. Cover the pan and cook over a low heat for about 10 minutes.

6 After this time, check that the chicken is cooked all the way through and the sauce is thick. Continue to cook for a little longer if necessary.

7 Transfer to a warmed serving dish and garnish with chopped fresh coriander. Plain boiled rice and a fruit chutney would go well with this dish.

SAMBAL KECAP, HOT TOMATO SAMBAL and CUCUMBER SAMBAL

Piquant sambals are placed on the table as a condiment for dipping meat and fish.

SAMBAL KECAP

MAKES ABOUT 150ML/¼ PINT/⅔ CUP

1 fresh red chilli, seeded and
   finely chopped
2 garlic cloves, crushed
60ml/4 tbsp dark soy sauce
20ml/4 tsp lemon juice, or
   15–25ml/1–1½ tbsp prepared tamarind
   juice or 5ml/1 tsp concentrated
   tamarind pulp
30ml/2 tbsp hot water
30ml/2 tbsp deep-fried onions

1 Mix the chilli, garlic, soy sauce, lemon
juice or tamarind juice or pulp and hot
water together in a bowl.

2 Stir in the deep-fried onions and
then leave the sambal to stand for
30 minutes before serving.

HOT TOMATO SAMBAL

MAKES 120ML/4FL OZ/½ CUP

3 ripe tomatoes
2.5ml/½ tsp salt
5ml/1 tsp chilli sauce
60ml/4 tbsp fish sauce or soy sauce
15ml/1 tbsp chopped fresh coriander
   (cilantro) leaves

1 Cover the tomatoes with boiling
water to loosen the skins. Remove the
skins, halve, discard the seeds and chop
the flesh finely.

2 Place the chopped tomatoes in a large
bowl, add the salt, chilli sauce, fish sauce
or soy sauce and chopped coriander

3 Mix together well. Leave the sambal
to stand for 30 minutes before serving.

CUCUMBER SAMBAL

MAKES 150ML/5FL OZ/⅔ CUP

1 clove garlic, crushed
5ml/1 tsp fennel seeds
10ml/2 tsp granulated sugar
2.5ml/½ tsp salt
2 shallots or 1 small onion, finely sliced
100ml/4fl oz/½ cup rice or white wine
   vinegar
¼ cucumber, finely diced

1 Place the garlic, fennel seeds, sugar
and salt in a pestle and mortar and
pound finely. Alternatively, grind the
ingredients thoroughly in a food
processor.

2 Stir in the shallots or onion, vinegar
and cucumber. Leave to stand for 6–8
hours to allow the flavours to combine.

CHICKEN DOPIAZA

With lashings of onions, dopiaza's popularity is timeless. The origin of the word is rather unclear. In the Hindi language Do means two and piaz is onion. Hence the popular belief that the word refers to the use of twice the amount or two different types of onions. However, dopiaza is essentially a Mogul dish and history has it that it was named after Emperor Akbar's courtier, Mullah Dopiaza.

SERVES 4

45ml/3 tbsp vegetable oil
8 small onions, halved
2 bay leaves
8 green cardamom pods
4 cloves
3 dried red chillies
8 black peppercorns
2 onions, finely chopped
2 garlic cloves, crushed
2.5cm/1in piece fresh root ginger,
    finely chopped
5ml/1 tsp ground coriander
5ml/1 tsp ground cumin
2.5ml/½ tsp ground turmeric
5ml/1 tsp chilli powder
2.5ml/½ tsp salt
4 tomatoes, skinned and finely chopped
120ml/4fl oz/½ cup water
8 chicken pieces, skinned
plain boiled rice or chapatis, to serve

1 Heat 30ml/2 tbsp oil in a wok, karahi or large pan and fry the halved small onions until soft. Remove and set aside.

2 Add the remaining oil and fry the bay leaves, cardamoms, cloves, chillies and peppercorns for 2 minutes. Add the chopped onions, garlic and ginger and fry for 5 minutes. Add the spices and salt and cook for 2 minutes.

COOK'S TIP
Soak the onions in boiling water for 2 minutes to make them easier to peel.

3 Add the tomatoes and water to the pan and simmer for 5 minutes until the sauce begins to thicken. Add the chicken pieces and cook for 15 minutes more.

4 Add the reserved small onions, then cover and cook for a further 10 minutes, or until the chicken is tender. Serve with plain boiled rice or chapatis.

FRUIT and RAW VEGETABLE GADO-GADO

Banana leaves, which can be bought from Asian markets, lend an authentic touch to all types of South-east Asian dishes. They are most frequently used as wrappers in which to cook small parcels of food, but if you are serving this salad for a special occasion, you could use a single banana leaf instead of the mixed salad leaves to line the platter.

SERVES 6

½ cucumber
2 pears (not too ripe) or 175g/6oz wedge
    of yam bean
1–2 eating apples
juice of ½ lemon
mixed salad leaves or 1–2 banana leaves
6 tomatoes, seeded and cut into wedges
3 fresh pineapple slices, cored and cut
    into wedges
3 eggs, hard-boiled (hard-cooked) and
    shelled
175g/6oz egg noodles, cooked, cooled
    and chopped
deep-fried onions, to garnish

For the peanut sauce
2–4 fresh red chillies, seeded and ground,
    or 15ml/1 tbsp Hot Tomato Sambal
300ml/½ pint/1¼ cups coconut milk
350g/12oz/1¼ cups crunchy peanut butter
15ml/1 tbsp dark soy sauce or dark brown
    sugar
5ml/1 tsp tamarind pulp, soaked in 45ml/
    3 tbsp warm water
coarsely crushed peanuts
salt

VARIATION
Quail's eggs can be used in place of hen's eggs. Hard boil for 3 minutes.

1 Make the peanut sauce. Put the ground chillies or Hot Tomato Sambal in a pan. Pour in the coconut milk, then stir in the peanut butter. Heat gently, stirring, until well blended.

2 Simmer gently until the sauce thickens, then stir in the soy sauce or sugar. Strain in the tamarind juice, add salt to taste and stir well. Spoon into a bowl and sprinkle with coarsely crushed peanuts.

3 To make the salad, core the cucumber and peel the pears or yam bean. Cut the flesh into fine matchsticks. Finely shred the apples and sprinkle them with the lemon juice. Spread a bed of mixed salad leaves on a flat platter and pile the cucumber, pear or yam bean, apple, tomato and pineapple on top.

4 Add the sliced or quartered hard-boiled eggs and the chopped noodles to the platter and garnish with deep-fried onions. Serve the salad at once, with the peanut sauce.

CHICKEN KORMA

Korma is not really a dish but a technique employed in Indian cooking; it simply means braising. It is a misconception to think that kormas are always rich and creamy as there are several different types. They can be light and aromatic or rich and creamy, and some kormas are fiery looking, with a taste to match. All depends on where the recipe originated. This recipe comes from Delhi, the centre of Mogul cuisine.

SERVES 4

25g/1oz blanched almonds
2 garlic cloves, crushed
2.5cm/1in piece fresh root ginger, chopped
30ml/2 tbsp vegetable oil
675g/1½lb chicken breast fillets, skinned and cubed
3 green cardamom pods
1 onion, finely chopped
10ml/2 tsp ground cumin
1.5ml/¼ tsp salt
150ml/¼ pint/⅔ cup natural (plain) yogurt
175ml/6fl oz/¾ cup single (light) cream
toasted flaked (sliced) almonds and fresh coriander (cilantro) sprigs, to garnish
plain boiled rice, to serve

1 Process the almonds, garlic and ginger in a food processor with 30ml/2 tbsp water.

2 Heat the oil in a wok, karahi or large pan, and cook the chicken for 10 minutes. Remove the chicken and set aside. Add the cardamom pods and fry for 2 minutes. Add the onion and fry for 5 minutes.

3 Stir the almond, garlic and ginger paste into the cardamom and onions in the pan. Add the cumin and season to taste with salt. Cook for 5 minutes more, stirring frequently.

4 Whisk the yogurt and add it to the onion mixture a tablespoonful at a time. Cook over a low heat, until the yogurt has all been absorbed. Return the chicken to the pan. Cover and simmer over a low heat for 5–6 minutes, or until the chicken is tender.

5 Stir in the cream and simmer for a further 5 minutes. Garnish with toasted flaked almonds and coriander, and serve with plain boiled rice.

COOK'S TIP
For a true Mogul flavour, replace the cumin with 15ml/1 tbsp ground coriander.

SQUID in CLOVE SAUCE

The island of Madura, between Bali and Java, makes use of various spices that were originally introduced to Indonesia by Indian and Arab traders. This recipe with cloves and nutmeg, along with tomato and soy sauce, is known as Cumi Cumi Smoor. *It is quite delicious, and not difficult to make.*

SERVES 3–4

675g/1½lb ready-cleaned squid
45ml/3 tbsp groundnut (peanut) oil
1 onion, finely chopped
2 garlic cloves, crushed
1 beefsteak tomato, skinned and chopped
15ml/1 tbsp dark soy sauce
2.5ml/½ tsp grated nutmeg
6 whole cloves
150ml/¼ pint/⅔ cup water
juice of ½ lemon or lime
salt and ground black pepper, to taste
shredded spring onions (scallions) and fresh
    coriander (cilantro) sprigs, to garnish
plain boiled rice, to serve

1 Wash the squid and pat dry on kitchen paper. Use a sharp kitchen knife to cut the squid into long, thin ribbons. Carefully remove the "bone" from each tentacle, and discard.

2 Heat a wok, toss in the squid and stir constantly for 2–3 minutes, when the squid will have curled into attractive shapes or into firm rings. Lift out and set aside in a warm place.

3 Heat the oil in a clean pan and fry the onion and garlic, until soft and beginning to brown. Add the tomato, soy sauce, nutmeg, cloves, water and lemon or lime juice. Bring to the boil and then reduce the heat and add the squid, with seasoning to taste.

4 Cook the squid in the sauce for 3–5 minutes, uncovered, over a gentle heat, stirring from time to time. Take care not to overcook the squid. Serve hot or warm, with plain rice, or as part of a buffet spread. Garnish with shredded spring onions and fresh coriander.

VARIATION
Instead of squid try using 450g/1lb cooked and peeled tiger prawns (shrimp) in this recipe. Add them to the pan for the final 1–2 minutes.

MUGHLAI-STYLE LEG of LAMB

In India, there are different names for this style of cooking a leg of lamb, two of which are shahi raan and peshawari raan. Roasting a whole leg of lamb was first popularized by the Mongolian warrior Genghis Khan (1162–1227) and is known as Chengezi Raan.

SERVES 4–6

4 large onions, chopped
4 garlic cloves
5cm/2in piece fresh root ginger,
    chopped
45ml/3 tbsp ground almonds
10ml/2 tsp ground cumin
10ml/2 tsp ground coriander
10ml/2 tsp ground turmeric
10ml/2 tsp garam masala
4–6 fresh green chillies
juice of 1 lemon
300ml/½ pint/1¼ cups natural (plain)
    yogurt, beaten
1.8kg/4lb leg of lamb
8–10 cloves
salt
15ml/1 tbsp blanched almond flakes,
    to garnish
4 firm tomatoes, halved and grilled
    (broiled), to serve

1 Place the first ten ingredients in a food processor or blender, with salt to taste, and process to a smooth paste. Gradually add the yogurt and blend. Grease a large, deep roasting pan and preheat the oven to 190°C/375°F/Gas 5.

2 Remove most of the fat and skin from the lamb. Using a sharp knife, make deep pockets above the bone at each side of the thick end. Make deep diagonal gashes on both sides of the lamb.

COOK'S TIP
If time permits, allow the joint to stand at room temperature for a couple of hours before putting it in the oven.

3 Push the cloves firmly into the meat, spaced evenly on all sides.

4 Push some of the spice mixture into the pockets and gashes and spread the remainder evenly all over the meat. Place the meat on the roasting pan and loosely cover the whole pan with foil. Roast for 2–2½ hours, or until the meat is cooked, removing the foil for the last 10 minutes of cooking time.

5 Remove from the oven and allow to rest for about 10 minutes before carving. Garnish the joint with almond flakes, and serve with grilled tomatoes.

PRAWN CURRY with QUAIL'S EGGS

This exotic combination lives up to all the promises of the East. The earthy flavour of ginger is blended with refreshing lemon grass, fiery red chillies and soothing coconut milk to create this exquisite dish. Quail's eggs are now stocked in most supermarkets.

SERVES 4

12 quail's eggs
30ml/2 tbsp vegetable oil
4 shallots or 1 onion, finely chopped
2.5cm/1in piece fresh galangal or
    2.5cm/1in piece fresh root ginger,
    chopped
2 garlic cloves, crushed
5cm/2in piece lemon grass,
    finely shredded
1–2 small fresh red chillies, seeded and
    finely chopped
2.5ml/½ tsp ground turmeric
12mm/½in cube shrimp paste or
    15ml/1 tbsp fish sauce
900g/2lb raw prawn (shrimp) tails,
    peeled and deveined
400g/14oz can coconut milk
300ml/½ pint/1¼ cups chicken stock
115g/4oz Chinese leaves,
    roughly shredded
10ml/2 tsp granulated sugar
2.5ml/½ tsp salt
2 spring onions (scallions), green part
    only, shredded, and 30ml/2 tbsp
    shredded coconut, to garnish

1 Boil the quail's eggs for 8 minutes. Refresh in cold water, peel by dipping in cold water to release the shells and set them aside.

2 Heat the vegetable oil in a large wok, add the shallots or onion, galangal or ginger and garlic and cook until the onions have softened, without colouring. Add the lemon grass, chillies, turmeric and shrimp paste or fish sauce and fry briefly to bring out their flavours.

3 Add the prawns to the wok and fry briefly. Pour the coconut milk through a sieve (strainer) over a bowl, then add the thin part of the milk with the chicken stock. Add the Chinese leaves, sugar and salt, and bring to the boil. Simmer for 6–8 minutes.

4 Turn out the prawn curry on to a warmed serving dish. Halve the quail's eggs, using a sharp knife for a clean cut, and toss them in the sauce until they are well coated. Sprinkle with the spring onions and the shredded coconut. Serve with plain boiled rice, if you like.

SHAMMI KABAB

Kababs came to India from the Middle East, where the word is spelt kebab and refers to a skewered meat. There is a delectable range of kababs in Indian cuisine, most of which can be served either as appetizers or side dishes with an accompanying raita or chutney.

SERVES 5–6

2 onions, finely chopped
250g/9oz lean lamb, boned and cubed
50g/2oz chana dhal or yellow split peas
5ml/1 tsp cumin seeds
5ml/1 tsp garam masala
4–6 fresh green chillies
5cm/2in piece fresh root ginger, grated
175ml/6fl oz/¾ cup water
a few fresh coriander (cilantro) and mint
    leaves, chopped, plus extra coriander
    (cilantro) sprigs to garnish
juice of 1 lemon
15ml/1 tbsp gram flour (besan)
2 eggs, beaten
vegetable oil, for shallow frying
salt

1 Put the first seven ingredients and the water into a large pan with salt, and bring to the boil. Simmer, covered, until the meat and dhal are cooked. Remove the lid and continue to cook for a few more minutes, to reduce the excess liquid. Set aside to cool.

2 Transfer the cooled meat and dhal mixture to a food processor or blender and process to a rough paste.

3 Put the paste into a large mixing bowl and add the chopped coriander and mint leaves, lemon juice and gram flour. Knead well with your hands to make sure the ingredients are evenly distributed through the mixture.

4 Divide the mixture into 10–12 even-size portions and use your hands to roll each into a ball, then flatten slightly. Chill for 1 hour. Dip the kababs in the beaten egg and shallow fry each side until golden brown. Pat dry on kitchen paper and serve hot.

SAMBAL GORENG with PRAWNS

This is an immensely useful and adaptable sauce. Here it is combined with prawns and green pepper, but you could use fine strips of calf's liver or chicken livers in place of the prawns, and tomatoes and green beans in place of the pepper.

SERVES 4–6

350g/12oz peeled cooked prawns (shrimp)
1 green (bell) pepper, seeded and
    thinly sliced
60ml/4 tbsp tamarind juice
pinch of granulated sugar
45ml/3 tbsp coconut milk or cream
lime strips and sliced red onion,
    to garnish
plain boiled rice, to serve

For the Sambal Goreng
2.5cm/1in cube shrimp paste
2 onions, roughly chopped
2 garlic cloves, roughly chopped
2.5cm/1in piece fresh galangal, sliced
2 fresh red chillies, seeded and sliced
1.5ml/¼ tsp salt
30ml/2 tbsp vegetable oil
45ml/3 tbsp tomato purée (paste)
600ml/1 pint/2½ cups vegetable stock
    or water

1 To make the Sambal Goreng, grind the shrimp paste with the onions and garlic using a mortar and pestle or a food processor. Add the galangal, chillies and salt. Pound or process to a paste.

2 Heat the oil in a wok or large pan and fry the paste for 2 minutes, without browning, until the mixture gives off a rich aroma. Stir in the tomato purée and the stock or water. Cook for 10 minutes. Ladle half the sauce into a bowl and leave to cool. This leftover sauce can be used in another recipe (see Cook's Tip).

VARIATIONS
To make Tomato Sambal Goreng, add 450g/1lb peeled, coarsely chopped tomatoes to the sauce mixture before stirring in the stock or water. To make Egg Sambal Goreng, add 3 or 4 chopped hard-boiled (hard-cooked) eggs, and 2 peeled, chopped tomatoes to the sauce.

3 Add the prawns and green pepper to the remaining sauce in the wok. Cook gently for 3–4 minutes, then stir in the tamarind juice, sugar and coconut milk or cream. Spoon into serving bowls and garnish with strips of lime rind and sliced red onion. Serve with plain boiled rice.

COOK'S TIP
Any remaining sauce can be stored in the refrigerator for up to 3 days. It can also be frozen for up to 3 months.

ROGAN JOSH

This is one of the most popular lamb dishes to have originated in Kashmir. Traditionally, fatty meat on the bone is slow cooked until most of the fat is separated from the meat. The fat that escapes from the meat in this way is known as rogan *and* josh *refers to the rich red colour. The Kashmiris achieve this colour by using a combination of mild and bright Kashmiri chillies and the juice extracted from a brightly coloured local flower.*

SERVES 4–6

45ml/3 tbsp lemon juice
250ml/8fl oz/1 cup natural (plain) yogurt
5ml/1 tsp salt
2 garlic cloves, crushed
2.5cm/1in piece fresh root ginger, finely
 grated
900g/2lb lean lamb fillet, cubed
60ml/4 tbsp vegetable oil
2.5ml/½ tsp cumin seeds
2 bay leaves
4 green cardamom pods
1 onion, finely chopped
10ml/2 tsp ground coriander
10ml/2 tsp ground cumin
5ml/1 tsp chilli powder
400g/14oz can chopped tomatoes
30ml/2 tbsp tomato purée (paste)
150ml/¼ pint/⅔ cup water
toasted cumin seeds and bay leaves,
 to garnish
plain boiled rice, to serve

1 In a large bowl, mix together the lemon juice, yogurt, salt, one crushed garlic clove and the ginger. Add the lamb and marinate in the refrigerator overnight.

2 Heat the oil in a wok, karahi or large pan and fry the cumin seeds for 2 minutes until they splutter. Add the bay leaves and cardamom pods and fry for 2 minutes.

3 Add the onion and remaining garlic and fry for 5 minutes. Add the coriander, cumin and chilli powder. Fry for 2 minutes.

4 Add the marinated lamb to the pan and cook for a further 5 minutes, stirring occasionally to prevent the mixture from sticking to the base of the pan.

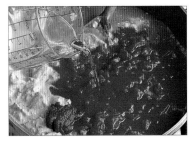

5 Add the tomatoes, tomato purée and water. Cover and simmer for 1–1½ hours. Garnish with toasted cumin seeds and bay leaves, and serve.

BALINESE FISH CURRY

On the beautiful island of Bali, along with neighbouring Java and Sumatra, fish curry and rice constitute the population's dietary staples. Food here has simple, uncomplicated yet delicious flavours. Handle the fish carefully as both cod and haddock flake easily. Alternatively, use a firm-textured fish such as monkfish, swordfish or fresh tuna.

SERVES 4–6

675g/1½lb cod or haddock fillet
1cm/½in cube shrimp paste
2 red or white onions, roughly chopped
2.5cm/1in piece fresh root ginger, sliced
1cm/½in piece fresh galangal, sliced,
    or 5ml/1 tsp galangal powder
2 garlic cloves
1–2 fresh red chillies, seeded, or
    10ml/2 tsp chilli sambal,
    or 5–10ml/1–2 tsp chilli powder
90ml/6 tbsp vegetable oil
15ml/1 tbsp dark soy sauce
5ml/1 tsp tamarind pulp, soaked in
    30ml/2 tbsp warm water
250ml/8fl oz/1 cup water
celery leaves or chopped fresh chilli,
    to garnish
plain boiled rice, to serve

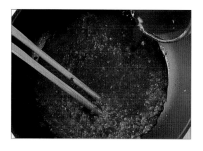

3 Heat 30ml/2 tbsp of the oil and fry the spice mixture, stirring, until it gives off a rich aroma. Add the soy sauce. Strain the tamarind and add the juice and water. Cook for 2–3 minutes.

4 In a separate pan, fry the fish in the remaining oil for 2–3 minutes. Turn once only so that the pieces stay whole. Lift out with a slotted spoon and put into the sauce.

5 Cook the fish in the sauce for a further 3 minutes. Garnish the dish with feathery celery leaves or a little chopped fresh chilli. Serve with plain boiled rice.

COOK'S TIP
Galangal paste is sold in Asian stores and can be used in place of galangal powder. It is worth buying a jar as it will keep in the refrigerator for several weeks.

1 Skin the fish and remove any bones, if necessary. Cut the flesh into bitesize pieces. Pat dry with kitchen paper and set aside.

2 Grind the shrimp paste, onions, ginger, fresh galangal, if using, garlic and fresh chillies, if using, to a paste in a food processor or with a pestle and mortar. Stir in the chilli sambal or chilli powder and galangal powder, if using.

VARIATION
Substitute 450g/1lb cooked tiger prawns (shrimp) for the fish. Add them to the sauce 3 minutes before the end of cooking and heat through thoroughly.

MINCED LAMB with PEAS

This dish, known as kheema mattar, *is a favourite all over India, although it originated in the north. Generally, in India minced mutton is used, as lamb is not very easy to obtain. Minced turkey, pork or chicken would all work equally well.*

SERVES 4

45ml/3 tbsp vegetable oil
1 onion, finely chopped
2 garlic cloves, crushed
2.5cm/1in piece fresh root ginger, grated
2 fresh green chillies, finely chopped
675g/1½lb minced (ground) lamb
5ml/1 tsp ground cumin
5ml/1 tsp ground coriander
5ml/1 tsp chilli powder
5ml/1 tsp salt
175g/6oz/1½ cups frozen peas, thawed
30ml/2 tbsp lemon juice
naan and natural (plain) yogurt, to serve

3 Stir in the cumin, coriander, chilli powder and salt with 300ml/½ pint/1¼ cups water. Cover the pan and simmer for about 25 minutes.

4 Add the peas and lemon juice. Cook for 10 minutes, uncovered. Garnish with fresh coriander and chilli powder and serve with warm naan and natural yogurt.

1 Heat the oil and fry the onion for about 5 minutes over a medium heat until browned. Add the garlic, ginger and chillies and fry for 2–3 minutes.

2 Add the minced lamb and stir-fry briskly for 5 minutes over a high heat.

COOK'S TIP
To reduce the fat content, dry-fry the lamb in a non-stick frying pan until the natural fat is released. Drain the fat and use the lamb as directed in the recipe.

FISH STEW with VEGETABLES

Sinigang, as it is known in the Philippines, is a soured soup-like stew, which many Filipinos consider to be their national dish. It is always served with noodles or rice, and seafood – either prawns or thin slivers of fish fillet – is often added for good measure.

SERVES 4–6

15ml/1 tbsp tamarind pulp or 5ml/1 tsp
   concentrated tamarind pulp
150ml/¼ pint/⅔ cup warm water
2 tomatoes, roughly chopped
115g/4oz spinach or Chinese
   kangkong leaves
115g/4oz peeled, cooked large prawns
   (jumbo shrimp), thawed if frozen
1.2 litres/2 pints/5 cups prepared fish
   stock (see Cook's Tip)
½ mooli (daikon), peeled and
   finely diced
115g/4oz/¾ cup French (green) beans,
   cut into 1cm/½in lengths
225g/8oz piece of cod or haddock fillet,
   skinned and cut into strips
fish sauce, to taste
squeeze of lemon juice, to taste
salt and ground black pepper
plain boiled rice or noodles, to serve

1 Put the tamarind pulp in a large bowl, if using, and pour over the warm water. Set aside. Peel and chop the tomatoes, and discard the seeds. Strip the spinach or kangkong leaves from the stems and tear into small pieces. Set aside.

2 Using your hands, remove the heads and shells from the prawns, if necessary, leaving the tails intact.

3 Pour the prepared fish stock into a large pan and add the finely diced mooli. Cook the mooli for 5 minutes, then add the chopped green beans. Continue to cook the stew gently for 3–5 minutes more.

4 Add the fish strips, tomatoes and spinach or kangkong leaves. Strain in the tamarind juice or add the concentrated tamarind, stir until dissolved, and cook for 2 minutes. Stir in the prawns and cook for 1–2 minutes to heat through.

5 Season the stew with salt and freshly ground black pepper, and add a little fish sauce and lemon juice to taste. Transfer the stew to individual warmed serving bowls, and serve with either plain boiled rice or noodles.

COOK'S TIP
A good fish stock is essential for Sinigang. Ask your fishmonger for about 675g/1½lb fish bones. Wash them, then place in a pan with 2 litres/3½ pints/8 cups water. Add half a peeled onion, a 2.5cm/1in piece of bruised fresh root ginger, and a little salt and pepper. Bring to the boil, skim, then simmer for 20 minutes. Cool slightly, then strain. Freeze any unused stock.

LAMB with APRICOTS

This recipe comes from the wonderful fruit-laden valley of Kashmir. The cuisine of Kashmir is renowned for the imaginative use of all the exotic fruits and nuts that grow abundantly in that state. Serve with an apricot chutney to complement the fruit in the recipe.

2 Heat the oil in a wok, karahi or large pan and fry the cinnamon stick and cardamoms for 2 minutes. Add the onion and fry for 6–8 minutes until soft.

3 Add the curry paste and fry for about 2 minutes. Stir in the cumin, coriander and salt and fry for 2–3 minutes.

4 Add the cubed lamb, dried apricots and the lamb stock to the pan. Cover with the lid and cook over a medium heat for 1–1½ hours.

SERVES 4–6

900g/2lb stewing lamb
30ml/2 tbsp vegetable oil
2.5cm/1in piece cinnamon stick
4 green cardamom pods
1 onion, chopped
15ml/1 tbsp curry paste
5ml/1 tsp ground cumin
5ml/1 tsp ground coriander
1.5ml/¼ tsp salt
175g/6oz/¾ cup ready-to-eat dried apricots
350ml/12fl oz/1½ cups lamb stock
fresh coriander (cilantro), to garnish

1 Cut away and discard any visible fat from the lamb, then cut the meat into 2.5cm/1in cubes.

5 Transfer to a serving dish and garnish with the fresh coriander. Classic Pulao and Apricot Chutney would make good accompaniments to this dish.

FISH in SPICED VINEGAR

This fish dish, cooked in the pickling style, is served hot and is known as escabeche. *It is eaten wherever there are or have been Spanish settlers. In the Philippines, palm vinegar is commonly used as a souring agent, but herb or cider vinegars will work just as well.*

SERVES 6

675–900g/1½–2lb white fish fillets,
    such as sole, plaice or flounder
45–60ml/3–4 tbsp seasoned flour
vegetable oil, for shallow frying

For the sauce
30ml/2 tbsp vegetable oil
2.5cm/1in piece fresh root ginger,
    thinly sliced
2–3 garlic cloves, crushed
1 onion, cut into thin rings
½ large green (bell) pepper, seeded and
    cut into small neat squares
½ large red (bell) pepper, seeded and
    cut into small neat squares
1 carrot, cut into thin batons
25ml/1½ tbsp cornflour (cornstarch)
450ml/¾ pint/scant 2 cups water
45–60ml/3–4 tbsp herb or cider vinegar
15ml/1 tbsp light soft brown sugar
5–10ml/1–2 tsp fish sauce
salt and ground black pepper
1 small fresh chilli, seeded and sliced and
    spring onions (scallions), finely
    shredded, to garnish
plain boiled rice, to serve

1 Wipe the fish fillets and leave them whole, or cut into serving portions, if you like. Pat dry on kitchen paper then dust lightly with the seasoned flour.

2 Heat oil for shallow frying in a frying pan and fry the fish in batches until golden and almost cooked. Transfer the fried fish to a large ovenproof dish and keep warm while you prepare the other ingredients.

3 Make the sauce in a wok or large pan. Fry the ginger, garlic and onion in the oil for 5 minutes or until the onion is softened but not browned.

4 Add the pepper squares and carrot strips and stir-fry for 1 minute.

5 Put the cornflour in a small bowl and add a little of the water to make a paste. Stir in the remaining water, the vinegar and the sugar. Pour the cornflour mixture over the vegetables in the wok and stir until the sauce boils and thickens a little. Season with fish sauce and salt and pepper if needed.

6 Add the fish to the sauce and reheat without stirring. Transfer to a serving platter and garnish with chilli and spring onions. Serve with plain boiled rice.

COOK'S TIP
Red snapper or small sea bass could be used for this recipe, in which case ask your fishmonger to cut it into fillets.

LAMB KOFTA CURRY

Koftas, or meatballs, reveal a Middle Eastern influence on Indian cuisine. The Middle Eastern technique for making the meatballs is still used, combined with the skilful blending of Indian spices. Koftas make an inexpensive but delicious main course.

SERVES 4

675g/1½lb minced (ground) lamb
1 fresh green chilli, roughly chopped
1 garlic clove, chopped
2.5cm/1in piece fresh root ginger, chopped
1.5ml/¼ tsp garam masala
1.5ml/¼ tsp salt
45ml/3 tbsp chopped fresh coriander
(cilantro)

For the sauce
30ml/2 tbsp vegetable oil
2.5ml/½ tsp cumin seeds
1 onion, chopped
1 garlic clove, chopped
2.5cm/1in piece fresh root ginger,
grated
5ml/1 tsp ground cumin
5ml/1 tsp ground coriander
2.5ml/½ tsp salt
2.5ml/½ tsp chilli powder
15ml/1 tbsp tomato purée (paste)
400g/14oz can chopped tomatoes
fresh coriander (cilantro) sprigs,
to garnish
coriander (cilantro) rice, to serve

1 To make the meatballs, put the lamb, chilli, garlic, ginger, garam masala, salt and coriander into a food processor and process until the mixture binds together.

2 Shape the mixture into 16 balls, using your hands. Cover with clear film (plastic wrap) and chill for 10 minutes.

COOK'S TIP
You can make the meatballs the day before. Store them in the refrigerator until needed.

3 To make the sauce, heat the oil and fry the cumin seeds until they splutter. Add the onion, garlic and ginger and fry for 5 minutes. Stir in the remaining sauce ingredients and simmer for 5 minutes.

4 Add the meatballs. Bring to the boil, cover and simmer for 25–30 minutes, or until the meatballs are cooked through. Garnish with sprigs of fresh coriander and serve with coriander rice.

BRAISED BEEF in a RICH PEANUT SAUCE

Like many dishes brought to the Philippines by Spanish settlers, this slow-cooking estofado, renamed kari kari, retains much of its original charm. Rice and peanuts are used to thicken the juices, yielding a rich glossy sauce.

SERVES 4–6

900g/2lb stewing beef, chuck, shin
    or blade steak
30ml/2 tbsp vegetable oil
15ml/1 tbsp annatto seeds, or 5ml/1 tsp
    paprika and a pinch of ground turmeric
2 onions, chopped
2 garlic cloves, crushed
275g/10oz celeriac or swede (rutabaga),
    peeled and roughly chopped
425ml/15fl oz/1¾ cups beef stock
350g/12oz new potatoes, peeled and
    cut into large dice
15ml/1 tbsp fish sauce
30ml/2 tbsp tamarind sauce
10ml/2 tsp granulated sugar
1 bay leaf
1 sprig thyme
45ml/3 tbsp long grain rice
50g/2oz/⅓ cup peanuts or 30ml/2 tbsp
    peanut butter
15ml/1 tbsp white wine vinegar
salt and ground black pepper

1 Cut the beef into 2.5cm/1in cubes and set aside.

2 Heat the vegetable oil in a wok or large pan. Add the annatto seeds, if using, and stir to colour the oil a dark red. Remove the seeds with a slotted spoon and discard. If you are not using annatto seeds, paprika and turmeric can be added later.

3 Soften the onions, garlic and the celeriac or swede in the oil without letting them colour. Add the beef cubes and fry over a high heat to seal. If you are not using annatto seeds to redden the sauce, stir in the paprika and ground turmeric with the beef.

4 Add the beef stock, potatoes, fish sauce and tamarind sauce, granulated sugar, bay leaf and thyme. Bring to a simmer and allow to cook on the top of the stove for about 2 hours.

5 Cover the rice with cold water and leave to stand for 30 minutes. Roast the peanuts under a hot grill (broiler), if using, then rub the skins off in a clean cloth. Drain the rice and grind with the peanuts or peanut butter, using a pestle and mortar, or food processor.

6 When the beef is tender, add 60ml/ 4 tbsp of the cooking liquid to the ground rice and nuts. Blend smoothly and stir into the contents of the pan. Simmer gently on the stove to thicken, for about 15–20 minutes. To finish, stir in the wine vinegar and season well.

STIR-FRIED CHILLI-GARLIC PRAWNS

Prawns have a particular affinity with garlic. To enhance the flavour of the garlic,
fry it very gently without letting it brown completely. The spice-coated prawns make
a mouthwatering appetizer or light lunch, when served with a salad, or they can be
transformed into a main meal with the addition of warm naan bread.

SERVES 4

15ml/1 tbsp vegetable oil
3 garlic cloves, roughly halved
3 tomatoes, chopped
2.5ml/½ tsp salt
5ml/1 tsp crushed dried red chillies
5ml/1 tsp lemon juice
Mango Chutney, to taste
1 fresh green chilli, chopped
16–20 peeled, cooked king prawns
    (jumbo shrimp)
fresh coriander (cilantro) sprigs and
    chopped spring onions (scallions),
    to garnish

1 In a wok, karahi or large pan, heat the vegetable oil over a low heat and fry the garlic halves gently until they are tinged with golden brown.

2 Add the chopped tomatoes, salt, crushed red chillies, lemon juice, Mango Chutney and the chopped fresh chilli. Stir the ingredients well.

3 Add the prawns to the pan, then raise the heat and stir-fry briskly, mixing the prawns with the other ingredients until they are thoroughly heated through.

4 Transfer the prawns in the sauce to a warm serving dish and garnish with fresh coriander sprigs and chopped spring onions. Serve immediately.

SWEET and SOUR PORK with COCONUT SAUCE

This is known as adobo *in the Philippines, which refers to a cooking style rather than the name of the dish. There are many variations of the recipe, and this version includes papaya, because the enzymes in the unripe fruit are excellent for tenderizing meat.*

SERVES 4–6

675g/1½lb lean pork, diced
1 garlic clove, crushed
5ml/1 tsp paprika
5ml/1 tsp crushed black peppercorns
15ml/1 tbsp granulated sugar
175ml/6fl oz/¾ cup palm or cider vinegar
2 small bay leaves
425ml/15fl oz/1¾ cups chicken stock
50g/2oz creamed coconut (coconut cream)
150ml/¼ pint/⅔ cup vegetable oil,
    for frying
1 under-ripe papaya, peeled, seeded and
    chopped
salt
½ cucumber, peeled and cut into batons,
    2 firm tomatoes, skinned, seeded and
    chopped, and 1 small bunch chives,
    chopped, to garnish

1 Marinate the pork with the garlic, paprika, black pepper, sugar, vinegar and bay leaves in a cool place for 2 hours. Add the chicken stock and coconut.

2 Transfer to a wok and simmer gently for 30–35 minutes, then remove the pork and drain. In a frying pan, heat the oil and brown the pork. Remove and drain.

3 Return the pork to the sauce with the papaya, season with salt and simmer for 15–20 minutes. Garnish with the cucumber batons, chopped tomatoes and chives and serve.

COOK'S TIP

If creamed coconut is not available, use 50ml/2fl oz/10 tsp coconut cream.

Indonesia and the Philippines

GRILLED KING PRAWNS with STIR-FRIED SPICES

Traditionally, king prawns are marinated and then grilled in the tandoor to produce the delectable tandoori king prawns. It is possible to achieve similar results by grilling the prawns under a very hot electric or gas grill as in this recipe.

SERVES 4

45ml/3 tbsp natural (plain) yogurt
5ml/1 tsp paprika
5ml/1 tsp grated fresh root ginger
16–20 peeled, cooked king prawns (jumbo shrimp), thawed if frozen
15ml/1 tbsp vegetable oil
3 onions, sliced
2.5ml/½ tsp fennel seeds, crushed
2.5cm/1in piece cinnamon stick
5ml/1 tsp crushed garlic
5ml/1 tsp chilli powder
1 yellow (bell) pepper, seeded and roughly chopped
1 red (bell) pepper, seeded and roughly chopped
salt
15ml/1 tbsp fresh coriander (cilantro) leaves, to garnish

1 Blend together the yogurt, paprika, ginger and add salt to taste. Add to the prawns and leave in a cool place to marinate for 30–45 minutes.

2 Meanwhile, heat the oil in a wok, karahi or large pan and fry the sliced onions with the fennel seeds and the cinnamon stick over a medium heat until the onions soften and turn golden.

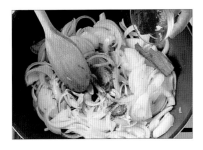

3 Lower the heat and stir in the crushed garlic and chilli powder.

4 Add the chopped yellow and red peppers to the pan and stir-fry gently for 3–5 minutes.

5 Remove the pan from the heat and transfer the onion and spice mixture to a warm serving dish, discarding the cinnamon stick. Set the dish aside.

COOK'S TIP
It is important not to overcook the prawns, they only need heating through.

6 Preheat the grill (broiler) to medium. Put the marinated prawns in a grill pan or flameproof dish and place under the grill to darken their tops and achieve a chargrilled effect. Add the prawns to the onion and spice mixture, and garnish with fresh coriander. Serve with plain rice and Creamy Black Lentils, if you like.

GINGER-FLAVOURED DUCK with CHINESE MUSHROOMS

Ducks are often seen, comically herded in single file, along the water channels between the rice paddies throughout Indonesia. There is a substantial Chinese population in Indonesia, among whom duck is a particular favourite. The delicious ingredients in this recipe give it an unmistakable flavour.

3 Cut the slices of fresh root ginger into thin batons and fry with the onion in the duck fat, until they give off a good aroma. Set aside the ginger and onion. Lift the duck pieces out of the soy sauce marinade and transfer to the pan. Fry them until browned on both sides. Add the mushrooms and reserved liquid.

4 Add 600ml/1 pint/2½ cups of stock or water to the browned duck pieces in the pan. Add the onion and ginger and season to taste with salt and ground black pepper. Cover the pan with a lid and cook over a gentle heat for about 1 hour, until the duck is tender.

SERVES 4

2.5kg/5½lb duck
5ml/1 tsp granulated sugar
50ml/2fl oz/¼ cup light soy sauce
2 garlic cloves, crushed
8 dried Chinese mushrooms, soaked in
　warm water for 15 minutes
5cm/2in piece fresh root ginger, sliced
1 onion, sliced
200g/7oz baby corn cobs
½ bunch spring onions (scallions)
15–30ml/1–2 tbsp cornflour (cornstarch),
　mixed with 60ml/4 tbsp water
salt and ground black pepper
plain boiled rice, to serve

1 Cut the duck along the breastbone, open it up and cut along each side of the backbone. Use the backbone, wings and giblets to make a stock to use later in the recipe. Any trimmings of fat can be rendered in a wok or large pan to use later. Cut each leg and each breast in half. Place in a bowl, rub with sugar and pour over the soy sauce and garlic.

2 Drain the mushrooms, reserving the soaking liquid. Trim, discarding the stalks.

VARIATION
Replace the corn with chopped celery and slices of canned water chestnuts.

5 Slice the spring onion tops and set aside. Add the corn cobs and the white part of the spring onions and cook for a further 10 minutes. Remove from the heat and add the cornflour paste. Return to the heat and bring to the boil, stirring. Cook for 1 minute until glossy. Sprinkle with the spring onion tops, and serve with plain boiled rice.

CORN on the COB in RICH ONION SAUCE

Corn is grown extensively in the Punjab region, where it is used in many delicacies. Corn bread, makki ki roti, along with spiced mustard greens, sarson ka saag, is a combination that is hard to beat and is what the Punjabis thrive on. Here, corn is cooked in a thick rich onion sauce, in another classic Punjabi dish. It is excellent served with naan bread.

SERVES 4–6

4 corn cobs, thawed if frozen
vegetable oil, for frying
1 large onion, finely chopped
2 cloves garlic, crushed
5cm/2in piece fresh root ginger, crushed
2.5ml/½ tsp ground turmeric
2.5ml/½ tsp onion seeds
2.5ml/½ tsp cumin seeds
2.5ml/½ tsp five-spice powder
6–8 curry leaves
2.5ml/½ tsp granulated sugar
200ml/7fl oz/scant 1 cup natural
   (plain) yogurt
chilli powder, to taste

1 Cut each corn cob in half, using a heavy knife or cleaver to make clean cuts. Heat the oil in a wok, karahi or large pan and fry the corn until golden brown. Remove the corn and set aside.

2 Remove any excess oil, leaving 30ml/ 2 tbsp in the wok. Grind the onion, garlic and ginger to a paste using a pestle and mortar or in a food processor. Transfer the paste to a bowl and mix in the spices, chilli powder, curry leaves and sugar.

3 Heat the oil gently and fry the onion paste mixture for 8–10 minutes until all the spices have blended well and the oil separates from the sauce.

4 Cool the mixture and fold in the yogurt. Mix to a smooth sauce. Add the corn and mix well, so that all the pieces are covered with the sauce. Reheat gently for about 10 minutes. Serve hot.

MADURA CHICKEN with AROMATIC SPICES

Spices, such as the coriander and cumin used in this recipe, are added to a dish mainly for their taste. With the inclusion of nutmeg and cloves, magadip, as it is known in Indonesia, combines both taste and aroma. It is best cooked a day or two in advance to allow the flavours to mellow and permeate the flesh of the chicken.

SERVES 4

1.3–1.6kg/3–3½lb chicken, cut into
   quarters, or 4 chicken quarters
5ml/1 tsp granulated sugar
30ml/2 tbsp coriander seeds
10ml/2 tsp cumin seeds
6 whole cloves
2.5ml/½ tsp grated nutmeg
2.5ml/½ tsp ground turmeric
1 small onion
2.5cm/1in piece fresh root ginger,
   thinly sliced
300ml/½ pint/1¼ cups chicken stock
   or water
salt and ground black pepper
deep-fried onions, to garnish
plain boiled rice, to serve

1 Cut each chicken quarter in half to make eight pieces. Place the pieces in a flameproof casserole, sprinkle with the sugar and season to taste with salt and pepper. Toss the chicken pieces and seasoning together. This helps release the juices in the chicken. Use the chicken backbone and any remaining carcass, if using, to make chicken stock for use later in the recipe, if you like (see Cook's Tip).

2 In a preheated wok or large pan, dry-fry the coriander and cumin seeds and the whole cloves until the spices give off a good aroma. Add the nutmeg and turmeric and heat briefly. Remove and cool. Grind in a spice mill or food processor or use a pestle and mortar.

3 In a food processor, process the onion and ginger until finely chopped. Otherwise, finely chop the onion and ginger and pound to a paste with a pestle and mortar. Add the spices and stock or water and mix well.

4 Pour the spice mixture over the chicken in the flameproof casserole, and stir to ensure the pieces are well coated. Cover the casserole with a lid and cook over a gentle heat for 45–50 minutes until the chicken pieces are tender.

5 Serve the chicken with the sauce on plain boiled rice, sprinkled with crisp deep-fried onions.

COOK'S TIP
Add a large piece of bruised fresh root ginger, a small onion studded with a clove, a carrot and a stick of celery and a few peppercorns to the chicken stock to ensure a good flavour.

Indonesia and the Philippines
134

STIR-FRIED INDIAN CHEESE with MUSHROOMS and PEAS

Indian cheese, known as paneer, is a very versatile ingredient. It is used in both sweet and savoury dishes. Indian housewives generally make this cheese at home, although in recent years it has become available commercially. It is a useful source of protein for the people in the north who are vegetarian.

SERVES 4–6

90ml/6 tbsp ghee or vegetable oil
225g/8oz paneer, cubed
1 onion, finely chopped
a few fresh mint leaves, chopped, plus
   extra sprigs to garnish
50g/2oz chopped fresh coriander (cilantro)
3 fresh green chillies, chopped
3 garlic cloves
2.5cm/1in piece fresh root ginger, sliced
5ml/1 tsp ground turmeric
5ml/1 tsp chilli powder (optional)
5ml/1 tsp garam masala
225g/8oz/3 cups tiny button (white)
   mushrooms, washed
225g/8oz/2 cups frozen peas, thawed
175ml/6fl oz/¾ cup natural (plain) yogurt,
   mixed with 5ml/1 tsp cornflour
   (cornstarch)
salt

1 Heat the ghee or oil in a wok, karahi or large pan, and fry the paneer cubes until they are golden brown on all sides. Remove, drain on kitchen paper, and keep to one side.

2 Grind the onion, mint, coriander, chillies, garlic and ginger with a pestle and mortar or in a food processor to a fairly smooth paste.

3 Remove to a bowl and mix in the turmeric, chilli powder, if using, and garam masala, and season with salt to taste.

4 Remove excess ghee or oil from the pan, leaving about 15ml/1 tbsp. Heat and fry the paste over a medium heat for 8–10 minutes, or until the raw onion smell disappears and the oil separates.

5 Add the mushrooms, thawed peas and paneer, and mix well. Cool the mixture slightly and gradually fold in the yogurt.

6 Simmer for about 10 minutes, until the vegetables are tender and the flavours well mixed. Remove to a serving dish, garnish with sprigs of fresh mint and serve immediately.

COOK'S TIP
If paneer is not available, you can use grilled goat's cheese instead. Add it just before the garnish.

CHICKEN COOKED in COCONUT MILK

Traditionally, the chicken pieces in this dish would be part-cooked by frying, but roasting in the oven can be a better option. This is an unusual recipe in that the sauce is white, as it does not contain chillies or turmeric, unlike many other Indonesian dishes. The dish is usually sprinkled with crisp deep-fried onions before serving.

SERVES 4

1.3–1.6kg/3–3½lb chicken or 4 chicken
   quarters
4 garlic cloves
1 onion, sliced
4 macadamia nuts or 8 almonds
15ml/1 tbsp coriander seeds, dry-fried,
   or 5ml/1 tsp ground coriander
45ml/3 tbsp vegetable oil
2.5cm/1in piece fresh galangal or
   4cm/1½in piece fresh root ginger,
   bruised
2 lemon grass stalks, fleshy part bruised
3 lime leaves
2 bay leaves
5ml/1 tsp granulated sugar
600ml/1 pint/2½ cups coconut milk
salt
deep-fried onions, to garnish
plain boiled rice, to serve

1 Preheat the oven to 190°C/375°F/ Gas 5. Cut the chicken into four or eight pieces. Season with salt. Put in an oiled roasting pan. Bake for 25–30 minutes.

COOK'S TIP
For fan assisted ovens, reduce the temperature by at least 10°C/20°F/Gas 1 when cooking the chicken in step 1. Check the chicken from time to time.

2 To make the sauce, grind the garlic, onion, nuts and coriander to a fine paste in a food processor or with a pestle and mortar. Heat the oil in a wok and lightly fry the paste to bring out the flavour.

3 Add the chicken pieces to the wok together with the galangal or ginger, lemon grass, lime and bay leaves, sugar, coconut milk and salt. Mix well.

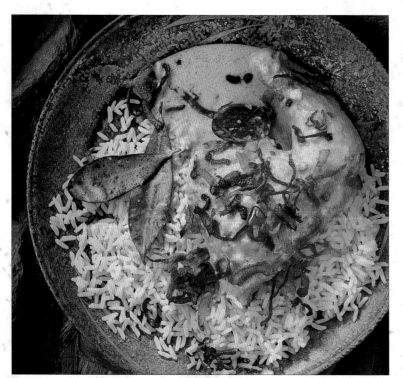

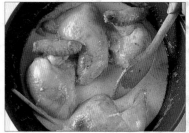

4 Bring to the boil and then reduce the heat and allow to simmer gently for 30–40 minutes, uncovered, until the chicken is tender and the coconut sauce is reduced and thickened. Stir the mixture occasionally during cooking.

5 Just before serving, remove the bruised galangal or ginger and lemon grass. Serve with plain boiled rice, sprinkled with deep-fried onions.

VARIATION
Instead of deep-frying the onions, coat them with oil, and bake until browned at the same time as the chicken.

DRY-SPICED POTATOES with CAULIFLOWER

This dish, known as aloo gobi in most Indian restaurants, has remained one of the most popular over the years. It is also a healthy dish, as potatoes are 90 per cent fat free and both potatoes and cauliflower are good sources of vitamin C.

2 Heat the oil in a wok, karahi or large pan over a medium heat and fry the cumin seeds for 2 minutes until they begin to splutter. Add the fresh green chilli and fry for a further 1 minute.

3 Add the cauliflower florets to the pan and fry, stirring, for 5 minutes.

SERVES 4

450g/1lb potatoes
30ml/2 tbsp vegetable oil
5ml/1 tsp cumin seeds
1 fresh green chilli, finely chopped
450g/1lb cauliflower, broken into florets
5ml/1 tsp ground coriander
5ml/1 tsp ground cumin
1.5ml/¼ tsp chilli powder
2.5ml/½ tsp ground turmeric
2.5ml/½ tsp salt
chopped fresh coriander (cilantro),
    to garnish
Tomato and Onion Salad and a pickle of
    your choice, to serve

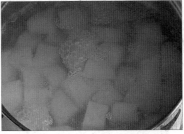

1 Cut the peeled and washed potatoes into 2.5cm/1in cubes, then par-boil them in a large pan of boiling water for about 10 minutes. Drain the potatoes well and set them aside.

4 Add the potatoes, the spices and salt and cook for a further 7–10 minutes, or until both vegetables are tender. Garnish with chopped coriander and serve with Tomato and Onion Salad and a pickle.

VARIATION
Use broccoli instead of some or all of the cauliflower, if you prefer.

INDONESIA AND THE PHILIPPINES

Numerous cultures have flourished among the 13,000 islands of this lush tropical archipelago, including the Dutch, Portuguese and British. The result is a rich culinary heritage that makes use of an abundance of indigenous ingredients, such as rice, chillies, limes, tamarind and spices.

KARAHI POTATOES with WHOLE SPICES

All spices work like magic with potatoes. Even just a light touch can bring about a complete transformation. For this recipe choose floury potatoes, as they will absorb the spice flavours better than the waxy variety.

SERVES 4

45ml/3 tbsp vegetable oil
2.5ml/½ tsp white cumin seeds
3 curry leaves
5ml/1 tsp crushed dried red chillies
2.5ml/½ tsp mixed onion, mustard
    and fenugreek seeds
2.5ml/½ tsp fennel seeds
3 garlic cloves, roughly chopped
2.5ml/½ tsp grated fresh root ginger
2 onions, sliced
6 new potatoes, cut into 5mm/¼in slices
15ml/1 tbsp chopped fresh coriander
    (cilantro)
1 fresh red chilli, seeded and sliced
1 fresh green chilli, seeded and sliced

1 Heat the oil in a wok, karahi or large pan. Lower the heat slightly and add the cumin seeds, curry leaves, dried chillies, mixed onion, mustard and fenugreek seeds, fennel seeds, chopped garlic and grated ginger.

2 Fry for about 1 minute, then add the sliced onions and fry gently for a further 5 minutes, or until the onions are golden brown. Add the sliced potatoes, fresh coriander and red and green chillies. Mix together well. Cover the pan tightly with a lid or foil, making sure the foil does not touch the food. Cook over a very low heat for about 7 minutes, or until the potatoes are tender.

3 Remove the lid or foil from the pan and serve the potatoes hot with parathas and any lentil dish for a vegetarian meal. Serve Shammi Kabab, Tandoori Chicken or Chicken Tikka instead of the lentils for meat eaters.

CUCUMBER and PINEAPPLE SAMBAL

Sambals are the little side dishes served at almost every Malay meal. In poorer societies, a main meal may simply be a bowl of rice and a sambal made from pounded shrimp paste, chillies and lime juice: the sambal is poured over the rice to give it flavour. This recipe is known as sambal nanas. *Use sparingly, as it is quite fiery.*

SERVES 8–10

1 small or ½ large fresh ripe pineapple
½ cucumber, halved lengthways
50g/2oz dried shrimps
1 large fresh red chilli, seeded
1.25cm/½ in cube shrimp paste, prepared
juice of 1 large lemon or lime
light brown sugar, to taste (optional)
salt

1 Cut off the top and the bottom of the pineapple. Stand it upright on a board, then slice off the skin from top to bottom, cutting out the spines. Slice the pineapple, removing the central core. Cut into thin slices and set aside.

2 Trim the ends from the cucumber and slice thinly. Sprinkle with salt and set aside. Place the dried shrimps in a food processor and chop finely. Add the chilli, prepared shrimp paste and lemon or lime juice, and process again to a paste.

3 Rinse the cucumber, drain and dry on kitchen paper. Mix the pineapple and chill. Just before serving, spoon in the spice mixture with sugar to taste, if liked. Mix well and serve.

COOK'S TIP
The pungent shrimp paste, also called blachan and terasi, is popular in many South-east Asian countries, and is available in Asian food markets. Since it can taste a bit raw in a sambal, dry fry it by wrapping it in foil and heating it in a frying pan over a low heat for 5 minutes, turning from time to time. If the shrimp paste is to be fried with other spices, this preliminary cooking can be eliminated.

MUSHROOM CURRY

*In India, mushrooms traditionally grow only in the northern state of Kashmir. However,
Indians have acquired the taste for them due to frequent travels abroad, and they are
now being cultivated in other northern areas where the climate is suitable.*

2 Add the onion and fry for 5 minutes
or until golden. Stir in the ground cumin,
coriander and garam masala and fry for
a further 2 minutes.

3 Add the chilli, garlic and ginger and fry
for 2–3 minutes, stirring constantly. Add
the tomatoes and salt. Bring to the boil
and simmer for 5 minutes.

SERVES 4

30ml/2 tbsp vegetable oil
2.5ml/½ tsp cumin seeds
1.5ml/¼ tsp black peppercorns
4 green cardamom pods
1.5ml/¼ tsp ground turmeric
1 onion, finely chopped
5ml/1 tsp ground cumin
5ml/1 tsp ground coriander
2.5ml/½ tsp garam masala
1 fresh green chilli, finely chopped
2 garlic cloves, crushed
2.5cm/1in piece fresh root ginger, grated
400g/4oz can chopped tomatoes
1.5ml/¼ tsp salt
450g/1lb/6 cups button (white) mushrooms
chopped fresh coriander (cilantro),
    to garnish

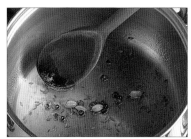

1 Heat the vegetable oil in a wok, karahi
or large pan and fry the cumin seeds,
black peppercorns, cardamom pods and
turmeric for 2–3 minutes.

COOK'S TIP
For authentic Kashmiri style, use ground
or crushed fennel in place of the cumin.

4 Halve the mushrooms, then add them
to the pan. Cover and simmer over a
low heat for 10 minutes. Transfer to
a warm serving platter and garnish with
chopped coriander. Serve with an Indian
bread, such as naan, parathas or chapatis,
and any dry meat or poultry dish, such
as Shammi Kabab or Tandoori Chicken.

MALAYSIAN FISH CURRY

The cooking styles of Malaysia have been greatly influenced by neighbouring countries such as India, Indonesia, China and the Middle East. The Malay people thrive on fish curry and rice. This is a superbly flavoured coconut-rich fish curry known as ikan moolee, *which is best served with a bowl of steaming hot boiled rice.*

SERVES 4

500g/1¼lb monkfish or other
    firm-textured fish fillets, skinned
    and cut into 2.5cm/1in cubes
2.5ml/½ tsp salt
50g/2oz/⅔ cup desiccated (dry,
    unsweetened, shredded) coconut
6 shallots or small onions, chopped
6 blanched almonds
2–3 garlic cloves, roughly chopped
2.5cm/1in piece fresh root ginger, sliced
2 lemon grass stalks, trimmed
10ml/2 tsp ground turmeric
45ml/3 tbsp vegetable oil
2 × 400g/14oz cans coconut milk
1–3 fresh red and green chillies, seeded
    and sliced
salt and ground black pepper, to taste
fresh chives, to garnish
plain boiled rice, to serve

1 Spread out the pieces of fish in a shallow dish and sprinkle them with the salt. Dry-fry the coconut in a wok over a gentle heat, turning all the time until it is crisp and golden (see Cook's Tip).

2 Transfer the coconut to a food processor and process to an oily paste. Scrape into a bowl and reserve.

3 Add the shallots or onions, almonds, garlic and ginger to the food processor. Cut off the lower 5cm/2in of the lemon grass stalks, chop them roughly and add to the processor. Process to a paste.

4 Add the turmeric to the mixture in the food processor and process briefly. Bruise the remaining lemon grass and set the stalks aside.

COOK'S TIP

Dry-frying is a feature of Malay cooking. When dry-frying do not be distracted. The coconut must be constantly on the move so that it becomes crisp and of a uniform golden colour.

5 Heat the oil in a wok. Add the onion mixture and cook for a few minutes without browning. Stir in the coconut milk and bring to the boil, stirring constantly to prevent curdling.

6 Add the cubes of fish to the wok, along with most of the sliced fresh chillies and the bruised lemon grass stalks. Cook for 3–4 minutes. Stir in the coconut paste (this can be moistened with some of the sauce if necessary) and cook for a further 2–3 minutes only. Do not overcook the fish. Taste the curry and adjust the seasoning, as required.

7 Remove the lemon grass. Transfer to a hot serving dish and sprinkle with the remaining slices of chilli. Garnish with chopped and whole chives and serve with plain boiled rice.

COURGETTES in SPICED TOMATO SAUCE

In India, tender marrow would be used for this recipe as courgettes are not grown there. Do try this recipe with a young marrow in the summer. It will also work well with winter squashes, such as butternut and acorn.

SERVES 4

675g/1½lb courgettes (zucchini)
45ml/3 tbsp vegetable oil
2.5ml/½ tsp cumin seeds
2.5ml/½ tsp mustard seeds
1 onion, thinly sliced
2 garlic cloves, crushed
1.5ml/¼ tsp ground turmeric
1.5ml/¼ tsp chilli powder
5ml/1 tsp ground coriander
5ml/1 tsp ground cumin
2.5ml/½ tsp salt
15ml/1 tbsp tomato purée (paste)
400g/14oz can chopped tomatoes
150ml/¼ pint/⅔ cup water
15ml/1 tbsp chopped fresh coriander
   (cilantro)
5ml/1 tsp garam masala

1 Trim the ends from the courgettes then cut them into 1cm/½in thick slices.

2 Heat the oil in a wok, karahi or large pan. Fry the cumin and mustard seeds for 2 minutes until they begin to splutter.

3 Add the onion and garlic and fry for about 5–6 minutes.

4 Add the ground turmeric, chilli powder, coriander, cumin and salt and fry for about 2–3 minutes.

5 Add the sliced courgettes, and cook for 5 minutes. Add the tomato purée and chopped tomatoes to the pan.

6 Add the water, then cover the pan and simmer for 10 minutes until the sauce thickens. Stir in the fresh coriander and garam masala, then cook for about 5 minutes, or until the courgettes are tender. Serve as an accompaniment to any meat, poultry or fish dish.

FRIED FISH with a SPICY SAUCE

Although this is not strictly a curry, it is one of the popular styles of cooking used in Malaysia. Locally known as ikan kecap, it comes from a small range of Eurasian recipes that combine Western techniques with Eastern flavours.

SERVES 3–4

450g/1lb fish fillets, such as mackerel, cod or haddock
30ml/2 tbsp plain (all-purpose) flour
groundnut (peanut) oil, for frying
1 onion, roughly chopped
1 small garlic clove, crushed
4cm/1½in piece fresh root ginger, grated
1–2 fresh red chillies, seeded and sliced
1cm/½in cube shrimp paste, prepared
60ml/4 tbsp water
juice of ½ lemon
15ml/1 tbsp brown sugar
30ml/2 tbsp dark soy sauce
salt
roughly torn lettuce leaves, to serve

1 Rinse the fish fillets under cold water and dry on kitchen paper. Cut into serving portions and remove any bones.

2 Season the flour and use it to dust the fish. Heat some oil and fry the fish on both sides for 3–4 minutes, or until cooked. Transfer to a plate and set aside.

3 Rinse out and dry the pan. Heat a little more oil in the clean frying pan and fry the onion, garlic, ginger and chillies to bring out the flavour. Do not brown.

4 Blend the shrimp paste with the water to make a smooth paste. Add it to the onion mixture, with a little extra water if necessary. Cook for 2 minutes and then stir in the lemon juice, brown sugar and soy sauce.

5 Pour the sauce over the fish and serve, hot or cold, with roughly torn lettuce leaves.

COOK'S TIP
If serving this dish as part of a buffet menu, cut the fish into bitesize pieces.

CUMIN-SCENTED VEGETABLES with TOASTED ALMONDS

Cabbage is a traditional vegetable in India, although neither baby corn cobs nor mangetouts are used in Indian cooking. Nonetheless, combining new and traditional ideas can create exciting and original dishes, as this recipe shows.

SERVES 4

15ml/1 tbsp vegetable oil
50g/2oz/4 tbsp butter
2.5ml/½ tsp crushed coriander seeds
2.5ml/½ tsp white cumin seeds
6 dried red chillies
1 small savoy cabbage, shredded
12 mangetouts (snow peas)
3 fresh red chillies, seeded and sliced
12 baby corn cobs, halved
salt
25g/1oz/¼ cup flaked (sliced) almonds, toasted and 15ml/1 tbsp chopped fresh coriander (cilantro), to garnish

1 Heat the oil and butter in a wok, karahi or large pan and add the crushed coriander seeds, white cumin seeds and dried red chillies.

2 Add the shredded cabbage and mangetouts to the spices in the pan and stir-fry briskly for about 5 minutes, until the cabbage starts to turn crisp.

3 Add the fresh red chillies, and baby corn cobs to the pan and season with salt to taste. Stir-fry for 3 minutes more.

4 Garnish with the toasted almonds and fresh coriander, and serve hot. This dish would go well with any meat curry and with Classic Pulao.

COOK'S TIP
Julienne strips of other vegetables will make this dish visually more appealing, and will add superb taste at the same time. Try julienne carrots and leeks instead of mangetouts and baby corn. Add the cabbage and carrots together, and add the leeks in step 3.

PRAWNS and CHAYOTE in COCONUT MILK

This delicious dish features chayote, which belongs to the squash family. Widely used in South-east Asia and some parts of India, it is pear-shaped, and generally pale yellow in colour. Larger supermarkets usually sell chayote, but you can use courgettes instead.

SERVES 4

1–2 chayotes or 2–3 courgettes (zucchini)
2 fresh red chillies, seeded
1 onion, quartered
5mm/¼in piece fresh galangal or 1cm/½in piece fresh root ginger, sliced
1 lemon grass stalk, lower 5cm/2in sliced, top bruised
2.5cm/1in piece fresh turmeric or 5ml/1 tsp ground turmeric
200ml/7fl oz/scant 1 cup water
lemon juice, to taste
400g/14oz can coconut milk
450g/1lb cooked, peeled prawns (shrimp)
salt
fresh red chilli shreds, to garnish
plain boiled rice or noodles, to serve

1 Peel the chayotes, remove the seeds and cut into strips. If using courgettes, cut into 5cm/2in strips.

2 Grind the fresh red chillies, onion, sliced galangal or root ginger, sliced lemon grass and the turmeric to a paste in a food processor or with a pestle and mortar. Add the water to the paste mixture, with a squeeze of lemon juice and salt to taste.

3 Pour into a pan. Add the top of the lemon grass stalk. Bring to the boil and cook for 1–2 minutes. Add the chayote or courgette pieces and then cook for 2 minutes. Stir in the coconut milk. Taste and adjust the seasoning.

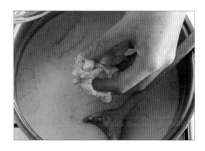

4 Add the peeled prawns and cook gently for 2–3 minutes. Remove the lemon grass stalk. Garnish with shreds of fresh red chilli, if using. This dish is usually served with plain boiled rice, but would taste equally good with rice noodles or egg noodles.

Malaysia

ROASTED AUBERGINES with SPRING ONIONS

This classic dish, made of roasted and mashed aubergines cooked with spring onions, is known as bharta *in the Punjab region. The term* bharta *means to mash. Traditionally, the aubergine is roasted over charcoal, but a hot electric or gas oven will produce similar results, although the smoky flavour will be missing.*

SERVES 4

2 large aubergines (eggplant)
45ml/3 tbsp vegetable oil
2.5ml/½ tsp black mustard seeds
1 bunch spring onions (scallions),
 finely chopped
115g/4oz/1½ cups button (white)
 mushrooms, halved
2 garlic cloves, crushed
1 fresh red chilli, finely chopped
2.5ml/½ tsp chilli powder
5ml/1 tsp ground cumin
5ml/1 tsp ground coriander
1.5ml/¼ tsp ground turmeric
5ml/1 tsp salt
400g/14oz can chopped tomatoes
15ml/1 tbsp chopped fresh coriander
 (cilantro), plus a few extra sprigs
 to garnish

1 Preheat the oven to 200°C/400°F/ Gas 6. Brush both of the aubergines with 15ml/1 tbsp of oil and prick with a fork. Bake for 30–35 minutes until soft.

2 Meanwhile, heat the remaining oil and fry the black mustard seeds for about 2 minutes until they splutter. Add the onions, mushrooms, garlic and chilli, and fry for 5 minutes more. Stir in the chilli powder, cumin, coriander, turmeric and salt and fry for 3–4 minutes. Add the tomatoes and simmer for 5 minutes.

COOK'S TIP
Roast the aubergines (eggplant) over a barbecue for an authentic smoky flavour.

3 Cut the aubergines in half lengthwise and scoop out the soft flesh into a large mixing bowl. Mash the flesh to a course texture, using a fork.

4 Add the aubergines to the pan with the coriander. Bring to the boil and simmer for 5 minutes until the sauce thickens. Serve garnished with coriander.

BEEF and AUBERGINE CURRY

The flavour of this versatile dish is subtle yet complex. As well as the fine combination of beef and aubergine, the dish successfully unites the mellow flavour of coconut milk with the pungency of fresh chillies, and the flavours of lemon grass and tamarind. The result is a dish that is equally suitable for a family meal or a dinner party.

SERVES 6

120ml/4fl oz/½ cup vegetable oil
2 onions, thinly sliced
2.5cm/1in piece fresh root ginger, sliced
　　and cut into thin batons
1 garlic clove, crushed
2 fresh red chillies, seeded and finely sliced
2.5cm/1in piece fresh turmeric, crushed,
　　or 5ml/1 tsp ground turmeric
1 lemon grass stalk, lower part sliced
　　finely, top bruised
675g/1½lb braising steak, cut into
　　even-size strips
400g/14oz can coconut milk
300ml/½ pint/1¼ cups water
1 aubergine (eggplant), sliced and
　　patted dry
5ml/1 tsp tamarind pulp, soaked in 60ml/
　　4 tbsp warm water
salt and ground black pepper
finely sliced fresh chilli (optional) and
　　deep-fried onions, to garnish
plain boiled rice, to serve

1 Heat half the oil in a wok or large pan, and fry the onions, ginger and garlic until they give off a rich aroma. Add the chillies, turmeric and the lower part of the lemon grass stalk. Push the contents of the pan to one side, then turn up the heat and add the steak, stirring until the meat changes colour.

2 Add the coconut milk, water and lemon grass top, with seasoning. Cover the pan or wok and simmer gently for 1½ hours, or until the meat is tender.

3 Towards the end of the cooking time heat the remaining oil in a frying pan. Fry the aubergine slices until they are brown on both sides.

COOK'S TIP

If you want to make this curry in advance, prepare to the end of step 2, then chill and store in the refrigerator until required.

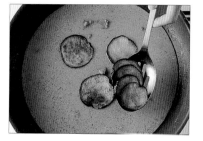

4 Add the browned aubergine slices to the beef curry and cook for a further 15 minutes. Stir gently from time to time. Strain the tamarind and stir the juice into the curry. Taste and adjust the seasoning. Put into a warm serving dish. Garnish with the sliced chilli, if using, and deep-fried onions, and serve with plain boiled rice.

KIDNEY BEAN CURRY

This dish, known as rajma in Punjabi, is a fine example of the area's hearty, robust cuisine. It is widely eaten dish all over the state, and is even sold by street vendors. Plain boiled rice makes the perfect accompaniment for this dish.

SERVES 4

225g/8oz/1¼ cups dried red kidney beans
30ml/2 tbsp vegetable oil
2.5ml/½ tsp cumin seeds
1 onion, thinly sliced
1 fresh green chilli, finely chopped
2 garlic cloves, crushed
2.5cm/1in piece fresh root ginger, grated
30ml/2 tbsp curry paste
5ml/1 tsp ground cumin
5ml/1 tsp ground coriander
2.5ml/½ tsp chilli powder
2.5ml/½ tsp salt
400g/14oz can chopped tomatoes
30ml/2 tbsp chopped fresh
    coriander (cilantro)

1 Place the kidney beans in a large bowl of cold water and then leave them to soak overnight.

2 Drain the beans and place in a large pan with double the volume of water. Boil vigorously for 10 minutes. Drain, rinse and return the beans to the pan. Add double the volume of water and bring to the boil. Reduce the heat, then cover and cook for 1–1½ hours, or until the beans are soft. This process is essential in order to remove the toxins that are present in dried kidney beans.

3 Meanwhile, heat the oil in a wok, karahi or large pan and fry the cumin seeds for 2 minutes until they begin to splutter. Add the onion, chilli, garlic and ginger and fry for 5 minutes. Stir in the curry paste, cumin, coriander, chilli powder and salt, and cook for 5 minutes.

4 Add the tomatoes and simmer for 5 minutes. Add the beans and fresh coriander, reserving a little for the garnish. Cover and cook for 15 minutes adding a little water if necessary. Serve garnished with the reserved coriander.

COOK'S TIP
Drained and well-rinsed canned beans work very well as an alternative.

CLAY-POT CHICKEN

This deliciously spiced dish is a refined version of the ancient cooking method, whereby the food was placed in a clay pot and buried in the dying embers of an open fire. Today, it is cooked in a low oven and the gentle heat is evenly distributed and retained by the clay pot, resulting in tender meat that melts in the mouth.

SERVES 4–6

1 × 1.3–1.6kg/3–3½lb oven-ready chicken
45ml/3 tbsp grated fresh coconut
30ml/2 tbsp vegetable oil
2 shallots or 1 small onion, finely chopped
2 garlic cloves, crushed
5cm/2in piece lemon grass
2.5cm/1in piece fresh galangal or fresh
   root ginger, thinly sliced
2 fresh green chillies, seeded and chopped
12mm/½in cube shrimp paste
400g/14oz can coconut milk
300ml/½ pint/1¼ cups chicken stock
2 kaffir lime leaves (optional)
15ml/1 tbsp granulated sugar
15ml/1 tbsp rice or white wine vinegar
2 ripe tomatoes
30ml/2 tbsp chopped fresh coriander
   leaves (cilantro), to garnish

1 To joint the chicken, remove the legs and wings with a sharp knife. Skin the pieces, divide the drumsticks from the thighs and, using kitchen scissors, remove the lower part of the chicken, leaving only the breast piece. Remove as many of the bones as you can, to make the dish easier to eat. Cut the breast piece into four or six and set aside.

2 Dry-fry the coconut in a large wok until evenly browned. Add the vegetable oil, shallots or onion, garlic, lemon grass, galangal or ginger, chillies and shrimp paste. Fry for 2–4 minutes to release the flavours. Preheat the oven to 180°C/350°F/Gas 4. Add the chicken joints to the wok and brown evenly with the spices for 2–3 minutes.

3 Strain the coconut milk, and add the thin part with the chicken stock, lime leaves, if using, sugar and vinegar. Transfer to a glazed clay pot, cover and bake in the centre of the oven for 50 minutes, or until the chicken is tender. Stir in the thick part of the coconut milk and return to the oven for 5–10 minutes.

4 Place the tomatoes in a bowl and cover with boiling water to loosen and remove the skins. Halve the tomatoes, then remove the seeds and chop into large dice. Add the chopped tomatoes to the finished dish, sprinkle with the chopped coriander and serve. Plain rice would make a good accompaniment.

CREAMY BLACK LENTILS

Black lentils or urad dhal are available whole, split, and skinned and split. Generally, both split, and skinned and split versions are used in west and south Indian cooking, whereas whole black lentils are a typical ingredient in the north.

SERVES 4–6

175g/6oz/³⁄₄ cup black lentils, soaked
50g/2oz/¹⁄₄ cup red split lentils
120ml/4fl oz/¹⁄₂ cup double (heavy) cream
120ml/4fl oz/¹⁄₂ cup natural (plain) yogurt
5ml/1 tsp cornflour (cornstarch)
45ml/3 tbsp ghee or vegetable oil
1 onion, finely chopped
5cm/2in piece fresh root ginger, crushed
4 fresh green chillies, chopped
1 tomato, chopped
2.5ml/¹⁄₂ tsp chilli powder
2.5ml/¹⁄₂ tsp ground turmeric
2.5ml/¹⁄₂ tsp ground cumin
2 garlic cloves, sliced
salt
coriander (cilantro) sprigs and sliced
    red chilli, to garnish

3 Heat 15ml/1 tbsp of the ghee or oil in a wok, karahi or large pan, and fry the onion, ginger, two green chillies and the tomato until the onion is soft. Add the ground spices and salt and fry for a further 2 minutes. Stir into the lentil mixture and mix well. Reheat, transfer to a heatproof serving dish and keep warm.

4 Heat the remaining ghee or oil in a frying pan over a low heat and fry the garlic slices and remaining chillies until the garlic slices are golden brown. Pour over the lentils and fold the garlic and chilli into the lentils just before serving. Place extra cream on the table for the diners to add more if they wish.

1 Drain the black lentils and place in a large pan with the red lentils. Cover with water and bring to the boil. Reduce the heat, cover the pan and simmer until tender. Mash with a spoon, and cool.

2 In a bowl, mix together the cream, yogurt and cornflour, and stir into the lentils in the pan.

CHICKEN with GOLDEN TURMERIC

As turmeric grows abundantly throughout South-east Asia, using it fresh is quite natural for the local people. The fresh version, which is a root like ginger, has a completely different taste and produces a luxurious golden colour in a dish. It is a difficult ingredient to find in the West. A little more than the normal amount of dried ground turmeric will produce an acceptable colour, although the flavour will be somewhat different.

SERVES 4

1.3–1.6kg/3–3½lb chicken, cut into
    8 pieces, or 4 chicken quarters, halved
15ml/1 tbsp light brown sugar
3 macadamia nuts or 6 almonds
2 garlic cloves, crushed
1 large onion, quartered
2.5cm/1in piece fresh galangal or
    1cm/½in piece fresh root ginger, sliced,
    or 5ml/1 tsp galangal powder
1–2 lemon grass stalks, lower 5cm/2in
    sliced, top bruised
1cm/½in cube shrimp paste
4cm/1½in piece fresh turmeric, sliced,
    or 10ml/2 tsp ground turmeric
15ml/1 tbsp tamarind pulp, soaked in
    150ml/¼ pint/⅔ cup warm water
60–90ml/4–6 tbsp vegetable oil
400g/14oz can coconut milk
salt and ground black pepper
deep-fried onions, to garnish

1 Rub each of the chicken joints with a little sugar and set them aside.

2 Grind the nuts and garlic in a food processor with the onion, galangal or ginger, sliced lemon grass, shrimp paste and turmeric. Alternatively, pound the ingredients to a paste with a pestle and mortar. Strain the tamarind pulp and reserve the juice.

COOK'S TIP

In step 3, start with a medium heat and reduce it to low after 1 minute.

3 Heat the oil in a wok or large pan, and cook the paste, without browning, until it gives off a spicy aroma. Add the pieces of chicken and toss well in the spices. Add the strained tamarind juice. Spoon the coconut cream off the top of the milk and set it to one side.

4 Add the coconut milk to the pan. Cover and cook for 45 minutes, or until the chicken is tender.

5 Before serving, stir in the coconut cream. Season to taste and serve, garnished with deep-fried onions.

EAST INDIA

The state of Bengal has developed a strong culinary identity, which makes use of local produce such as mustard, coconut, vegetables, lentils and rice. Fish from the Bay of Bengal is eaten throughout eastern India, and in areas close to the sea, fish is eaten daily, in place of meat.

CHICKEN with SPICES and SOY SAUCE

This simple but delicious dish, known as ayam kecap, suggests a Chinese influence. Although a significant number of people from China had already settled in Malaysia, by the 15th century Malacca was established as one of the important trading posts in the world, and more Chinese poured into the area. Together with the local Malay people, they developed a unique style of cuisine known as Nonya.

SERVES 4

1.3–1.6kg/3–3½lb chicken, jointed and
    cut into 16 pieces
3 onions, sliced
about 1 litre/1¾ pints/4 cups water
3 garlic cloves, crushed
3–4 fresh red chillies, seeded and sliced,
    or 15ml/1 tbsp chilli powder
45ml/3 tbsp vegetable oil
2.5ml/½ tsp grated nutmeg
6 whole cloves
5ml/1 tsp tamarind pulp, soaked in 45ml/
    3 tbsp warm water
30–45ml/2–3 tbsp dark or light soy sauce
salt
fresh green and red chilli shreds, to garnish
plain boiled rice, to serve

1 Place the prepared chicken pieces in a large pan with one of the sliced onions. Pour over enough water to just cover. Bring to the boil and then reduce the heat and allow to simmer gently for about 20 minutes.

2 Grind the remaining onions, with the garlic and chillies or chilli powder, to a fine paste in a food processor or with a pestle and mortar. Heat a little of the oil in a wok or frying pan and cook the paste to bring out the flavour. Do not allow the paste to brown.

COOK'S TIP
When adding salt, start with a very small quantity and taste before adding more.

3 When the chicken has cooked for 20 minutes, lift it out of the stock and into the spicy mixture. Toss everything together over a fairly high heat so that the spices permeate the chicken pieces. Reserve 300ml/½ pint/1¼ cups of the chicken stock to add to the pan later.

4 Stir in the nutmeg and cloves. Strain the tamarind and add the tamarind juice and the soy sauce to the chicken. Cook for a further 2–3 minutes, then add the reserved stock.

5 Taste and adjust the seasoning to taste and cook, uncovered, for a further 25–35 minutes, or until the chicken pieces are tender.

6 Transfer the chicken to a bowl, topped with shredded green and red chillies, and serve with plain boiled rice.

COOK'S TIP
Dark soy sauce is thicker and more salty than light. Adding the dark variety will give a deeper colour to the chicken.

CHICKEN JHALFRAZI

Jhalfrazi was created by Indian chefs during the British Raj. Leftover cold meat, generally from the Sunday roast, was stir-fried with spices. The dish originated in Calcutta, where the East India Company was established as an important trading post by the British.

SERVES 4

675g/1½lb chicken breast fillets, skinned
30ml/2 tbsp vegetable oil
5ml/1 tsp cumin seeds
1 onion, finely chopped
1 green (bell) pepper, finely chopped
1 red (bell) pepper, finely chopped
1 garlic clove, crushed
2cm/¾in piece fresh root ginger, chopped
15ml/1 tbsp curry paste
1.5ml/¼ tsp chilli powder
5ml/1 tsp ground coriander
5ml/1 tsp ground cumin
2.5ml/½ tsp salt
400g/14oz can chopped tomatoes
30ml/2 tbsp chopped fresh coriander
   (cilantro)
fresh coriander (cilantro) sprig, to garnish
plain boiled rice or naan bread, to serve

3 Add the curry paste to the other ingredients in the pan and stir-fry for about 2 minutes. Stir in the chilli powder, ground coriander, cumin and salt, and add 15ml/1 tbsp water. Stir-fry for a further 2 minutes.

4 Add the chicken and stir-fry for about 5 minutes. Add the tomatoes and fresh coriander. Cook, covered, for about 15 minutes until the chicken is tender. Garnish with a sprig of fresh coriander. Serve with plain boiled rice or naan.

1 Remove any visible fat and cut the chicken into 2.5cm/1in cubes.

2 Heat the oil in a wok, karahi or large pan, and fry the cumin seeds for 30–40 seconds until they begin to splutter. Add the onion, peppers, garlic and ginger and fry for 6–8 minutes.

MALAYSIA

The food of Malaysia is a rich blend of some of the world's most exciting cuisines: Malay, Chinese and Indian. The result is a harmonious mixture of flavours, some cool and some famously hot and spicy, such as the dishes cooked in the traditional style known as Nonya.

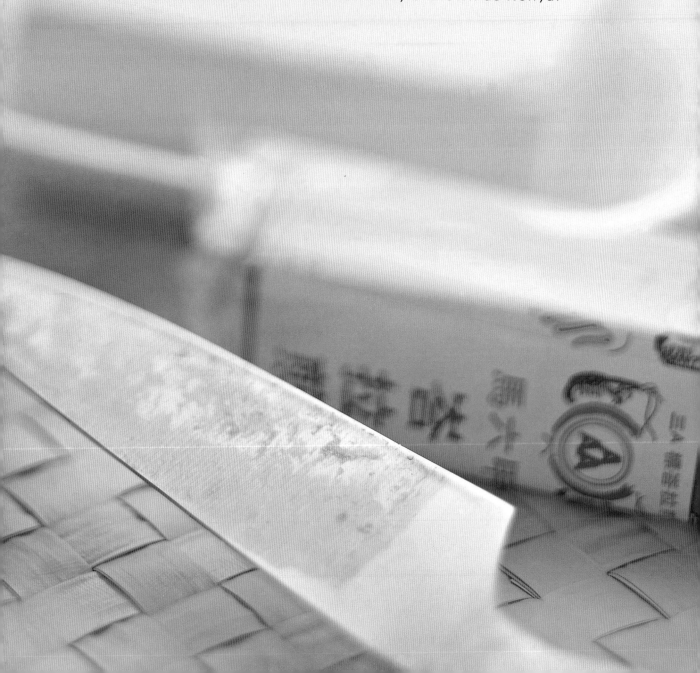

CUMIN-SCENTED CHICKEN

Cumin is a wonderful spice that is full of pungency, but without any harshness. Its rather warm and assertive nature gives this dish a distinctive flavour and aroma. Cumin is also known to have curative properties.

SERVES 4

45ml/3 tbsp cumin seeds
45ml/3 tbsp vegetable oil
2.5ml/½ tsp black peppercorns
4 green cardamom pods
2 fresh green chillies, finely chopped
2 garlic cloves, crushed
2.5cm/1in piece fresh root ginger, grated
5ml/1 tsp ground coriander
10ml/2 tsp ground cumin
2.5ml/½ tsp salt
8 chicken pieces, such as thighs and
    drumsticks, skinned
5ml/1 tsp garam masala
Spiced Yogurt and Cucumber Raita,
    garnished with fresh coriander (cilantro)
    and chilli powder, to serve (optional)

1 Preheat a wok or round-based frying pan over a medium heat and dry-roast 15ml/1 tbsp of the cumin seeds for 1–2 minutes until they release their aroma. Set aside.

2 Heat the oil in a wok or large pan and fry the remaining cumin seeds, black peppercorns and cardamoms for about 2 minutes.

3 Add the green chillies, garlic and grated fresh root ginger to the spices in the pan and fry for 2 minutes.

4 Add the ground coriander and cumin to the pan with the salt, and cook over a medium heat, stirring, for a further 1–2 minutes.

5 Add the chicken pieces, stir and mix thoroughly with the spices. Cover and allow to simmer for 20–25 minutes.

6 Add the garam masala and reserved dry-roasted cumin seeds, and cook for a further 5 minutes. Serve with Spiced Yogurt and Cucumber Raita, if you like.

GREEN PAPAYA SALAD

This salad appears in many guises in South-east Asia. If green papaya is not easy to get hold of, finely grated carrots, cucumber or green apple can be used instead. Alternatively, use very thinly sliced white cabbage.

SERVES 4

1 green papaya
4 garlic cloves, roughly chopped
15ml/1 tbsp chopped shallots
3–4 fresh red chillies, seeded and sliced
2.5ml/½ tsp salt
2–3 snake beans or 6 green beans
2 tomatoes, seeded and cut into very
    thin wedges
45ml/3 tbsp Thai fish sauce
15ml/1 tbsp granulated sugar
juice of 1 lime
30ml/2 tbsp coarsely crushed
    roasted peanuts
1 fresh red chilli, seeded and sliced,
    to garnish

1 Cut the papaya in half lengthwise. Scrape out the seeds with a spoon, then peel using a vegetable peeler or a small sharp knife. Shred the flesh finely using a food processor grater.

2 Put the garlic, shallots, chillies and salt in a large mortar and grind to a rough paste with a pestle. Add the shredded papaya, a little at a time, pounding until it becomes slightly limp and soft.

3 Cut the snake beans or green beans into 2cm/¾in lengths. Add the sliced beans and the wedges of tomato to the mortar and crush them very lightly with the pestle.

4 Season the mixture with the Thai fish sauce, sugar and lime juice. Transfer the salad to a serving dish and sprinkle with the crushed peanuts. Garnish with slices of red chilli and serve.

CHICKEN in COCONUT MILK

In Bengal, this dish is known as murgi malai, *and in the Bengali language, the word* murgi *means chicken and* malai *is cream, either dairy or coconut. Coconut is a favourite ingredient of the region, and it grows in abundant supply in Bengal, Orissa and Assam.*

2 Add the coconut milk, fromage frais or ricotta cheese, ground coriander, chilli powder, garlic, ginger and salt to the bowl. Mix together well.

3 Heat the vegetable oil in the pan, and add the chicken cubes, cardamom pods and bay leaf. Stir-fry for about 2 minutes to seal the chicken.

SERVES 4

15ml/1 tbsp ground almonds
15ml/1 tbsp desiccated (dry, unsweetened, shredded) coconut
85ml/3fl oz/⅔ cup coconut milk
175g/6oz/⅔ cup fromage frais or ricotta cheese
7.5ml/1½ tsp ground coriander
5ml/1 tsp chilli powder
5ml/1 tsp crushed garlic
7.5ml/1½ tsp grated fresh root ginger
5ml/1 tsp salt
30ml/2 tbsp vegetable oil
450g/1lb chicken breast fillets, skinned and cubed
3 green cardamom pods
1 bay leaf
1 dried red chilli, crushed
30ml/2 tbsp chopped fresh coriander (cilantro)

1 Dry-roast the almonds and coconut in a wok, karahi or large pan, until they turn a shade darker. Transfer the mixture to a large glass bowl.

COOK'S TIP
Fromage frais and ricotta cheese are used here in order to reduce the fat content. For a more authentic taste and aroma, use extra coconut milk.

4 Pour in the coconut mixture and stir well. Lower the heat, add the chilli and coriander, then cover and cook for 10–12 minutes, stirring occasionally to prevent the contents from sticking to the pan. Uncover the pan, then stir and cook for 2 minutes more. Classic Pulao would make a good accompaniment.

BEANCURD and GREEN BEAN CURRY

These days, beancurd is widely available from supermarkets and Asian stores. It has a silky appearance and an extremely soft texture. Tofu makes an excellent substitute; like beancurd, tofu is made of soya bean paste, but is much firmer. It is also much more easily available and can be found in most supermarkets and health food stores.

SERVES 4–6

600ml/1 pint/2½ cups coconut milk
15ml/1 tbsp red curry paste
45ml/3 tbsp Thai fish sauce
10ml/2 tsp palm sugar or soft light
   brown sugar
225g/8oz button (white) mushrooms
115g/4oz French (green) beans, trimmed
175g/6oz beancurd, rinsed and cut into
   2cm/¾in cubes
4 kaffir lime leaves, torn
2 fresh red chillies, sliced
fresh coriander (cilantro) sprigs, to garnish

1 Put about one-third of the coconut milk in a wok or large pan. Cook until an oily sheen appears on the surface.

2 Add the red curry paste, fish sauce and sugar to the coconut milk. Mix together thoroughly.

3 Add the button mushrooms. Stir well and cook over a medium heat for about 1 minute. Stir in the rest of the coconut milk and bring back to the boil.

4 Add the French beans and cubes of beancurd and allow to simmer gently for another 4–5 minutes.

5 Stir in the kaffir lime leaves and red chillies. Serve garnished with the fresh coriander sprigs.

FISH JHALFRAZI

In Bengal, fish curry and rice are eaten together on a daily basis. This is a rather unusual dish, using canned tuna cooked in the style of jhalfrazi, and is ideal for lunch or supper. Served with boiled basmati rice and tarka dhal, it will also make a satisfying family meal.

SERVES 4

1 onion
1 red (bell) pepper
1 green (bell) pepper
45ml/3 tbsp vegetable oil
1.5ml/¼ tsp cumin seeds
2.5ml/½ tsp ground cumin
2.5ml/½ tsp ground coriander
2.5ml/½ tsp chilli powder
1.5ml/¼ tsp salt
2 garlic cloves, crushed
400g/14oz can tuna, drained
1 fresh green chilli, finely chopped
2.5cm/1in piece fresh root ginger, grated
1.5ml/¼ tsp garam masala
5ml/1 tsp lemon juice
30ml/2 tbsp chopped fresh coriander (cilantro)
fresh coriander (cilantro) sprig, to garnish
pitta bread and Spiced Yogurt and Cucumber Raita, to serve

4 Stir-fry the vegetables for 5–7 minutes until the onions have browned.

5 Stir in the tuna, fresh chilli and grated ginger and cook for 5 minutes more.

6 Add the garam masala, lemon juice and fresh coriander and continue to cook for 3–4 minutes. Serve in warmed pitta bread with Spiced Yogurt and Cucumber Raita, garnished with fresh coriander.

1 Thinly slice the onion and the red and green peppers. Set aside.

2 Heat the oil in a wok, karahi or large pan over a medium heat and fry the cumin seeds for 30–40 seconds until they begin to splutter.

3 Add the ground cumin and coriander, chilli powder and salt to the pan. Cook for 2 minutes. Add the garlic, onion and peppers and increase the heat a little.

COOK'S TIP
Place the pitta bread on a grill (broiler) rack and grill (broil) until it puffs up. It will then be easy to split with a sharp knife.

PRAWNS with YELLOW CURRY PASTE

*Fish and shellfish, such as prawns, and coconut milk were made for each other. This is a
very quick recipe if you make the yellow curry paste in advance, or buy it ready-made.
It keeps well in a screw-top jar in the refrigerator for up to four weeks.*

SERVES 4–6

600ml/1 pint/2½ cups coconut milk
30ml/2 tbsp yellow curry paste
15ml/1 tbsp fish sauce
2.5ml/½ tsp salt
5ml/1 tsp granulated sugar
450g/1lb raw king prawns
    (jumbo shrimp), thawed if frozen,
    peeled and deveined
225g/8oz cherry tomatoes
juice of ½ lime
red (bell) peppers, seeded and cut into
    thin strips, and fresh coriander
    (cilantro) leaves, to garnish
plain boiled rice or rice noodles,
    to serve

1 Put half the coconut milk in a wok
or large pan and bring to the boil. Add
the yellow curry paste, and stir until it
disperses. Lower the heat and simmer
gently for about 10 minutes.

2 Add the fish sauce, salt, sugar and
remaining coconut milk to the sauce.
Simmer for 5 minutes more.

3 Add the prawns and cherry tomatoes.
Simmer very gently for about 5 minutes
until the prawns are pink and tender.

4 Spoon into a serving dish, sprinkle
with lime juice and garnish with strips
of pepper and coriander.

VARIATION
Use cooked prawns if preferred. Add in
step 3 and heat through.

COOK'S TIP
• Unused coconut milk can be stored in
the refrigerator for 1 2 days, or poured
into a freezer container and frozen.
• If making your own coconut milk,
instead of discarding the spent coconut,
it can be reused to make a second batch
of coconut milk. This will be of a poorer
quality and should only be used to extend
a good quality first quantity of milk.
• Leave newly made coconut milk to
stand for 10 minutes. The coconut cream
will float to the top: skim off with a spoon.

FISH STEW

Cooking fish with vegetables is very much a tradition in eastern regions. This hearty dish with potatoes, peppers and tomatoes is perfect served with breads such as chapatis or parathas. You can try other combinations, such as green beans and spinach, but you do need a starchy vegetable in order to thicken the sauce.

SERVES 4

30ml/2 tbsp vegetable oil
5ml/1 tsp cumin seeds
1 onion, chopped
1 red (bell) pepper, thinly sliced
1 garlic clove, crushed
2 fresh red chillies, finely chopped
2 bay leaves
2.5ml/½ tsp salt
5ml/1 tsp ground cumin
5ml/1 tsp ground coriander
5ml/1 tsp chilli powder
400g/14oz can chopped tomatoes
2 large potatoes, cut into 2.5cm/1in chunks
300ml/½ pint/1¼ cups fish stock
4 cod fillets
chapatis, to serve

1 Heat the oil in a wok, karahi or large pan over a medium heat and fry the cumin seeds for 30–40 seconds until they begin to splutter. Add the onion, red pepper, garlic, chillies and bay leaves and fry for 5–7 minutes more until the onions have browned.

2 Add the salt, ground cumin, ground coriander and chilli powder and cook for 1–2 minutes.

COOK'S TIP
Avoid reheating this dish. Serve it as soon as it is cooked because cod flesh flakes very easily. If preparing in advance, follow the recipe up to the end of step 3, then cover the sauce and store in the refrigerator. Cook step 4 before serving.

3 Stir in the tomatoes, potatoes and fish stock. Bring to the boil and simmer for a further 10 minutes, or until the potatoes are almost tender.

4 Add the fish fillets, then cover the pan and allow to simmer for 5–6 minutes until the fish is just cooked. Serve hot with chapatis, if you like.

GREEN PRAWN CURRY

Green Curry has become a firm favourite in the West, and this prawn dish is just one of a range of delicious green curry recipes. Home-made green curry paste has the best flavour, but you can also buy it ready-made from good supermarkets.

SERVES 4–6

30ml/2 tbsp vegetable oil
30ml/2 tbsp green curry paste
450g/1lb raw king prawns (jumbo shrimp), peeled and deveined
4 kaffir lime leaves, torn
1 lemon grass stalk, bruised and chopped
250ml/8fl oz/1 cup coconut milk
30ml/2 tbsp fish sauce
½ cucumber, seeded and cut into thin batons
10–15 basil leaves
4 fresh green chillies, sliced, to garnish

1 Heat the oil in a wok or large pan. Add the green curry paste and fry gently until bubbling and fragrant.

2 Add the prawns, kaffir lime leaves and chopped lemon grass. Fry for 2 minutes, until the prawns are pink.

3 Stir in the coconut milk and bring to a gentle boil. Simmer, stirring occasionally, for about 5 minutes or until the prawns are tender.

4 Stir in the fish sauce, cucumber batons and whole basil leaves, then top with the green chillies and serve from the pan.

VARIATION
Strips of skinned chicken breast fillet can be used in place of the prawns if you prefer. Add them to the pan in step 2 and fry until browned on all sides.

FISH in a RICH TOMATO and ONION SAUCE

It is difficult to imagine the cuisine of eastern India without fish. Bengal is as well known for its fish and shellfish dishes as Goa on the west coast. In both regions, coconut is used extensively, and the difference in the taste, as always, lies in the spicing. This onion-rich dish is known as kalia in Bengal, and a firm-fleshed fish is essential.

SERVES 4

675g/1½lb steaks of firm-textured fish
    such as tuna or monkfish, skinned
30ml/2 tbsp lemon juice
5ml/1 tsp salt
5ml/1 tsp ground turmeric
vegetable oil, for shallow frying
40g/1½ oz/½ cup plain (all-purpose) flour
2.5ml/¼ tsp ground black pepper
60ml/4 tbsp vegetable oil
10ml/2 tsp granulated sugar
1 large onion, finely chopped
15ml/1 tbsp grated fresh root ginger
15ml/1 tbsp crushed garlic
5ml/1 tsp ground coriander
2.5–5ml/½–1 tsp hot chilli powder
175g/6 oz canned chopped tomatoes,
    including the juice
300ml/½ pint/1¼ cups warm water
30ml/2 tbsp chopped fresh coriander
    (cilantro) leaves, to garnish
plain boiled rice, to serve

1 Cut the fish into 7.5cm/3in pieces and put into a large bowl. Add the lemon juice and sprinkle with half the salt and half the turmeric. Mix gently with your fingertips and set aside for 15 minutes.

2 Pour enough oil into a 23cm/9in frying pan to cover the base to a depth of 1cm/½in and heat over a medium setting. Mix the flour and pepper and dust the fish in the seasoned flour. Add to the oil in a single layer and fry until browned on both sides and a light crust has formed. Drain on kitchen paper.

3 In a wok, karahi or large pan, heat 60ml/4 tbsp oil. When the oil is hot, but not smoking, add the sugar and let it caramelize. As soon as the sugar is brown, add the onion, ginger and garlic and fry for 7–8 minutes, until just beginning to colour. Stir regularly.

4 Add the ground coriander, chilli powder and the remaining turmeric. Stir-fry for about 30 seconds and add the tomatoes. Cook until the tomatoes are mushy and the oil separates from the spice paste, stirring regularly.

5 Pour the warm water and remaining salt into the pan, and bring to the boil. Carefully add the fried fish, reduce the heat to low and simmer, uncovered, for 5–6 minutes. Transfer to a serving dish and garnish with the coriander leaves. Serve with plain boiled rice.

COOK'S TIP
Like all ground spices, ground turmeric will lose its potency on keeping. Buy only small quantities, and store the powder in an airtight container, in a cupboard away from strong light.

BURMESE FISH STEW

Housewives in Burma buy this well-known and delicious one-course meal, known as Mohingha, from hawkers, who can be recognized by a bamboo pole carried across their shoulders. At one end of the pole is a container with a charcoal fire and at the other end is everything else they need to make the meal.

SERVES 8

675g/1½lb huss, cod or mackerel,
   cleaned but left on the bone
3 lemon grass stalks
2.5cm/1in piece fresh root ginger
30ml/2 tbsp fish sauce
3 onions, roughly chopped
4 garlic cloves, roughly chopped
2–3 fresh red chillies, seeded and chopped
5ml/1 tsp ground turmeric
75ml/5 tbsp groundnut (peanut) oil,
   for frying
400g/14oz can coconut milk
25g/1oz/¼ cup rice flour
25g/1oz/¼ cup gram flour (besan)
540g/1lb/5oz canned bamboo shoots,
   rinsed, drained and sliced
salt and ground black pepper
wedges of hard-boiled (hard-cooked) egg,
   thinly sliced red onions, finely chopped
   spring onions (scallions), deep-fried
   prawns (shrimp) and fried chillies,
   to garnish
rice noodles, to serve

1 Place the fish in a large pan and pour in cold water to cover. Bruise two lemon grass stalks and half the peeled fresh root ginger and add to the pan. Bring to the boil, add the fish sauce and cook for 10 minutes. Lift out the fish with a slotted spoon, and allow to cool. Meanwhile, strain the stock into a large bowl. Discard any skin and bones from the fish and break the flesh into small pieces, using a fork.

2 Cut off the lower 5cm/2in of the remaining lemon grass stalk and discard; roughly chop the remaining lemon grass. Put it in a food processor or blender, along with the remaining ginger, the onions, garlic, chillies and turmeric. Process to a smooth paste. Heat the oil in a wok or large pan, and fry the paste until it gives off a rich, fragrant aroma. Remove the pan from the heat and add the fish pieces.

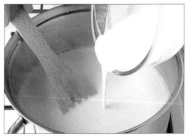

3 Stir the coconut milk into the reserved fish stock and pour into a large pan. Add water to make up to 2.5 litres/4 pints/10 cups. In a jug (pitcher), mix the rice flour and gram flour (besan) to a thin cream with some of the stock. Stir into the mixture. Bring to the boil, stirring.

4 Add the bamboo shoots to the pan and cook for 10 minutes until tender. Stir in the fish mixture, season to taste, and cook until heated through. Guests pour the soup over the noodles, and add hard-boiled egg, onions, spring onions, prawns and chillies as a garnish.

PRAWN CURRY

The Bay of Bengal provides Bengal and Orissa with enormous quantities of fish and shellfish. Eating plenty of fish, greens, lentils and peas is a way of life here. The food is generally cooked in mustard oil, which lends a distinctive, nutty flavour to the final dish.

SERVES 4

675g/1½lb raw tiger prawns (jumbo shrimp)
4 dried red chillies
50g/2oz/1 cup desiccated (dry, unsweetened, shredded) coconut
5ml/1 tsp black mustard seeds
1 large onion, chopped
45ml/3 tbsp vegetable oil
4 bay leaves
2.5cm/1in piece fresh root ginger, chopped
2 garlic cloves, crushed
15ml/1 tbsp ground coriander
5ml/1 tsp chilli powder
5ml/1 tsp salt
4 tomatoes, finely chopped
plain boiled rice, to serve

1 Peel the prawns. Run a sharp knife along the back of each prawn to make a shallow cut and carefully remove the thin black intestinal vein. You might like to leave a few of the prawns unpeeled, setting them aside to use as a garnish for the finished dish.

2 Put the dried red chillies, coconut, mustard seeds and onion in a wok, karahi or large pan and dry-fry over a medium heat for 5–6 minutes, or until the mixture begins to brown. Stir continuously to ensure even browning and to avoid burning the coconut. Put into a food processor or blender and process to a coarse paste.

3 Heat the vegetable oil in the pan and fry the bay leaves for 1 minute. Add the chopped ginger and the garlic, and fry for 2–3 minutes.

4 Add the ground coriander, chilli powder, salt and the paste and fry for about 5 minutes.

5 Stir in the tomatoes and about 175ml/6fl oz/¾ cup water and simmer for 5–6 minutes or until thickened.

6 Add the prawns and cook for about 4–5 minutes, or until they turn pink. Grill (broil) the reserved whole prawns, if using, until pink. Serve the curry on a ring of plain boiled rice and garnish with the whole prawns, if using.

MUSSAMAN CURRY

Unlike its neighbouring countries, Thailand managed to remain free from colonization by European powers. As a result, its food has no outside influence, although the Thais have borrowed cooking styles from other countries, such as India and China. Mussaman Curry is one such example, which originated within the Muslim community in India.

SERVES 4–6

600ml/1 pint/2½ cups coconut milk (see Cook's Tip)
675g/1½lb stewing beef, cut into 2.cm/1in chunks
250ml/8fl oz/1 cup coconut cream
45ml/3 tbsp mussaman curry paste
30ml/2 tbsp Thai fish sauce
15ml/1 tbsp palm sugar or soft light brown sugar
60ml/4 tbsp tamarind juice or concentrated tamarind pulp
6 cardamom pods
2.5cm/1in piece cinnamon stick
225g/8oz potatoes, cut into even-size chunks
1 onion, cut into wedges
50g/2oz/⅓ cup roasted peanuts
plain boiled rice, to serve

1 Bring the coconut milk to a gentle boil in a wok or large pan. Add the beef and simmer for 40 minutes, until tender.

2 Pour the coconut cream into a small pan, then cook for 5–8 minutes, stirring constantly, until an oily sheen appears on the surface. Add the Thai mussaman curry paste and cook until fragrant.

3 Stir the curry paste into the beef. Add the fish sauce, sugar, tamarind, cardamom pods, cinnamon stick, potatoes and onions. Simmer gently for 10–15 minutes. Add the peanuts and cook for a further 5 minutes. Serve with plain boiled rice.

COOK'S TIP
Coconut milk can be made at home from desiccated (dry, unsweetened, shredded) coconut. In a food processor, process 225g/8oz/2⅔ cups desiccated coconut with 450ml/¾ pint/scant 2 cups boiling water for 20–30 seconds. Allow to cool, then ladle into a sieve (strainer) lined with muslin (cheesecloth) set over a bowl. Bring up the ends of the cloth and twist to extract the liquid. Discard the spent coconut and use the milk as directed in recipes. Unused milk will keep in the refrigerator for 1–2 days.

KING PRAWN KORMA

Prawns are the most popular shellfish in Bengal. This dish is cooked in the style of malai chingri, *which means prawns cooked in dairy or coconut cream. Because of the richness of the ingredients, serve plain boiled rice with this korma.*

SERVES 4

10–12 peeled, cooked king prawns
   (jumbo shrimp), thawed if frozen
45ml/3 tbsp natural (plain) yogurt
5ml/1 tsp paprika
5ml/1 tsp garam masala
15ml/1 tbsp tomato purée (paste)
60ml/4 tbsp coconut milk
5ml/1 tsp chilli powder
150ml/¼ pint/⅔ cup water
15ml/1 tbsp vegetable oil
5ml/1 tsp crushed garlic
5ml/1 tsp grated fresh root ginger
2.5cm/1in piece cinnamon stick, halved
2 green cardamom pods
salt
15ml/1 tbsp chopped fresh coriander
   (cilantro), to garnish

1 If the prawns had been frozen, drain thoroughly in a sieve (strainer) over a bowl to ensure that all excess liquid is removed before cooking.

2 Place the yogurt, paprika, garam masala, tomato purée, coconut milk, chilli powder and water into a large glass bowl, and season to taste with salt.

3 Blend the ingredients together. Set aside.

4 Heat the oil in a wok, karahi or large pan, add the garlic, ginger, cinnamon, cardamoms and season to taste with salt. Fry over a low heat for 1–2 minutes.

5 Pour in the spice mixture and bring to the boil, stirring occasionally.

6 Add the prawns and cook, stirring constantly, until the sauce starts to thicken. Garnish and serve.

GREEN BEEF CURRY with THAI AUBERGINE

Thai cuisine is packed with sensational yet perfectly balanced flavours. This dish, which is cooked in the well-known green curry paste, creates a taste explosion. Thai aubergines are much smaller than the large, purple variety sold in Western supermarkets. You can buy small aubergines from Asian stores or, alternatively, use baby aubergines.

SERVES 4–6

15ml/1 tbsp vegetable oil
45ml/3 tbsp green curry paste
600ml/1 pint/2½ cups coconut milk
450g/1lb beef sirloin
4 kaffir lime leaves, torn
15–30ml/1–2 tbsp Thai fish sauce
5ml/1 tsp palm sugar or soft light
  brown sugar
150g/5oz small Thai aubergines
  (eggplant) or baby aubergines,
  halved
2 fresh green chillies and a small handful
  of Thai basil, to garnish
plain boiled rice or noodles, to serve

1 Heat the oil in a wok or large pan. Add the green curry paste and fry gently until the paste begins to release its fragrant aromas.

2 Stir in half the coconut milk, a little at a time. Cook over a medium heat for about 5–6 minutes, until the oil begins to separate and an oily sheen appears on the surface.

3 Cut the beef into long thin slices and add to the pan with the kaffir lime leaves, fish sauce, sugar and aubergines. Cook for 2–3 minutes, then stir in the remaining coconut milk.

4 Bring back to a simmer and cook until the meat and aubergines are tender. Finely shred the green chillies and use to garnish the curry, along with the Thai basil leaves.

MASALA CHANNA

This is a typical Calcutta street food known as ghughni. Plates full of ghughni, with the wholesome taste of chickpeas laced with spices and tamarind juice, are enjoyed with flat breads such as chapatis and parathas.

SERVES 4

225g/8oz/1¼ cups dried chickpeas
50g/2oz tamarind pulp
120ml/4fl oz/½ cup boiling water
45ml/3 tbsp vegetable oil
2.5ml/½ tsp cumin seeds
1 onion, finely chopped
2 garlic cloves, crushed
2.5cm/1in piece fresh root ginger, grated
1 fresh green chilli, finely chopped
5ml/1 tsp ground cumin
5ml/1 tsp ground coriander
1.5ml/¼ tsp ground turmeric
2.5ml/½ tsp salt
225g/8oz tomatoes, skinned and
　　finely chopped
2.5ml/½ tsp garam masala
chopped chillies and chopped onion,
　　to garnish

1 Put the chickpeas in a large bowl and cover with plenty of cold water. Leave to soak overnight.

2 Drain the chickpeas and place in a large pan with double the volume of cold water. Bring to the boil and boil vigorously for 10 minutes. Skim off any scum, then cover and simmer for 1½–2 hours or until soft.

3 Meanwhile, break up the tamarind pulp and soak in the boiling water for about 15 minutes. Use the back of a spoon to rub the tamarind through a sieve (strainer) into a bowl, discarding any stones and fibre. (Leave out this step if you are using commercial tamarind paste in place of the fresh pulp.)

4 Heat the vegetable oil in a wok, karahi or large pan and fry the cumin seeds for 2 minutes until they begin to splutter. Add the chopped onion, garlic, ginger and chilli and fry for 5 minutes.

5 Add the cumin, coriander, turmeric and salt and fry for 3–4 minutes. Add the tomatoes and tamarind juice. Bring to the boil and simmer for 5 minutes.

6 Add the chickpeas and garam masala, cover and simmer for about 15 minutes. Garnish with the chillies and onion.

COOK'S TIP
Make double the quantity of tamarind juice and freeze in ice-cube trays. It will keep for up to 12 months. Alternatively, buy tamarind paste sold in Indian stores. It is ready to use and will keep for an indefinite period at room temperature.

BEEF CURRY in SWEET PEANUT SAUCE

The consistency of this curry is quite thick, unlike most other Thai curries. Roasted and ground peanuts add a rich taste, and thicken the sauce at the same time. You can grind the peanuts in a coffee grinder or use a pestle and mortar. For a quick alternative, you could use peanut butter, but you will need to reduce the quantity of salt.

SERVES 4–6

600ml/1 pint/2½ cups coconut milk
45ml/3 tbsp red curry paste
45ml/3 tbsp Thai fish sauce
30ml/2 tbsp palm sugar or soft light
  brown sugar
2 lemon grass stalks, bruised
450g/1lb rump steak cut into thin strips
75g/3oz roasted ground peanuts
2 fresh red chillies, sliced
5 kaffir lime leaves, torn
salt and ground black pepper
10–15 Thai basil leaves, to garnish
2 salted eggs, to serve

1 Put half the coconut milk into a wok or large pan. Heat the milk gently, stirring constantly, until it begins to boil and separate.

2 Add the red curry paste and cook over a medium heat until fragrant. Add the fish sauce, palm or light brown sugar and lemon grass.

3 Continue to cook until the colour of the curry sauce deepens.

4 Add the remaining coconut milk and bring back to the boil. Add the beef and ground peanuts. Cook for 8–10 minutes.

5 Add the sliced chillies and torn kaffir lime leaves and adjust the seasoning. Garnish with the whole Thai basil leaves, and serve with salted eggs, if you like.

MIXED VEGETABLE CURRY

Curries based on a variety of vegetables are cooked throughout India, but they all differ from one another according to the spicing and the method of cooking. This particular version, made with onion seeds, is a typical example from the east and north-east of the country, where the dish is known as chorchori.

SERVES 4–6

350g/12oz mixed vegetables such as green
    beans, peas, potatoes, cauliflower,
    carrots, cabbage, mangetouts (snow
    peas) and button (white) mushrooms
30ml/2 tbsp vegetable oil
2.5ml/½ tsp mustard seeds
5ml/1 tsp cumin seeds, freshly roasted
2.5ml/½ tsp onion seeds
5ml/1 tsp ground turmeric
2 garlic cloves, crushed
6–8 curry leaves
1 dried red chilli
5ml/1 tsp granulated sugar
150ml/¼ pint/⅔ cup natural (plain) yogurt
    mixed with 5ml/1 tsp cornflour
    (cornstarch), well beaten
salt
fresh bay leaves, to garnish

1 Prepare all the vegetables you have chosen: string the beans; cube the potatoes; cut the cauliflower into florets; dice the carrots; shred the cabbage; trim the mangetouts; wash the mushrooms and leave them whole.

2 Heat a large, deep-sided pan with enough water to cook all the vegetables and bring to the boil. First add the potatoes and carrots and cook until nearly tender then add all the other vegetables and cook until nearly tender but still firm. All the vegetables should be only just tender except the potatoes, which should be tender. Drain well.

COOK'S TIP
If you have gram flour (besan), mix this with the yogurt instead of cornflour. It prevents the yogurt from curdling and lends a nutty taste.

3 Heat the oil in a large pan and add the mustard and cumin seeds. As they pop, add the remaining spices and fry gently until the garlic is golden and the chilli nearly burnt. Reduce the heat.

4 Fold in the drained vegetables, add the sugar and salt and gradually add the yogurt mixed with the cornflour. Heat through and serve immediately, garnished with fresh bay leaves.

CHICKEN with GINGER and LEMON GRASS

This quick and easy recipe from Vietnam contains the unusual combination of ginger and lemon grass with mandarin orange and chillies. The dish is served topped with peanuts, which are first roasted, then skinned.

SERVES 4–6

3 chicken legs (thighs and drumsticks)
15ml/1 tbsp vegetable oil
2cm/¾in piece fresh root ginger,
   finely chopped
1 garlic clove, crushed
1 small fresh red chilli, seeded and
   finely chopped
5cm/2in piece lemon grass, shredded
150ml/¼ pint/⅔ cup chicken stock
15ml/1 tbsp fish sauce
10ml/2 tsp granulated sugar
2.5ml/½ tsp salt
juice of ½ lemon
50g/2oz raw peanuts
2 spring onions (scallions),
   shredded
zest of 1 mandarin or satsuma,
   shredded
plain boiled rice or rice noodles, to serve

3 To prepare the peanuts, the red skin must be removed. To do this grill (broil) or roast the peanuts under a medium heat until evenly brown, for 2–3 minutes. Turn the nuts out on to a clean cloth and rub briskly to loosen the skins.

4 Transfer the chicken from the pan to a warmed serving dish, and sprinkle with the roasted peanuts, shredded spring onions and the zest of the mandarin or satsuma. Serve hot with plain boiled rice or rice noodles.

1 With the heel of a knife, chop through the narrow end of each of the chicken drumsticks. Remove the jointed parts of the chicken, then remove the skin. Rinse and pat dry with kitchen paper.

2 Heat the oil in a wok or large pan. Add the chicken, ginger, garlic, chilli and lemon grass and cook for 3–4 minutes. Add the chicken stock, fish sauce, sugar, salt and lemon juice. Cover the pan and simmer for 30–35 minutes.

COOK'S TIP
To save yourself time and effort, buy ready-roasted peanuts. These are now available with reduced sodium for a low-salt alternative.

Thailand, Burma and Vietnam

CRISP FRIED AUBERGINE

The vegetarian community in Bengal would happily eat begun bhaja, fried aubergine, and a lentil dish with rice for a main meal. Choose the large variety of aubergine with an unblemished, glossy skin. There is no need to soak the aubergine in salted water as today's aubergines generally have less bitterness in the skin than they used to.

2 Halve the aubergine lengthwise and cut each half into 5mm/¼in thick slices. Rinse them and shake off the excess water, but do not pat dry. With some of the water still clinging to the slices, add them to the spiced gram flour mixture. Toss them around until they are evenly coated with the flour. Use a spoon if necessary to ensure that all the flour is incorporated.

3 Heat the oil in a deep-fat fryer or other suitable pan over a medium-high heat. If you have a thermometer, check that the oil has reached190°C/375°F. Alternatively, drop a small piece of day-old bread into the oil. If it floats immediately, then the oil has reached the right temperature.

SERVES 4

50g/2oz/½ cup gram flour (besan)
15ml/1tbsp semolina or ground rice
2.5ml/½ tsp onion seeds
5ml/1 tsp cumin seeds
2.5ml/½ tsp fennel seeds or aniseeds
2.5–5ml/½–1 tsp hot chilli powder
2.5ml/½ tsp salt, or to taste
1 large aubergine (eggplant)
vegetable oil, for deep-frying

COOK'S TIP
Fennel and aniseeds aid digestion, and most deep-fried Indian recipes use them.

1 Sieve the gram flour into a large mixing bowl and add the remaining ingredients except the aubergine and the vegetable oil.

4 Fry the spice-coated aubergine slices in a single layer. Avoid overcrowding the pan as this will lower the oil temperature, resulting in a soggy texture. Fry until the aubergines are crisp and well browned. Drain on kitchen paper and serve with a chutney.

BURMESE-STYLE PORK CURRY

The cuisine of Burma is influenced by its two neighbours, China and India. Soy sauce and noodles are obviously the result of a Chinese influence, but curry itself is definitely an Indian invention. Burmese curries are, however, much lighter.

SERVES 4–6

2.5cm/1in piece fresh root ginger,
    crushed
8 dried red chillies, soaked in warm
    water for 20 minutes
2 lemon grass stalks, finely chopped
15ml/1 tbsp chopped galangal or
    chopped fresh root ginger
15ml/1 tbsp shrimp paste
30ml/2 tbsp brown sugar
675g/1½lb pork, with some of its fat
600ml/1 pint/2½ cups water
10ml/2 tsp ground turmeric
5ml/1 tsp dark soy sauce
4 shallots, finely chopped
15ml/1 tbsp chopped garlic
45ml/3 tbsp tamarind juice or 5ml/1 tsp
    concentrated tamarind pulp
5ml/1 tsp granulated sugar
15ml/1 tbsp fish sauce
fresh red chillies, to garnish
French (green) beans, to serve

1 In a mortar, pound the ginger, chillies, lemon grass and galangal into a coarse paste with a pestle, then add the shrimp paste and brown sugar to produce a dark, grainy purée.

2 Cut the pork into large chunks and place in a wok or large pan. Add the curry purée and stir well to make sure the meat is well coated.

3 Cook the pork over a low heat, stirring occasionally, until the meat has changed colour and rendered some of its fat, and the curry paste has begun to release its aroma.

4 Stir the water, turmeric and soy sauce into the meat in the pan. Simmer gently for about 40 minutes, until the meat is tender. The pan does not need to be kept covered.

5 Add the shallots, garlic, tamarind juice, sugar and fish sauce. If you are using concentrated tamarind pulp, stir until dissolved. Garnish with fresh chillies and serve with French beans.

SWEET-and-SOUR PINEAPPLE

This may sound like a Chinese recipe, but it is a traditional Bengali dish known as tok. The predominant flavour is ginger, and the pieces of golden pineapple, dotted with plump, juicy raisins have plenty of visual appeal with a taste to match. It is equally delicious if made with mangoes instead of the pineapple. Serve as a side dish or digestive.

SERVES 4

800g/1¾lb pineapple rings or chunks
    in natural juice
15ml/1 tbsp vegetable oil
2.5ml/½ tsp black mustard seeds
2.5ml/½ tsp cumin seeds
2.5ml/½ tsp onion seeds
10ml/2 tsp grated fresh root ginger
5ml/1 tsp crushed dried chillies
50g/2oz/⅓ cup seedless raisins
125g/4oz/⅔ cup granulated sugar
7.5ml/1½ tsp salt

3 Add the pineapple, raisins, sugar and salt. Add 300 ml/½ pint/1¼ cups of the juice (make up with cold water if necessary) and add to the pineapple.

VARIATION
Two or three mangoes can be used for this dish instead of the pineapple, if you prefer. Choose ripe fruits that will be full of flavour. To prepare, cut off both sides of the fruit, keeping close to the stone, then peel off the skin and chop the flesh into chunks. Canned mangoes in natural juice could also be used.

4 Bring the mixture to the boil, reduce the heat to medium and cook, uncovered, for 20–25 minutes.

1 Drain the pineapple in a sieve (strainer) and reserve the juice. Chop the pineapple rings or chunks finely (you should have approximately 500g/1¼lb).

2 Heat the vegetable oil in a wok, karahi or large pan over a medium heat and immediately add the mustard seeds. As soon as they pop, add the cumin seeds, then the onion seeds. Add the ginger and chillies and stir-fry the spices briskly for 30 seconds until they release their flavours.

THAILAND, BURMA AND VIETNAM

To eat a Thai meal is an experience in itself, with subtle spice blends and exquisite flavours. Burmese food is more robust yet equally exciting, while Vietnamese cuisine shows the influence of neighbouring China, and there is evidence of traditions left over from French colonial rule.

POTATOES with ROASTED POPPY SEEDS

Poppy seeds are used in Indian cooking as thickening agents, and to lend a nutty taste to sauces. It is the creamy white variety of poppy seed that is used here, rather than the ones with a blue-grey hue that are used for baking.

SERVES 4

45ml/3 tbsp white poppy seeds
45–60ml/3–4 tbsp vegetable oil
675g/1½lb potatoes, peeled and cut into
    1cm/½in cubes
2.5ml/½ tsp black mustard seeds
2.5ml/½ tsp onion seeds
2.5ml/½ tsp cumin seeds
2.5ml/½ tsp fennel seeds
1–2 dried red chillies, chopped or broken
    into small pieces
2.5ml/½ tsp ground turmeric
2.5ml/½ tsp salt
150ml/¼ pint/⅔ cup warm water
fresh coriander (cilantro) sprigs, to garnish
pooris and natural (plain) yogurt, to serve

1 Preheat a wok, karahi or large pan over a medium setting. When the pan is hot, reduce the heat slightly and add the poppy seeds. Stir them around in the pan until they are just a shade darker. Remove from the pan and allow to cool.

2 In the pan, heat the vegetable oil over a medium heat and fry the cubes of potatoes until they are light brown. Remove them with a slotted spoon and drain on kitchen paper.

COOK'S TIP
Do not allow the dried chillies to burn or they will become bitter. Remove them from the pan when they have blackened.

3 To the same oil, add the mustard seeds. As soon as they begin to pop, add the onion, cumin and fennel seeds and the chillies. Let the chillies blacken.

4 Stir in the turmeric and follow quickly with the fried potatoes and salt. Stir well and add the warm water. Cover the pan with the lid and reduce the heat to low. Cook for 8–10 minutes, or until the potatoes are tender.

5 Grind the cooled poppy seeds in a pestle and mortar or coffee grinder. Stir the ground seeds into the potatoes. It should form a thick paste which should cling to the potatoes. If there is too much liquid, continue to stir over a medium heat until you have the right consistency. Transfer to a serving dish. Garnish with coriander and serve with pooris and natural yogurt.

COOK'S TIP
As they are ground, poppy seeds release a natural oil, which may prevent the blade of a spice mill or coffee grinder from moving. Scrape away anything that sticks to the blades and start again.

FRUIT RAITA and TOMATO and ONION SALAD

Refreshing yogurt raitas can be made with almost any fruit. Raw vegetable salads, known as cachumbers, are another classic way of adding a tangy touch to a meal.

FRUIT RAITA

SERVES 4

350ml/12fl oz/1½ cups natural
   (plain) yogurt
75g/3oz seedless grapes, washed and dried
50g/2oz shelled walnuts
2 firm bananas, sliced
5ml/1 tsp granulated sugar
5ml/1 tsp freshly ground cumin seeds
salt
1.5ml/¼ tsp freshly roasted cumin seeds,
   chilli powder, to garnish

1 Put the yogurt, grapes and walnuts in a bowl. Fold in the bananas.

2 Stir in the sugar, ground cumin and salt. Chill and sprinkle on the roasted cumin seeds and chilli powder before serving.

TOMATO AND ONION SALAD

SERVES 4–6

2 limes
2.5ml/½ tsp granulated sugar
a few fresh coriander (cilantro) sprigs,
   chopped, plus extra for garnishing
2 onions, finely chopped
4 firm tomatoes, finely chopped
½ cucumber, finely chopped
1 fresh green chilli, finely chopped
salt and ground black pepper
a few fresh mint sprigs, to garnish

1 Extract the juice of the limes into a small bowl. Add the sugar, salt and pepper and allow to rest until the sugar and salt have completely dissolved. Mix together well.

2 Add the remaining ingredients and mix well. Chill, and garnish with fresh coriander and mint sprigs before serving.

VARIATION
For Banana and Coconut Raita, slice 2 bananas and fold into 350ml/12fl oz/ 1½ cups natural yogurt. Stir in 30ml/2 tbsp desiccated coconut and add a pinch of chilli powder, and salt and lemon juice to taste.

SPINACH with GOLDEN POTATOES

The combination of spinach and potato is generally known as aloo saag *or* saag aloo.
*As with most Indian dishes, there are different versions using the same or similar
ingredients. This recipe is from Bengal, where it is known as* palong saaker ghonto.

SERVES 4–6

450g/1lb spinach
30ml/2 tbsp vegetable oil
5ml/1 tsp black mustard seeds
1 onion, thinly sliced
2 garlic cloves, crushed
2.5cm/1in piece fresh root ginger,
   finely chopped
675g/1½lb firm potatoes, cut into
   2.5cm/1in chunks
5ml/1 tsp chilli powder
5ml/1 tsp salt
120ml/4fl oz/½ cup water

1 Blanch the spinach in boiling water
for 3–4 minutes, then drain in a sieve
(strainer) and leave to cool. When it is
cool enough to handle, squeeze out any
remaining liquid using the back of a
wooden spoon or with your hands.

2 Heat the oil in a large pan over a
medium heat and fry the mustard seeds
until they begin to splutter.

3 Add the sliced onion, crushed garlic
and chopped ginger and fry for about
5 minutes, stirring.

4 Stir in the potatoes, chilli powder,
salt and water and cook for 8 minutes,
stirring occasionally.

VARIATION
For an excellent alternative to spinach,
use 450g/1lb spring greens.

5 Add the spinach to the pan. Cover
and simmer for 10–15 minutes until the
potatoes are tender. Serve.

COOK'S TIP
Enhance the flavour by adding fresh red
chillies in step 3. Omit the chilli powder.

SPICED YOGURT and CUCUMBER RAITA

These slightly sour, yogurt-based accompaniments have a cooling effect on the palate when eaten with spicy foods, and they help to balance the flavours of an Indian meal.

SPICED YOGURT

MAKES 450ML/¾ PINT/SCANT 2 CUPS

450ml/¾ pint/scant 2 cups natural (plain)
    yogurt
2.5ml/½ tsp freshly ground fennel seeds
2.5ml/½ tsp granulated sugar
60ml/4 tbsp vegetable oil
1 dried red chilli
1.5ml/¼ tsp mustard seeds
1.5ml/¼ tsp cumin seeds
4–6 curry leaves
a pinch each of asafoetida and
    ground turmeric
salt

1 Mix together the yogurt, fennel and sugar, and add salt to taste. Chill.

2 Heat the oil and fry the remaining ingredients. When the chilli turns dark, pour the oil and spices over the yogurt and mix. Cover and chill before serving.

CUCUMBER RAITA

MAKES ABOUT 600ML/1 PINT/2½ CUPS

½ cucumber
1 fresh green chilli, seeded and chopped
300ml/½ pint/1¼ cups natural (plain)
    yogurt
1.5ml/¼ tsp salt
1.5ml/¼ tsp ground cumin

1 Dice the cucumber finely and place in a large mixing bowl. Add the chilli.

2 Beat the natural yogurt with a fork until smooth, then stir into the cucumber and chilli mixture.

3 Stir in the salt and cumin. Cover the bowl with clear film (plastic wrap) and chill before serving.

VARIATION
Instead of cucumber, use two skinned, seeded and chopped tomatoes and 15ml/ 1 tbsp chopped fresh coriander (cilantro).

CHANA DHAL and BOTTLE GOURD CURRY

Chana dhal, also known as Bengal gram, is a very small type of chickpea grown in India. It has a nutty taste and gives fabulous earthy flavour to the food. Chana dhal is available from good Indian stores. Yellow split peas make a good substitute in terms of appearance and require the same cooking time, but the flavour is not quite the same.

SERVES 4–6

175g/6oz/⅔ cup chana dhal or yellow
   split peas, washed
450ml/¾ pint/scant 2 cups water
60ml/4 tbsp vegetable oil
2 fresh green chillies, chopped
1 onion, chopped
2 cloves garlic, crushed
5cm/2in piece fresh root ginger, grated
6–8 curry leaves
5ml/1 tsp chilli powder
5ml/1 tsp ground turmeric
450g/1lb bottle gourd or marrow (large
   zucchini), courgettes (zucchini), squash
   or pumpkin, peeled, pithed and sliced
60ml/4 tbsp tamarind juice
2 tomatoes, chopped
salt
a handful fresh coriander (cilantro) leaves,
   chopped

2 Heat the oil in a large pan and fry the chillies, onion, garlic, ginger, curry leaves, chilli powder and turmeric and salt until the onions have softened. Add the gourd (or other vegetable) pieces and mix.

3 Add the chana dhal and water and bring to the boil. Add the tamarind juice, tomatoes and coriander. Simmer until the gourd is cooked. Serve hot with a dry meat curry.

1 In a large pan, cook the chana dhal in the water, seasoned with salt, for about 30 minutes until the chana dhal grains are tender but not mushy. Put aside without draining away any excess water.

COOK'S TIP
If using courgettes (zucchini), add them along with the tamarind juice, tomatoes and coriander in step 3. Courgettes need much less cooking time than the other vegetables in the recipe.

HOT LIME PICKLE and GREEN CHILLI PICKLE

Spicy pickles are a perennial favourite with all types of curry. Leaving the pickles to rest for a week after preparation will greatly enhance the flavours.

HOT LIME PICKLE

MAKES 450G/1LB/2 CUPS

25 limes, cut into wedges
225g/8oz/1 cup salt
50g/2oz/¼ cup fenugreek powder
50g/2oz/¼ cup mustard powder
150g/5oz/¾ cup chilli powder
15ml/1 tbsp ground turmeric
600ml/1 pint/2½ cups mustard oil
5ml/1 tsp asafoetida
25g/1oz yellow mustard seeds, crushed

1 Place the limes in a large sterilized jar or glass bowl. Add the salt and toss with the limes. Cover and leave in a warm place for 1–2 weeks, until they become soft and dull brown in colour.

2 Mix the fenugreek, mustard powder, chilli powder and turmeric and add to the limes. Cover and leave to rest in a warm place for a further 2–3 days.

3 Heat the oil and fry the asafoetida and mustard seeds. When the oil reaches smoking point, pour it over the limes. Mix well. Cover and leave in a warm place for 1 week before serving.

GREEN CHILLI PICKLE

MAKES 450–550G/1–1¼LB/2–2½ CUPS

50g/2oz/¼ cup mustard seeds, crushed
50g/2oz/¼ cup freshly ground cumin seeds
25ml/1½ tbsp ground turmeric
50g/2oz/¼ cup crushed garlic
150ml/¼ pint/⅔ cup white vinegar
75g/3oz/scant ½ cup granulated sugar
10ml/2 tsp salt
150ml/¼ pint/⅔ cup mustard oil
20 small garlic cloves
450g/1lb small fresh green chillies, halved

1 Mix the mustard seeds, cumin, turmeric, crushed garlic, vinegar, sugar and salt in a sterilized jar or glass bowl. Cover and allow to rest for 24 hours. This enables the spices to infuse (steep)and the sugar and salt to melt.

2 Heat the mustard oil and gently fry the spice mixture for about 5 minutes. (Keep a window open while cooking with mustard oil as it is pungent and the smoke may irritate the eyes.) Add the whole garlic cloves and fry for a further 5 minutes.

3 Add the halved fresh chillies and cook gently until tender but still green in colour. This will take about 30 minutes on a low heat. Cool thoroughly.

4 Pour into the sterilized jar, ensuring that the oil is evenly distributed if you are using more than one bottle. Leave to rest for 1 week before serving.

TARKA DHAL

Tarka, also spelt tadka, *is a hot oil seasoning that is folded into a dish before serving.
In an Indian household, dhal is cooked every day and for most family meals a much
simpler version is made. Tarka dhal is commonly found in Bengal, Assam and Bangladesh
and it is the combination of spices that gives away its origin.*

SERVES 4–6

115g/4oz/½ cup red lentils, washed
50g/2oz/¼ cup chana dhal or yellow split
    peas, washed
600ml/1 pint/2½ cups water
5ml/1 tsp grated fresh root ginger
5ml/1 tsp crushed garlic
2.5ml/¼ tsp ground turmeric
2 fresh green chillies, chopped
7.5ml/1½ tsp salt

For the tarka
30ml/2 tbsp vegetable oil
1 onion, sliced
2.5ml/¼ tsp mixed mustard and onion
    seeds
4 dried red chillies
1 tomato, sliced

To garnish
15ml/1 tbsp chopped fresh coriander
    (cilantro), 1–2 fresh green chillies,
    seeded and sliced, 15ml/1 tbsp
    chopped mint

1 Pick over the washed chana dhal or
lentils for any stones, then place in a
large pan and boil in the water with
the ginger, garlic, turmeric and chopped
green chillies for 15–20 minutes or until
the lentils are soft.

2 Mash the lentils with the back of
a spoon until they are of the same
consistency as chicken soup. If the
mixture looks too dry, add a little
more water.

3 To prepare the tarka, heat the oil
in another pan and fry the onion with
the mustard and onion seeds, dried red
chillies and sliced tomato for 2 minutes.

4 Pour the dhal into serving bowls,
garnished with the tarka, chopped
fresh coriander, fresh green chillies
and chopped mint.

BOMBAY DUCK PICKLE

Boil is the name of a fish that is found off the west coast of India during the monsoon season. It is salted and dried in the sun and is characterized by a strong smell and distinctive piquancy. How this fish acquired the name Bombay duck in the Western world is still unknown. Bombay duck can be served hot or cold, and is usually eaten with Indian breads as an accompaniment to vegetable dishes.

SERVES 4–6

6–8 pieces boil (Bombay duck), soaked
 in water for 5 minutes
60ml/4 tbsp vegetable oil
2 fresh red chillies, chopped
15ml/1 tbsp granulated sugar
450g/1lb cherry tomatoes, halved
115g/4oz deep-fried onions
red onion rings, to garnish (optional)

COOK'S TIP
As an alternative to boil, try skinned
mackerel fillets, without frying them.
You will need only 30ml/2 tbsp vegetable
oil to make the sauce.

1 Pat the fish dry with kitchen paper.
Heat the oil in a frying pan and fry the
fish pieces for about 30–45 seconds on
both sides until crisp. Be careful not to
burn them as they will taste bitter. Drain
well. When cool, break into small pieces.

2 Cook the remaining ingredients until
the tomatoes become pulpy and the
onions are blended into a sauce. Fold in
the Bombay duck and mix well. Leave to
cool, then garnish and serve, or ladle
into a hot sterilized jar and cover.

Indian Chutneys, Pickles and Salads

SOUTH INDIA

The food in the southern states is light and refreshing, with plenty of

fish and shellfish; it is also fiery, with much use being made of the

chillies that are grown throughout the region. In south India, coconut

milk is used to enrich sauces in place of the dairy cream and nuts

that are used in the north.

MINT and COCONUT, APRICOT and TOMATO and FRESH CHILLI CHUTNEYS

Chutneys can be made by grinding fresh ingredients together, or by slow-cooking.

MINT AND COCONUT CHUTNEY

MAKES ABOUT 350ML/12FL OZ/1½ CUPS

50g/2oz fresh mint leaves
90ml/6 tbsp desiccated (dry, unsweetened, shredded) coconut
15ml/1 tbsp sesame seeds
1.5ml/¼ tsp salt
175ml/6fl oz/¾ cup natural (plain) yogurt

1 Finely chop the fresh mint leaves, using a sharp kitchen knife.

2 Put all the ingredients into a food processor or blender and process until smooth. Transfer to a sterilized jar, cover and chill until needed.

COOK'S TIP
This chutney can be stored in the refrigerator for up to 5 days.

APRICOT CHUTNEY

MAKES ABOUT 450G/1LB/2 CUPS

450g/1lb/2 cups dried apricots, finely diced
5ml/1 tsp garam masala
275g/10oz/1¼ cups soft light brown sugar
450ml/¾ pint/scant 2 cups malt vinegar
5ml/1 tsp grated fresh root ginger
5ml/1 tsp salt
75g/3oz/½ cup sultanas (golden raisins)
450ml/¾ pint/scant 2 cups water

1 Put all the ingredients together into a pan and stir well to mix. Bring to the boil, then simmer for 30–35 minutes, stirring occasionally.

2 When the chutney becomes syrupy, remove from the heat. Leave to cool, then ladle into a hot sterilized jar and cover. Chill after opening.

TOMATO AND FRESH CHILLI CHUTNEY

MAKES ABOUT 475ML/16FL OZ/2 CUPS

1 red (bell) pepper
4 tomatoes, chopped
2 fresh green chillies, chopped
1 garlic clove, crushed
1.5ml/¼ tsp salt
2.5ml/½ tsp granulated sugar
5ml/1 tsp chilli powder
45ml/3 tbsp tomato purée (paste)
15ml/1 tbsp chopped fresh coriander (cilantro)

1 Halve the red pepper and remove the core and seeds. Roughly chop the red pepper halves.

2 Process all the ingredients with 30ml/2 tbsp water in a food processor until smooth. Transfer to a sterilized jar, cover and chill until needed.

MUGHLAI-STYLE CHICKEN

The cuisine of Andhra Pradesh is renowned for its pungency because the hottest variety of chilli is grown there. In sharp contrast, however, the region is also home to the subtle flavours of a style of cooking known as nizami, *which has a distinct Mogul influence. This recipe, with the heady aroma of saffron and the captivating flavour of a silky almond and cream sauce, is a typical example.*

SERVES 4–6

4 chicken breast fillets, rubbed with
   a little garam masala
2 eggs, beaten with salt and pepper
90ml/6 tbsp ghee or vegetable oil
1 large onion, finely chopped
5cm/2in piece fresh root ginger,
   finely crushed
4 garlic cloves, finely crushed
4 cloves
4 green cardamom pods
5cm/2in piece cinnamon stick
2 bay leaves
15–20 saffron threads
150ml/¼ pint/⅔ cup natural (plain)
   yogurt, beaten with 5ml/1 tsp
   cornflour (cornstarch)
75ml/5 tbsp/⅓ cup double (heavy) cream
50g/2oz ground almonds
salt

3 Return the chicken to the pan, along with any juices, and gently cook until the chicken is tender. Adjust the seasoning if necessary.

4 Just before serving, fold in the double cream and ground almonds. Make sure the curry is piping hot before serving. Tricolour Pulao goes well with this dish.

1 Brush the chicken fillets with the beaten eggs. In a wok, karahi or large pan, heat the ghee or vegetable oil and fry the chicken until cooked through and browned on both sides. Remove the chicken from the pan and keep warm.

2 In the same pan, fry the chopped onion, ginger, garlic, cloves, cardamom pods, cinnamon and bay leaves. When the onion turns golden, remove the pan from the heat, allow the contents to cool a little and add the saffron and natural yogurt. Mix well to prevent the yogurt from curdling.

MANGO, CORIANDER and TOMATO CHUTNEYS

Chutneys are always vegetarian, but ingredients vary between regions. Mango and tomato chutneys are made all over India, while herb chutneys are eaten in the north and west.

MANGO CHUTNEY

MAKES 450G/1LB/2 CUPS

3 firm green mangoes, cut into chunks
150ml/¼ pint/⅔ cup cider vinegar
130g/4½oz/⅔ cup light muscovado (brown) sugar
1 small fresh red chilli, split
2.5cm/1in piece resh root ginger, grated
1 garlic clove, crushed
5 cardamom pods, bruised
2.5ml/½ tsp coriander seeds, crushed
1 bay leaf
2.5ml/½ tsp salt

1 Put the mango chunks into a pan, add the cider vinegar and cover. Cook over a low heat for 10 minutes, then stir in the remaining ingredients. Bring to the boil slowly, stirring.

2 Lower the heat and simmer gently for 30 minutes, until the mixture is syrupy. Leave to cool, then ladle into a hot sterilized jar and cover. Leave to rest for 1 week before serving.

CORIANDER CHUTNEY

MAKES 400G/14OZ/1¾ CUPS

30ml/2 tbsp vegetable oil
1 dried red chilli
1.5ml/¼ tsp each cumin, fennel and onion seeds
1.5ml/¼ tsp asafoetida
4 curry leaves
115g/4oz desiccated (dry, unsweetened, shredded) coconut
10ml/2 tsp granulated sugar
3 fresh green chillies, chopped
175–225g/6–8oz coriander (cilantro) leaves
60ml/4 tbsp mint sauce
juice of 3 lemons
salt

1 Heat the oil and fry the next eight ingredients until the coconut turns golden. Season and allow to cool.

2 Use a mortar and pestle to grind the spice mixture with the chillies, coriander and mint sauce. Stir in the lemon juice. Transfer to a sterilized jar, cover and chill.

TOMATO CHUTNEY

MAKES 450–500G/16–18OZ/2–2¼ CUPS

90ml/6 tbsp vegetable oil
5cm/2in piece cinnamon stick
4 cloves
5ml/1 tsp freshly roasted cumin seeds
5ml/1 tsp nigella seeds
4 bay leaves
5ml/1 tsp mustard seeds, crushed
4 cloves garlic, crushed
5cm/2in piece fresh root ginger, grated
5ml/1 tsp chilli powder
5ml/1 tsp ground turmeric
60ml/4 tbsp brown sugar
800g/¾lb canned, chopped tomatoes, drained, juices reserved

1 Heat the oil, then fry the first six spices. Add the garlic and fry until golden.

2 Add the remaining spices, sugar and reserved tomato juices. Simmer until reduced, then add the tomatoes and cook for 15–20 minutes. Leave to cool, then ladle into a sterilized jar and cover.

CHICKEN MADRAS

Madras, one of India's largest cities, is the capital of Tamil Nadu. The city is generally regarded as the heartland of southern Indian cuisine. It is surrounded by long stretches of beautiful beaches, shared between the Bay of Bengal to the east and the Indian Ocean to the south. The food is mainly vegetarian, but the small Muslim and Christian communities have a wonderful range of meat- and poultry-based dishes, such as this one.

SERVES 4

450g/1lb chicken breast fillets, skinned
45ml/3 tbsp tomato purée (paste)
large pinch ground fenugreek
1.5ml/¼ tsp ground fennel seeds
5ml/1 tsp grated fresh root ginger
7.5ml/1½ tsp ground coriander
5ml/1 tsp crushed garlic
5ml/1 tsp chilli powder
1.5ml/¼ tsp ground turmeric
30ml/2 tbsp lemon juice
5ml/1 tsp salt
300ml/½ pint/1¼ cups water
45ml/3 tbsp vegetable oil
2 onions, diced
2–4 curry leaves
2 fresh green chillies, seeded
    and chopped
15ml/1 tbsp chopped fresh coriander
    (cilantro), plus extra sprigs to garnish
naan bread, to serve

1 Cut the chicken breast fillets into cubes. Mix the tomato purée in a bowl with the fenugreek, fennel, ginger, ground coriander, garlic, chilli powder, turmeric, lemon juice, salt and water.

2 Heat the oil in a wok, karahi or large pan and fry the onions with the curry leaves until the onions are golden. Add the chicken and stir for 1 minute to seal.

COOK'S TIP
Take care not to use too much ground fenugreek, as it can be quite bitter.

3 Pour the tomato sauce and spice mixture into the pan. Stir for 2 minutes to ensure the ingredients are well mixed.

4 Lower the heat and cook for 8–10 minutes, then add the chillies and fresh coriander. Garnish and serve.

INDIAN CHUTNEYS, PICKLES AND SALADS

Indians believe that eating sour foods with a meal is good for the health, and they have created a huge range of tart, tangy chutneys and pickles, refreshing yogurt-based raitas, and raw vegetable salads, which all taste good with hot, spicy dishes.

MADRAS BEEF CURRY

Although Madras is renowned for the best vegetarian food in the country, meat-based recipes such as this one are also extremely popular. This particular recipe is a contribution by the area's small Muslim community.

SERVES 4–6

60ml/4 tbsp vegetable oil
1 large onion, finely sliced
3–4 cloves
4 green cardamoms
2 whole star anise
4 fresh green chillies, chopped
2 fresh or dried red chillies, chopped
45ml/3 tbsp Madras masala paste
5ml/1 tsp ground turmeric
450g/1lb lean beef, cubed
60ml/4 tbsp tamarind juice
granulated sugar, to taste
salt
a few fresh coriander (cilantro) leaves,
    chopped, to garnish

1 Heat the vegetable oil in a wok, karahi or large pan over a medium heat and fry the onion slices for 8–9 minutes until they turn golden brown. Lower the heat, add all the spice ingredients, and fry for a further 2–3 minutes.

2 Add the beef and mix well. Cover and cook on low heat until the beef is tender. Cook uncovered on a higher heat for the last few minutes to reduce any excess liquid.

COOK'S TIP
To tenderize the meat, add 60ml/4 tbsp white wine vinegar in step 2, along with the meat, and omit the tamarind juice.

3 Fold in the tamarind juice, sugar and salt. Reheat the dish and garnish with the chopped coriander leaves. Tricolour Pulao and Tomato and Onion Salad would both make excellent accompaniments to this dish.

BHATURAS

These leavened and deep-fried breads are from Punjab, where the local people enjoy them with a bowl of spicy chickpea curry. The combination has become a classic over the years and is known as choley bhature. *Bhaturas must be eaten hot and cannot be reheated.*

MAKES 10 BHATURAS

15g/½oz fresh yeast
5ml/1 tsp granulated sugar
120ml/4fl oz/½ cup lukewarm water
200g/7oz/1¾ cups plain (all-purpose) flour
50g/2oz/½ cup semolina
2.5ml/½ tsp salt
15g/½oz/1 tbsp ghee or butter
30ml/2 tbsp natural (plain) yogurt
oil, for frying

COOK'S TIP

Ghee is availabe from Indian stores and some supermarkets. However, it is easy to make at home. Melt unsalted (sweet) butter over a low heat. Simmer very gently until the residue becomes light golden, then leave to cool. Strain through muslin (cheesecloth) before using.

1 Mix the yeast with the sugar and water in a jug (pitcher). Sift the flour into a large bowl and stir in the semolina and salt. Rub in the butter or ghee.

2 Add the yeast mixture and yogurt and mix to a dough. Turn out on to a lightly floured surface and knead for 10 minutes until smooth and elastic.

3 Place the dough in an oiled bowl, cover with oiled clear film (plastic wrap) and leave to rise, in a warm place, for about 1 hour, or until doubled in size.

4 Turn out on to a lightly floured surface and knock back (punch down). Divide into ten equal pieces and shape each into a ball. Flatten into discs with the palm of your hand. Roll out on a lightly floured surface into 13cm/5in rounds.

5 Heat oil to a depth of 1cm/½in in a deep frying pan and slide one bhatura into the oil. Fry for about 1 minute, turning over after 30 seconds, then drain well on kitchen paper. Keep each bhatura warm in a low oven while frying the remaining bhaturas. Serve immediately, while hot.

CHILLI MEAT with CURRY LEAVES

Curry leaves and chillies are two of the hallmark ingredients used in the southern states of India. This recipe is from the state of Andhra Pradesh, where the hottest chillies, known as Guntur after the region where they are produced, are grown in abundance.

SERVES 4–6

30ml/2 tbsp vegetable oil
1 large onion, finely sliced
5cm/2in piece fresh root ginger, grated
4 garlic cloves, crushed
12 curry leaves
45ml/3 tbsp extra hot curry paste, or
   60ml/4 tbsp hot curry powder
15ml/1 tbsp chilli powder
5ml/1 tsp five-spice powder
5ml/1 tsp ground turmeric
900g/2lb lean lamb, beef or pork, cubed
175ml/6fl oz/¾ cup thick coconut milk
salt
red onion, finely sliced, to garnish
Indian bread and Fruit Raita, to serve

1 Heat the oil in a wok, karahi or large, pan, and fry the onion, ginger, garlic and curry leaves until the onion is soft. Add the curry paste or powder, chilli and five-spice powder, turmeric and salt.

2 Add the meat and stir well over a medium heat to seal and evenly brown the meat pieces. Keep stirring until the oil separates. Cover the pan and cook for about 20 minutes.

COOK'S TIP
For extra flavour, reserve half the curry leaves and add in step 3, along with the coconut milk.

3 Stir in the coconut milk and simmer, covered, until the meat is cooked. Towards the end of cooking, uncover the pan to reduce the excess liquid. Garnish and serve with any Indian bread, and with Fruit Raita, for a cooling effect.

POORIS

These delicious little deep-fried breads, shaped into discs, make it temptingly easy to overindulge. In most areas, they are made of wholemeal flour, but in the east and north-east of India, they are made from plain refined flour, and are known as loochis.

MAKES 12

115g/4oz/1 cup unbleached plain
   (all-purpose) flour
115g/4oz/1 cup wholemeal (whole-wheat)
   flour
2.5ml/½ tsp salt
2.5ml/½ tsp chilli powder
30ml/2 tbsp vegetable oil
100–120ml/3½–4fl oz/scant ⅓–½ cup
   water
oil, for frying

VARIATION
For spinach-flavoured pooris, thaw 50g/2oz frozen spinach, drain, and add to the dough with a little grated fresh root ginger and 2.5ml/½ tsp ground cumin.

1 Sift the flours, salt and chilli powder, if using, into a large mixing bowl. Add the vegetable oil then add sufficient water to mix to a dough. Turn out on to a lightly floured surface and knead for 8–10 minutes until smooth.

2 Place in an oiled bowl and cover with oiled clear film (plastic wrap). Leave for 30 minutes.

3 Turn out on to the floured surface. Divide the dough into 12 equal pieces. Keeping the rest of the dough covered, roll one piece into a 13cm/5in round. Repeat with the remaining dough. Stack the pooris, layered between clear film, to keep them moist.

4 Pour the oil for frying to a depth of 2.5cm/1in in a deep frying pan and heat it to 180°C/350°F. Using a metal fish slice (spatula), lift one poori and gently slide it into the oil; it will sink but will then return to the surface and begin to sizzle. Gently press the poori into the oil. It will puff up. Turn the poori over after a few seconds and allow it to cook for a further 20–30 seconds.

5 Remove the poori from the pan and pat dry with kitchen paper. Place the cooked poori on a large baking tray, in a single layer, and keep warm in a low oven while you cook the remaining pooris. Serve warm.

LAMB KORMA

Although south Indian food is generally free of foreign influences, the city of Hyderabad in Andhra Pradesh has a rich heritage of Mogul cuisine. It was here that the last of the Mogul emperors retired before finally handing over power to the Nizam dynasty.

SERVES 4–6

15ml/1 tbsp white sesame seeds
15ml/1 tbsp white poppy seeds
50g/2oz/½ cup blanched almonds
2 fresh green chillies, seeded
6 garlic cloves, sliced
5cm/2in piece fresh root ginger, sliced
1 onion, finely chopped
45ml/3 tbsp ghee or vegetable oil
6 green cardamom pods
5cm/2in piece cinnamon stick
4 cloves
900g/2lb lean lamb, boned and cubed
5ml/1 tsp ground cumin
5ml/1 tsp ground coriander
300ml/½ pint/1¼ cups double (heavy) cream mixed with 2.5ml/½ tsp cornflour (cornstarch)
salt
roasted sesame seeds, to garnish

1 Preheat a wok, karahi or large pan over a medium heat without any fat, and add the first seven ingredients. Stir until they begin to change colour. They should go just a shade darker.

2 Allow the mixture to cool, then grind to a fine paste using a pestle and mortar or in a food processor. Heat the ghee or oil in the pan over a low heat.

3 Fry the cardamoms, cinnamon and cloves until the cloves swell. Add the lamb, ground cumin and coriander and the prepared paste, and season with salt, to taste. Increase the heat to medium and stir well. Reduce the heat to low, then cover the pan and cook until the lamb is almost done.

4 Remove from the heat, allow to cool a little and gradually fold in the cream, reserving 5ml/1 tsp to garnish. To serve, gently reheat the lamb, uncovered. Garnish with the sesame seeds and the reserved cream. This korma is very good served with Classic Pulao.

COOK'S TIP
If white poppy seeds are not available, use sunflower seeds instead.

TANDOORI ROTIS

Roti means bread and is the most common food eaten in central and northern India. For generations, roti has been made with just wholemeal flour, salt and water, although the art of making rotis is generally more refined these days. Tandoori roti is traditionally baked in a tandoor, or clay oven, but it can also be made successfully in an electric or gas oven at the highest setting.

MAKES 6

350g/12oz/3 cups chapati flour or ground
  wholemeal (whole-wheat) flour
5ml/1 tsp salt
250ml/8fl oz/1 cup water
30–45ml/2–3 tbsp melted ghee or unsalted
  (sweet) butter, for brushing

1 Sift the flour and salt into a large mixing bowl. Add the water and mix to a soft, pliable dough.

2 Knead on a lightly floured surface for 3–4 minutes until smooth. Place the dough in a lightly oiled bowl, cover with lightly oiled clear film (plastic wrap) and leave to rest for 1 hour.

3 Turn out the dough on to a lightly floured surface. Divide the dough into six pieces and shape each into a ball. Press out into a larger round with the palm of your hand, cover with lightly oiled clear film and leave to rest for about 10 minutes.

4 Meanwhile, preheat the oven to 230°C/450°F/Gas 8. Place three baking sheets in the oven to heat. Roll the rotis into 15cm/6in rounds, place two on each baking sheet and bake for 8–10 minutes. Brush with melted ghee or butter and serve warm.

MARINATED FRIED FISH

Fish and shellfish are a strong feature of the cuisine in the coastal region of southern India. Kerala, in the southernmost tip of the country, produces some of the finest fish and shellfish dishes. These are flavoured with local spices, grown in the fabulous spice plantation that is the pride and joy of the state.

SERVES 4–6

1 small onion, coarsely chopped
4 garlic cloves, crushed
5cm/2in piece fresh root ginger, chopped
5ml/1 tsp ground turmeric
10ml/2 tsp chilli powder
4 red mullets or snappers
vegetable oil, for shallow frying
5ml/1 tsp cumin seeds
3 fresh green chillies, finely sliced
salt
lemon or lime wedges, to serve

COOK'S TIP
To enhance the flavour, add 15ml/1 tbsp chopped fresh coriander (cilantro) leaves to the spice paste in step 1.

1 In a food processor, grind the first five ingredients with salt to a smooth paste. Make several slashes on both sides of the fish and rub them with the paste. Leave to rest for 1 hour. Excess fluid will be released as the salt dissolves, so lightly pat the fish dry with kitchen paper without removing the paste.

2 Heat the oil and fry the cumin seeds and sliced chillies for 1 minute. Add the fish, in batches if necessary, and fry on one side. When the first side is sealed, turn them over very gently to ensure they do not break. Fry until golden brown on both sides, drain and serve hot, with lemon or lime wedges.

MISSI ROTIS

These delicious unleavened breads are a speciality from Punjab in India. Gram flour, known as besan, is made from chickpeas and is combined here with the more traditional wheat flour. In Punjab, missi rotis are very popular with a glass of lassi, a refreshing yogurt drink.

MAKES 4

115g/4oz/1 cup gram flour (besan)
115g/4oz/1 cup wholemeal (whole-wheat) flour
1 fresh green chilli, seeded and chopped
½ onion, finely chopped
15ml/1 tbsp chopped fresh coriander (cilantro)
2.5ml/½ tsp ground turmeric
2.5ml/½ tsp salt
15ml/1 tbsp vegetable oil or melted butter
120–150ml/4–5fl oz/½–⅔ cup lukewarm water
30–45ml/2–3 tbsp melted unsalted (sweet) butter or ghee

1 Mix the two types of flour, chilli, onion, coriander, turmeric and salt together in a large bowl. Stir in the 15ml/1 tbsp oil or melted butter.

2 Mix in sufficient water to make a pliable soft dough. Turn out the dough on to a lightly floured surface and knead until smooth.

3 Place in a lightly oiled bowl, cover with lightly oiled clear film (plastic wrap) and leave to rest for 30 minutes.

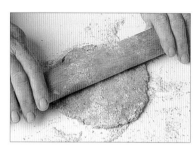

4 Turn the dough out on to a lightly floured surface. Divide into four equal pieces and shape into balls in the palms of your hands. Roll out each ball into a thick round about 15–18cm/6–7in in diameter.

5 Heat a griddle or heavy frying pan over a medium heat for a few minutes until hot.

6 Brush both sides of one roti with some melted butter or ghee. Add it to the griddle or frying pan and cook for about 2 minutes, turning after 1 minute. Brush the cooked roti lightly with melted butter or ghee again, slide it on to a plate and keep warm in a low oven while cooking the remaining rotis in the same way. Serve the rotis warm.

CAULIFLOWER in COCONUT SAUCE

Coconut is used for both sweet and savoury dishes in south Indian cooking. This versatile fruit with its many by-products, including coconut oil, which is widely used as a cooking medium, provides the basis for a huge manufacturing industry all over the southern states.

SERVES 4–6

15ml/1 tbsp gram flour (besan)
120ml/4fl oz/½ cup water
5ml/1 tsp chilli powder
15ml/1 tbsp ground coriander
5ml/1 tsp ground cumin
5ml/1 tsp mustard powder
5ml/1 tsp ground turmeric
60ml/4 tbsp vegetable oil
6–8 curry leaves
5ml/1 tsp cumin seeds
1 cauliflower, broken into florets
175ml/6fl oz/¾ cup thick coconut milk
juice of 2 lemons
salt
lime slices, to garnish

1 Mix the gram flour with a little water to make a smooth paste. Add the chilli, coriander, cumin, mustard, turmeric and salt. Add the remaining water and mix to blend the ingredients.

2 Heat the oil in a wok, karahi or large pan, and fry the curry leaves and the cumin seeds. Add the spice paste and simmer for about 5 minutes. If the sauce is too thick, add a little hot water.

COOK'S TIP
Serve this dish southern-style, with plain rice and Spiced Lentils with Spinach. If you prefer, serve a northern-style meal with parathas and Kashmiri Chicken Curry.

3 Add the cauliflower and coconut milk. Bring to the boil, reduce the heat, cover and cook until the cauliflower is tender but crunchy. Cook longer if you prefer. Add the lemon juice, mix throughly and serve hot, garnished with lime slices.

PARATHAS

Making a paratha is somewhat similar to the technique used when making flaky pastry. The difference lies in the handling of the dough; this can be handled freely, unlike that for a flaky pastry. Parathas are rich in saturated fat, so reserve for special occasions.

MAKES 12–15

350g/12oz/3 cups chapati flour or ground wholemeal (whole-wheat), plus 50g/2oz/½ cup for dusting
50g/2oz/½ cup plain (all-purpose) flour
30ml/2 tbsp ghee or unsalted (sweet) butter, plus 10ml/2 tsp, melted
water, to mix
salt

1 Sift the flours and salt into a bowl. Make a well in the centre and add 10ml/2 tsp of unmelted ghee and fold into the flour to make a crumbly texture. Gradually add water to make a soft, pliable dough. Knead until smooth. Cover and leave to rest for 30 minutes.

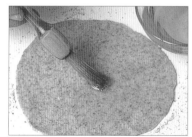

2 Divide the dough into 12–15 equal portions and keep covered. Take one portion at a time and roll out on a lightly floured surface to about 10cm/4in in diameter. Brush the dough with a little of the melted ghee or sweet butter and sprinkle with chapati flour.

3 With a sharp knife, make a straight cut from the centre to the edge of the dough, then lift a cut edge and roll the dough into a cone shape. Lift it and flatten it again into a ball. Roll the dough again on a lightly floured surface until it is 18cm/7in wide.

4 Heat a griddle and cook one paratha at a time, placing a little of the remaining ghee along the edges. Cook on each side until golden brown. Serve hot.

COOK'S TIP

If you cannot find chapati flour, known as atta, substitute an equal quantity of wholemeal flour and plain flour.

MIXED VEGETABLES IN COCONUT SAUCE

A vegetable dish is an essential part of an Indian meal, even for a simple occasion, where one or two vegetable dishes may be served with a lentil dhal, a raita, and bread or boiled rice. There are many ways to make a vegetable curry, but this recipe, in which the vegetables are simmered in coconut milk, is typical of South India.

SERVES 4

225g/8oz potatoes, cut into 5cm/2in cubes
125g/4oz/³⁄₄ cup French (green) beans
150g/5oz carrots, scraped and cut into
   5cm/2in cubes
500ml/17fl oz/2¼ cups hot water
1 small aubergine (eggplant), about
   225g/8oz, quartered lengthwise
75g/3oz coconut milk powder
5ml/1 tsp salt
30ml/2 tbsp vegetable oil
6–8 fresh or 8–10 dried curry leaves
1–2 dried red chillies, chopped into
   small pieces
5ml/1 tsp ground cumin
5ml/1 tsp ground coriander
2.5ml/½ tsp ground turmeric

1 Put the potatoes, beans and carrots in a large pan and add 300ml/½ pint/ 1¼ cups of the hot water and bring to the boil. Reduce the heat a little, cover the pan and cook for 5 minutes.

2 Cut the aubergine quarters into 5cm/2in pieces. Rinse. Add to the pan.

3 Blend the coconut milk powder with the remaining hot water and add to the vegetables, with the salt. Bring to a slow simmer, cover and cook for 6–7 minutes.

4 In a small pan heat the oil over a medium heat and add the curry leaves and the chillies. Immediately follow with the cumin, coriander and turmeric. Stir-fry the spices for 15–20 seconds and pour the entire contents of the pan over the vegetables. Stir to distribute the spices evenly and remove from the heat. Serve with any Indian bread.

RED LENTIL PANCAKES

This is a type of dosa, *which is essentially a pancake from southern India, but used in the similar fashion to north Indian bread. North Indian breads are made of wholemeal or refined flour; in the south they are made of ground lentils and rice.*

2 Drain off the water and reserve. Place the rice and lentils in a food processor and blend until smooth. Blend in the reserved water.

3 Scrape into a bowl, cover with clear film (plastic wrap) and leave the lentil and rice mixture in a warm place to ferment for about 24 hours.

4 Stir in the salt, turmeric, pepper and coriander. Heat a heavy frying pan over a medium heat for a few minutes until hot. Smear with oil and add about 30–45ml/ 2–3 tbsp batter.

5 Using the rounded base of a soup spoon, gently spread the batter out, using a circular motion, to make a pancake that is 15cm/6in in diameter.

6 Cook in the pan for 1½–2 minutes, or until set. Drizzle a little oil over the pancake and around the edges. Turn over and cook for about 1 minute, or until golden brown. Keep the cooked pancakes warm in a low oven on a heatproof plate placed over simmering water while cooking the remaining pancakes. Serve warm.

MAKES 6 PANCAKES

150g/5oz/¾ cup long grain rice
50g/2oz/¼ cup red lentils
250ml/8fl oz/1 cup warm water
5ml/1 tsp salt
2.5ml/½ tsp ground turmeric
2.5ml/½ tsp ground black pepper
30ml/2 tbsp chopped fresh coriander
    (cilantro)
oil, for frying and drizzling

VARIATION
Add 60ml/4 tbsp grated coconut to the batter just before cooking.

1 Place the long grain rice and lentils in a large mixing bowl, cover with the warm water, and set aside to soak for at least 8 hours or overnight.

POTATOES in CHILLI TAMARIND SAUCE

In this favourite potato dish from the state of Karnataka, the combination of chilli and tamarind awakens the taste buds immediately. This version adapts the traditional recipe slightly, to reduce the pungency and enhance the dish's fiery appearance.

SERVES 4–6

450g/1lb small new potatoes, washed
   and dried
25g/1oz whole dried red chillies,
   preferably Kashmiri
7.5ml/1½ tsp cumin seeds
4 garlic cloves
90ml/6 tbsp vegetable oil
60ml/4 tbsp thick tamarind juice
30ml/2 tbsp tomato purée (paste)
4 curry leaves
5ml/1 tsp granulated sugar
1.5ml/¼ tsp asafoetida
salt
coriander (cilantro) sprigs and lemon
   wedges, to garnish

1 Boil the potatoes until they are fully cooked, ensuring they do not break. To test, insert a thin sharp knife into the potatoes. It should come out clean when the potatoes are fully cooked. Drain and cool the potatoes in iced water to prevent further cooking.

2 Soak the chillies for 5 minutes in warm water. Drain and grind with the cumin seeds and garlic to a coarse paste either using a pestle and mortar or in a food processor.

COOK'S TIP

Chunks of sweet potatoes can be used as an alternative to new potatoes.

3 Heat the oil and fry the paste, tamarind juice, tomato purée, curry leaves, salt, sugar and asafoetida until the oil separates from the spice paste. Add the potatoes. Reduce the heat, cover and simmer for 5 minutes. Garnish and serve.

NAAN

This bread was introduced to India by the Moguls who originally came from Persia via Afghanistan. In Persian, the word naan means bread. Traditionally, naan is not rolled, but patted and stretched until the teardrop shape is achieved. You can, of course, roll it out to a circle, then gently pull the lower end, which will give you the traditional shape.

MAKES ABOUT 3

225g/8oz/2 cups unbleached white
    bread flour
2.5ml/½ tsp salt
15g/½oz fresh yeast
60ml/4 tbsp lukewarm milk
15ml/1 tbsp vegetable oil
30ml/2 tbsp natural (plain) yogurt
1 egg
30–45ml/2–3 tbsp melted ghee or butter,
    for brushing

1 Sift the flour and salt together into a large bowl. In a smaller bowl, cream the yeast with the milk. Set aside for 15 minutes.

2 Add the yeast mixture, oil, yogurt and egg to the flour and mix to a soft dough.

VARIATION
Onion seeds or chopped fresh coriander (cilantro) may also be used as a topping. You could also make wholemeal (whole-wheat) naan by substituting wholemeal flour for some or all of the white flour.

3 Turn the dough out on to a lightly floured surface and knead for about 10 minutes, or until smooth. Return the dough to the bowl, cover and leave in a warm place for about 1 hour, until it has doubled in size. Preheat the oven to its highest setting, at least 230°C/450°F/Gas 8.

4 Turn out the dough back on to the floured surface and knead for a further 2 minutes.

5 Divide into three equal pieces, shape into balls and roll each out into a teardrop shape about 25cm/10in long, 13cm/5in wide and 5mm–8mm/¼–⅓in thick.

6 Preheat the grill (broiler) to its highest setting. Meanwhile, place the naan on preheated baking sheets and bake for 3–4 minutes, or until puffed up.

7 Remove the naan from the oven and place under the hot grill for a few seconds until the tops brown slightly. Brush with ghee or butter and serve warm.

Indian Rices and Breads

MASALA BEANS with FENUGREEK

The term masala refers to the blending of several spices to achieve a distinctive taste, with different spice-combinations being used to complement specific ingredients. Households will traditionally create their own blends, and many are quite unique.

SERVES 4

1 onion
5ml/1 tsp ground cumin
5ml/1 tsp ground coriander
5ml/1 tsp sesame seeds
5ml/1 tsp chilli powder
2.5ml/½ tsp crushed garlic
1.5ml/¼ tsp ground turmeric
5ml/1 tsp salt
30ml/2 tbsp vegetable oil
1 tomato, quartered
225g/8oz/1½ cups French (green) beans,
    blanched
1 bunch fresh fenugreek leaves,
    stems discarded
60ml/4 tbsp chopped fresh coriander
    (cilantro)
15ml/1 tbsp lemon juice

1 Roughly chop the onion. Mix together the cumin and coriander, sesame seeds, chilli powder, garlic, turmeric and salt.

2 Put the chopped onion and spice mixture into a food processor or blender, and process for 30–45 seconds until you have a rough paste.

3 In a wok, karahi or large pan, heat the oil over a medium heat and fry the spice paste for about 5 minutes, stirring the mixture occasionally.

VARIATION
Instead of fresh fenugreek, you can also use 15ml/1 tbsp dried fenugreek for this recipe. Dried fenugreek is readily available from Indian stores and markets. It may be sold by its Indian name, *kasuri methi*.

4 Add the tomato quarters, blanched French beans, fresh fenugreek and chopped coriander.

5 Stir-fry the contents of the pan for about 5 minutes, then sprinkle in the lemon juice and serve.

CHAPATIS

A chapati is an unleavened bread made from chapati flour, a ground wholemeal flour known as atta, which is finer than the Western equivalent. An equal quantity of standard wholemeal flour and plain flour will also produce satisfactory results, although chapati flour is available from Indian grocers. This is the everyday bread of the Indian home.

MAKES 8–10

225g/8oz/2 cups chapati flour or ground
   wholemeal (whole-wheat) flour
2.5ml/½ tsp salt
175ml/6fl oz/¾ cup water

1 Place the flour and salt in a mixing bowl. Make a well in the middle and gradually stir in the water, mixing well with your fingers. Form a supple dough and knead for 7–10 minutes. Ideally, cover with clear film and leave on one side for 15–20 minutes to rest.

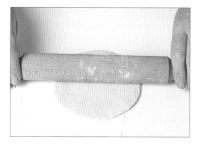

2 Divide the dough into 8–10 equal portions. Roll out each piece in a circle on a well-floured surface.

3 Place a *tava* (chapati griddle) or heavy frying pan over a high heat. When steam rises from it, lower the heat to medium and add the first chapati to the pan.

4 When the chapati begins to bubble, turn it over. Press down with a clean dish towel or a flat spoon and turn once again. Remove the cooked chapati from the pan and keep warm in a piece of foil lined with kitchen paper while you cook the other chapatis. Repeat the process until all the breads are cooked. Serve the chapatis immediately.

Indian Rices and Breads

CHILLI and MUSTARD FLAVOURED PINEAPPLE

Pineapple is cooked with coconut milk and a blend of spices in this South Indian dish, which could be served with any meat, fish or vegetable curry. The chilli adds heat, and the mustard seeds lend a rich, nutty flavour that complements the sharpness of the pineapple, while the coconut milk provides a delectable creamy sweetness.

2 Put the pineapple in a wok, karahi or large pan and add the measured water, with the coconut milk, turmeric and crushed chillies. Bring to a slow simmer over a low heat, and cook, covered, for 10–12 minutes, or until the pineapple is soft, but not mushy.

3 Add the salt and sugar, and cook, uncovered, until the sauce thickens.

4 Heat the oil in a second pan, and add the mustard seeds. As soon as they begin to pop, add the cumin seeds and the onion. Fry for 6–7 minutes, stirring regularly, until the onion is soft.

SERVES 4

1 pineapple
50ml/2fl oz/¼ cup water
150ml/¼ pint/⅔ cup can coconut milk
2.5ml/½ tsp ground turmeric
2.5ml/½ tsp crushed dried chillies
5ml/1 tsp salt
10ml/2 tsp granulated sugar
15ml/1 tbsp groundnut (peanut) oil
2.5ml/½ tsp mustard seeds
2.5ml/½ tsp cumin seeds
1 small onion, finely chopped
1–2 dried red chillies, broken
6–8 curry leaves

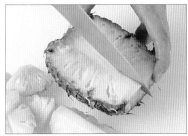

1 Halve the pineapple lengthwise and cut each half into two, so that you end up with four boat-shaped pieces. Peel them and remove the eyes and the central core. Cut into bitesize pieces.

5 Add the chillies and curry leaves. Fry for a further 1–2 minutes and pour the entire contents over the pineapple. Stir well, then remove from the heat. Serve hot or cold, but not chilled.

COOK'S TIP
Use canned pineapple in natural juice to save time. You will need approximately 500g/1¼lb drained pineapple.

CHICKEN BIRYANI

Biryani is a meal in itself and needs no accompaniment, except for a raita and some grilled or fried poppadums. It is a dish that is equally at home on the family dining table or as a dinner-party centrepiece.

SERVES 4

10 whole green cardamom pods
275g/10oz/1½ cups basmati rice, soaked
    and drained
2.5ml/½ tsp salt
2–3 whole cloves
5cm/2in piece cinnamon stick
45ml/3 tbsp vegetable oil
3 onions, sliced
4 chicken breast fillets, each about 175g/
    6oz, skinned and cubed
1.5ml/¼ tsp ground cloves
1.5ml/¼ tsp hot chilli powder
5ml/1 tsp ground cumin
5ml/1 tsp ground coriander
2.5ml/½ tsp ground black pepper
3 garlic cloves, chopped
5ml/1 tsp finely chopped fresh root ginger
juice of 1 lemon
4 tomatoes, sliced
30ml/2 tbsp chopped fresh coriander
    (cilantro)
150ml/¼ pint/⅔ cup natural (plain) yogurt,
    plus extra to serve
4–5 saffron threads, soaked in 10ml/2 tsp
    warm milk
150ml/¼ pint/⅔ cup water
toasted flaked (sliced) almonds and fresh
    coriander (cilantro) sprigs, to garnish

1 Preheat the oven to 190°C/375°F/
Gas 5. Remove the seeds from half the
cardamom pods and grind them finely,
using a pestle and mortar. Set aside the
ground seeds.

2 Bring a pan of water to the boil and
add the rice, salt, whole cardamom
pods, cloves and cinnamon stick. Boil for
2 minutes, then drain, leaving the whole
spices in the rice. Keep the rice hot in
a covered pan.

3 Heat the oil in a wok, karahi or large
pan, and fry the onions for 8 minutes,
until softened and browned. Add the
chicken and the ground spices, including
the ground cardamom seeds. Mix well,
then add the garlic, ginger and lemon
juice. Stir-fry for about 5 minutes.

4 Transfer the chicken mixture to a
casserole and arrange the tomatoes
on top. Sprinkle on the fresh coriander,
spoon the yogurt evenly on top and
cover with the drained rice.

5 Drizzle the saffron milk over the rice
and pour over the water. Cover, then
bake for 1 hour. Transfer to a serving
platter and discard the whole spices.
Garnish and serve immediately.

LENTILS SEASONED with GARLIC-INFUSED OIL

This recipe, known as sambhar, *varies considerably within the southern states. Vegetables are added to the lentils, and this can be a single vegetable or a combination of two or more. It is traditionally served with steamed rice dumplings (idlis) or stuffed rice pancakes (dosai). It is also extremely satisfying with plain boiled rice.*

SERVES 4–6

120ml/8 tbsp vegetable oil
2.5ml/½ tsp mustard seeds
2.5ml/½ tsp cumin seeds
2 dried red chillies
1.5ml/¼ tsp asafoetida
6–8 curry leaves
2 garlic cloves, crushed, plus 2 garlic
    cloves, sliced
30ml/2 tbsp desiccated (dry, unsweetened,
    shredded) coconut
225g/8oz/1 cup red lentils, picked over,
    washed and drained
10ml/2 tsp sambhar masala
2.5ml/½ tsp ground turmeric
450ml/¾ pint/scant 2 cups water
450g/1lb mixed vegetables, such as okra,
    courgettes (zucchini), aubergine
    (eggplant) cauliflower, shallots and
    (bell) peppers
60ml/4 tbsp tamarind juice
4 firm tomatoes, quartered
a few coriander (cilantro) leaves, chopped

2 Cover the pan and leave to simmer for 25–30 minutes, until the lentils are mushy. Add the mixed vegetables, tamarind juice and tomato quarters. Cook until the vegetables are just tender.

3 Heat the remaining oil in a small pan over a low heat, and fry the garlic slices until golden. Stir in the coriander leaves, then pour over the lentils and vegetables. Mix at the table before serving.

1 Heat half the oil in a wok, karahi or large pan, and stir-fry the next seven ingredients until the coconut begins to brown. Stir in the prepared red lentils, sambhar masala and turmeric. Stir-fry for 2–3 minutes and add the water. Bring it to the boil and reduce the heat to low.

COOK'S TIP
Red lentils are used in this recipe, but the traditional choice would be yellow split lentils, known as toor dhal or tuvar dhal, which are available from Indian stores.

TOMATO and SPINACH PULAO

A tasty and nourishing dish for vegetarians and meat eaters alike. Serve it with another vegetable curry, or with tandoori chicken, marinated fried fish or shammi kabab. Add a cooling fruit raita for a completely balanced meal.

2 Drain the rice, add it to the pan and cook for a further 1–2 minutes, stirring, until the rice is coated.

3 Stir in the dhana jeera powder or coriander and cumin, then add the carrots. Season with salt and pepper. Pour in the stock and stir well to mix.

SERVES 4

30ml/2 tbsp vegetable oil
15ml/1 tbsp ghee or unsalted (sweet) butter
1 onion, chopped
2 garlic cloves, crushed
3 tomatoes, peeled, seeded and chopped
225g/8oz/generous 1 cup brown basmati rice, soaked
10ml/2 tsp dhana jeera powder or 5ml/1 tsp ground coriander and 5ml/1 tsp ground cumin
2 carrots, coarsely grated
900ml/1½ pints/3¾ cups vegetable stock
275g/10oz young spinach leaves
50g/2oz/½ cup unsalted cashew nuts, toasted
salt and ground black pepper
naan bread, to serve

1 Heat the oil and ghee or butter in a wok, karahi or large pan, and fry the onion and garlic for 4–5 minutes until soft. Add the tomatoes and cook for 3–4 minutes, stirring, until thickened.

COOK'S TIP
Leaving to rest for 6–8 minutes before serving makes the rice dry and fluffy.

4 Bring to the boil, then cover tightly and simmer over a very gentle heat for 20–25 minutes, until the rice is tender. Lay the spinach on the surface of the rice, cover again, and cook for a further 2–3 minutes, until the spinach has wilted. Fold the spinach into the rest of the rice and check the seasoning. Sprinkle with toasted cashews and serve with naan.

STUFFED BANANAS

Bananas are cooked with spices in many different ways in southern India. Some recipes contain large quantities of chillies, but the taste is skilfully mellowed by adding coconut milk and tamarind juice. Green bananas are available from Indian stores, or you can use plantains or unripe eating bananas that are firm to the touch.

SERVES 4

4 green bananas or plantains
30ml/2 tbsp ground coriander
15ml/1 tbsp ground cumin
5ml/1 tsp chilli powder
2.5ml/½ tsp salt
1.5ml/¼ tsp ground turmeric
5ml/1 tsp granulated sugar
15ml/1 tbsp gram flour (besan)
45ml/3 tbsp chopped fresh coriander
    (cilantro), plus extra sprigs
    to garnish
90ml/6 tbsp vegetable oil
1.5ml/¼ tsp cumin seeds
1.5ml/¼ tsp black mustard seeds

1 Trim the bananas or plantains and cut each crossways into three equal pieces, leaving the skin on. Make a lengthwise slit along each piece of banana, without cutting all the way through the flesh.

2 On a plate mix together the ground coriander, cumin, chilli powder, salt, turmeric, sugar, gram flour, chopped fresh coriander and 15ml/1 tbsp of the oil. Use your fingers to combine well.

3 Carefully stuff each piece of banana with the spice mixture, taking care not to break the bananas in half.

4 Heat the remaining oil in a wok, karahi or large pan, and fry the cumin and mustard seeds for 2 minutes or until they begin to splutter. Add the bananas and toss gently in the oil. Cover and simmer over a low heat for 15 minutes, stirring from time to time, until the bananas are soft but not mushy.

5 Garnish with the fresh coriander sprigs, and serve with warm chapatis, if you like. Other good accompaniments include Prawn Biryani and yogurt.

COOK'S TIP
Baby courgettes (zucchini) would make a delicious alternative to bananas.

PRAWN BIRYANI

The recipe for biryani originated with mutton, but its popularity has tempted Indian chefs to create versions using other ingredients. As with all biryanis, this one using prawns is a meal in itself. The classic accompaniment to any biryani is a raita.

SERVES 4–6

2 large onions, finely sliced and
    deep-fried
300ml/½ pint/1¼ cups natural
    (plain) yogurt
30ml/2 tbsp tomato purée (paste)
60ml/4 tbsp green masala paste
30ml/2 tbsp lemon juice
5ml/1 tsp black cumin seeds
5cm/2in piece cinnamon stick, or
    1.5ml/¼ tsp ground cinnamon
4 green cardamom pods
450g/1lb raw king prawns (jumbo
    shrimp), peeled and deveined
225g/8oz/3 cups small whole button
    (white) mushrooms
225g/8oz/2 cups frozen peas, thawed
450g/1lb/2⅓ cups basmati rice,
    soaked for 5 minutes in boiled
    water and drained
300ml/½ pint/1¼ cups water
1 sachet saffron powder, mixed in
    90ml/6 tbsp milk
30ml/2 tbsp ghee or unsalted (sweet)
    butter
salt

1 In a bowl, mix the onions, yogurt, tomato purée, masala paste, lemon juice, cumin seeds, cinnamon and cardamom, with salt to taste. Fold in the prawns, mushrooms and peas. Leave for 2 hours. Preheat the oven to 190°C/375°F/Gas 5.

2 Grease the base of a heavy pan and add the prawns, vegetables and any marinade juices. Cover with the drained rice and smooth the surface gently until you have an even layer.

3 Pour the water over the surface of the rice. Make holes through the rice with the handle of a spoon and pour into each a little saffron milk. Place knobs (pats) of ghee or butter on the surface.

4 Place a circular piece of foil on top of the rice. Cover and cook in the oven for 45–50 minutes. Allow to stand for 8–10 minutes, then stir the biryani and serve hot.

SPICED LENTILS with SPINACH

Spinach cooked with chana dhal *lentils makes a wholesome, healthy dish. It is perfect for a vegetarian diet, as it provides protein, vitamins and minerals in one dish. Serve it with naan bread, chapatis or plain boiled rice to make a satisfying main course. A salad or a chutney will add an extra special zest to the meal.*

2 Drain the chana dhal or split peas and put in a large pan with the water. Bring to the boil, cover, and simmer for about 20–25 minutes until the dhal are soft. Cook, uncovered, until the cooking liquid has evaporated completely.

3 Heat the oil in a wok, karahi or large pan and fry the mustard seeds for about 2 minutes until they begin to splutter. Add the onion, garlic, ginger and chilli and fry for 5–6 minutes, then add the spinach and cook for 10 minutes or until the spinach is dry and the liquid is absorbed. Stir in the remaining spices and salt and cook for 2–3 minutes.

4 Add the chana dhal or split peas to the spinach in the pan and cook, stirring, for about 5 minutes. Serve hot with warm naan bread, or with plain boiled rice, if you like.

SERVES 4

175g/6oz/¾ cup chana dhal or yellow
   split peas
175ml/6fl oz/¾ cup water
30ml/2 tbsp vegetable oil
1.5ml/¼ tsp black mustard seeds
1 onion, thinly sliced
2 garlic cloves, crushed
2.5cm/1in piece fresh root ginger, grated
1 red chilli, finely chopped
275g/10oz frozen spinach, thawed
1.5ml/¼ tsp chilli powder
2.5ml/½ tsp ground coriander
2.5ml/½ tsp garam masala
2.5ml/½ tsp salt

1 Wash the chana dhal or split peas in several changes of cold water. Put the dhal or peas into a large bowl and cover with plenty of cold water. Leave to soak for about 30 minutes.

COOK'S TIP

Use canned chickpeas in place of chana dhal for a quick alternative. Drain, rinse in water, drain again, and add in step 4.

TRICOLOUR PULAO

Most Indian restaurants in the West serve this popular vegetable pulao, which has three different vegetables. The effect is easily achieved with canned or frozen vegetables, but for entertaining or a special occasion dinner, you may prefer to use fresh produce.

SERVES 4–6

225g/8oz/1 cup basmati rice, rinsed
    and soaked for 30 minutes
30ml/2 tbsp vegetable oil
2.5ml/½ tsp cumin seeds
2 dried bay leaves
4 green cardamom pods
4 cloves
1 onion, finely chopped
1 carrot, finely diced
50g/2oz/½ cup frozen peas, thawed
50g/2oz/⅓ cup frozen sweetcorn, thawed
25g/1oz/¼ cup cashew nuts, lightly fried
475ml/16fl oz/2 cups water
1.5ml/¼ tsp ground cumin
salt

1 Heat the oil in a wok, karahi or large pan over a medium heat, and fry the cumin seeds for 2 minutes. Add the bay leaves, cardamoms and cloves, and fry gently for 2 minutes more, stirring the spices from time to time.

2 Add the onion and fry until lightly browned. Stir in the diced carrot and cook, stirring, for 3–4 minutes.

3 Drain the soaked basmati rice and add to the contents in the pan. Stir well to mix. Add the peas, sweetcorn and fried cashew nuts.

4 Add the measured water and the remaining spices, and add salt to taste. Bring to the boil, cover and simmer for 15 minutes over a low heat until all the water is absorbed.

5 Leave to stand, covered, for 10 minutes. Transfer to a warmed dish and serve.

WEST INDIA

The western states of Gujarat and Maharashtra have developed an excellent repertoire of vegetarian dishes, using fresh vegetables, dairy products and lentils and peas. Goa, to the south of Bombay, shows Portuguese influences; its most famous culinary export is vindaloo.

CHICKEN PULAO

Like biryanis, pulaos cooked with meat and poultry make a convenient one-pot meal.
A vegetable curry makes a good accompaniment, although for a simpler meal, such as
supper, you could serve the pulao with a simple raita, combining natural yogurt with
any raw vegetable, such as white cabbage, grated carrots, or cauliflower florets.

SERVES 4

400g/14oz/2 cups basmati rice
75g/3oz/6 tbsp ghee or unsalted
    (sweet) butter
1 onion, sliced
1.5ml/¼ tsp mixed onion and mustard
    seeds
3 curry leaves
5ml/1 tsp grated fresh root ginger
5ml/1 tsp crushed garlic
5ml/1 tsp ground coriander
5ml/1 tsp chilli powder
7.5ml/1½ tsp salt
2 tomatoes, sliced
1 potato, cubed
50g/2oz/½ cup frozen peas, thawed
175g/6oz chicken breast fillets, skinned
    and cubed
60ml/4 tbsp chopped fresh coriander
    (cilantro)
2 fresh green chillies, chopped
700ml/1¼ pints/3 cups water

1 Wash the rice thoroughly under
running water, then leave to soak for
30 minutes. Drain and set aside in a
sieve (strainer).

2 In a pan, melt the ghee or butter and
fry the sliced onion until golden.

3 Add the onion and mustard seeds,
the curry leaves, ginger, garlic, ground
coriander, chilli powder and salt. Stir-fry
for about 2 minutes over a low heat:
ground spices require only gentle
warmth to release their flavours.

4 Add the sliced tomatoes, cubed
potato, peas and chicken and mix
everything together well.

5 Add the rice and stir gently to
combine with the other ingredients.

6 Add the coriander and chillies. Mix
and stir-fry for 1 minute. Pour in the
water, bring to the boil and then lower
the heat. Cover and cook for 20 minutes.
Remove from the heat and leave the
pulao to stand for 6–8 minutes. Serve.

GOAN CHICKEN CURRY

Lines of swaying palm trees and the raised borders of a vast patchwork of paddy fields are just two of the features that constitute the superb landscape of Goa. Not surprisingly, coconut, in all of its forms, is widely used to enrich Goan cuisine.

SERVES 4

75g/3oz/1½ cups desiccated (dry, unsweetened, shredded) coconut
30ml/2 tbsp vegetable oil
2.5ml/½ tsp cumin seeds
4 black peppercorns
15ml/1 tbsp fennel seeds
15ml/1 tbsp coriander seeds
2 onions, finely chopped
2.5ml/½ tsp salt
8 small chicken pieces, such as thighs and drumsticks, skinned
fresh coriander (cilantro) sprigs and lemon wedges, to garnish

1 Put the desiccated coconut in a bowl with 45ml/3 tbsp water. Leave to soak for 15 minutes.

2 Heat 15ml/1 tbsp of the oil in a wok, karahi or large pan and fry the cumin seeds, peppercorns, fennel and coriander seeds over a low heat for 3–4 minutes until they begin to splutter.

COOK'S TIP
If you prefer, make the spiced coconut mixture the day before and chill it in the refrigerator, then continue from step 6 when required.

3 Add the finely chopped onions and fry for about 5 minutes, stirring occasionally, until the onion has softened and turned opaque.

4 Stir in the coconut, along with the soaking water and salt, and continue to fry for a further 5 minutes, stirring occasionally to prevent the mixture from sticking to the pan.

5 Put the coconut mixture into a food processor or blender and process to form a coarse paste. Spoon into a bowl and set aside until required.

6 Heat the remaining oil and fry the chicken for 10 minutes. Add the coconut paste and cook over a low heat for 15–20 minutes, or until the coconut mixture is golden brown and the chicken is tender.

7 Transfer the curry to a warmed serving plate, and garnish with sprigs of fresh coriander and lemon wedges. Mint and Coconut Chutney, plain boiled rice or a lentil dish would all make good accompaniments to this recipe.

PULAO in AROMATIC LAMB STOCK

A typical north Indian dish known as yakhni pulao, *this is rich and highly aromatic.*
Traditionally, lamb is cooked on the bone, which adds extra flavour to the stock.
If you buy a leg of lamb and bone it yourself, do save the bones and add them to
the stock at step 1; they can be discarded later in the recipe.

SERVES 4–6

900g/2lb chicken pieces or lean lamb, cubed
600ml/1 pint/2½ cups water
4 green cardamom pods
2 black cardamom pods
10 whole peppercorns
4 cloves
1 onion, sliced
450g/1lb/2⅓ cups basmati rice, washed
    and drained
8–10 saffron threads
2 garlic cloves, crushed
5cm/2in piece fresh root ginger, crushed
5cm/2in piece cinnamon stick
salt
175g/6oz/generous 1 cup sultanas
    (golden raisins) and almonds, sautéed,
    to garnish

1 Place the chicken pieces or cubed lamb in a large pan with the water, cardamoms, peppercorns, cloves and sliced onion. Add salt to taste, and cook until the meat is tender. Remove the meat with a slotted spoon and keep warm. Strain the stock, if you wish, and return it to the pan.

2 Add the drained rice, saffron, garlic, ginger and cinnamon to the stock in the pan and bring the contents to the boil.

3 Quickly add the meat and stir well. Bring the stock back to the boil, reduce the heat and cover. Cook for about 15–20 minutes.

4 Remove from the heat and stand for 5 minutes. Transfer the contents of the pan to a warmed serving platter and garnish with the sultanas and sautéed almonds before serving.

COOK'S TIP
When washing rice, toss and turn it very gently to avoid damage to the delicate grains of basmati.

CHICKEN with GREEN MANGO

Green or unripe mango is meant only for cooking purposes. These fruits are smaller than eating mangoes, and they have a sharper taste. They can be bought from Indian stores and markets, but if not available, cooking apples make an easy alternative.

SERVES 4

1 green (unripe) mango or cooking apple
450g/1lb chicken breast fillets, skinned
    and cubed
1.5ml/¼ tsp onion seeds
5ml/1 tsp grated fresh root ginger
2.5ml/½ tsp crushed garlic
5ml/1 tsp chilli powder
1.5ml/¼ tsp ground turmeric
5ml/1 tsp salt
5ml/1 tsp ground coriander
30ml/2 tbsp vegetable oil
2 onions, sliced
4 curry leaves
300ml/½ pint/1¼ cups water
2 tomatoes, quartered
2 fresh green chillies, chopped
30ml/2 tbsp chopped fresh
    coriander (cilantro)

1 To prepare the mango, peel the skin and slice the flesh thickly. Discard the stone (pit) from the middle. Place the mango slices in a bowl, cover and set aside. If using apple, coat the slices with lemon juice to prevent discoloration.

2 Put the cubed chicken into a large mixing bowl and add the onion seeds, ginger, garlic, chilli powder, turmeric, salt and ground coriander. Mix the spices with the chicken, then stir in half the mango or apple slices.

3 Heat the oil in a wok, karahi or large pan over a medium heat, and fry the sliced onions until golden brown. Add the curry leaves to the pan, and stir very gently to release their flavour.

4 Gradually add the chicken to the pan, stirring all the time. Stir-fry briskly over a medium heat until the chicken is opaque.

5 Pour in the water, lower the heat and cook for 12–15 minutes, stirring, until the chicken is cooked through and the water has been completely absorbed.

6 Add the remaining mango or apple slices, the tomatoes, green chillies and fresh coriander. Plain boiled rice and Stuffed Okra are good accompaniments to serve with this dish.

VARIATION
Try fillets of rabbit for an unusual treat.

NUT PULAO

Known as pilau in Persia, pilaff in Turkey and pulao in India, these rice dishes are always made with the best-quality long grain rice. In India, basmati rice is the natural choice. There are different variations of this recipe, and this one, with walnuts and cashews, makes an ideal dish for vegetarians when served with a raita or natural yogurt.

SERVES 4

15–30ml/1–2 tbsp vegetable oil
1 onion, chopped
1 garlic clove, crushed
1 large carrot, coarsely grated
225g/8oz/generous 1 cup basmati rice,
   soaked for 20–30 minutes
5ml/1 tsp cumin seeds
10ml/2 tsp ground coriander
10ml/2 tsp black mustard seeds (optional)
4 green cardamom pods
450ml/¾ pint/scant 2 cups vegetable stock
1 bay leaf
75g/3oz/¾ cup unsalted walnuts and
   cashew nuts
salt and ground black pepper
fresh coriander (cilantro) sprigs, to garnish

1 Heat the oil in a wok, karahi or large pan. Fry the onion, garlic and carrot for 3–4 minutes. Drain the rice and add to the spices. Cook for 2 minutes, stirring to coat the grains in oil.

2 Pour in the vegetable stock, stirring. Add the bay leaf and season well.

3 Bring to the boil, lower the heat, cover and simmer very gently for 10–12 minutes.

4 Remove the pan from the heat without lifting the lid. Leave to stand for 5 minutes, then check the rice. If it is cooked, there will be small steam holes on the surface of the rice. Discard the bay leaf and the cardamom pods.

COOK'S TIP
Use a metal slotted spoon or a fork while stirring in the nuts. Wooden spoons will squash the delicate rice grains.

5 Stir in the walnuts and cashew nuts and check the seasoning. Spoon on to a warmed platter, garnish with the fresh coriander and serve.

Indian Rices and Breads

BEEF VINDALOO

Vindaloo is Goa's most famous export, but its origins are in fact Portuguese. In the 16th century, when Portuguese traders embarked on their long voyage to India, they carried pork, preserved in vinegar, garlic and black pepper. The word vin comes from vinegar and aloo is derived from alho, the Portuguese word for garlic.

SERVES 4

15ml/1 tbsp cumin seeds
4 dried red chillies
5ml/1 tsp black peppercorns
5 green cardamom pods, seeds only
5ml/1 tsp fenugreek seeds
5ml/1 tsp black mustard seeds
2.5ml/½ tsp salt
2.5ml/½ tsp demerara (raw) sugar
60ml/4 tbsp white wine vinegar
60ml/4 tbsp vegetable oil
1 large onion, finely chopped
900g/2lb stewing beef, cut into
    2.5cm/1in cubes
2.5cm/1in piece fresh root ginger, shredded
1 garlic clove, crushed
10ml/2 tsp ground coriander
2.5ml/½ tsp ground turmeric
plain and yellow rice, to serve

1 Use a pestle and mortar to grind the cumin seeds, chillies, peppercorns, cardamom seeds, fenugreek seeds and mustard seeds to a fine powder. Add the salt, sugar and white wine vinegar and mix to a thin paste.

2 Heat 30ml/2 tbsp of the oil and fry the onion over a medium heat for 8–10 minutes. Put the onion and the spice mixture into a food processor or blender and process to a coarse paste.

VARIATION
Pork tenderloin or leg is the traditional meat for vindaloo. If using leg, remove the crackling and trim off all visible fat.

3 Heat the remaining oil in the pan and fry the meat cubes over a medium heat for 10 minutes or until lightly browned. Remove the beef cubes with a slotted spoon and set aside.

4 Add the shredded ginger and crushed garlic to the pan and fry for 2 minutes. Stir in the coriander and turmeric and fry for 2 minutes more.

COOK'S TIP
To make plain and yellow rice, infuse (steep) a pinch of saffron threads or dissolve a little turmeric in 15ml/1 tbsp hot water in a small bowl. Stir into half the cooked rice until it is uniformly yellow. Carefully mix the yellow rice into the plain rice.

5 Add the spice and onion paste and fry for about 5 minutes.

6 Return the meat to the pan, together with 300ml/½ pint/1¼ cups water. Cover and simmer for 1–1½ hours or until the meat is tender. Serve with plain and yellow rice, and a raita, if you like.

CLASSIC PULAO

The exquisite flavour of basmati rice flavoured with stock and the heady aroma of saffron is the classic character of a traditional pulao. The secret of a perfect pulao is to wash the rice thoroughly, then soak it briefly. Soaking before cooking softens and moistens the grains, enabling the rice to absorb moisture during cooking, and resulting in fluffier rice.

SERVES 4

600ml/1 pint/2½ cups hot chicken
    stock
generous pinch of saffron threads
50g/2oz/¼ cup butter
1 onion, chopped
1 garlic clove, crushed
2.5cm/1in piece cinnamon stick
6 green cardamom pods
1 bay leaf
250g/9oz/1⅓ cups basmati rice, soaked
    for 20–30 minutes
50g/2oz/⅓ cup sultanas (golden raisins)
15ml/1 tbsp vegetable oil
50g/2oz/½ cup cashew nuts
naan bread and Tomato and Onion
    Salad, to serve

3 Drain the rice and add to the pan, then cook, stirring, for 2 minutes more. Pour in the saffron stock and add the sultanas. Bring to the boil, stir, then lower the heat, cover and cook gently for 10 minutes or until the rice is tender and the liquid has all been absorbed.

4 Meanwhile, heat the oil in a wok, karahi or large pan and fry the cashew nuts until browned. Drain on kitchen paper, then sprinkle the cashew nuts over the rice. Serve with naan bread and Tomato and Onion Salad, or with Mughlai-style Leg of Lamb.

1 Pour the hot chicken stock into a jug (pitcher). Stir in the saffron threads and set aside.

2 Heat the butter in a pan and fry the onion and garlic for 5 minutes. Stir in the cinnamon stick, cardamoms and bay leaf and cook for 2 minutes.

PORK BALCHAO

Pork and beef dishes are not very common in India, but Goa, on the west coast of the country, has a cuisine that has been influenced by three religions: Hinduism, Islam and Christianity. Goa was colonized by the Portuguese for nearly four centuries and during this time a Jesuit father, Francis Xavier, brought about a calming influence between the religions. The region became known for its religious tolerance, and this is one tradition that has not faded with the passing of time.

SERVES 4

60ml/4 tbsp vegetable oil
15ml/1 tbsp grated fresh root ginger
15ml/1 tbsp crushed garlic
2.5cm/1in piece cinnamon stick,
    broken up
2–4 dried red chillies, chopped or torn
4 cloves
10ml/2 tsp cumin seeds
10 black peppercorns
675g/1½ lb cubed leg of pork, crackling
    and visible fat removed
5ml/1 tsp ground turmeric
200ml/7fl oz/scant 1 cup warm water
25ml/1½ tbsp tomato purée (paste)
2.5ml/½ tsp chilli powder (optional)
1 large onion, finely sliced
5ml/1 tsp salt
5ml/1 tsp granulated sugar
10ml/2 tbsp cider vinegar

1 Heat 30ml/2 tbsp of the oil in a wok, karahi or large pan, and add the ginger and garlic. Fry for 30 seconds.

2 Grind the next five ingredients to a fine powder, using a spice mill or coffee grinder. Add the spice mix to the pan and fry for a further 30 seconds, stirring.

3 Add the pork and turmeric and increase the heat slightly. Fry for 5–6 minutes or until the meat starts to release its juices, stirring regularly.

4 Add the water, tomato purée and chilli powder, if using, and bring to the boil. Cover the pan and simmer gently for 35–40 minutes.

5 Heat the remaining oil and fry the onion for 8–9 minutes until browned, stirring regularly.

6 Add the fried onion to the pork along with the salt, sugar and vinegar. Stir, cover and simmer for 30–35 minutes or until the pork is tender. Remove from the heat and serve.

COOK'S TIP
Balchao will keep well in the refrigerator for up to 7 days. Before reheating, bring to room temperature. Add a little warm water during reheating, if necessary.

CARAMELIZED BASMATI RICE

This is the traditional accompaniment to a dhansak curry. Sugar is caramelized in hot oil before the rice is added, along with a few whole spices.

SERVES 4

225g/8oz/generous 1 cup basmati rice,
    washed and soaked for 20–30 minutes
45ml/3 tbsp vegetable oil
20ml/4 tsp granulated sugar
4–5 green cardamom pods, bruised
2.5cm/1in piece cinnamon stick
4 cloves
1 bay leaf, crumbled
½ tsp salt
475ml/16fl oz/2 cups hot water

1 Put the basmati rice in a colander and leave to drain.

2 In a large pan, heat the vegetable oil over a medium heat. When the oil is hot, add the granulated sugar and wait until it is caramelized.

3 Reduce the heat to low and add the spices and bay leaf. Let sizzle for about 15–20 seconds, then add the rice and salt. Fry gently, stirring, for 2–3 minutes.

4 Pour in the water and bring to the boil. Let it boil steadily for 2 minutes and then reduce the heat to very low. Cover the pan and cook for 8 minutes.

5 Remove the rice from the heat and let it stand for 6–8 minutes. Gently fluff up the rice with a fork and transfer to a warmed dish to serve.

GOAN PRAWN CURRY

The cuisine of Goa is well known for its excellent range of fish and shellfish-based recipes, such as this one for prawns. Numerous varieties of fish and shellfish are found along the extended coastline and the network of inland waterways.

SERVES 4

15g/½oz/1 tbsp ghee or butter
2 garlic cloves, crushed
450g/1lb small raw prawns (shrimp),
    peeled and deveined
15ml/1 tbsp groundnut (peanut) oil
4 cardamom pods
4 cloves
5cm/2in piece cinnamon stick
15ml/1 tbsp mustard seeds
1 large onion, finely chopped
½–1 fresh red chilli, seeded and sliced
4 tomatoes, peeled, seeded and chopped
175ml/6fl oz/¾ cup fish stock or water
350ml/12fl oz/1½ cups coconut milk
45ml/3 tbsp Fragrant Spice Mix (see
    Cook's Tip)
10–20ml/2–4 tsp chilli powder
salt
turmeric-coloured basmati rice, to serve

1 Melt the ghee or butter in a wok, karahi or large pan, add the garlic and stir over a low heat for a few seconds. Add the prawns and stir-fry briskly to coat. Transfer to a plate and set aside.

VARIATION
For a reduced fat version, use the same quantity of semi-skimmed (low-fat) milk instead of the coconut milk.

2 In the same pan, heat the oil and fry the cardamom, cloves and cinnamon for 2 minutes. Add the mustard seeds and fry for 1 minute. Add the onion and chilli and fry for 7–8 minutes or until softened and lightly browned.

3 Add the remaining ingredients and bring to a slow simmer. Cook gently for 6–8 minutes and add the prawns. Simmer for 5–8 minutes until the prawns are cooked through. Serve the curry with turmeric-coloured basmati rice.

COOK'S TIP
To make a Fragrant Spice Mix, dry-fry 25ml/1½ tbsp coriander seeds, 15ml/1 tbsp mixed peppercorns, 5ml/1 tsp cumin seeds, 1.5ml/¼ tsp fenugreek seeds and 1.5ml/¼ tsp fennel seeds until aromatic, then grind finely in a spice mill.

SAFFRON RICE

The saffron crocus is a perennial bulb that only flowers for two weeks of the year, and each stigma has to be removed by hand and dried with care. Consequently, saffron is said to be worth its weight in gold. Kashmir in the northern region of India and La Manche in Spain are the world's two major producers of saffron. In Indian cooking, saffron is used as a colorant in both sweet and savoury dishes.

SERVES 6

450g/1lb/2⅓ cups basmati rice, soaked
   for 20–30 minutes
750ml/1¼ pints/3 cups water
3 green cardamom pods
2 cloves
5ml/1 tsp salt
45ml/3 tbsp semi-skimmed (low-fat) milk
2.5ml/½ tsp saffron threads, crushed

COOK'S TIP
The saffron milk can be heated in the microwave. Mix the milk and saffron threads in a suitable container and warm them for 1 minute on Low.

1 Drain the basmati rice and place in a large pan. Pour in the water. Add the cardamoms, cloves and salt. Stir, then bring to the boil. Lower the heat and cover tightly, and simmer for 5 minutes.

2 Meanwhile, place the milk in a small pan. Add the saffron threads and heat through gently.

3 Add the saffron milk to the rice and stir. Cover again and continue cooking over a low heat for 5–6 minutes.

4 Remove the pan from the heat without lifting the lid. Leave the rice to stand for about 5 minutes, then fork through just before serving.

COOK'S TIP
Wash the rice in cold water before soaking for longer, fluffier cooked rice.

PARSI PRAWN CURRY

After landing on the west coast of India, the Parsi community migrated to different parts of the country. The majority, however, made Bombay their home. They have cleverly integrated their cooking style into the exotic tastes of Indian cuisine, as this curry shows.

2 Add the chopped onions to the other ingredients in the pan and fry gently until the chopped onions become translucent, then fold in the tamarind juice, mint sauce, sugar and salt. Simmer for a further 3 minutes.

3 Carefully peel and devein the king prawns, then pat them dry with kitchen paper. Add the prawns to the spice mixture with a small amount of water and stir-fry until the prawns turn bright orange/pink.

SERVES 4–6

60ml/4 tbsp vegetable oil
1 onion, finely sliced, plus 2 onions,
    finely chopped
6 garlic cloves, crushed
5ml/1 tsp chilli powder
7.5ml/1½ tsp ground turmeric
50ml/2fl oz/¼ cup tamarind juice
5ml/1 tsp mint sauce
15ml/1 tbsp demerara (raw) sugar
450g/1lb raw king prawns (jumbo shrimp)
75g/3oz coriander (cilantro) leaves,
    chopped, plus extra leaves to garnish
salt

1 Heat the oil and fry the sliced onion. In a bowl, mix the garlic, chilli powder and turmeric with water to form a paste. Add to the onion and cook.

4 When the prawns are cooked, add the coriander leaves and stir-fry on a high heat to thicken the sauce. Garnish with extra coriander leaves and serve.

INDIAN RICES
AND BREADS

An Indian meal is always served with rice or bread. Basmati rice, with its distinctive aromatic flavour, is the most popular variety. Leavened breads, such as naan, are widely eaten in the north and west, while flat, unleavened chapatis and parathas are the breads of the south.

FISH CAKES

Goan fish and shellfish are skilfully prepared with spices to make cakes of all shapes and sizes, while the rest of India makes fish kababs. Although haddock is used in this recipe, you can use other less expensive white fish, such as coley or whiting.

MAKES 20

450g/1lb skinned haddock or cod
2 potatoes, peeled, boiled and
    coarsely mashed
4 spring onions (scallions),
    finely chopped
4 fresh green chillies, finely chopped
5cm/2in piece fresh root ginger, crushed
a few coriander (cilantro) and mint
    sprigs, chopped
2 eggs
breadcrumbs, for coating
vegetable oil, for shallow frying
salt and ground black pepper
lemon wedges and chilli sauce,
    to serve

1 Place the skinned fish in a lightly greased steamer and steam gently until cooked. Remove the steamer from the hob (stovetop) but leave the fish on the steaming tray until cool.

2 When the fish is cool, crumble it coarsely into a large bowl, using a fork. Mix in the mashed potatoes, spring onions, chillies, crushed ginger, chopped coriander and mint, and one of the eggs. Season to taste with salt and pepper.

COOK'S TIP

For a quick version, used canned tuna in brine and omit step 1. Make sure the tuna is thoroughly drained before use.

3 Shape into cakes. Beat the remaining egg and dip the cakes in it, then coat with the breadcrumbs. Heat the oil and fry the cakes until brown on all sides. Serve as an appetizer or as a side dish, with the lemon wedges and chilli sauce.

STUFFED VEGETABLES

It is hard to beat the Gujarati community when it comes to the creation of imaginative vegetarian dishes. In this fabulous recipe, two different vegetables are stuffed with an irresistible blend of spices and peanuts.

SERVES 4

12 small potatoes
8 baby aubergines (eggplant)
single (light) cream, to garnish

For the stuffing
15ml/1 tbsp sesame seeds
30ml/2 tbsp ground coriander
30ml/2 tbsp ground cumin
2.5ml/½ tsp salt
1.5ml/¼ tsp chilli powder
2.5ml/½ tsp ground turmeric
10ml/2 tsp granulated sugar
1.5ml/¼ tsp garam masala
15ml/1 tbsp peanuts, roughly crushed
15ml/1 tbsp gram flour (besan)
2 garlic cloves, crushed
15ml/1 tbsp lemon juice
30ml/2 tbsp chopped fresh coriander
    (cilantro)

For the sauce
30ml/2 tbsp vegetable oil
2.5ml/½ tsp black mustard seeds
400g/14oz can chopped tomatoes
30ml/2 tbsp chopped fresh coriander
    (cilantro)
150ml/¼ pint/⅔ cup water

1 Preheat the oven to 200°C/400°F/ Gas 6. Make slits in the potatoes and baby aubergines, making sure that you do not cut right through.

2 Mix all the ingredients for the stuffing together on a plate.

3 Carefully stuff the potatoes and aubergines with the spice mixture.

4 Place the potatoes and aubergines in a greased ovenproof dish.

5 Heat the oil in a pan and fry the mustard seeds for 2 minutes until they begin to splutter, then add the tomatoes, coriander and any leftover stuffing, together with the water. Simmer for 5 minutes until the sauce thickens.

6 Pour the sauce over the potatoes and aubergines. Cover and bake for 25–30 minutes until the vegetables are soft. Garnish with single cream, if using. Serve with any Indian bread or with a meat or chicken curry of your choice.

SPICY OMELETTE

*Another popular contribution by the Parsis, this irresistible omelette is known as poro
in their language. Parsi food originated along the shores of the Caspian Sea, and the
cuisine offers some unique flavours, which appeal to both Eastern and Western palates.*

SERVES 4–6

30ml/2 tbsp vegetable oil
1 onion, finely chopped
2.5ml/½ tsp ground cumin
1 garlic clove, crushed
1 or 2 fresh green chillies, finely chopped
a few coriander (cilantro) sprigs,
    chopped, plus extra, to garnish
1 firm tomato, chopped
1 small potato, cubed and boiled
25g/1oz/¼ cup cooked peas
25g/1oz/¼ cup cooked sweetcorn,
    or canned sweetcorn, drained
2 eggs, beaten
25g/1oz/¼ cup grated cheese
salt and ground black pepper

1 Heat the vegetable oil in a wok, karahi
or large pan, and fry the next nine
ingredients until they are well blended
but the potato and tomato are still firm.
Season to taste with salt and ground
black pepper.

2 Increase the heat and pour in the
beaten eggs. Reduce the heat, cover and
cook until the bottom layer is brown.
Turn the omelette over and sprinkle with
the grated cheese. Place under a hot grill
(broiler) and cook until the egg sets and
the cheese has melted.

3 Garnish the omelette with sprigs of
coriander and serve with salad for a light
lunch. If you prefer, serve it for breakfast,
in the typical Parsi style.

VARIATION
You can use any vegetable with the
potatoes. Try thickly sliced button
(white) mushrooms, added in step 1.

POTATOES in a YOGURT SAUCE

The potato was first introduced to India by Dutch traders, and it has since been elevated to gourmet status. In Indian cuisine, the humble potato takes on delicious flavourings of simple whole spices, or of blends of spices ground together.

SERVES 4

12 new potatoes, halved
300ml/½ pint/1¼ cups natural (plain)
    yogurt, whisked
300ml/½ pint/1¼ cups water
1.5ml/¼ tsp ground turmeric
5ml/1 tsp chilli powder
5ml/1 tsp ground coriander
2.5ml/½ tsp ground cumin
5ml/1 tsp salt
5ml/1 tsp soft brown sugar
30ml/2 tbsp vegetable oil
5ml/1 tsp cumin seeds
15ml/1 tbsp chopped fresh coriander
    (cilantro), plus extra sprigs to
    garnish (optional)
2 fresh green chillies, sliced

1 Boil the halved new potatoes with their skins on in a large pan of salted water, until they are just tender. Drain the potatoes and set aside.

2 Mix together the natural yogurt, water, turmeric, chilli powder, ground coriander, ground cumin, salt and sugar in a bowl. Set the mixture aside.

COOK'S TIPS
• If new potatoes are out of season and unavailable, you could use 450g/1lb ordinary potatoes instead. Peel and wash them and cut into large chunks, then cook as described above.
• Add 10ml/2 tsp gram flour (besan) to the yogurt to prevent it curdling.

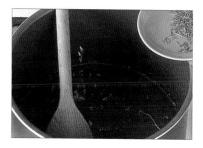

3 Heat the vegetable oil in a wok, karahi or large pan, and add the cumin seeds. Fry gently until they begin to splutter.

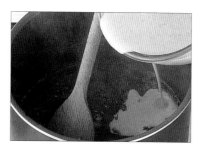

4 Reduce the heat, stir in the yogurt mixture and cook for about 3 minutes over a medium heat.

5 Add the chopped fresh coriander, green chillies and cooked potatoes. Blend everything together and cook for a further 5–7 minutes, stirring the mixture occasionally.

6 Transfer to a warmed serving dish and garnish with the coriander sprig, if you like. This dish goes very well with hot bhaturas or chapatis.

EGGS BAKED on CHIPSTICKS

This is an unusual and delicious way of combining eggs with potato sticks, and is known as sali pur eeda in the Parsi language. The potato sticks are cooked with spices to form a pancake. Eggs are then placed on top of the potato pancake and gently cooked.

SERVES 4–6

225g/8oz salted chipsticks
2 fresh green chillies, finely chopped
a few coriander (cilantro) sprigs, chopped
1.5ml/¼ tsp ground turmeric
60ml/4 tbsp vegetable oil
75ml/5 tbsp water
6 eggs
3 spring onions (scallions), finely chopped
salt and ground black pepper

1 In a bowl, mix the salted chipsticks, chopped chillies, coriander and turmeric. Heat 30ml/2 tbsp of the oil in a heavy frying pan. Add the chipstick mixture and water. Cook until the chipsticks turn soft, and then crisp.

2 Place a dinner plate over the frying pan, and hold in place as you turn the pan over and carefully transfer the chipstick pancake on to the plate. Heat the remaining oil in the pan and slide the pancake back into the frying pan to brown the other side.

3 Gently break the eggs over the pancake, cover the frying pan and allow the eggs to set over a low heat. Season well and sprinkle with spring onions. Cook until the base is crisp. Serve hot for breakfast in the Parsi style, or with chapatis and a salad for lunch or supper.

CHICKPEAS with SPICED POTATO CAKES

This is a typical Mumbai street snack; the kind that the locals would happily eat while walking along the beach or watching a cricket match. It is the kind of food that brings together the cosmopolitan population of the city.

MAKES 10–12

30ml/2 tbsp vegetable oil
30ml/2 tbsp ground coriander
30ml/2 tbsp ground cumin
2.5ml/½ tsp ground turmeric
2.5ml/½ tsp salt
2.5ml/½ tsp granulated sugar
30ml/2 tbsp gram flour (besan), mixed
 with a little water to make a paste
450g/1lb/3 cups boiled chickpeas, drained
2 fresh green chillies, chopped
5cm/2in piece fresh root ginger, crushed
85g/3oz chopped fresh coriander
 (cilantro)
2 firm tomatoes, chopped
fresh mint sprigs, to garnish

For the potato cakes
450g/1lb potatoes, boiled and mashed
4 fresh green chillies, finely chopped
50g/2oz finely chopped fresh coriander
 (cilantro)
7.5ml/1½ tsp ground cumin
5ml/1 tsp amchur (dry mango powder)
vegetable oil, for shallow frying
salt

1 To prepare the chickpeas, heat the oil in a wok, karahi or large pan. Fry the coriander, cumin, turmeric, salt, sugar and gram flour paste until the water has evaporated and the oil has separated.

2 Add the chickpeas to the spices in the pan, and stir in the chopped chillies, ginger, fresh coriander and tomatoes. Toss the ingredients well and simmer gently for about 5 minutes. Transfer to a serving dish and keep warm.

3 To make the potato cakes, place the mashed potato in a large bowl and add the green chillies, chopped fresh coriander, cumin and amchur powder and salt. Mix together until all the ingredients are well blended.

4 Using your hands, shape the potato mixture into little cakes. Heat the oil in a shallow frying pan and fry the cakes on both sides until golden brown. Transfer to a serving dish, garnish with mint sprigs and serve with the chickpeas.

SAMOSAS

The origin of samosas can be attributed to the western states of Maharashtra and Gujarat, which are famous for these fabulous crispy pastries with spiced vegetable fillings. The original samosa is vegetarian, but meat fillings are also used, especially in northern India. In this recipe, ready-made spring roll pastry is used as a quick alternative.

MAKES 30

1 packet spring roll pastry, thawed and
   wrapped in a damp towel
vegetable oil, for deep-frying
Fresh Coriander Chutney, to serve

For the filling
3 large potatoes, boiled and mashed
75g/3oz/¾ cup frozen peas, thawed and
   cooked
50g/2oz/⅓ cup canned sweetcorn, drained
5ml/1 tsp ground coriander
5ml/1 tsp ground cumin
5ml/1 tsp amchur (dry mango powder)
1 small red onion, finely chopped
2 fresh green chillies, finely chopped
30ml/2 tbsp each fresh coriander (cilantro)
   and mint leaves, chopped
juice of 1 lemon
salt

1 Toss all the filling ingredients together in a large mixing bowl until well blended. Adjust the seasoning with salt and lemon juice, if necessary.

2 Working with one strip of pastry at a time, place 15ml/1 tbsp of the filling mixture at one end of the strip and diagonally fold the pastry to form a triangle. Repeat with the other strips.

3 Heat enough oil for deep-frying and fry the samosas in small batches until they are golden brown. Serve hot. Fresh Coriander Chutney or a chilli sauce are ideal for dipping.

COOK'S TIP
Filo pastry is an excellent alternative. Brush the filo samosas with oil and bake in a preheated hot oven for 25 minutes.

BOMBAY POTATO

This well-known dish is served in most Indian restaurants in the West, but it does not exist in Bombay (now called Mumbai). The origin of the name Bombay potato remains a mystery, although one theory is that it resembles a dish sold by street vendors in Mumbai.

SERVES 4–6

450g/1lb whole new potatoes
5ml/1 tsp ground turmeric
60ml/4 tbsp vegetable oil
2 dried red chillies
6–8 curry leaves
2 onions, finely chopped
2 fresh green chillies, finely chopped
50g/2oz coarsely chopped fresh coriander
  (cilantro)
1.5ml/¼ tsp asafoetida
2.5ml/½ tsp each cumin, mustard,
  onion, fennel and nigella seeds
lemon juice, to taste
salt

1 Scrub the potatoes under running water and cut into small pieces. Boil the potatoes in water with a little salt and 2.5ml/½ tsp of the turmeric until tender. Drain well then coarsely mash. Set aside.

2 Heat the oil and fry the dried chillies and curry leaves until the chillies are nearly burnt. Add the onions, green chillies, coriander, remaining turmeric, asafoetida and spice seeds and cook until the onions are soft.

3 Fold in the potatoes and add a few drops of water. Cook gently over a low heat for 10 minutes, mixing well to ensure even distribution of the spices. Add lemon juice to taste.

4 Serve the potatoes with parathas or, as they would be eaten in Mumbai, as a snack with soft white bread rolls.

STUFFED OKRA

*The Gujarati community excels in the art of vegetarian cooking. Although some meat-
and poultry-based dishes originated in Gujarat due to the presence of the Parsis, the
native Gujaratis are strict vegetarians, who do not even eat eggs. Stuffed okra is easy
to make and will happily accompany most meat and poultry dishes.*

SERVES 4–6

225g/8oz large okra
15ml/1 tbsp amchur (dry
   mango powder)
2.5ml/½ tsp ground ginger
2.5ml/½ tsp ground cumin
2.5ml/½ tsp chilli powder
   (optional)
2.5ml/½ tsp ground turmeric
vegetable oil, for frying and mixing
30ml/2 tbsp cornflour (cornstarch),
   placed in a plastic bag
salt

1 Wash the okra and trim the tips.
Make a slit lengthwise in the centre of
each okra; do not cut all the way through.

2 In a bowl, mix the amchur, ginger,
cumin, chilli, if using, turmeric and salt
with a few drops of vegetable oil. Leave
the mixture to rest for 1–2 hours or
refrigerate overnight.

3 Using your fingers, part the slit of
each okra carefully without opening it
all the way and fill each with as much
filling as possible. Put all the okra into
the plastic bag with the cornflour and
shake the bag carefully to cover the
okra evenly.

4 Fill a wok, karahi or large pan with
enough oil to sit 2.5cm/1in deep. Heat
the oil and fry the okra in small batches
for 5–8 minutes or until they are brown
and slightly crisp. Serve hot with any
meat, poultry or fish curry.

COOK'S TIP
When buying okra, choose those without
any blemishes. Wash them thoroughly,
rubbing each one gently with a soft
vegetable brush or your fingertips.

OKRA in YOGURT

This tangy vegetable dish can be served as an accompaniment, but also makes an excellent vegetarian meal served with tarka dhal and chapatis. The secret of cooking okra is not to disturb its glutinous tendencies by overcooking, as the results can be unpleasant. Do follow the temperature and timing carefully.

SERVES 4

450g/1lb okra
30ml/2 tbsp vegetable oil
2.5ml/½ tsp onion seeds
3 fresh red or green chillies, chopped
1 onion, sliced
1.5ml/¼ tsp ground turmeric
10ml/2 tsp desiccated (dry, unsweetened, shredded) coconut
2.5ml/½ tsp salt
15ml/1 tbsp natural (plain) yogurt
2 tomatoes, quartered
15ml/1 tbsp chopped fresh coriander (cilantro)

1 Wash and trim the okra, cut into 1cm/½in pieces and set aside.

2 Heat the oil in a wok, karahi or large pan. Add the onion seeds, green chillies and onion, and fry for 5 minutes.

3 When the onion is golden brown, lower the heat and add the turmeric, desiccated coconut and salt. Fry for about 1 minute, stirring all the time.

4 Add the okra pieces to the pan. Turn the heat to medium-high and stir-fry briskly for a few minutes, until the okra has turned lightly golden.

5 Add the yogurt, tomatoes and fresh coriander. Cook for a further 2 minutes. Transfer to a warmed serving dish and serve immediately, as a side dish.

fifth edition

COLOR ATLAS of HISTOLOGY

LESLIE P. GARTNER, Ph.D.
Professor of Anatomy (Retired)

JAMES L. HIATT, Ph.D.
Professor Emeritus

Department of Biomedical Sciences
Baltimore College of Dental Surgery
Dental School
University of Maryland
Baltimore, Maryland

Wolters Kluwer | Lippincott Williams & Wilkins
Health

Philadelphia • Baltimore • New York • London
Buenos Aires • Hong Kong • Sydney • Tokyo

Acquisitions Editor: Crystal Taylor
Managing Editor: Jessica Heise
Marketing Manager: Valerie Sanders
Production Editor: John Larkin
Creative Director: Doug Smock
Compositor: Maryland Composition

351 West Camden Street
Baltimore, Maryland 21201-2436 USA

530 Walnut Street
Philadelphia, Pennsylvania 19106-3621 US

Printed in China.

First Edition, 1990
Second Edition, 1994
Third Edition, 2000
Fourth Edition, 2006

Translations:
Chinese (Taiwan), Ho-Chi Book Publishing Company, 2002
Chinese (Mainland China), Liaoning Education Press/CITIC, 2004
Greek, Parissianos, 2003
Italian, Masson Italia, 1999
Japanese, Igaku-Shoin, 1997
Portuguese, Editora Guanabara Koogan, 2002
Spanish, Editorial Medica Panamericana, 2002
French
Korean
Russian

Library of Congress Cataloging-in-Publication Data

Gartner, Leslie P., 1943-
    Color atlas of histology / Leslie P. Gartner, James L. Hiatt. — 5th ed.
        p. ; cm.
    Includes index.
    ISBN 978-0-7817 8872-4
1. Histology—Atlases. I. Hiatt, James L., 1934- II. Title.
    [DNLM: 1. Histology—Atlases. QS 517 G244c 2009]
    QM557.G38 2009
    611'.0180222—dc22

                                                                    2008021813

To purchase additional copies of this book, call our customer service department at **(800) 638-3030** or fax orders to **(301) 824-7390**. International customers should call **(301) 714-2324**.

Visit **Lippincott Williams & Wilkins on the Internet: http://www.LWW.com.** Lippincott Williams & Wilkins customer service representatives are available from 8:30 am to 6:00 pm, EST.

09101112
1 2 3 4 5 6 7 8 9 10

● Dedication

To my wife Roseann,
my daughter Jen,
and my mother Mary
LPG

To my wife Nancy
and my children
Drew, Beth, and Kurt
JLH

Preface to the Fifth Edition

We are very pleased to be able to present the fifth edition of our *Color Atlas of Histology*, an atlas that has been in continuous use since its first publication as a black and white atlas in 1987. The success of that atlas prompted us to revise it considerably, retake all of the images in full color, change its name, and publish it in 1990 under its current title. In the past 22 years the Atlas has undergone many changes. We added color paintings, published a corresponding set of Kodachrome slides, and added histophysiology to the text. The advent of high resolution digital photography allowed us to reshoot all of the photomicrographs for the fourth edition and we created a CD-ROM that accompanied and was packaged with our Atlas.

For the fifth edition, the Interactive Color Atlas of Histology has been updated and made available to the student on the Lippincott Williams & Wilkins website, http://thePoint.lww.com, and can be accessed from anywhere in the world via an Internet connection. The online Atlas contains every photomicrograph and electron micrograph and accompanying legends present in the Atlas. The student has the capability to study select chapters or to look up a particular item via a keyword search. Images may be viewed with or without labels and/or legends, enlarged using the "zoom" feature, and compared side-by-side to other images. Also, the updated software now allows students to self-test on all labels using the "hotspot" mode, facilitating learning and preparation for practical examinations. For examination purposes, the online Atlas contains over 300 additional photomicrographs with more than 700 interactive fill-in and true/false questions organized in a fashion to facilitate the student's learning and preparation for practical exams. Additionally, we have included approximately 100 USMLE Part I format multiple-choice questions, based on photomicrographs created specifically for the questions, that can be accessed in test or study mode.

We are grateful to the many faculty members throughout the world who have assigned our Atlas to their students whether in its original English or in its translated form that now counts nine languages. We have received many complements and constructive suggestions not only from faculty members but also from students and we tried to incorporate those ideas into each new edition. One suggestion that we have resisted, however, was to change the order of the chapters. There were several faculty members who suggested a number of varied sequences and they all made sense to us and would have been very easy for us to adopt any one of the suggested chapter orders. However, we feel partial to and very comfortable with the classical sequence that we adopted so many years ago; it is just as valid and logical an arrangement as all the others that were suggested and, in the final analysis, instructors can simply tell their classes to use the chapters of the Atlas in a different sequence without harming the coherence of the material.

In this fifth edition, labels have been added to the thumbnails of the pertinent four-color illustrations that are present in each chapter. These illustrations are designed to trigger the student's memory by providing a three-dimensional representation of the two-dimensional photomicrographs on the facing page. These should prove to be helpful to the student in providing a framework on which the student may base detailed knowledge of histology. Also, while the didactic information remains at the beginning of each chapter, the Summary of the Histological Organization has been moved to the end of the chapter. Moreover, the Histophysiology components of each chapter has been revised to reflect new information that has been published in the literature since the publication of the 4th edition.

As in the previous editions, most of the photomicrographs of this atlas are of tissues stained with hematoxylin and eosin. Each figure is supplied with a final magnification, which takes into consideration the photographic enlargement, as well as that achieved by the microscope. Many of the sections were prepared from plastic-embedded specimens, as noted. Most of the exquisite electron micrographs included in this Atlas were kindly provided by our colleagues throughout the world as identified in the legends.

As with all of our textbooks, this Atlas has been written with the student in mind, thus the material is complete but not esoteric. We wish to help the student learn and enjoy histology, not be overwhelmed by it. Furthermore, this Atlas is designed not only for use in the laboratory, but also as preparation for both didactic and practical examinations. Although we have attempted to be accurate and complete, we know that errors and omissions may have escaped our attention. Therefore, we welcome criticisms, suggestions, and comments that could help improve this atlas; please address them to LPG21136@yahoo.com.

Acknowledgments

We would like to thank Todd Smith for the rendering of the outstanding full-color plates and thumbnail figures, Jerry Gadd for his paintings of blood cells, and our many colleagues who provided us with electron micrographs. We are especially thankful to Dr. Stephen W. Carmichael of the Mayo Medical School for his suggestions concerning the suprarenal medulla and Dr. Cheng Hwee Ming of the University of Malaya Medical School for his comments on the distal tubule of the kidney. Additionally, we are grateful to our good friends at Lippincott Williams & Wilkins, including our always cheerful, and exceptionally helpful, Managing Editor, Jessica Heise; and to Acquisitions Editor, Crystal Taylor; Senior Developmental Editor, Kathleen Scogna; Production Editor, John Larkin; and Editorial Assistant, Kelsi Loos. Finally, we wish to thank our families again for encouraging us during the preparation of this work. Their support always makes the labor an achievement.

Contents

The Cell

Cells not only constitute the basic units of the human body but also function in executing all of the activities that the body requires for its survival. Although there are more than 200 different cell types, most cells possess common features that permit them to perform their varied responsibilities. The living component of the cell is the **protoplasm**, which is subdivided into the **cytoplasm** and the **nucleoplasm** (see Graphic 1-1). The protoplasm also contains nonliving material such as crystals and pigment.

● CYTOPLASM

Plasmalemma

Cells possess a membrane, the **plasmalemma**, which provides a selective, structural barrier between the cell and the outside world. This phospholipid bilayer, with **integral** and **peripheral proteins** and **cholesterol** embedded in it, functions in cell-cell recognition, in exocytosis and endocytosis, as a receptor site for signaling molecules, and as an initiator and controller of the secondary messenger system. Materials may enter the cell by several means, such as **pinocytosis** (nonspecific uptake of molecules in an aqueous solution), **receptor-mediated endocytosis** (specific uptake of substances, such as low density lipoproteins), or **phagocytosis** (uptake of particulate matter). Secretory products may leave the cell by two means: **constitutive** or **regulated secretion. Constitutive secretion,** using non–clathrin-coated vesicles, is the default pathway that does not require an extracellular signal for release and thus the secretory product (e.g., procollagen) leaves the cell in a continuous fashion. **Regulated secretion** requires the presence of clathrin-coated storage vesicles whose contents (e.g., pancreatic enzymes) are released only after the initiation of an extracellular signaling process.

Cells possess a number of distinct organelles, many of which are formed from membranes that are similar but not identical to the biochemical composition of the plasmalemma.

Mitochondria

Mitochondria are composed of an outer and an inner membrane with an intervening compartment between them known as the **intermembrane space** (see Graphic 1-2). The inner membrane is folded to form flat, shelf-like structures (or tubular in steroid-manufacturing cells) known as **cristae** and encloses a viscous fluid-filled space known as the **matrix space**. Mitochondria function in the **generation of ATP**, utilizing a chemiosmotic coupling mechanism that employs a specific sequence of enzyme complexes and proton translocator systems (**electron transport chain** and the ATP-synthase containing **elementary particles**) embedded in their cristae. In brown fat, this organelle instead of producing ATP generates heat. Mitochondria also assist in the **synthesis** of certain **lipids** and **proteins;** they possess the enzymes of the **TCA cycle, circular DNA** molecules, and matrix granules in their matrix space. These organelles increase in number by undergoing **binary fission**.

Ribosomes

Ribosomes are small, bipartite, nonmembranous organelles that exist as individual particles that do not coalesce with each other until protein synthesis begins. Each portion is composed of proteins and r-RNA and functions as an interactive "workbench" that not only provides a surface on which protein synthesis occurs but also as a catalyst that facilitates the synthesis of proteins.

Endoplasmic Reticulum

The **endoplasmic reticulum** is composed of tubules, sacs, and flat sheets of membranes that occupy much of the intracellular space (see Graphic 1-2). There are two types of endoplasmic reticula: rough and smooth. The **rough endoplasmic reticulum (RER)**, whose cytoplasmic surface possesses receptor molecules for ribosomes and signal recognition particles (known as **ribophorins** and **docking proteins**, respectively), is continuous with the outer nuclear membrane. The RER functions in the **synthesis** and **modification of proteins** that are to

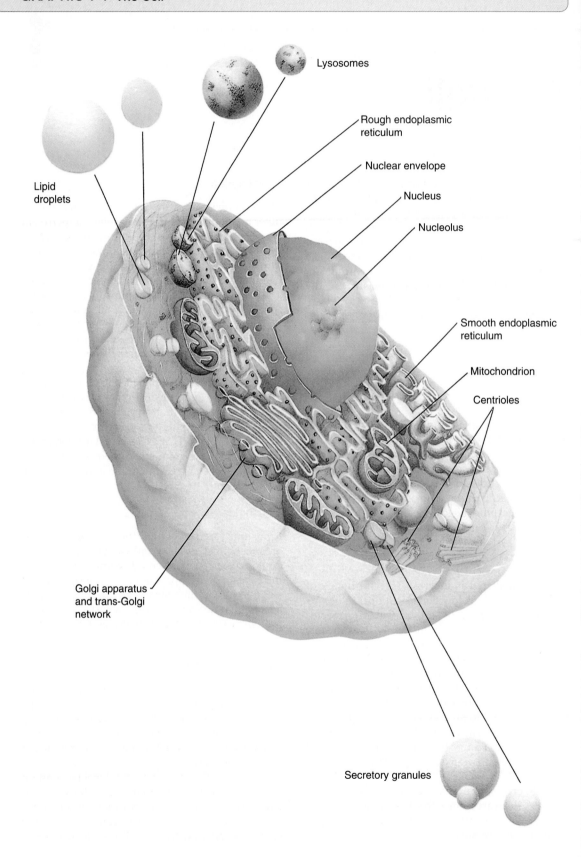

Lysosomes

Rough endoplasmic
reticulum

Nuclear envelope

Nucleus

Nucleolus

Lipid
droplets

Smooth endoplasmic
reticulum

Mitochondrion

Centrioles

Golgi apparatus
and trans-Golgi
network

Secretory granules

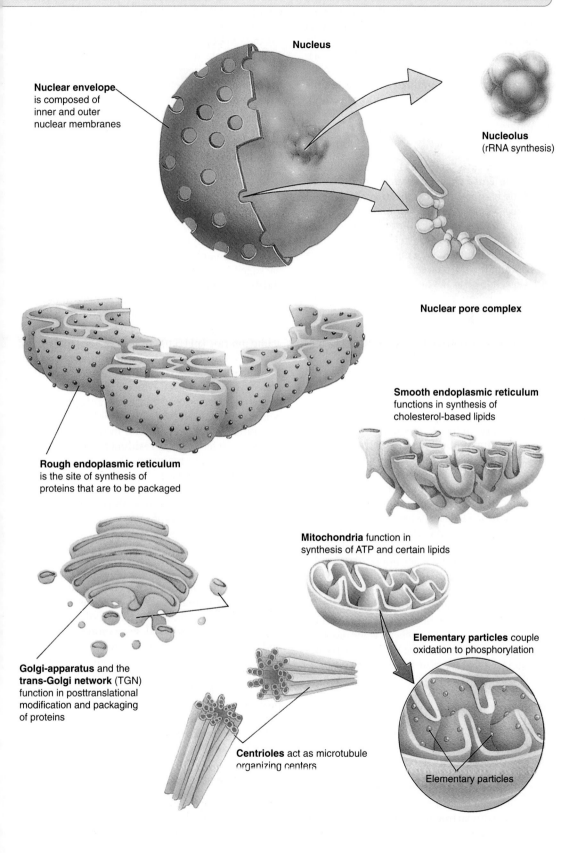

Nucleus

Nuclear envelope is composed of inner and outer nuclear membranes

Nucleolus (rRNA synthesis)

Nuclear pore complex

Smooth endoplasmic reticulum functions in synthesis of cholesterol-based lipids

Rough endoplasmic reticulum is the site of synthesis of proteins that are to be packaged

Mitochondria function in synthesis of ATP and certain lipids

Elementary particles couple oxidation to phosphorylation

Golgi-apparatus and the **trans-Golgi network** (TGN) function in posttranslational modification and packaging of proteins

Centrioles act as microtubule organizing centers

Elementary particles

be **packaged**, as well as in the synthesis of membrane lipids and proteins. **Smooth endoplasmic reticulum (SER)** functions in the synthesis of **cholesterols** and **lipids** as well as in the **detoxification** of certain drugs and toxins (such as barbiturates and alcohol). Additionally, in skeletal muscle cells this organelle is specialized to sequester and release calcium ions and thus regulate muscle contraction and relaxation.

Golgi Apparatus, *cis*-Golgi Network, and *trans*-Golgi Network

The **Golgi apparatus (complex)** is composed of a specifically oriented cluster of vesicles, tubules, and flattened membrane-bounded cisternae. Each Golgi complex has a convex entry face, known as the *cis* **face**, and a concave exit face, known as the *trans* **face**. The *cis* face is closer to the nucleus and the *trans* face is oriented toward the cell membrane. Between the *cis* face and the *trans* face are several intermediate cisternae, known as the **medial face** (see Graphic 1-2). The Golgi complex not only **packages** but also **modifies** macromolecules synthesized on the surface of the RER. Newly synthesized proteins pass from the RER to the **vesicular-tubular cluster** (**VTC**, formerly referred to as the ERGIC) by COPII-coated **transfer vesicles**, whose outer membrane has the protein coatamer II (COPII-coated vesicles), and from there to the *cis*-Golgi network, probably via COPI-coated (coatamer I) vesicles. The proteins continue to travel to the *cis*, medial, and *trans* faces of the Golgi apparatus by non–clathrin-coated **vesicles** (or, according to some authors, via cisternal maturation). Lysosomal oligosaccharides are phosphorylated in the VTC and/or in the *cis* face; mannose groups are removed and other sugar residues are added in the medial face, whereas the addition of galactose and sialic acid as well as the sulfation of selected residues occur in the *trans* face. **Sorting** and the final **packaging** of the macromolecules are the responsibility of the *trans*-**Golgi network** (TGN). It should be noted that material can travel through the Golgi complex in an **anterograde fashion**, as just described, as well as in a **retrograde fashion**, which occurs in situations such as when escaped proteins that are residents of the RER or of a particular Golgi face must be returned to their compartments of origin.

Endosomes

Endosomes are intermediate compartments within the cell, utilized in the destruction of endocytosed, phagocytosed, or autophagocytosed materials as well as in the formation of lysosomes. Endosomes possess **proton pumps** in their membranes, which pump H^+ into the endosome, thus acidifying the interior of this compartment. Also, these organelles are intermediate stages in the formation of lyso-somes. **Early endosomes** are located at the periphery of the cell; they contain receptor-ligand complexes, and their acidic content (pH 6) is responsible for the uncoupling of receptors from ligands. The receptors are usually carried into a system of tubular vesicles, the **recycling endosomes**, from which the receptors are returned to the plasmalemma, whereas the ligands are translocated to **late endosomes**. Within late endosomes the pH is even more acidic (pH 5.5). Many investigators have suggested that early endosomes mature into late endosomes by the fusion of vesicles with one another as well as with late endosomes that have been formed earlier.

Lysosomes

Lysosomes are formed by the utilization of **late endosomes** as an intermediary compartment. Both lysosomal membranes and lysosomal enzymes are packaged in the TGN and are delivered in separate **clathrin-coated vesicles** to late endosomes, forming **endolysosomes**, which then mature to become **lysosomes**. These membrane-bounded vesicles whose proton pumps are responsible for their very acidic interior (pH 5.0) contain various **hydrolytic enzymes** that function in **intracellular digestion**. They degrade certain macromolecules as well as phagocytosed particulate matter (**phagolysosomes**) and autophagocytosed material (**autophagolysosomes**). Frequently, the indigestible remnants of lysosomal degradation remain in the cell, enclosed in vesicles referred to as **residual bodies**. The lysosomal membrane maintains its integrity possibly because the luminal aspects of the membrane proteins are glycosylated to a much greater extent than those of other membranes, thus preventing the degradation of the membrane.

Peroxisomes

Peroxisomes are membrane-bounded organelles housing **oxidative enzymes** such as **urate oxidase**, **D-amino acid oxidase**, and **catalase**. These organelles function in the formation of free radicals (e.g., superoxides), which destroy various substances, and in the protection of the cell by degrading hydrogen peroxide by catalase. They also function in **detoxification** of certain toxins and in elongation of some fatty acids during **lipid synthesis**. Most of the proteins intended for inclusion into peroxisomes are synthesized in the cytosol rather than on the RER. All peroxisomes are formed by **fission** from preexisting peroxisomes.

Proteasomes

Proteasomes are small, barrel-shaped organelles that function in the degradation of cytosolic proteins. The practice of cytosolic proteolysis is highly regulated, and the candidate protein must be tagged by several ubiquitin molecules before it is permitted to be destroyed by the proteasome system.

Cytoskeleton

The **cytoskeleton** is composed of a filamentous array of proteins that act not only as the structural framework of the cell but also to **transport** material within it from one region of the cell to another and to provide it with the capability of **motion** and cell division. Components of the cytoskeleton include **microtubules** (consisting of α- and β-tubulins arranged in 13 protofilaments) and **thin** (actin) **filaments** (also known as **microfilaments**). Thin filaments function in the movement of cells from one place to another as well as in the movement of regions in the cell with respect to itself. **Intermediate filaments** are thicker than thin filaments and thinner than thick filaments. They function in providing a structural framework to the cell and resisting mechanical stress placed on cells. **Thick filaments**, included here although not traditionally included as part of the cytoskeleton, are composed of myosin, and they interact with thin filaments to facilitate cell movement either along a surface or movement of cellular regions with respect to the cell.

Microtubules are also associated with **microtubule-associated proteins** (MAPs), which permit organelles, vesicles, and other components of the cytoskeleton to bind to microtubules. Most microtubules originate from **the microtubule-organizing center** (MTOC) of the cell, located in the vicinity of the Golgi apparatus. These elements of the cytoskeleton are pathways for intracellular translocation of organelles and vesicles, and, during cell division, chromosomes are moved into their proper locations. Two important MAPs, **kinesin** and **dynein**, are motor proteins that facilitate anterograde and retrograde intracellular vesicular and organelle movement, respectively. The **axoneme** of cilia and flagella, as well as a framework of centrioles, are formed mostly of microtubules.

Inclusions

Cytoplasmic **inclusions**, such as **lipids, glycogen, secretory granules**, and **pigments**, are also consistent constituents of the cytoplasm. Many of these inclusions are transitory in nature, although some pigments, e.g., **lipofuscin**, are permanent residents of certain cells.

● NUCLEUS

The **nucleus** is enclosed by the **nuclear envelope**, composed of an **inner** and an **outer nuclear membrane** with an intervening **perinuclear cistern** (see Graphic 1-2). The outer nuclear membrane is studded with **ribosomes** and is continuous, in places, with the RER. In areas where the inner and outer membranes fuse with each other, circular profiles (known as **nuclear pores**) form that permit communication between the nucleoplasm and the cytoplasm. These perforations of the nuclear envelope are guarded by protein assemblies, which, together with the perforations, are known as **nuclear pore complexes**, providing regulated passageways for the transport of materials in and out of the nucleus. The nucleus houses **chromosomes** and is the location of **RNA synthesis**. Both **mRNA** and **tRNA** are transcribed in the nucleus, whereas **rRNA** is transcribed in the region of the nucleus known as the **nucleolus**. The nucleolus is also the site of assembly of ribosomal proteins and rRNA into the small and large subunits of **ribosomes**. These ribosomal subunits enter the cytosol individually.

● CELL CYCLE

The **cell cycle** is governed by the cell cycle control system, which not only ensures the occurrence of the correct sequence of events in a timely fashion but also monitors and controls them. The cell cycle is subdivided into four phases: G_1, S, G_2, and M. During the presynthetic phase, G_1, the cell increases its size and organelle content. During the **S phase**, DNA (plus histone and other chromosome-associated protein) synthesis and centriole replication occur. During G_2, ATP is accumulated, centriole replication is completed, and tubulin is accumulated for spindle formation. G_1, S, and G_2 are also referred to as **interphase**. M represents **mitosis**, which is subdivided into prophase, prometaphase, metaphase, anaphase, and telophase. The result is the division of the cell and its genetic material into two identical daughter cells. The sequence of events in the cell cycle is controlled by a number of trigger proteins known as **cyclins**.

Histophysiology

I. MEMBRANES AND MEMBRANE TRAFFICKING

The fluidity of the plasmalemma is an important factor in the processes of membrane synthesis, endocytosis, exocytosis, and **membrane trafficking** (see Graphic 1-3)—conserving the membrane as it is transferred through the various cellular compartments. The degree of fluidity is influenced directly by temperature and the degree of unsaturation of the fatty acyl tails of the membrane phospholipids and is influenced indirectly by the amount of cholesterol present.

Ions and other hydrophilic molecules are incapable of passing across the lipid bilayer; however, small nonpolar molecules, such as oxygen and carbon dioxide, as well as uncharged polar molecules, such as water and glycerol, all diffuse rapidly across the lipid bilayer. Specialized multipass integral proteins known as **membrane transport proteins** function in the transfer of substances across the plasmalemma. Transport across the cell membrane may be **passive** down an ionic or concentration gradient (**simple diffusion** or **facilitated diffusion** via ion channel or carrier proteins; no energy required) or **active** (energy required, usually against a gradient). **Ion channel** proteins possess an aqueous pore and may be **ungated** or **gated**. The former are always open, whereas gated ion channels require the presence of a stimulus (alteration in voltage, mechanical stimulus, presence of a ligand, G protein, neurotransmitter substance, etc.) that opens the gate. These **ligands** and **neurotransmitter substances** are types of signaling molecules.

Signaling molecules are either hydrophobic (lipid soluble) or hydrophilic and are used for cell-to-cell communication. Lipid-soluble molecules diffuse through the cell membrane to activate **intracellular messenger systems** by binding to receptor molecules located in either the cytoplasm or the nucleus. Hydrophilic signaling molecules initiate a specific sequence of responses by binding to **receptors** (integral proteins) embedded in the cell membrane.

Endocytosis is the process of taking fluid and/or larger molecules into the cell by the invagination of the cell membrane and the subsequent formation of intracellular endocytic vesicles. The size of the endocytic vesicles, determined by the material to be engulfed, discriminates two types of endocytosis, namely, **pinocytosis** ("cell drinking"), involving small vesicles (<150 nm in diameter) and **phagocytosis** ("cellular eating"), involving larger vesicles, **phagosomes** (usually >250 nm in diameter). Receptors permit the endocytosis of a much greater concentration of ligands than would be possible without receptors. This process is referred to as **receptor-mediated endocytosis** and involves the formation of a **clathrin-coated endocytic vesicle**, which, once within the cell, sheds its clathrin coat and fuses with an **early endosome**. The receptors and ligands are uncoupled in this compartment, permitting the receptors to be transported to a system of tubular vesicles, the recycling endosome, from which the receptors are recycled to the cell membrane. The ligands, left in the **early endosome** (pH 6), are ferried to **late endosomes** (pH 5.5), deeper in the cytoplasm. Two groups of clathrin-coated vesicles derived from the TGN ferry lysosomal enzymes and lysosomal membranes (containing additional ATP-energized **proton pumps**) to the late endosome, forming an **endolysosome** (or **lysosome**). The newly delivered proton pumps further decrease the pH of the endolysosomal interior (to a pH of 5.0). Hydrolytic enzymes of the lysosome degrade the ligand, releasing the usable substances for use by the cell. The indigestible remnants of the ligand may remain enclosed within special vesicles known as **residual bodies**, located in the cytoplasm.

II. PROTEIN SYNTHESIS AND EXOCYTOSIS

Protein synthesis requires the code-bearing mRNA, amino acid–carrying tRNAs, and ribosomes (see Graphic 1-4). Proteins that will not be packaged are synthesized on **ribosomes** in the cytosol, whereas **noncytosolic proteins** (secretory, lysosomal, and membrane proteins) are synthesized on ribosomes that are translocated to the surface of the RER. The complex of mRNA and ribosomes is referred to as a **polysome**.

The **signal hypothesis** states that mRNAs that code for noncytosolic proteins possess a constant initial segment, the **signal codon**, which codes for a **signal protein**. As the mRNA enters the cytoplasm, it becomes associated with the small subunit of a ribosome. The small subunit has a binding site for mRNA as well as three binding sites (A, P, and E) for tRNAs.

Once the initiation process is completed, the **start codon** (AUG for the amino acid methionine)

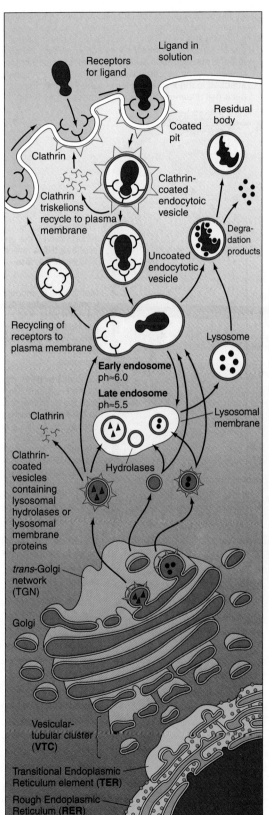

Signaling molecules bind to **receptors** (integral proteins) embedded in the cell membrane and initiate a specific sequence of responses. Receptors permit the endocytosis of a much greater concentration of ligands than would be otherwise possible. This process, **receptor-mediated endocytosis**, involves the formation of **clathrin-coated endocytic vesicles**. Once within the cell, the vesicle sheds its clathrin coat and fuses with an early endosome (pH ≅ 6) where the receptor is uncoupled from the ligand. The receptors are carried from the early endosome into a system of tubular vesicles, known as the **recycling endosome**, from which the receptors are returned to the cell membrane.

The ligand is transferred by the use of multivesicular bodies from the early endosome to another system of vesicles, late endosomes, located deeper in the cytoplasm. **Late endosomes** are more acidic (pH ≅ 5.5) and it is here that the ligand begins to be degraded. Late endosomes receive lysosomal hydrolases and lysosomal membranes, and in that fashion late endosomes probably are transformed into lysosomes (pH ≅ 5.0). Hydrolytic enzymes of the lysosomes degrade the ligand, releasing the usable substances for utilization by the cell, whereas the indigestible remnants of the ligand may remain in vesicles, **residual bodies**, within the cytoplasm.

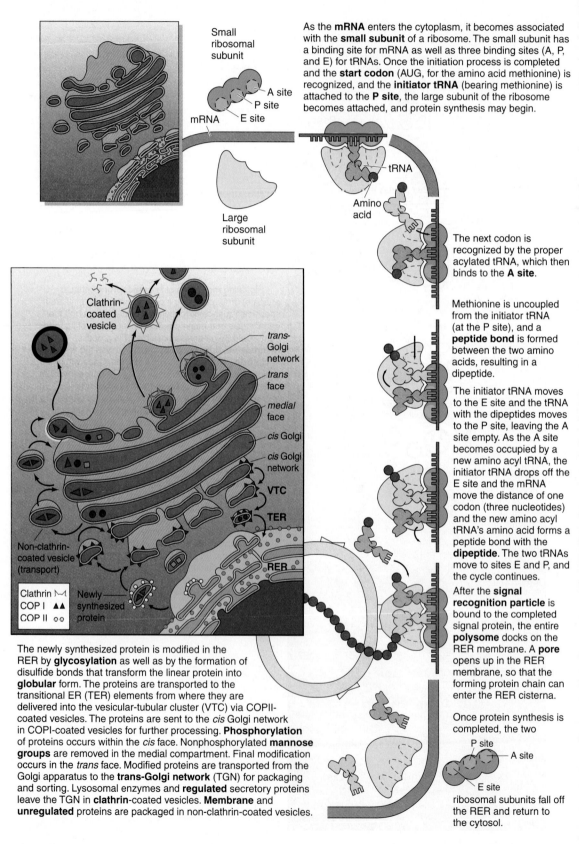

Small ribosomal subunit

A site
P site
E site

mRNA

Large ribosomal subunit

As the **mRNA** enters the cytoplasm, it becomes associated with the **small subunit** of a ribosome. The small subunit has a binding site for mRNA as well as three binding sites (A, P, and E) for tRNAs. Once the initiation process is completed and the **start codon** (AUG, for the amino acid methionine) is recognized, and the **initiator tRNA** (bearing methionine) is attached to the **P site**, the large subunit of the ribosome becomes attached, and protein synthesis may begin.

tRNA

Amino acid

The next codon is recognized by the proper acylated tRNA, which then binds to the **A site**.

Methionine is uncoupled from the initiator tRNA (at the P site), and a **peptide bond** is formed between the two amino acids, resulting in a dipeptide.

The initiator tRNA moves to the E site and the tRNA with the dipeptides moves to the P site, leaving the A site empty. As the A site becomes occupied by a new amino acyl tRNA, the initiator tRNA drops off the E site and the mRNA move the distance of one codon (three nucleotides) and the new amino acyl tRNA's amino acid forms a peptide bond with the **dipeptide**. The two tRNAs move to sites E and P, and the cycle continues.

After the **signal recognition particle** is bound to the completed signal protein, the entire **polysome** docks on the RER membrane. A **pore** opens up in the RER membrane, so that the forming protein chain can enter the RER cisterna.

Once protein synthesis is completed, the two

P site
A site
E site

ribosomal subunits fall off the RER and return to the cytosol.

Clathrin-coated vesicle

trans-Golgi network
trans face
medial face
cis Golgi
cis Golgi network
VTC
TER
RER

Non-clathrin-coated vesicle (transport)

Clathrin
COP I
COP II
Newly synthesized protein

The newly synthesized protein is modified in the RER by **glycosylation** as well as by the formation of disulfide bonds that transform the linear protein into **globular** form. The proteins are transported to the transitional ER (TER) elements from where they are delivered into the vesicular-tubular cluster (VTC) via COPII-coated vesicles. The proteins are sent to the *cis* Golgi network in COPI-coated vesicles for further processing. **Phosphorylation** of proteins occurs within the *cis* face. Nonphosphorylated **mannose groups** are removed in the medial compartment. Final modification occurs in the *trans* face. Modified proteins are transported from the Golgi apparatus to the **trans-Golgi network** (TGN) for packaging and sorting. Lysosomal enzymes and **regulated** secretory proteins leave the TGN in **clathrin**-coated vesicles. **Membrane** and **unregulated** proteins are packaged in non-clathrin-coated vesicles.

is recognized, and the **initiator tRNA** (bearing methionine) is attached to the **P site** (peptidyl-tRNA-binding site), the large subunit of the ribosome, which has corresponding A, P, and E sites, becomes attached, and protein synthesis may begin. The next codon is recognized by the proper acylated tRNA, which then binds to the **A site** (aminoacyl-tRNA-binding site). Methionine is uncoupled from the initiator tRNA (at the P site), and a **peptide bond** is formed between the two amino acids (forming a **dipeptide**) so that the tRNA at the P site loses its amino acid and the tRNA at the A site now has two amino acids attached to it. The formation of this peptide bond is catalyzed by the enzyme **peptidyl transferase**, a part of the large ribosomal subunit. As the peptide bond is formed, the large subunit shifts in relation to the small subunit and the attached tRNAs wobble just enough to cause them to move just a little bit, so that the initiator tRNA (that lost its amino acid at the P site) moves to the **E site** (Exit site) and the tRNA that has two amino acids attached to it moves from the A site to the P site, freeing the A site. As this shifting occurs, the small ribosomal subunit moves the space of a single codon along the mRNA, so that the two ribosomal subunits are once again aligned with each other and the A site is located above the next codon on the mRNA strand. As a new tRNA with its associated amino acid occupies the A site (assuming that its anticodon matches the newly exposed codon of the mRNA), the initiator RNA drops off the E site, leaving the ribosome. The dipeptide is uncoupled from the tRNA at the P site, and a peptide bond is formed between the dipeptide and the new amino acid, forming a tripeptide. The empty tRNA again moves to the E site to fall off the ribosome, as the tRNA bearing the tripeptide moves from the A site to the P site. In this fashion, the peptide chain is elongated to form the signal protein.

The cytosol contains proteins known as **signal recognition particles** (SRP). An SRP binds to each signal protein, inhibits the continuation of protein synthesis, and the entire polysome proceeds to the RER. A **signal recognition particle receptor**, a transmembrane protein located in the membrane of the RER, recognizes and properly positions the polysome. The docking of the polysome results in the movement of the SRP-ribosome complex to a protein translocator, a pore in the RER membrane. The large subunit of the ribosome binds to and forms a tight seal with the protein translocator, aligning the pore in the ribosome with the pore in the protein translocator. The signal recognition particle and SRP receptor leave the polysome, permitting protein synthesis to resume, and the forming protein chain can enter the RER cisterna through the aqueous channel that penetrates the protein translocator. During this process, the enzyme **signal peptidase**, located in the RER cisterna, cleaves signal protein from the growing polypeptide chain. Once protein synthesis is complete, the two ribosomal subunits fall off the RER and return to the cytosol. The newly synthesized protein is modified in the RER by glycosylation as well as by the formation of disulfide bonds, following which the linear protein is transformed into a globular form. The newly formed protein is transported in COPII-coated **transfer vesicles** to the vesicular-tubular cluster and from there in COPI-coated vesicles to the *cis*-Golgi network and from there to the *cis* face for further processing.

Within the *cis* face, the mannose groups of lysosomal enzymes are phosphorylated. Nonphosphorylated mannose groups are removed, and galactose and sialic acid residues are added (**terminal glycosylation**) in the **medial** compartment of the Golgi apparatus. Final modification occurs in the *trans* compartment, where selected amino acid residues are phosphorylated and sulfated. Modified proteins are then transported from the Golgi apparatus to the TGN for packaging and sorting.

All transfers between the various faces of the Golgi apparatus including the TGN probably occur via COPI-coated vesicles. (A concurrent theory suggests the possibility of cisternal maturation, that is, as the vesicular-tubular cluster matures, it is transformed into the various faces of the Golgi and it is replaced by the coalescence of newly derived transfer vesicles.) Mannose 6-phosphate receptors in the TGN recognize and package enzymes destined for lysosomes. These **lysosomal enzymes** leave the TGN in clathrin-coated vesicles. **Regulated secretory proteins** are separated and are also packaged in clathrin-coated vesicles. **Membrane proteins** and proteins destined for constitutive (unregulated) transport are packaged in non–clathrin-coated vesicles.

Certain individuals suffer from **lysosomal storage diseases**, which involve a hereditary deficiency in the ability of their lysosomes to degrade the contents of their endolysosomes. One of the best-characterized examples of these diseases is **Tay-Sachs disease**, which occurs mostly in children whose parents are descendants of Northeast European Jews. Because the lysosomes of these children are unable to catabolize GM2 gangliosides, due to hexoaminidase deficiency, their neurons accumulate massive amounts of this ganglioside in endolysosomes of ever-increasing diameters. As the endolysosomes increase in size, they obstruct neuronal function and the child dies by the third year of life.

Zellweger's disease is an inherited autosomal recessive disorder that interferes with normal peroxisomal biogenesis whose characteristics include renal cysts, hepatomegaly, jaundice, hypotonia of the muscular system, and cerebral demyelination, resulting in psychomotor retardation.

Recent studies have suggested that most **cancers** arise not from mutations in individual genes but from the formation of aneuploidy. In fact, within the same tumor the chromosomal configurations of individual cells vary greatly, and the DNA content of the cells may be 50% to 200% of the normal somatic cell. It is interesting to note that in the apparently chaotic reshuffling and recombination of chromosomes in cancer cells, there appears to be an order, as in Burkitt's lymphoma, in which chromosomes 3, 13, and 17 usually display translocations and chromosomes 7 and 20 are usually missing segments.

FIGURE 1 • Cells. Monkey. Plastic section. ×1323.

The typical cell is a membrane-bound structure that con-sists of a **nucleus** (N) and **cytoplasm** (C). Although the cell membrane is too thin to be visualized with the light microscope, the outline of the cell approximates the cell membrane (*arrowheads*). Observe that the outline of these particular cells more or less approximates a square shape. Viewed in three dimensions, these cells are said to be cuboidal in shape, with a centrally placed nucleus. The **nucleolus** (n) is clearly evident, as are the chromatin gran-ules (*arrows*) that are dispersed around the periphery as well as throughout the nucleoplasm.

FIGURE 3 • Cells. Monkey. Plastic section. ×540.

Cells come in a variety of sizes and shapes. Note that the **epithelium** (E) that lines the **lumen** of the bladder is com-posed of numerous layers. The surface-most layer consists of large, dome-shaped cells, some occasionally displaying two **nuclei** (N). The granules evident in the cytoplasm (*arrowhead*) are glycogen deposits. Cells deeper in the ep-ithelium are elongated and narrow, and their nuclei (*arrow*) are located in their widest region.

FIGURE 2 • Cells. Monkey. Plastic section. ×540.

Cells may possess tall, thin morphologies, like those of a collecting duct of the kidney. Their **nuclei** (N) are located basally, and their lateral cell membranes (*arrowheads*) are outlined. Because these cells are epithelially derived, they are separated from **connective tissue elements** (CT) by a **basal membrane** (BM).

FIGURE 4 • Cells. Monkey. Plastic section. ×540.

Some cells possess a rather unusual morphology, as ex-emplified by the **Purkinje cell** (PC) of the cerebellum. Note that the **nucleus** (N) of the cell is housed in its widest portion, known as the soma (perikaryon). The cell possesses several cytoplasmic extensions, **dendrites** (De), and axon. This nerve cell integrates the numerous digits of information that it receives from other nerve cells that synapse on it.

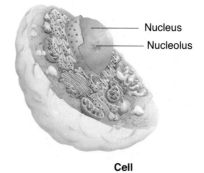

Nucleus
Nucleolus

Cell

KEY							
BM	basal membrane	De	dendrite			N	nucleus
C	cytoplasm	E	epithelium			n	nucleolus
CT	connective tissue	L	lumen			PC	Purkinje cell

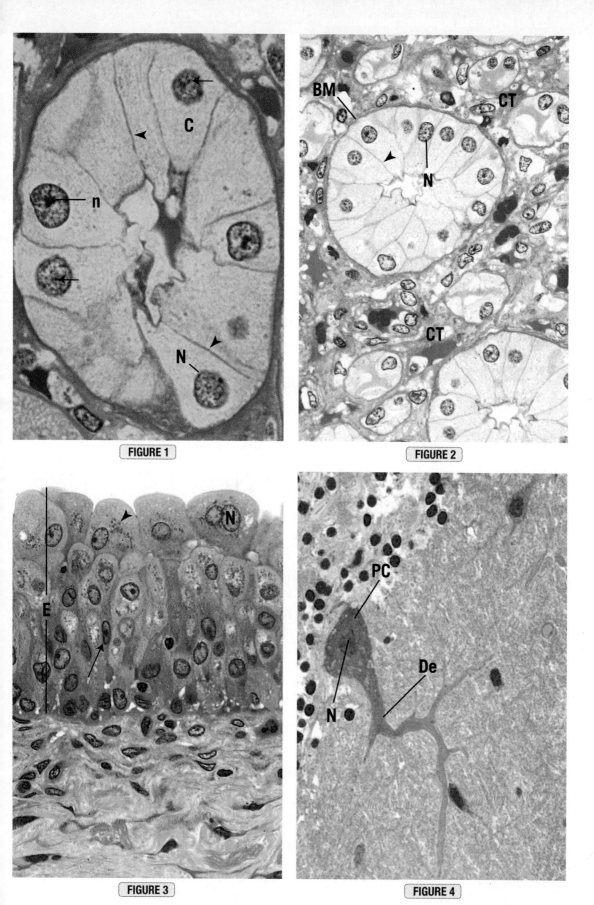

FIGURE 1

FIGURE 2

FIGURE 3

FIGURE 4

FIGURE 1 • Nucleus and Nissl bodies. Spinal cord. Human. Paraffin section. ×540.

The motor neurons of the spinal cord are multipolar neurons because they possess numerous processes arising from an enlarged **soma** (S), which houses the **nucleus** (N) and various organelles. Observe that the nucleus displays a large, densely staining **nucleolus** (n). The cytoplasm also presents a series of densely staining structures known as **Nissl bodies** (NB), which have been demonstrated by electron microscopy to be rough endoplasmic reticulum. The staining intensity is due to the presence of ribonucleic acid of the ribosomes studding the surface of the rough endoplasmic reticulum.

FIGURE 3 • Zymogen granules. Pancreas. Monkey. Plastic section. ×540.

The exocrine portion of the pancreas produces enzymes necessary for proper digestion of ingested food materials. These enzymes are stored by the pancreatic cells as **zymogen granules** (ZG) until their release is effected by hormonal activity. Note that the parenchymal cells are arranged in clusters known as **acini** (Ac), with a central lumen into which the secretory product is released. Observe that the zymogen granules are stored in the apical region of the cell, away from the basally located **nucleus** (N). Arrows indicate the lateral cell membranes of adjacent cells of an acinus.

FIGURE 2 • Secretory products. Mast cell. Monkey. Plastic section. ×540.

The **connective tissue** (CT) subjacent to the epithelial lining of the small intestines is richly endowed with **mast cells** (MC). The granules (*arrows*) of mast cells are distributed throughout their cytoplasm and are released along the entire periphery of the cell. These small granules contain histamine and heparin as well as additional substances. Note that the **epithelial cells** (EC) are tall and columnar in morphology and that **leukocytes** (Le) are migrating, via intercellular spaces, into the **lumen** (L) of the intestines. Arrowheads point to terminal bars, junctions between epithelial cells. The **brush border** (BB) has been demonstrated by electron microscopy to be microvilli.

FIGURE 4 • Mucous secretory products. Goblet cells. Large intestines. Monkey. Plastic section. ×540.

The glands of the large intestine house **goblet cells** (GC), which manufacture a large amount of mucous material that acts as a lubricant for the movement of the compacted residue of digestion. Each goblet cell possesses an expanded apical portion, the **theca** (T), which contains the secretory product of the cell. The base of the cell is compressed and houses the **nucleus** (N) as well as the organelles necessary for the synthesis of the mucus—namely, the rough endoplasmic reticulum and the Golgi apparatus. Arrows indicate the lateral cell membranes of contiguous goblet cells.

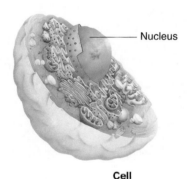

Nucleus

Cell

KEY					
Ac	acinus	L	lumen	NB	Nissl body
BB	brush border	Le	leukocyte	S	soma
CT	connective tissue	MC	mast cell	T	theca
EC	epithelial cell	N	nucleus	ZG	zymogen granule
GC	goblet cell	n	nucleolus		

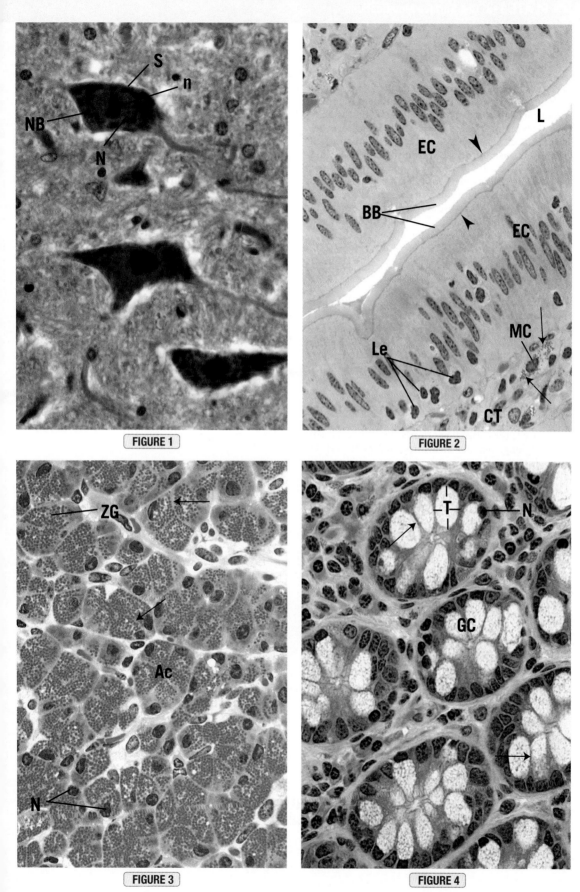

FIGURE 1

FIGURE 2

FIGURE 3

FIGURE 4

FIGURE 1 • Brush border. Small intestines. Monkey. Plastic section. ×540.

The cells lining the **lumen** (L) of the small intestine are columnar cells, among which are numerous mucus-producing **goblet cells** (GC). The columnar cells' function is absorbing digested food material along their free, apical surface. To increase their free surface area, the cells possess a **brush border** (BB), which has been demonstrated by electron microscopy to be microvilli—short, narrow, finger-like extensions of plasmalemma-covered cytoplasm. Each microvillus bears a glycocalyx cell coat, which also contains digestive enzymes. The core of the microvillus contains longitudinally arranged actin filaments as well as additional associated proteins.

FIGURE 3 • Stereocilia. Epididymis. Monkey. Plastic section. ×540.

The lining of the epididymis is composed of tall, columnar **principal cells** (Pi) and short **basal cells** (BC). The principal cells bear long stereocilia (*arrows*) that protrude into the lumen. It was believed that stereocilia were long, nonmotile, cilia-like structures. However, studies with the electron microscope have shown that stereocilia are actually long microvilli that branch as well as clump with each other. The function, if any, of stereocilia within the epididymis is not known. The lumen is occupied by numerous spermatozoa, whose dark heads (*asterisks*) and pale flagella (*arrowhead*) are clearly discernible. Flagella are very long, cilia-like structures used by the cell for propulsion.

FIGURE 2 • Cilia. Oviduct. Monkey. Plastic section. ×540.

The lining of the oviduct is composed of two types of epithelial cells: bleb-bearing **peg cells** (pc), which probably produce nutritional factors necessary for the survival of the gametes, and pale **ciliated cells** (CC). Cilia (*arrows*) are long, motile, finger-like extensions of the apical cell membrane and cytoplasm that transport material along the cell surface. The core of the cilium, as shown by electron microscopy, contains the axoneme, composed of microtubules arranged in a specific configuration of nine doublets surrounding a central pair of individual microtubules.

FIGURE 4 • Intercellular bridges. Skin. Monkey. Plastic section. ×540.

The epidermis of thick skin is composed of several cell layers, one of which is the stratum spinosum shown in this photomicrograph. The cells of this layer possess short, stubby, finger-like extensions that interdigitate with those of contiguous cells. Before the advent of electron microscopy, these intercellular bridges (*arrows*) were believed to represent cytoplasmic continuities between neighboring cells; however, it is now known that these processes merely serve as regions of desmosome formation so that the cells may adhere to each other.

Cell

KEY					
BB	brush border	GC	goblet cell	pc	peg cell
BC	basal cell	L	lumen	Pi	principal cell
CC	ciliated cell				

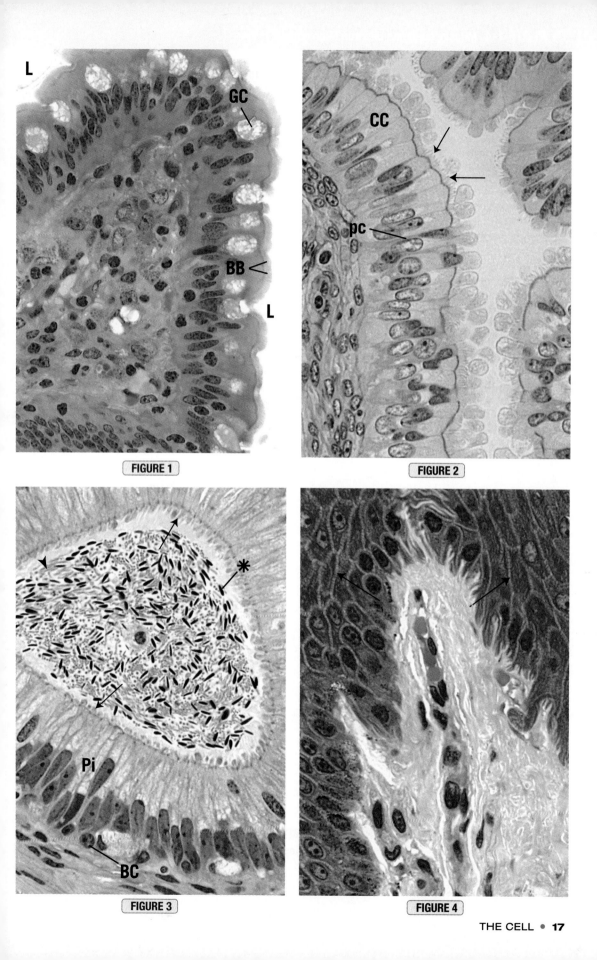

FIGURE 1

FIGURE 2

FIGURE 3

FIGURE 4

FIGURE 1 ● Mitosis. Whitefish blastula. Paraffin section. ×270.

This photomicrograph of whitefish blastula shows different stages of mitosis. The first mitotic stage, **prophase** (P), displays the short, threadlike chromosomes (*arrow*) in the center of the cell. The nuclear membrane is no longer present. During **metaphase** (M), the chromosomes line up at the equatorial plane of the cell. The chromosomes begin to migrate toward the opposite poles of the cell in early **anaphase** (A) and proceed farther and farther apart as anaphase progresses (*arrowheads*). Note the dense regions, **centrioles** (c), toward which the chromosomes migrate.

FIGURE 3 ● Mitosis. Mouse. Electron microscopy. ×9423.

Neonatal tissue is characterized by mitotic activity, in which numerous cells are in the process of proliferation. Observe that the interphase **nucleus** (N) possesses a typical **nuclear envelope** (NE), perinuclear chromatin (*asterisk*), nucleolus, and nuclear pores. A cell that is undergoing the mitotic phase of the cell cycle loses its nuclear membrane and nucleolus, whereas its **chromosomes** (Ch) are quite visible. These chromosomes are no longer lined up at the equatorial plate but are migrating to opposite poles, indicating that this cell is in the early- to mid-anaphase stage of mitosis. Observe the presence of cytoplasmic organelles, such as mitochondria, rough endoplasmic reticulum, and Golgi apparatus.

FIGURE 2 ● Mitosis. Whitefish blastula. Paraffin section. ×540.

During the early telophase stage of mitotic division, the **chromosomes** (Ch) have reached the opposite poles of the cell. The cell membrane constricts to separate the cell into the two new daughter cells, forming a cleavage furrow (*arrowheads*). The spindle apparatus is visible as parallel, horizontal lines (*arrow*) that eventually form the midbody. As telophase progresses, the two new daughter cells will uncoil their chromosomes and the nuclear membrane and nucleoli will become reestablished.

KEY							
A	anaphase	M	metaphase	NE	nuclear envelope
c	centriole	N	nucleus	P	prophase
Ch	chromosome				

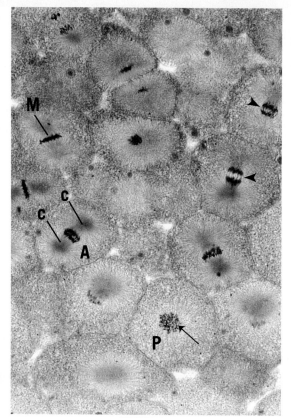

FIGURE 1

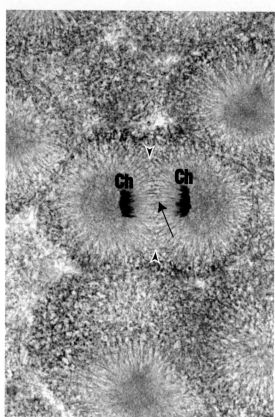

FIGURE 2

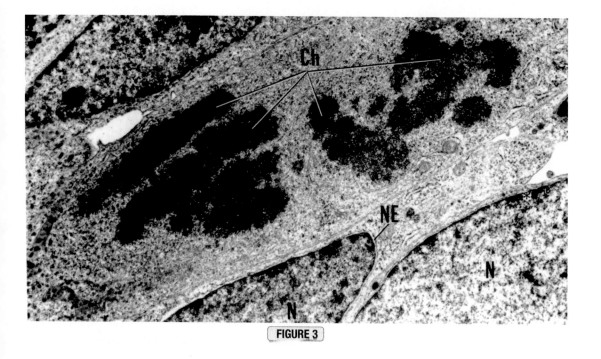

FIGURE 3

FIGURE 1 • Typical cell. Pituitary. Rat. Electron microscopy. ×8936.

The gonadotrophs of the pituitary gland provide an excellent example of a typical cell because they house many of the cytoplasmic organelles possessed by most cells. The cytoplasm is limited by a cell membrane (*arrowheads*) that is clearly evident, especially where it approximates the plasmalemma of the adjacent electron-dense cells. **Mitochondria** (m) are not numerous but are easily recognizable, especially in longitudinal sections, because their cristae (*arrows*) are arranged in a characteristic fashion. Because this cell actively manufactures a secretory product that must be packaged and delivered outside of the cell, it possesses a well developed **Golgi apparatus** (GA), positioned near the **nucleus** (N). Observe that the Golgi is formed by several stacks of flattened membranes. Additionally, this cell is well-endowed with **rough endoplasmic reticulum**, indicating active protein synthesis. The

cytoplasm also displays secretory products (*asterisks*), which are transitory inclusions.

The nucleus is bounded by the typical **nuclear envelope** (NE), consisting of a ribosome-studded outer nuclear membrane and an inner nuclear membrane. The peripheral chromatin and chromatin islands are clearly evident, as is the **nucleolus-associated chromatin** (NC). The clear area within the nucleus is the nucleoplasm representing the fluid component of the nucleus. The **nucleolus** (n) presents a spongelike appearance composed of electron-lucent and electron-dense materials, suspended free in the nucleoplasm. The electron-dense region is composed of the pars granulosa and the pars fibrosa, whereas the electron-lucent region is probably the nucleoplasm in which the nucleolus is suspended. (From Stokreef JC, Reifel CW, Shin SH. A possible phagocytic role for folliculo-stellate cells of anterior pituitary following estrogen withdrawal from primed male rats. Cell Tissue Res 1986;243:255–261.)

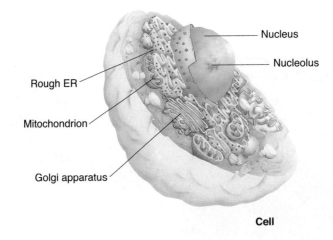

Nucleus

Nucleolus

Rough ER

Mitochondrion

Golgi apparatus

Cell

KEY					
GA	Golgi apparatus	n	nucleolus	NE	nuclear envelope
m	mitochondrion	NC	nucleolus-associated	rER	rough endoplasmic
N	nucleus		chromatin		reticulum

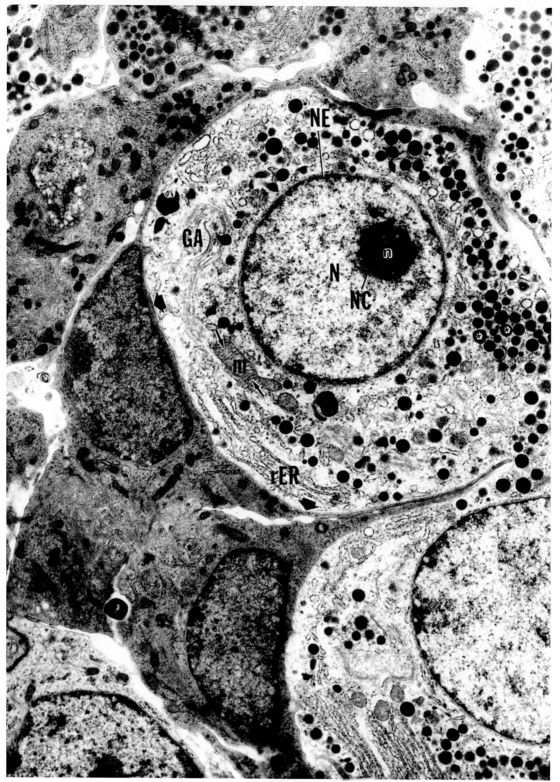

FIGURE 1 • Nucleus and cytoplasm. Liver. Mouse. Electron microscopy. ×48,176.

The **nucleus** (N) displays its nucleoplasm and **chromatin** (c) to advantage in this electron micrograph. Note that the inner (*arrowheads*) and outer (*double arrows*) mem- branes of the nuclear envelope fuse to form **nuclear pores** (NP). The **rough endoplasmic reticulum** is richly en- dowed by **ribosomes** (R). Note the presence of numerous **mitochondria** (m), whose double membrane and **cristae** (Cr) are quite evident. Observe the slightly electron-dense **microtubule** (Mi) as it courses through the cytoplasm.

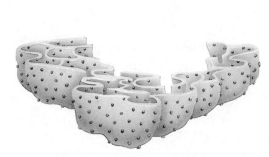

Rough endoplasmic reticulum

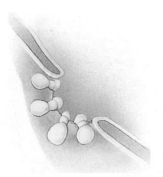

Nuclear pore complex

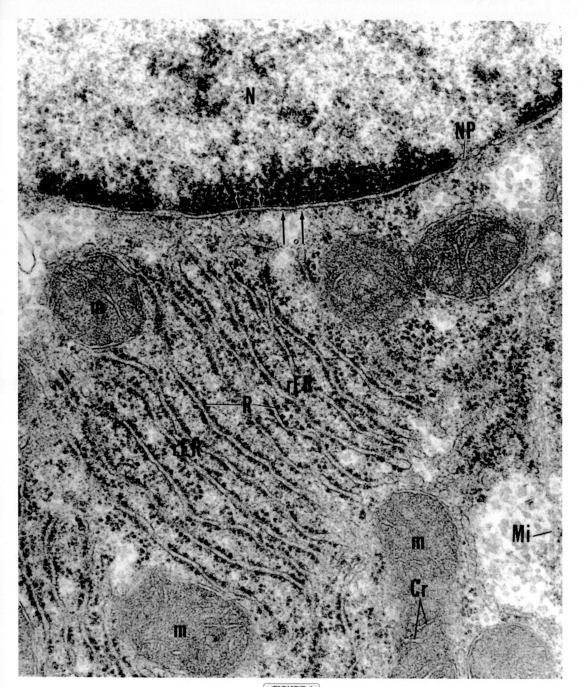

FIGURE 1

FIGURE 1 • Nucleus and cytoplasm. Liver. Mouse. Electron microscopy. ×20,318.

This electron micrograph of a liver cell displays the **nucleus** (N), with its condensed **chromatin** (c), as well as many cytoplasmic organelles. Note that the **mitochondria** (m) possess electron-dense matrix granules (*arrows*)

scattered in the matrix of the intercristal spaces. The perinuclear area presents the **Golgi apparatus** (GA), which is actively packaging material in **condensing vesicles** (CV). The **rough endoplasmic reticulum** is obvious due to its **ribosomes** (R), whereas the **smooth endoplasmic reticulum** is less obvious.

Golgi apparatus

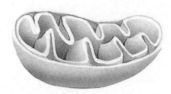

Mitochondrion

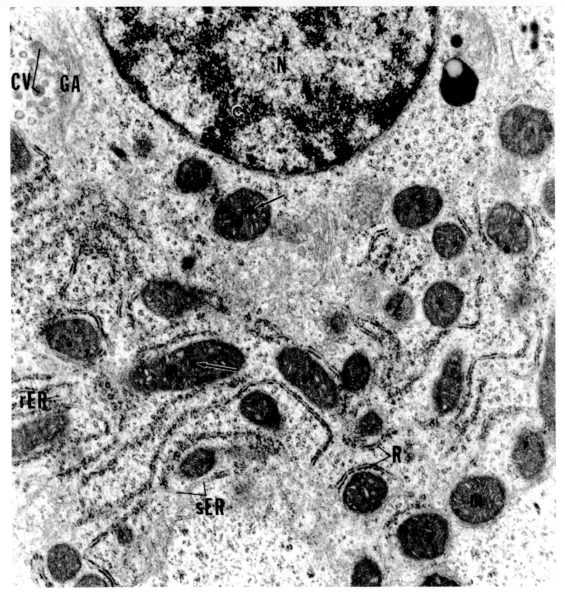

FIGURE 1

FIGURE 1 • Golgi apparatus. Mouse. Electron microscopy. ×28,588.

The extensive Golgi apparatus of this secretory cell presents several flattened membrane-bound **cisternae** (Ci), stacked one on top of the other. The convex face (*cis* face) (ff) receives **transfer vesicles** (TV) derived from the rough endoplasmic reticulum. The concave, *trans*-**Golgi network** (mf) releases **condensing vesicles** (CV), which house the secretory product. (From Gartner LP, Seibel W, Hiatt JL, et al. A fine-structural analysis of mouse molar odontoblast maturation. Acta Anat (Basel) 1979;103:16–33.)

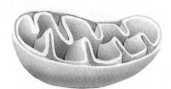

Golgi apparatus   **Mitochondrion**

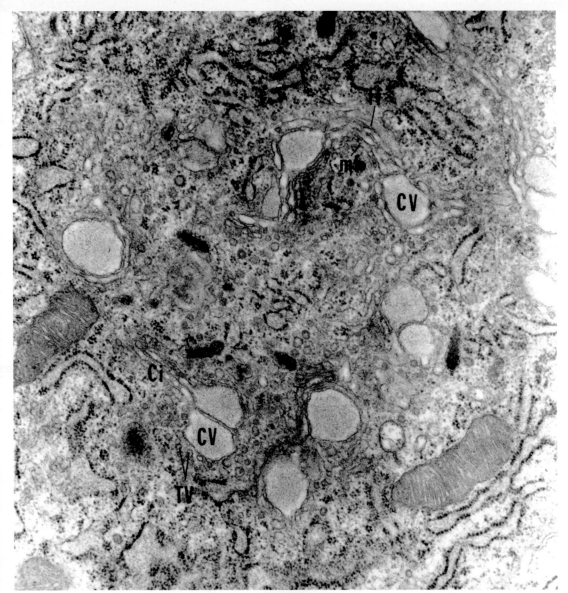

FIGURE 1

FIGURE 1 • Mitochondria. Kidney. Mouse. Electron microscopy. ×18,529.

The basal aspect of the proximal tubule cell presents numerous interdigitating processes, many of which house longitudinally oriented **mitochondria** (m). The outer membrane of each mitochondrion is smooth, whereas its inner membrane is folded to form **cristae** (Cr). Note that the matrix houses matrix granules (*arrowheads*). Observe also the basal lamina whose lamina densa (*open arrowheads*) and lamina lucida (*arrows*) are clearly evident.

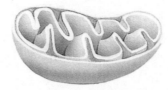

Mitochondrion

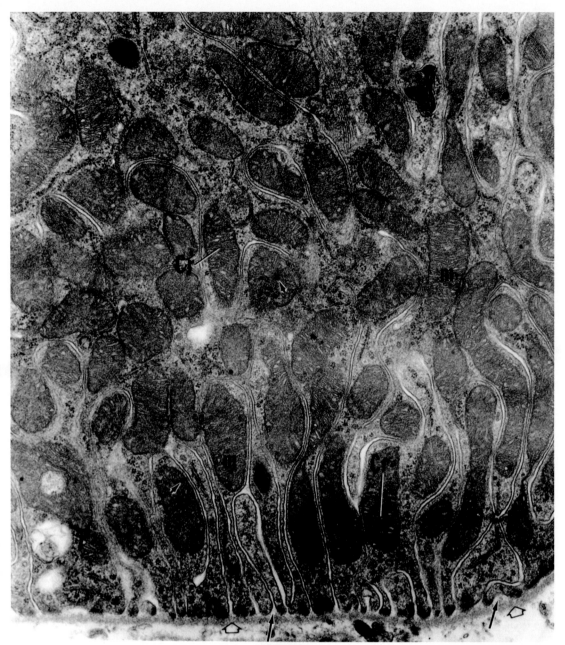

FIGURE 1

Epithelium and Glands

2

Epithelium is one of the four basic tissues of the body and is derived from all three germ layers. It is composed of very closely packed, contiguous cells, with very little or no extracellular material in the extracellular spaces. Epithelia either form membranes that are represented as sheets covering the body surface and lining its internal surface or occur as secretory elements known as glands. Almost always, epithelia and their derivatives are separated from underlying or surrounding connective tissues by a thin, noncellular layer, the **basal membrane (basement membrane)**. This is usually composed of two regions, the epithelially derived **basal lamina** and the connective tissue–derived **lamina reticularis**.

● EPITHELIUM

Epithelial Membranes

Epithelial membranes are avascular, deriving their nutrients by diffusion from blood vessels in the adjacent connective tissues. These membranes can cover a surface, line a cavity, or line a tube. Surfaces covered may be dry, as the outer body surface, or wet, as the covering of the ovary. However, all lining epithelia have a wet surface (e.g., those lining the body cavities, blood vessels, and gastrointestinal tract). Membranes that line serous body cavities are referred to as **mesothelia**, whereas those lining blood and lymph vessels and the chambers of the heart are known as **endothelia**.

Epithelial membranes are classified according to the shape of the most superficial cell layer, which may be **squamous** (flat), **cuboidal**, or **columnar**, as observed when sectioned perpendicular to the exposed surface of the membrane. Moreover, the number of cell layers composing the epithelium also determines its classification, in that a single layer of cells constitutes a **simple epithelium**, whereas two or more layers of cells are referred to as a **stratified epithelium** (Table 2-1). In a simple epithelium, all of the cells contact the basal lamina and reach the free surface. In **pseudostratified epithelia** (which may or may not possess cilia or stereocilia) all of the cells contact the basal lamina, although some cells are much shorter than others and do not reach the free surface. Therefore, this is a simple epithelium that appears to be stratified.

Stratified squamous epithelium may be **keratinized, nonkeratinized**, or even **parakeratinized**. Since stratified squamous epithelium is the thickest of the epithelia, as a barrier, it affords the greatest protection of the body from the external milieu. To enhance this protection, stratified squamous epithelium may possess an outer surface composed of dying or dead epithelial cells; the epithelium then is known as parakeratinized or keratinized, respectively. The stratified epithelium lining much of the urinary tract is known as **transitional epithelium**; its free surface is characterized by large, dome-shaped cells (Table 2-1).

Epithelial cell membranes are frequently specialized. Their free surface may form **microvilli (brush border)**, **cilia**, or **stereocilia**. The lateral cell membranes maintain various types of intercellular junctions between contiguous cells, namely, **zonulae occludentes, zonulae adherentes, maculae adherentes**, and **gap junctions**. The basal cell membrane forms **hemidesmosomes**, maintaining the cell's attachment to the basal membrane (Graphic 2-1).

Epithelial membranes possess numerous functions that include protection from mechanical abrasion, chemical penetration, and bacterial invasion; reduction of friction; absorption of nutrients as a result of its polarized cells that are capable of performing vectorial functions; secretion; excretion of waste products; synthesis of various proteins, enzymes, mucins, hormones, and a myriad of other substances; receiving sensory signals from the external (or internal) milieu; **forming glands** whose function is **secreting** enzymes, hormones, lubricants, or other products; and movement of material along the epithelial sheet (such as mucus along the respiratory tract) by the assistance of cilia.

● GLANDS

Most glands are formed by epithelial downgrowth into the surrounding connective tissue. Glands that deliver their secretions onto the epithelial surface

TABLE 2-1 • Classification of Epithelia

Type	Surface Cell Shape	Examples (Some)
Simple		
Simple squamous	Flattened	Lining blood and lymphatic vessel walls (endothelium), pleural and abdominal cavities (mesothelium)
Simple cuboidal	Cuboidal	Lining ducts of most glands
Simple columnar	Columnar	Lining much of digestive tract, gall bladder
Pseudostratified	All cells rest on basal lamina with only some reaching the surface. Cells that reach the surface are columnar.	Lining of nasal cavity, trachea, bronchi, epididymis
Stratified		
Stratified squamous (nonkeratinized)	Flattened (with nuclei)	Lining mouth, esophagus, vagina
Stratified squamous (keratinized)	Flattened (without nuclei)	Epidermis of the skin
Stratified cuboidal	Cuboidal	Lining ducts of sweat glands
Stratified columnar	Columnar	Conjunctiva of eye, lining some large excretory ducts
Transitional	Large dome-shaped cells when bladder is empty; flattened when bladder is distended	Lining renal calyces, renal pelvis, ureter, urinary bladder, proximal portion of urethra

do so via ducts and are known as **exocrine glands**. Glands that do not maintain a connection to the outside (ductless) and whose secretions enter the vascular system for delivery are known as **endocrine glands**. The secretory cells of a gland are referred to as its **parenchyma** and are separated from surrounding connective tissue and vascular elements by a basement membrane. Exocrine glands are classified according to various parameters, e.g., morphology of their functional units, branching of their ducts, types of secretory products that they manufacture, and the method whereby their component cells release secretory products. The classification of endocrine glands is much more complex, but, morphologically, their secretory units either are composed of **follicles** or are arranged in **cords** and clumps of cells (see Graphic 2-2).

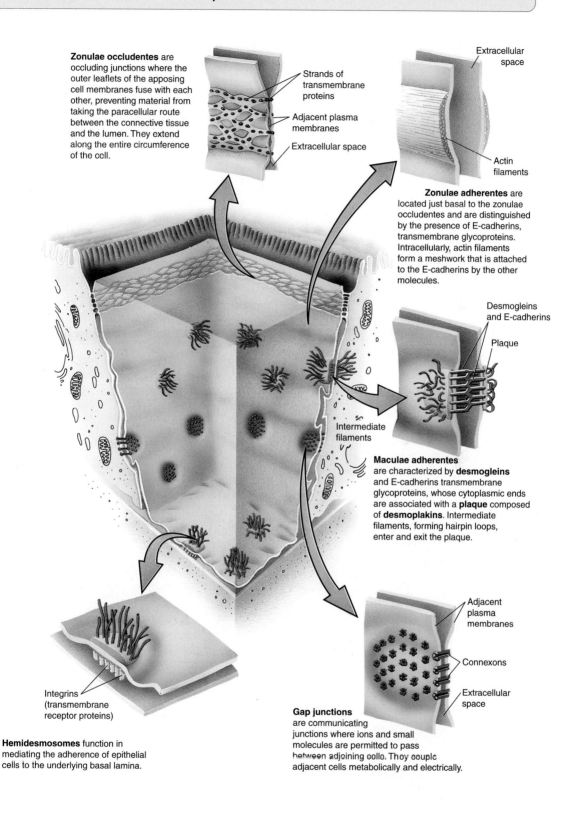

Zonulae occludentes are occluding junctions where the outer leaflets of the apposing cell membranes fuse with each other, preventing material from taking the paracellular route between the connective tissue and the lumen. They extend along the entire circumference of the cell.

Strands of transmembrane proteins

Adjacent plasma membranes

Extracellular space

Extracellular space

Actin filaments

Zonulae adherentes are located just basal to the zonulae occludentes and are distinguished by the presence of E-cadherins, transmembrane glycoproteins. Intracellularly, actin filaments form a meshwork that is attached to the E-cadherins by the other molecules.

Desmogleins and E-cadherins

Plaque

Intermediate filaments

Maculae adherentes are characterized by **desmogleins** and E-cadherins transmembrane glycoproteins, whose cytoplasmic ends are associated with a **plaque** composed of **desmoplakins**. Intermediate filaments, forming hairpin loops, enter and exit the plaque.

Adjacent plasma membranes

Connexons

Extracellular space

Integrins (transmembrane receptor proteins)

Hemidesmosomes function in mediating the adherence of epithelial cells to the underlying basal lamina.

Gap junctions are communicating junctions where ions and small molecules are permitted to pass between adjoining cells. They couple adjacent cells metabolically and electrically.

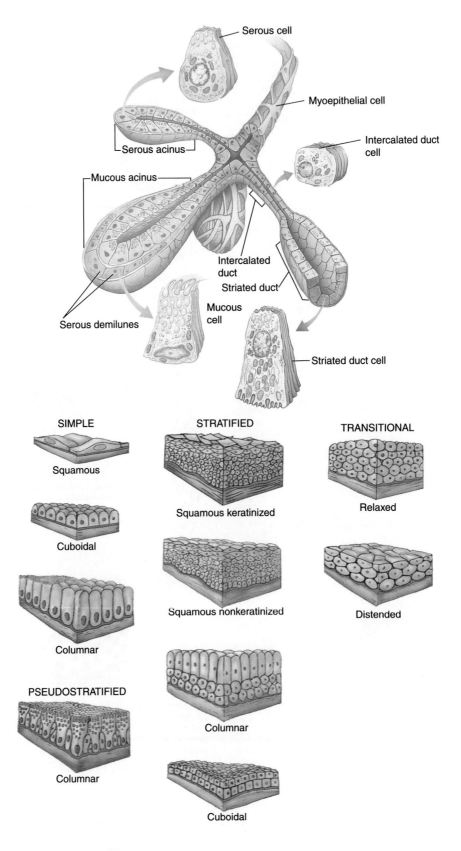

Serous cell

Myoepithelial cell

Serous acinus

Intercalated duct cell

Mucous acinus

Intercalated duct

Striated duct

Mucous cell

Serous demilunes

Striated duct cell

SIMPLE

Squamous

Cuboidal

Columnar

PSEUDOSTRATIFIED

Columnar

STRATIFIED

Squamous keratinized

Squamous nonkeratinized

Columnar

Cuboidal

TRANSITIONAL

Relaxed

Distended

Histophysiology

I. EPITHELIUM

Epithelial cells may present specializations along their various surfaces. These surfaces are **apical** (microvilli, stereocilia, cilia, and flagella), **lateral or basolateral** (junctional complexes, zonula occludens, zonula adherens, macula adherens, and gap junctions), and **basal** (hemidesmosomes and basal lamina).

A. Apical Surface Modifications

Microvilli are closely spaced, finger-like extensions of the cell membrane that increase the surface area of cells that function in absorption and secretion. Dense clusters of microvilli are evident in light micrographs, as a striated or brush border. The core of each microvillus possesses a cluster of 15 or so microfilaments (actin filaments) that are embedded in **villin** at the tip of the microvillus and are anchored in the terminal web of the cell. The actin filaments are linked to each other by **fimbrin** and **fascin** and to the membrane of the microvillus by **myosin I**. Where the actin filaments are anchored in the terminal web, myosin II molecules abound, and these assist in the spreading of the microvilli apart to increase the intervillar spaces and facilitate absorption or secretion.

Stereocilia are located in the epididymis, as well as in a few limited regions of the body. They were named cilia because of their length; however, electron micrography proved them to be elongated microvilli whose functions are, as yet, unknown. The core of these stereocilia is composed of actin filaments that are bound to one another by **fimbrin** and to the membrane of the stereocila by **erzin**.

Cilia are elongated, motile, plasmalemma-covered extensions of the cytoplasm that move material along the cell surface. Each cilium arises from a centriole (**basal body**) and possesses an **axoneme** core composed of nine pairs of peripheral (doublets) and two single, centrally placed microtubules (singlets). Microtubules of the doublets possess **dynein** arms with ATPase activity, which functions in energizing ciliary motion. Each doublet is composed of a complete microtubule, **microtubule A**, consisting of of 13 protofilaments and a **microtubule B**, composed of only 10 protofilaments. Microtubule A shares three of its protofilaments with microtubule B. The two singlets are surrounded by a **central sheet**, composed of an elastic material, and each doublet is attached to the central sheet by a **radial spoke**, also composed of

an elastic material. Moreover, **nexin bridges** bind adjacent doublets to each other.

B. Basolateral Surface Modifications
(see Graphic 2-1)

Junctional complexes, which occupy only a minute region of the basolateral cell surfaces, are visible with light microscopy as **terminal bars**, a structure that encircles the entire cell. Terminal bars are composed of three components: **zonula occludens** (tight or occluding junction), **zonula adherens** (adhering junction), and **macula adherens** (**desmosomes**, also adhering junction). The first two encircle the cell, whereas desmosomes do not. Additionally, another type of junction, the **gap junction**, permits two cells to communicate with each other.

Occluding junctions are formed in such a fashion that the plasma membranes of the two adjoining cells are very close to each other and the transmembrane proteins of the two cells contact each other in the extracellular space. There are a number of transmembrane proteins that participate in the formation of the zonula occludens, **caludins, occludins, junctional adhesion molecules, ZO-1, ZO-2**, and **ZO-3** proteins, among others. Although all of these proteins are necessary to exclude material from traversing the paracellular route, it is the claudins that form a physical barrier that cannot be penetrated. However, there are some claudins that possess aqueous channels that are designed to permit the movement of ions, water, and some very small molecules. These proteins are preferentially adherent to the P-face (protoplasmic face) of the membrane and form characteristic ridges evident in freeze-fracture preparation, whereas the E-face (extracellular face) presents corresponding grooves. The zonulae occludentes are also responsible for preventing integral proteins of the cell from migrating from the apical surface to the basolateral surface and vice versa.

The plasma membranes of adjacent epithelial cells are farther apart in the region of the zonula adherens. **Cell adhesion molecules** (CAMs) are the most significant components of adhering junctions of epithelial cells, and in the zonulae adherentes they are calcium-dependent proteins, known as **E-cadherins**. The cytoplasmic moiety of the E-cadherins have binding sites for **catenins**, which, in turn, bind to **vinculin** and **α-actinin**, which are capable of forming bonds with the thin filaments of the cytoskeleton. In this fashion, in the presence of calcium in the extracellular space, the two epithelial cells adhere to each other and the adherence is reinforced by the cytoskeleton of the two cells. Moreover, the zonulae adherentes reinforce and stabilize the zonulae occludentes as well as distribute stresses across the epithelial sheet.

Maculae adherentes (**desmosomes**) resemble spot welding that holds the two cells together. As their name implies, they are not continuous structures like the two zonulae but are discrete entities. Desmosomes require the presence of two cells, and they are composed of an intracellular **attachment plaque**, composed of **plakoglobins** and **desmoplakins**, which adhere to the cytoplasmic aspect of the two adjacent cell membranes as mirror images. Intermediate filaments enter and leave the plaques, resembling hairpins. Embedded into the plaques are transmembrane, calcium-dependent cadherins, **desmogleins** and **desmocollins**. The extracellular moieties of desmogleins and desmocollins contact each other and, in the presence of calcium, attach the two cells to each other.

In the regions of **gap junctions** (communicating junctions, **nexus**) the two cell membranes are very close to each other, about 2 nm apart. Interposed within the cell membrane of each cell and meeting each other are **connexons**, composed of six subunits known as a **connexins**; these are multipass proteins from a cylindrical structure with a central pore. A connexon of one cell matches the connexon of the other cell and thus forms an aqueous channel, about 2 nm in diameter, between the two cells that permits the water, ions, and molecules smaller than 1 kD in size to traverse the channel and go from one cell into the next. Each cell has the ability to open or close the channel, and this regulation is calcium as well as pH dependent. In this fashion a healthy cell can shut off communication with a cell that may be damaged.

C. Basal Surface Modifications

The basal cell membrane of the cell is affixed to the basal lamina by adhering junctions known as the **hemidesmosomes**. Morphologically, this structure resembles half of a desmosome, but its biochemical composition and clinical significance demonstrate enough dissimilarity that hemidesmosomes are no longer viewed as being merely one half of a desmosome. Therefore, a hemidesmosome has an intracellular plaque, composed mostly of **plectin**, **BP230**, and **erbin**. Intermediate filaments terminate in the plaque by interacting with BP230 and plectin. Hemidesmosomes also possess transmembrane protein components known as **integrin molecules**, whose cytoplasmic moiety is embedded in the plaque and is attached to it by interacting with

BP230 and erbin. The extracellular region of the integrin molecules contact laminin and type IV collagen of the basal lamina and bind to them if extracellular calcium is present. In this manner, hemidesmosomes assist in the anchoring of epithelial sheets to the adjacent basal lamina.

The **basement membrane**, interposed between epithelium and connective tissue, is composed of an epithelially derived component, the **basal lamina**, and a connective tissue–derived region, the **lamina reticularis**. The basal lamina is further subdivided into two regions, the **lamina lucida** and the **lamina densa**. Although some investigators, using low-temperature, high-pressure freezing techniques of fixation, are beginning to question the existence of the lamina lucida, this *Atlas* will continue to adhere to the concept of a lamina lucida component of the basal lamina. The lamina lucida is that region of the basal lamina that houses the extracellular moieties of the transmembrane **laminin receptors**, **integrin** and **dystroglycans** molecules, and the glycoproteins **laminin**, **entactin**, and **perlacans**. The lamina densa is composed of **type IV collagen**, coated by laminin, entactin, and perlacan on its epithelial surface, and **fibronectin** on the lamina reticularis surface. Additionally, two other **collagen types, XV and XVIII**, are also present in the lamina densa. The lamina densa adheres to the lamina reticularis, composed mostly of **type III collagen**, proteoglycans, glycoproteins, and slender elastic fibers, by **anchoring fibers** (**type VII collagen**) and **microfibrills** (**fibrillin**). Basal laminae function as structural supports for the epithelium, as molecular filters (e.g., in the renal glomerulus), in regulating the migration of certain cells across epithelial sheaths (e.g., preventing entry to fibroblasts but permitting access to lymphoid cells), in epithelial regeneration (e.g., in wound healing, where it forms a surface along which regenerating epithelial cells migrate), and in cell-to-cell interactions (e.g., formation of myoneural junctions).

D. Epithelial Cell Renewal

Epithelial cells usually undergo regular turnover because of their function and location. For example, cells of the epidermis that are sloughed from the surface originated approximately 28 days earlier by mitosis from cells of the basal layers. Other cells, such as those lining the small intestine, are replaced every few days. Still others continue to proliferate until adulthood is reached, at which time the mechanism is shut down. However, when large numbers of cells are lost, for example, because of injury, certain mechanisms trigger the proliferation of new cells to restore the cell population.

CLINICAL CONSIDERATIONS

Bullous Pemphigoid

Bullous pemphigoid, a rare autoimmune disease, is caused by autoantibodies binding to some of the protein components of hemidesmosomes. Individuals afflicted with this disease exhibit skin blistering of the groin and axilla, about the flexure areas, and often in the oral cavity. Fortunately, it can be controlled by steroids and immunosuppressive drugs.

Pemphigus Vulgaris

Pemphigus vulgaris is an autoimmune disease, caused by autoantibodies binding to some of the components of desmosomes. This disease causes blistering and is usually found occurring in middle-aged individuals. It is a relatively dangerous disease because the blistering can easily lead to infections. Frequently this disease also responds to steroid therapy.

Tumor Formation

Under certain pathologic conditions, mechanisms that regulate cell proliferation do not function properly; thus, epithelial proliferation gives rise to tumors that may be benign if they are localized or malignant if they wander from their original site and metastasize (seed) to another area of the body and continue to proliferate. Malignant tumors that arise from surface epithelium are termed carcinomas, whereas those developing from glandular epithelium are called adenocarcinomas.

Metaplasia

Epithelial cells are derived from certain germ cell layers, possess a definite morphology and location, and perform specific functions; however, under certain pathological conditions, they may undergo metaplasia, transforming into another epithelial cell type. An example of such metaplasia occurs in the lining epithelium of the oral cavity of individuals who smoke or use chewing tobacco.

Cholera

Cholera toxins cause the release of tremendous volumes of fluid from the individual afflicted by that disease. The toxin attacks the zonulae occludentes by disturbing the proteins ZO-1 and ZO-2, thereby disrupting the zonula occludentes and permitting the paracellular movement of water and electrolytes. The patient has uncontrolled diarrhea and subsequent fluid and electrolyte loss. If the fluids and salts are not replaced in a timely manner, the patient dies.

FIGURE 1 • Simple squamous epithelium. Kidney. Monkey. Plastic section. ×540.

The lining of the **lumen** (L) of this small arteriole is composed of a **simple squamous epithelium** (SE) (known as the endothelium). The cytoplasm of these cells is highly attenuated and can only be approximated in this photomicrograph as a thin line (between the *arrowheads*). The boundaries of two contiguous epithelial cells cannot be determined with the light microscope. The **nuclei** (N) of the squamous epithelial cells bulge into the lumen, characteristic of this type of epithelium. Note that some of the nuclei appear more flattened than others. This is due to the degree of agonal contraction of the **smooth muscle** (M) cells of the vessel wall.

FIGURE 3 • Simple columnar epithelium. Monkey. Plastic section. ×540.

The simple columnar epithelium of the duodenum in this photomicrograph displays a very extensive **brush border** (MV) on the apical aspect of the cells. The **terminal web** (TW), where microvilli are anchored, appears as a dense line between the brush border and the apical cytoplasm. Distinct dots (*arrowheads*) are evident, which, although they appear to be part of the terminal web, are actually terminal bars, resolved by the electron microscope to be junctional complexes between contiguous cells. Note that the cells are tall and slender, and their **nuclei** (N), more or less oval in shape, are arranged rather uniformly at the same level in each cell. The basal aspects of these cells lie on a basal membrane (*arrows*), separating the epithelium from the **connective tissue** (CT). The round **nuclei** (rN) noted within the epithelium actually belong to leucocytes migrating into the **lumen** (L) of the duodenum. A few **goblet cells** (GC) are also evident.

FIGURE 2 • Simple squamous and simple cuboidal epithelia. x.s. Kidney. Paraffin section. ×270.

The medulla of the kidney provides ideal representation of simple squamous and simple cuboidal epithelia. Simple squamous epithelium, as in the previous figure, is easily recognizable due to flattened but somewhat bulging **nuclei** (N). Note that the cytoplasm of these cells appears as thin, dark lines (between *arrowheads*); however, it must be stressed that the dark lines are composed of not only attenuated cells but also the surrounding basal membranes. The **simple cuboidal epithelium** (CE) is very obvious. The lateral cell membranes (*arrow*) are clearly evident in some areas; even when they cannot be seen, the relationships of the round nuclei permit an imaginary approximation of the extent of each cell. Note that simple cuboidal cells, in *section*, appear more or less like small squares with centrally positioned nuclei.

FIGURE 4 • Pseudostratified columnar epithelium with cilia. Paraffin section. ×270.

The first impression conveyed by this epithelium from the nasal cavity is that it is stratified, being composed of at least four layers of cells; however, careful observation of the *inset* (× 540) demonstrates that these are closely packed cells of varying heights and girth, each of which is in contact with the basal membrane. Here, unlike in the previous photomicrograph, the **nuclei** (N) are not uniformly arranged, and they occupy about three-fourths of the epithelial layer. The location and morphology of the nuclei provide an indication of the cell type. The short **basal cells** (BC) display small, round to oval nuclei near the basal membrane. The tall, ciliated cells (*arrows*) possess large, oval nuclei. The **terminal web** (TW) supports tall, slender **cilia** (C), which propel mucus along the epithelial surface. The connective tissue is highly vascularized and presents good examples of simple squamous epithelia (*arrowheads*) that compose the endothelial lining of **blood** (BV) and **lymph vessels** (LV).

PSEUDOSTRATIFIED

SIMPLE

Squamous

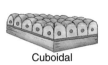
Cuboidal

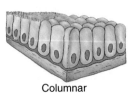
Columnar

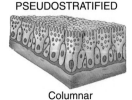
Columnar

KEY					
BC	basal cell	GC	goblet cell	N	nucleus
BV	blood vessel	L	lumen	rN	round nucleus
C	cilia	LV	lymph vessel	SE	simple squamous epithelium
CE	simple cuboidal epithelium	M	smooth muscle	TW	terminal web
CT	connective tissue	MV	brush border		

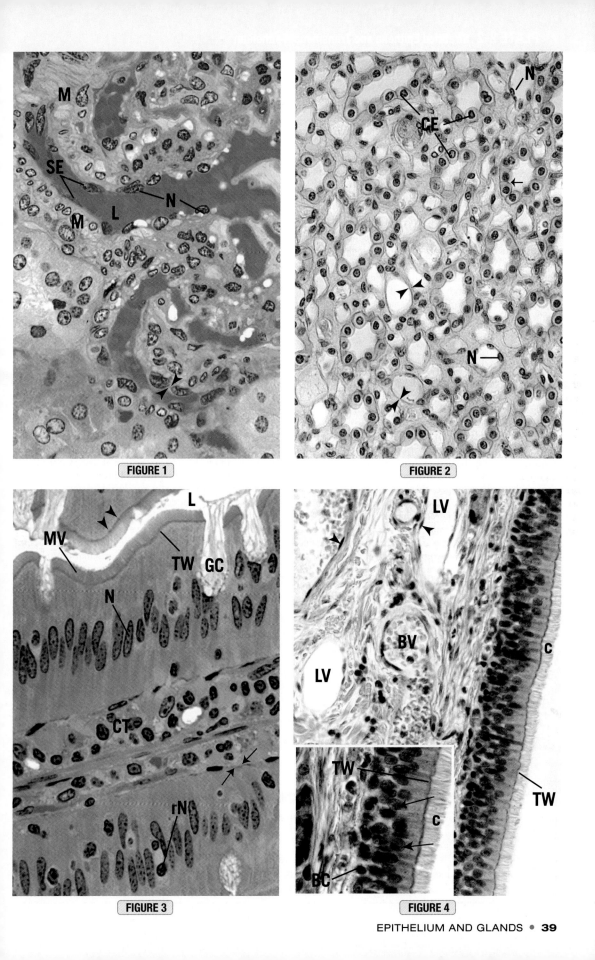

FIGURE 1

FIGURE 2

FIGURE 3

FIGURE 4

PLATE 2-2 Stratified Epithelia and Transitional Epithelium

FIGURE 1 • Stratified cuboidal epithelium. Monkey. Plastic section. ×540.

Stratified cuboidal epithelium is characterized by two or more layers of cuboid-shaped cells, as illustrated in this photomicrograph of a sweat gland duct. The **lumen** (L) of the duct is surrounded by cells whose cell boundaries are not readily evident, but the layering of the **nuclei** (N) demonstrates that this epithelium is truly stratified. The epithelium of the duct is surrounded by a **basal membrane** (BM). The other thick tubular profiles are tangential sections of the **secretory** (s) portions of the sweat gland, composed of simple cuboidal epithelium. Note the presence of a **capillary** (Cp), containing a single red blood cell, and the bulging nucleus (*arrow*) of the epithelial cell constituting the endothelial lining. The large empty space in the lower right-hand corner of this photomicrograph represents the lumen of a **lymph vessel** (LV) whose endothelial lining presents a flattened nucleus bulging into the lumen. Note that more cytoplasm is evident near the pole of the nucleus (*arrowhead*) than elsewhere.

FIGURE 3 • Stratified squamous keratinized epithelium. Skin. Paraffin section. ×132.

The palm of the hand is covered by a thick stratified squamous keratinized epithelium. The definite difference between this and the preceding photomicrograph is the thick layer of nonliving cells containing **keratin** (K), which functions in protecting the deeper living cells and tissues from abrasion, desiccation, and invasion by bacterial flora. Although the various layers of this epithelium will be examined in greater detail in Chapter 11, certain features need to be examined here. Note that the interdigitation between the connective tissue **dermal ridges** (P) and the **epithelial ridges** (R) provides a larger surface area for adhesion and providing nutrients than would be offered by a merely flat interface. The **basal membrane** (BM) is a definite interval between the epithelium and the connective tissue. The basal layer of this epithelium, composed of cuboidal cells, is known as the stratum germinativum, which possesses a high mitotic activity. Cells originating here press toward the surface, and, while on their way, change their morphology, manufacture proteins, and acquire different names. Note the **duct** (D) of a sweat gland piercing the base of an epidermal ridge as it continues toward the outside (*arrows*).

FIGURE 2 • Stratified squamous nonkeratinized epithelium. Plastic section. ×270.

The lining of the esophagus provides a good example of stratified squamous nonkeratinized epithelium. The lack of vascularity of the epithelium, which is approximately 30–35 cell layers thick, is clearly evident. Nourishment must reach the more superficial cells via diffusion from blood vessels of the **connective tissue** (CT). Note that the deepest cells, which lie on the basal membrane and are known as the **basal layer** (BL), are actually cuboidal in shape. Due to their mitotic activity, they give rise to the cells of the epithelium, which, as they migrate toward the surface, become increasingly flattened. By the time they reach the surface, to be sloughed off into the **esophageal lumen** (EL), they are squamous in morphology. The endothelial lining of a vessel is shown as scattered **nuclei** (N) bulging into the **lumen** (L), providing an obvious contrast between stratified and simple squamous epithelia.

FIGURE 4 • Transitional epithelium. Bladder. Monkey. Plastic section. ×132.

The urinary bladder, as most of the excretory portion of the urinary tract, is lined by a specialized type of stratified epithelium—the transitional epithelium. This particular specimen was taken from an empty, relaxed bladder, as indicated by the large, **round**, dome-**shaped** (rC) **cells**, some of which are occasionally binucleated (*arrow*), abutting the **lumen** (L). The epithelial cells lying on the **basal membrane** (BM) are quite small but increase in size as they migrate superficially and begin to acquire a pear shape. When the bladder is distended, the thickness of the epithelium decreases and the cells become flattened, more squamous-like. The connective tissue–epithelium interface is flat, with very little interdigitation between them. The **connective tissue** (CT) is very vascular immediately deep to the epithelium, as is evident from the sections of the **arterioles** (A) and **venules** (V) in this field. Observe the simple squamous endothelial linings of these vessels, characterized by their bulging nuclei (*arrowheads*).

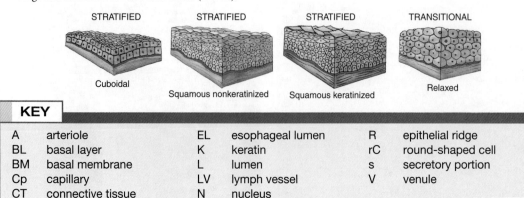

STRATIFIED | STRATIFIED | STRATIFIED | TRANSITIONAL

Cuboidal | Squamous nonkeratinized | Squamous keratinized | Relaxed

KEY					
A	arteriole	EL	esophageal lumen	R	epithelial ridge
BL	basal layer	K	keratin	rC	round-shaped cell
BM	basal membrane	L	lumen	s	secretory portion
Cp	capillary	LV	lymph vessel	V	venule
CT	connective tissue	N	nucleus		
D	duct	P	dermal ridge		

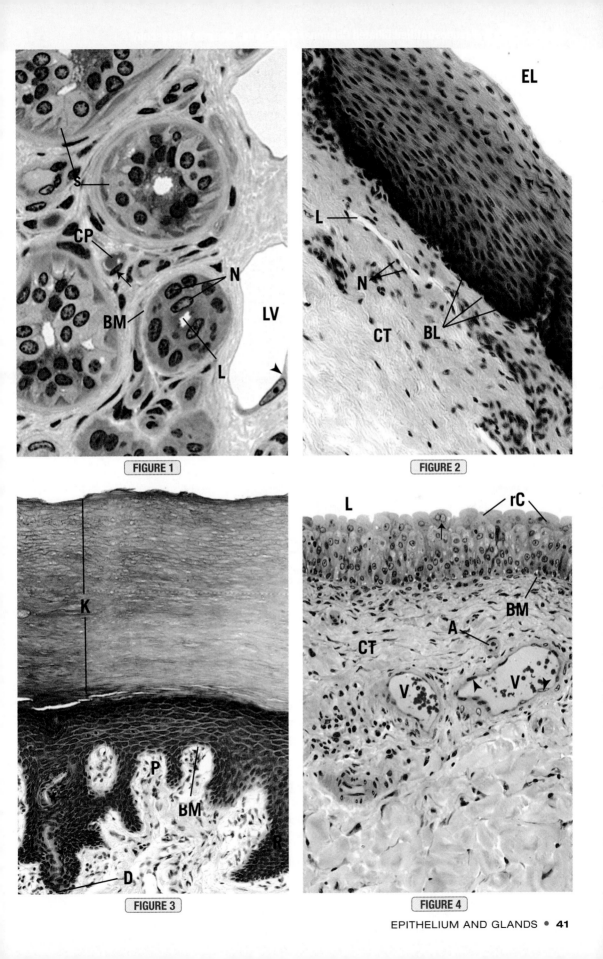

FIGURE 1

FIGURE 2

FIGURE 3

FIGURE 4

FIGURE 1 • Pseudostratified ciliated columnar epithelium.
Hamster trachea. Electron microscopy. ×6480.

The pseudostratified ciliated columnar epithelium of the trachea is composed of several types of cells, some of which are presented here. Since this is an oblique section through the epithelium, it is not readily evident here that all of these cells touch the **basal lamina** (BL). Note that the pale-staining **ciliated cells** (CC) display **rough endoplasmic reticulum** (rER), **mitochondria** (M), **Golgi apparatus** (G), and numerous **cilia** (**C**) interspersed with **microvilli** (MV). Each cilium, some of which are seen in cross-section, displays its plasma membrane and its **axoneme** (A). The cilia are anchored in the terminal web via their **basal bodies** (BB). The mitochondria appear to be concentrated in this area of the cell. The second cell types to be noted are the **mucous cells** (MC), also known as goblet cells. These cells produce a thick, viscous secretion,

which appears as **secretory granules** (SG) within the apical cytoplasm. The protein moiety of the secretion is synthesized on the **rough endoplasmic reticulum** (rER), whereas most of the carbohydrate groups are added to the protein in the **Golgi apparatus** (G). The mucous cells are nonciliated but do present short, stubby **microvilli** (MV) on their apical surface. When these cells release their secretory product, they change their morphology. They no longer contain secretory granules, and their microvilli become elongated and are known as brush cells. They may be recognized by the filamentous structures within the supranuclear cytoplasm. The lower right-hand corner of this electron micrograph presents a portion of a **capillary** (Ca) containing a **red blood cell** (RBC). Observe that the highly attenuated **endothelial cell** (EC) is outside of but very close to the **basal lamina** (BL) of the tracheal epithelium. (Courtesy of Dr. E. McDowell.)

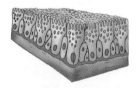

**Pseudostratified columnar
epithelium**

KEY						
A	axoneme	CC	ciliated cell	MV	microvillus
BB	basal body	EC	endothelial cell	RBC	red blood cell
BL	basal lamina	G	Golgi apparatus	rER	rough endoplasmic reticulum
C	cilium	M	mitochondrion	SG	secretory granule
Ca	capillary	MC	mucous cell		

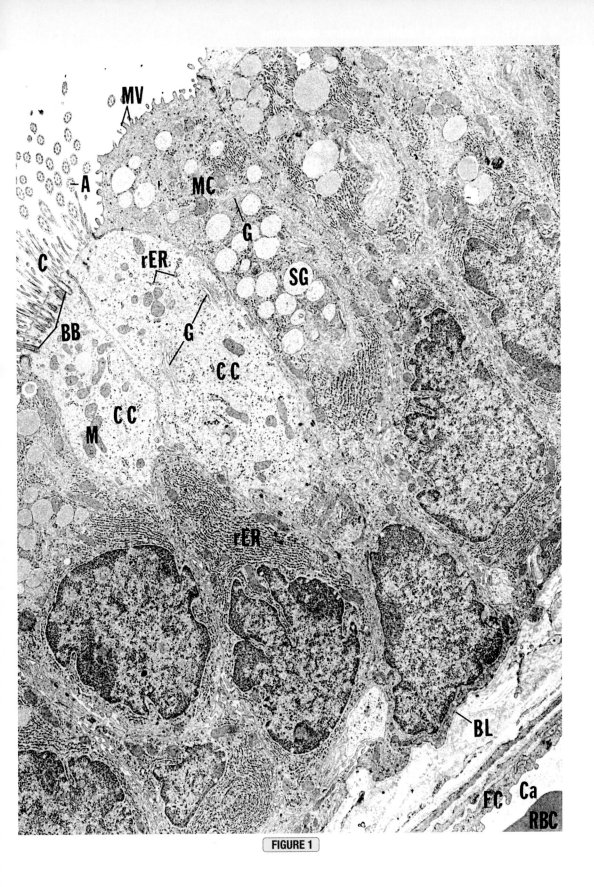

FIGURE 1

EPITHELIUM AND GLANDS • 43

FIGURE 1 • Epithelial junction. Human. Electron microscopy. ×27,815.

This electron micrograph represents a thin section of an intercellular canaliculus between clear cells of a human eccrine sweat gland stained with ferrocyanide-reduced osmium tetroxide. A tight junction (*arrows*) separates the lumen of the **intercellular canaliculus** (IC) from the basolateral intercellular space. Observe the **nucleus** (N). (From Briggman JV, Bank HL, Bigelow JB, Graves JS, Spicer SS. Structure of the tight junctions of the human eccrine sweat gland. Am J Anat 1981;162:357–368.)

FIGURE 2 • Epithelial junction. Zonula occludens. Human. Electron microscopy. ×83,700.

This is a freeze-fracture replica of an elaborate tight junction along an intercellular canaliculus between two clear cells. Note the smooth transition from a region of wavy, nonintersecting, densely packed junctional elements to an area of complex anastomoses. At the step fracture (*arrows*), it can be seen that the pattern of ridges on the E face corresponds to that of the grooves on the P face of the plasma membrane of the adjacent clear cell. In certain areas (*arrowheads*), several of the laterally disposed, densely packed junctional elements are separated from the luminal band. The direction of platinum shadowing is indicated by the *circled arrow*. (From Briggman JV, Bank HL, Bigelow JB, Graves JS, Spicer SS. Structure of the tight junctions of the human eccrine sweat gland. Am J Anat 1981;162:357–368.)

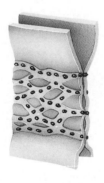

Zonulae occludentes

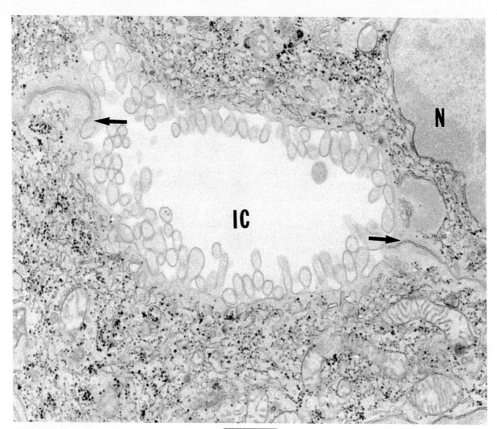

FIGURE 1

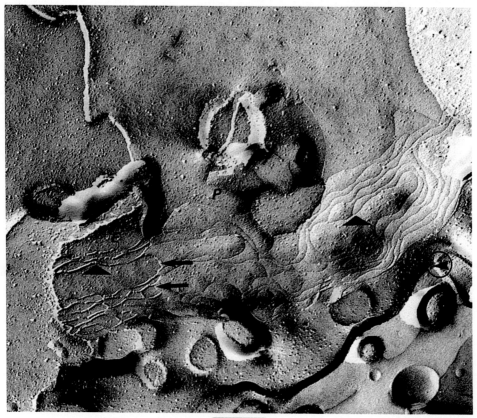

FIGURE 2

FIGURE 1 ● Goblet cells. Ileum. Monkey. Plastic section. ×270.

Goblet cells are unicellular exocrine glands that are found interspersed among simple columnar and pseudostratified columnar epithelia. This photomicrograph of an ileal villus displays numerous **goblet cells** (GC) located among the **simple columnar epithelial cells** (EC). The brush border (*arrowhead*) of the columnar cells is only scantly present on the goblet cells. The expanded apical region of the goblet cell is known as the **theca** (T) and is filled with **mucin** (m), which, when released into the lumen of the gut, coats and protects the intestinal lining. The lower right-hand corner of the simple columnar epithelium was sectioned somewhat obliquely through the nuclei of the epithelial cells, producing the appearance of a stratified epithelium (*asterisk*). Looking at the epithelium above the *double arrows*, however, it is clearly simple columnar. The occasional **round nuclei** (rN) are those of lymphocytes migrating through the epithelium into the **lumen** (L). Figure 2 is a higher magnification of the *boxed area*.

FIGURE 3 ● Sebaceous gland. Scalp. Paraffin section. ×132.

Sebaceous glands are usually associated with hair follicles. They discharge their sebum into the follicle, although in certain areas of the body they are present independent of hair follicles. These glands, surrounded by slender connective tissue **capsules** (Ca), are pear-shaped saccules with short ducts. Each saccule is filled with large, amorphous cells with nuclei in various states of degeneration (*arrows*). The periphery of the saccule is composed of small, cuboidal **basal cells** (BC), which act in a regenerative capacity. As the cells move away from the periphery of the saccule, they enlarge and increase their cytoplasmic **fat** (f) content. Near the duct, the entire cell degenerates and becomes the **secretion** (se). Therefore, sebaceous glands are classified as simple, branched, acinar glands with a holocrine mode of secretion. **Smooth muscles** (M), arrector pili, are associated with sebaceous glands. Observe the **secretory** (s) and **duct** (D) portions of a sweat gland above the sebaceous gland.

FIGURE 2 ● Goblet cells. Ileum. Monkey. Plastic section. ×540.

This photomicrograph is a higher magnification of the *boxed area* of the previous figure, demonstrating the light microscopic morphology of the goblet cell. The **mucin** (m) in the expanded **theca** (T) of the goblet cell has been partly precipitated and dissolved during the dehydration procedure. The **nucleus** (N) of the goblet cell is relatively dense due to the condensed chromatin. Between the nucleus and the theca is the **Golgi zone** (GZ), where the protein product of the cell is modified and packaged into secretory granules for delivery. The **base** (b) of the goblet cell is slender, almost as if it were "squeezed in" between neighboring columnar epithelial cells, but it touches the **basal membrane** (BM). The terminal web and brush border of the goblet cell are greatly reduced but not completely absent (*arrowheads*). The **round nuclei** (rN) belong to leucocytes migrating through the epithelium into the **lumen** (L) of the ileum.

FIGURE 4 ● Eccrine sweat glands. Skin. Paraffin section. ×270.

Eccrine sweat glands are the most numerous glands in the body, and they are extensively distributed. The glands are simple, unbranched, coiled tubular, producing a watery solution. The **secretory portion** (s) of the gland is composed of a simple cuboidal type of epithelium with two cell types, a lightly staining cell that makes up most of the secretory portion, and a darker staining cell that usually cannot be distinguished with the light microscope. Surrounding the secretory portion are **myoepithelial cells** (MC), which, with their numerous branching processes, encircle the secretory tubule and assist in expressing the fluid into the ducts. The **ducts** (D) of sweat glands are composed of a stratified cuboidal type of epithelium, whose cells are smaller than those of the secretory unit. In histologic sections, therefore, the ducts are always darker than the secretory units. The large, empty-looking spaces are **adipose** (fat) **cells** (AC). Note the numerous small blood vessels (*arrows*) in the vicinity of the sweat gland.

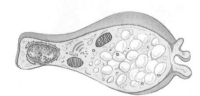

Goblet cell

KEY							
AC	adipose cell	f	fat	N	nucleus		
b	base	GC	goblet cell	rN	round nucleus		
BC	basal cell	GZ	Golgi zone	s	secretory		
BM	basal membrane	L	lumen	se	secretion		
Ca	capsule	M	smooth muscle	T	theca		
D	duct	m	mucin				
EC	simple columnar epithelial cell	MC	myoepithelial cell				

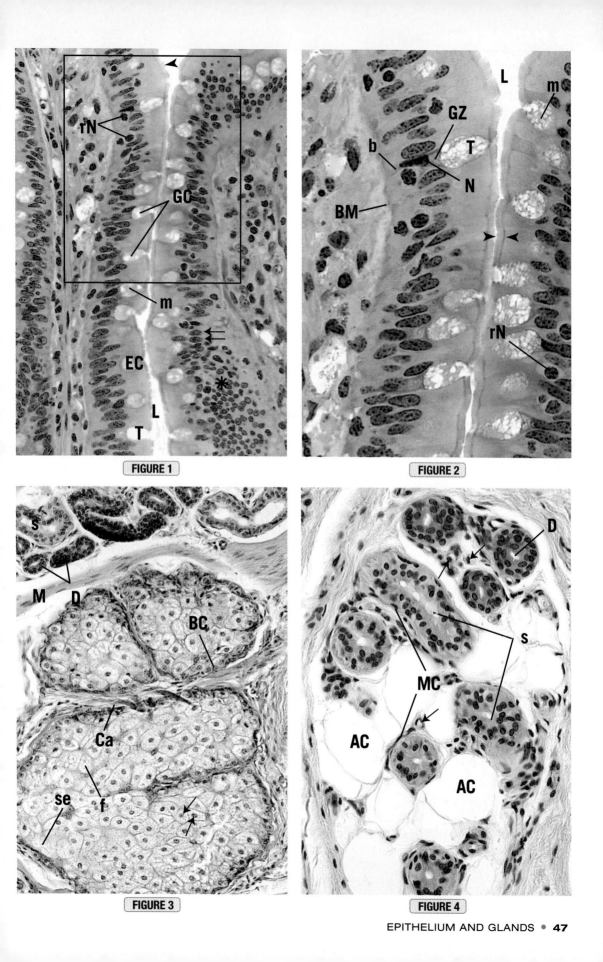

FIGURE 1

FIGURE 2

FIGURE 3

FIGURE 4

FIGURE 1 • Compound tubuloacinar (alveolar) serous gland. Pancreas. Monkey. Plastic section. ×540.

This is a photomicrograph of the exocrine portion of the pancreas, a compound tubuloacinar (alveolar) serous gland. The duct system of this gland will be studied in Chapter 15 on the Digestive System. Only its secretory cells will be considered at this point. Each acinus, when sectioned well, presents a round appearance with a small central **lumen** (L), with the secretory cells arranged like a pie cut into pieces. The **connective tissue** (CT) investing each acinus is flimsy in the pancreas. The secretory cells are more or less trapezoid-shaped, with a round, basally situated **nucleus** (N). The cytoplasm contains numerous **zymogen granules** (ZG), which are the membrane-bound digestive enzymes packaged by the Golgi apparatus.

FIGURE 3 • Compound tubuloacinar (alveolar) mixed gland. Sublingual gland. Monkey. Plastic section. ×540.

The sublingual gland is a mostly mucous, compound tubuloacinar gland that contains many mucous tubules and acini. These profiles of mucous acini are well represented in this photomicrograph. Note the open **lumen** (L) bordered by several trapezoid-shaped cells whose lateral plasma membranes are clearly evident (*double arrows*). The **nuclei** (N) of these mucous cells appear to be flattened against the basal plasma membrane and are easily distinguishable from the round nuclei of the cells of serous acini. The cytoplasm appears to possess numerous vacuole-like structures that impart a frothy appearance to the cell. The serous secretions of this gland are derived from the few serous cells that appear to cap the mucous units, known as **serous demilunes** (SD). The secretory products of the serous demilunes gain entrance to the lumen of the secretory unit via small intercellular spaces between neighboring mucous cells.

FIGURE 2 • Compound tubuloacinar (alveolar) mucous glands. Soft palate. Paraffin section. ×132.

The compound tubuloacinar glands of the palate are purely mucous and secrete a thick, viscous fluid. The secretory acini of this gland are circular in section and are surrounded by fine **connective tissue** (CT) elements. The **lumina** (L) of the mucous acini are clearly distinguishable, as are the trapezoid-shaped **parenchymal cells** (PC), which manufacture the viscous fluid. The **nuclei** (N) of the trapezoid-shaped cells are dark, dense structures that appear to be flattened against the basal cell membrane. The cytoplasm has an empty, frothy appearance, which stains a light grayish-blue with hematoxylin and eosin.

FIGURE 4 • Compound tubuloacinar (alveolar) mixed gland. Submandibular gland. Monkey. Plastic section. ×540.

The submandibular gland is a compound tubuloacinar gland that produces a mixed secretion, as does the sublingual gland of the previous figure. However, this gland contains many purely **serous acini** (SA) and very few purely mucous ones, namely because the mucous acini are capped by **serous demilunes** (SD). Also, this gland possesses an extensive system of **ducts** (D). Note that the cytoplasm of the serous cells appears to be blue when stained with hematoxylin and eosin. Also notice that the lumina of the acini are so small that they are not apparent, whereas those of mucous units (L) are obvious. Observe the difference in the cytoplasms of serous and mucus-secreting cells as well as the density of the nuclei of individual cells. Finally, note that the lateral cell membranes (*arrows*) of mucus-producing cells are clearly delineated, whereas those of the serous cells are very difficult to observe.

Salivary gland

KEY							
CT	connective tissue	N	nucleus	SD	serous demilunes
D	duct	PC	parenchymal cell	ZG	zymogen granules
L	lumen	SA	serous acini		

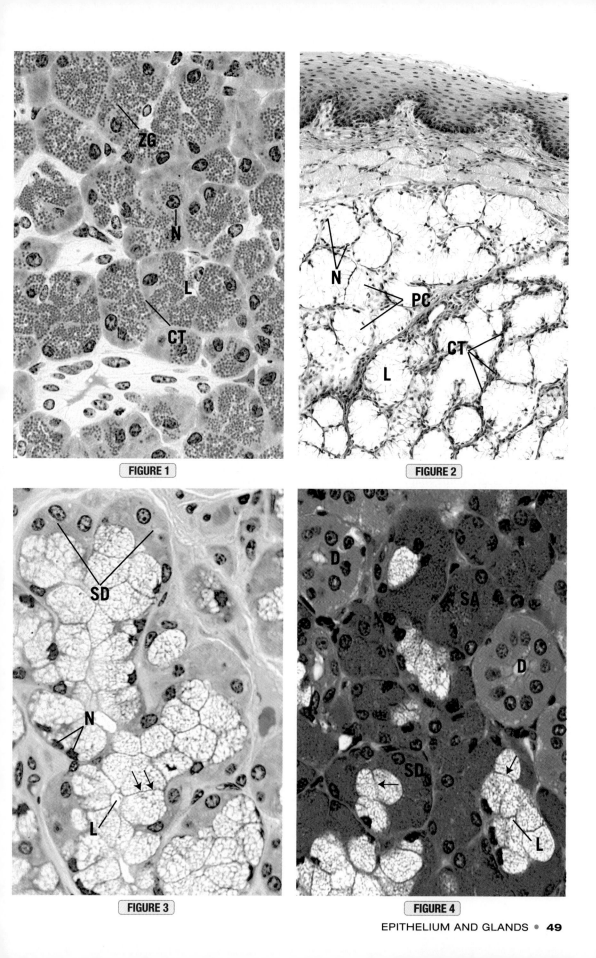

FIGURE 1

FIGURE 2

FIGURE 3

FIGURE 4

● Summary of Histological Organization

I. EPITHELIUM

A. Types

1. *Simple Squamous*—single layer of uniform flat cells.
2. *Simple Cuboidal*—single layer of uniform cuboidal cells.
3. *Simple Columnar*—single layer of uniform columnar cells.
4. *Pseudostratified Columnar*—single layer of cells of varied shapes and heights.
5. *Stratified Squamous*—several layers of cells whose superficial layers are flattened. These may be nonkeratinized, parakeratinized, or keratinized.
6. *Stratified Cuboidal*—two or more layers of cells whose superficial layers are cuboidal in shape.
7. *Stratified Columnar*—two or more layers of cells whose superficial layers are columnar in shape.
8. *Transitional*—several layers of cells, characterized by large, dome-shaped cells at the free surface, that help maintain the integrity of the epithelium during distention of the various components of the urinary tract.

B. General Characteristics

1. Free Surface Modifications
Cells may possess **microvilli** (brush border, striated border), short finger-like projections that increase the surface area of the cell; **stereocilia** (long anastomosing microvilli), which are only found in the epididymis; and **cilia**, which are long, motile projections of the cell with a 9 + 2 microtubular substructure (**axoneme**).

2. Lateral Surface Modifications
For the purposes of adhesion, the cell membranes form junctional complexes involving the lateral plasmalemma of contiguous cells. These junctions are known as **desmosomes** (maculae adherentes), **zonulae occludentes**, and **zonulae adherentes**. For the purpose of intercellular communication, the lateral cell membranes form **gap junctions (nexus, septate junctions)**.

3. Basal Surface Modifications
The basal cell membrane that lies on the basal membrane forms **hemidesmosomes** to assist the cell to adhere to the underlying connective tissue.

4. Basal Membrane
The **basal (basement) membrane** of light microscopy is composed of an epithelially derived **basal lamina** (which has two parts, **lamina densa** and **lamina lucida**) and a **lamina reticularis** derived from connective tissue, which may be absent.

II. GLANDS

A. Exocrine Glands

Exocrine glands, which deliver secretions into a system of ducts to be conveyed onto an epithelial surface, may be **unicellular** (goblet cells) or **multicellular**.

Multicellular glands may be classified according to the branching of their **duct system**. If the ducts are not branched, the gland is **simple**; if they are branched, the gland is **compound**. Moreover, the three-dimensional shape of the secretory units may be **tubular**, **acinar (alveolar)**, or a combination of the two, namely **tubuloacinar (alveolar)**. Additional criteria include 1) the **type** of secretory product produced: **serous** (parotid, pancreas), **mucous** (palatal glands), and **mixed** (sublingual, submandibular), possessing serous and mucous acini and **serous demilunes**; and 2) the **mode of secretion: merocrine** (only the secretory product is released, as in the parotid gland), **apocrine** (the secretory product is accompanied by some of the apical cytoplasm, as perhaps in mammary glands), and **holocrine** (the entire cell becomes the secretory product, as in the sebaceous gland, testes, and ovary). Glands are subdivided by connective tissue septa into lobes and lobules, and the ducts that serve them are interlobar, intralobar, interlobular, and intralobular (striated, intercalated).

Myoepithelial (basket) cells are ectodermally derived myoid cells that share the basement lamina of the glandular parenchyma. These cells possess long processes that surround secretory acini and, by occasional contraction, assist in the delivery of the secretory product into the system of ducts.

B. Endocrine Glands

Endocrine glands are ductless glands that release their secretion into the bloodstream. These glands are described in Chapter 10.

Connective Tissue

3

Connective tissues encompass the major structural constituents of the body. Although seemingly diverse, structurally and functionally they possess many shared qualities; therefore, they are considered in a single category. Most connective tissues are derived from mesoderm, which form the multipotential mesenchyme from which bone, cartilage, tendons, ligaments, capsules, blood and hematopoietic cells, and lymphoid cells develop. Functionally, connective tissues serve in support, defense, transport, storage, and repair, among others. Connective tissues, unlike epithelia, are composed mainly of **extracellular elements** with a limited number of **cells**. They are classified mostly on the basis of their nonliving components rather than on their cellular constituents. Although the precise ordering of the various subtypes differs from author to author, the following categories are generally accepted:

   A. Embryonic connective tissues
      1. Mesenchymal
      2. Mucous
   B. Adult connective tissues
      1. Connective tissue proper
         a. Loose (areolar)
         b. Reticular
         c. Adipose
         d. Dense irregular
         e. Dense regular
            (1) Collagenous
            (2) Elastic
      2. Specialized connective tissues
         a. Supporting tissues
            (1) Cartilage
            (2) Bone
         b. Blood

● EXTRACELLULAR MATRIX

The extracellular matrix of connective tissue proper may be subdivided into **fibers**, **amorphous ground substance**, and **extracellular (tissue) fluid**.

Three types of fibers are recognized histologically: collagen, reticular, and elastic. **Collagen** fibers, forming about 25% of the protein content of humans, usually occur as bundles of nonelastic fibers of varied thickness whose basic subunits, **tropocollagen molecules**, each composed of three α chains wound around each other, aggregate into specific staggered associations, producing a 67-nm banding once believed to be characteristic of this protein (see Graphic 3-1). Some collagen types, such as type IV collagen, which is present in basal laminae, do not exhibit this banding characteristic. **Reticular fibers** (once believed to have different composition) are thin, branching, carbohydrate-coated fibers composed of type III collagen that form delicate networks around smooth muscle cells, certain epithelial cells, adipocytes, nerve fibers, and blood vessels. They also constitute the structural framework of certain organs, such as the liver and the spleen. **Elastic fibers**, as their name implies, are highly elastic and may be stretched to about 150% of their resting length without breaking. They are composed of an amorphous protein, **elastin**, surrounded by a **microfibrillar** component, consisting of **fibrillin**. Elastic fibers do not display a periodicity and are found in regions of the body that require considerable flexibility and elasticity.

The **amorphous ground substance** constitutes the gel-like matrix in which the fibers and cells are embedded and through which tissue fluid diffuses. Ground substance is composed of glycosaminoglycans (GAGs), proteoglycans, and glycoproteins. The major GAGs constituents are **hyaluronic acid, chondroitin 4-sulfate, chondroitin 6-sulfate, dermatan sulfate**, and **heparan sulfate**. **Proteoglycans** are composed of a protein core to which GAGs are covalently bound. **Glycoproteins** have also been localized in connective tissue proper. These substances, especially **fibronectin**, appear to be essential in facilitating the attachment and migration of cells along connective tissue elements, such as collagen fibers.

The basement membrane, interposed between epithelia and connective tissues, is described in Chapter 2, Epithelium and Glands.

● CELLS

The following are cells of connective tissue proper—or, more accurately, loose (areolar) connective tissue (see Graphic 3-2).

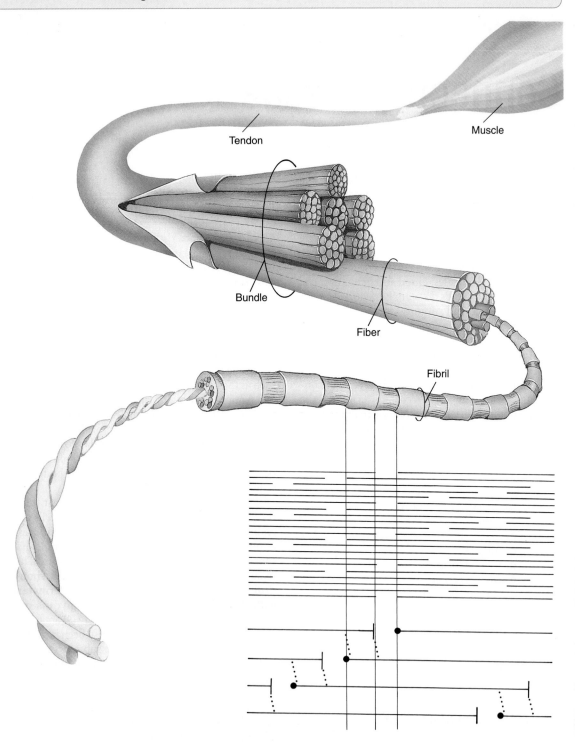

Tendon

Muscle

Bundle

Fiber

Fibril

Each collagen fiber bundle is composed of smaller fibrils, which in turn consist of aggregates of **tropocollagen molecules**. Tropocollagen molecules self-assemble in the extracellular environment in such a fashion that there is a gap between the tail of the one and the head of the succeeding molecule of a single row. As fibrils are formed, tails of tropocollagen molecules overlap the heads of tropocollagen molecules in adjacent rows. Additionally, the **gaps** and **overlaps** are arranged so that they are in register with those of neighboring (but not adjacent) rows of tropocollagen molecules. When stained with a heavy metal, such as osmium, the stain preferentially precipitates in the gap regions, resulting in the repeating **light** and **dark** banding of collagen.

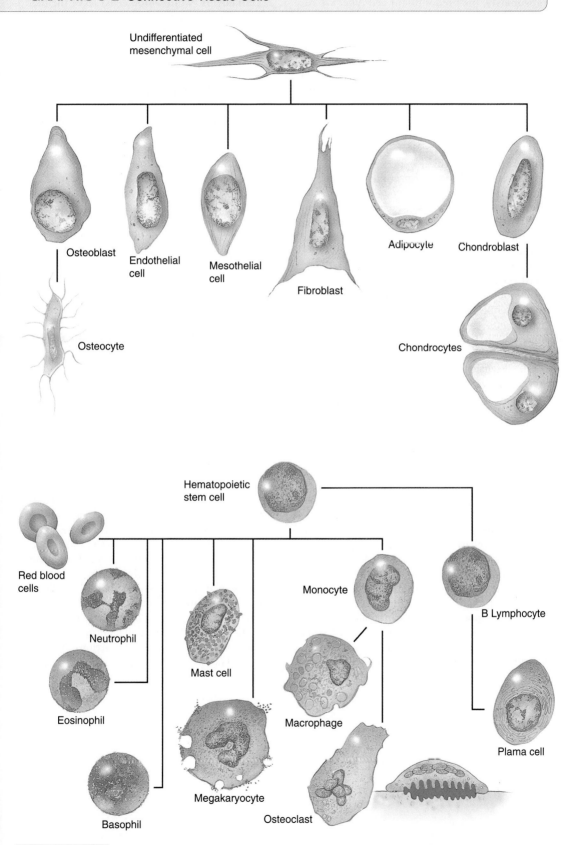

Undifferentiated mesenchymal cell

Osteoblast

Endothelial cell

Mesothelial cell

Fibroblast

Adipocyte

Chondroblast

Osteocyte

Chondrocytes

Hematopoietic stem cell

Red blood cells

Neutrophil

Eosinophil

Basophil

Mast cell

Megakaryocyte

Monocyte

Macrophage

Osteoclast

B Lymphocyte

Plama cell

* Please note that the cells are not drawn to scale.

Fibroblasts, the predominant cell type, are responsible for the **synthesis** of collagen and elastic and reticular fibers and much if not all of the ground substance. The morphology of these cells appears to be a function of their synthetic activities and therefore resting (or inactive fibroblasts) cells were often referred to as fibrocytes, a term that is rapidly disappearing from the literature.

Macrophages (**histiocytes**) are derived from monocytes in bone marrow. They migrate to the connective tissue and function in ingesting (**phagocytosing**) foreign particulate matter. These cells also participate in enhancing the immunologic activities of lymphocytes.

Plasma cells are the major cell type present during **chronic inflammation**. These cells are derived from a subpopulation of lymphocytes and are responsible for the synthesis and release of humoral antibodies.

Mast cells are usually observed in the vicinity of small blood vessels, although the relationship between them is not understood. These cells house numerous metachromatic granules containing histamine, which is a smooth muscle contractant, and heparin, which is an anticoagulant. Mast cells also release **eosinophilic chemotactic agent** and **leukotriene**. Because of the presence of immunoglobulins on the external surface of the mast cell plasmalemma, these cells, in sensitized individuals, may become degranulated (i.e., release their granules), resulting in **anaphylactic reactions** or even in life-threatening anaphylactic shock.

Pericytes are also associated with minute blood vessels, but much more closely than are mast cells, since they share the basal laminae of the endothelial cells. Pericytes are believed to be **contractile cells**, which assist in the regulation of blood flow through the capillaries. Additionally, they may also be **pluripotential cells**, which assume the responsibilities of mesenchymal cells in adult connective tissue. It is now believed that mesenchymal cells are probably not present in the adult.

Fat cells (**adipocytes**) may form small clusters or aggregates in loose connective tissue. They **store lipids** and form adipose tissue, which protects, insulates, and cushions organs of the body.

Leukocytes (white blood cells) leave the bloodstream and enter the connective tissue spaces. Here they assume various functions, which are discussed in Chapter 5.

● CONNECTIVE TISSUE TYPES

Mesenchymal and **mucous connective tissues** are limited to the embryo. The former consists of mesenchymal cells and fine reticular fibers interspersed in a semifluid matrix of ground substance. Mucous connective tissue is more viscous in consistency, contains collagen bundles and numerous fibroblasts, and is found deep to the fetal skin and in the umbilical cord (where it is known as Wharton's jelly), surrounding the umbilical vessels.

Loose (areolar) connective tissue is distributed widely, since it constitutes much of the superficial fascia and invests neurovascular bundles. The cells and intercellular elements described above help form this more or less amorphous, watery tissue.

Reticular connective tissue forms a network of thin reticular fibers that constitute the structural framework of bone marrow and many lymphoid structures as well as a framework enveloping certain cells.

Adipose tissue is composed of fat cells, reticular fibers, and a rich vascular supply. It acts as a depot for fat, a thermal insulator, and a shock absorber.

Dense irregular connective tissue consists of coarse, almost haphazardly arranged bundles of collagen fibers interlaced with few elastic and reticular fibers. The chief cellular constituents are fibroblasts, macrophages, and occasional mast cells. The dermis of the skin and capsules of some organs are composed of dense irregular connective tissue.

Dense regular connective tissue may be composed either of thick, parallel arrays of collagenous fibers, as in tendons and ligaments, or of parallel bundles of elastic fibers, as in the ligamentum nuchae, the ligamentum flava, and the suspensory ligament of the penis. The cellular constituents of both dense regular collagenous and elastic connective tissues are almost strictly limited to fibroblasts.

Histophysiology

I. EXTRACELLULAR MATRIX

A. Ground Substance

Ground substance is composed of GAGs, proteoglycans, and glycoproteins. **Glycosaminoglycans** are linear polymers of repeating disaccharides, one of which is always a **hexosamine**, whereas the other is a **hexuronic acid**. All of the GAGs, with the exception of **hyaluronic acid**, are sulfated and thus possess a predominantly **negative charge**.

Most GAGs are linked to protein cores, forming huge **proteoglycan** molecules. Many of these proteoglycan molecules are also linked to hyaluronic acid, forming massive molecules, such as **aggregans aggregate**, of enormous electrochemical **domains** that attract osmotically active cations (e.g., Na^+), forming hydrated molecules that provide a gel-like consistency to connective tissue proper and function in resisting compression and slowing down the flow of extracellular fluid, thus permitting more time for the exchange of materials by the cells and retarding the spread of invading microorganisms. The sulfated GAGs include chondroitin sulfate, dermatan sulfate, heparan sulfate, heparin, and keratan sulfate. **Glycoproteins** are large polypeptide molecules with attendant carbohydrate side chains. The best characterized are laminin, fibronectin, chondronectin, osteonectin, entactin, and tenascin. Laminin and entactin are derived from epithelial cells, and tenascin is made by glial cells of the embryo, whereas the remainder are manufactured by cells of connective tissue. Many cells possess **integrins**, transmembrane proteins, with receptor sites for one or more of these glycoproteins. Moreover, glycoproteins also bind to collagen, thus facilitating cell adherence to the extracellular matrix.

B. Fibers

1. Collagen

Collagen, the most abundant of the fibers, is inelastic and is composed of a staggered array of the protein **tropocollagen**, composed of three α chains. Interestingly, every third amino acid is **glycine**, and a significant amount of **proline, hydroxyproline, lysine**, and **hydroxylysine** constitute much of the tropocollagen subunit. Since glycine is a very small amino acid, the three α chains can form a tight helix as they wrap around each other. The hydrogen bonds of hydroxyproline residues of individual α chains hold the three chains together to maintain the stability of the tropocollagen molecule; hydroxylysine residues hold the tropocollagen molecules to each other to form collagen fibrils.

Currently, there are at least 25 different types of collagens that are known, depending on the amino acid composition of their α chains. The most common collagens are type I (dermis, bone, capsules of organs, fibrocartilage, dentin, and cementum), type II (hyaline and elastic cartilages), type III (reticular fibers), type IV (lamina densa of the basal lamina), type V (placenta), and type VII (anchoring fibrils of the basal lamina). With the exception of type IV, all collagen fibers display a **67-nm periodicity** as the result of the specific arrangement of the tropocollagen molecules.

a. Collagen Synthesis

Synthesis of collagen occurs on the rough endoplasmic reticulum, where polysomes possess different mRNAs coding for the three **α chains** (**preprocollagens**). Within the rough endoplasmic reticulum (RER) cisternae, specific proline and lysine residues are **hydroxylated**, and hydroxylysine residues are **glycosylated**. Each α chain possesses **propeptides** (**telopeptides**) located at both amino and carboxyl ends. These propeptides are responsible for the precise **alignment** of the α chains, resulting in the formation of the **triple helical procollagen** molecule.

Coatomer-coated transfer vesicles convey the procollagen molecules to the **Golgi apparatus** for modification, mostly the addition of carbohydrate side chains. Subsequent to transfer to the *trans*-Golgi network, the **procollagen** molecule is exocytosed (via non–clathrin-coated vesicles), and the propeptides are cleaved by the enzyme **procollagen peptidase**, resulting in the formation of tropocollagen.

Tropocollagen molecules self-assemble, forming fibrils with 67-nm characteristic banding. Type IV collagen is composed of procollagen rather than tropocollagen subunits, hence the absence of periodicity and fibril formation in this type of collagen.

b. Reticular Fibers

Reticular fibers (type III collagen) are thinner than type I collagen and possess a higher content of carbohydrate moieties than do the remaining collagen types. As a result, when stained with silver stain, the silver preferentially deposits on these fibers, giving them a brown to black appearance in the light microscope.

2. Elastic Fibers

Elastic fibers may be stretched up to 150% of their resting length before breaking. The elasticity of elastin is due to its lysine content in that four lysine molecules, each belonging to a different elastin chain, form covalent **desmosine crosslinks** with one another. These links are highly deformable and can stretch as tensile forces are applied to them. Once the tensile force ceases, the elastic fibers return to their resting length.

C. Extracellular Fluid

Extracellular fluid (tissue fluid) is the fluid component of blood, similar to plasma, that percolates throughout the ground substance, carrying nutrients, oxygen, and other blood-borne materials to cells and carbon dioxide and waste products from cells. Extracellular fluid leaves the vascular supply at the arterial end of the capillaries and returns into the circulatory system at the venous end of capillaries, the venules, and the excess fluid enters lymphatic capillaries.

II. ADIPOSE TISSUE

There are two types of adipose tissue, white (unilocular) and brown (multilocular).

A. Unilocular Adipose Tissue

Cells of **unilocular adipose tissue** store triglycerides in a single, large fat droplet that occupies most of the cell. Fat cells of adipose tissue make the enzyme **lipoprotein lipase**, which is transported to the luminal surface of the capillary endothelial cell membrane, where it hydrolyzes chylomicrons and very low density lipoproteins. The fatty acids and monoglycerides are transported to the adipocytes, diffuse into their cytoplasm, and are reesterified into triglycerides. **Hormone-sensitive lipase**, activated by **cAMP**, hydrolyzes the stored lipids into fatty acids and glycerol, which are released from the cell as the need arises, to enter the capillaries for distribution to the remainder of the body.

B. Multilocular Adipose Tissue

Multilocular adipose cells are rare in the adult human. They are present in the neonate as well as in animals that hibernate. These cells possess numerous droplets of lipid in their cytoplasm and a rich supply of mitochondria. These mitochondria are capable of uncoupling oxidation from phosphorylation, and instead of producing ATP, they release heat, thus arousing the animal from hibernation.

CLINICAL CONSIDERATIONS

Keloid Formation
Surgical wounds are repaired by the body first with weak type III collagen that is later replaced by type I collagen, which is much stronger. Some individuals, especially African-Americans, form an overabundance of collagen in the healing process, thus developing elevated scars called keloids.

Scurvy
Scurvy, a condition characterized by bleeding gums and loose teeth among other symptoms, results from a vitamin C deficiency. Vitamin C is necessary for hydroxylation of proline for proper tropocollagen formation, giving rise to fibrils necessary for maintaining teeth in their bony sockets.

Marfan's Syndrome
Patients with Marfan's syndrome, a genetic defect in chromosome 15 that codes for fibrillin, possess undeveloped elastic fibers in their body and are predisposed to rupture of the aorta.

Edema
The release of histamine and leukotrienes from mast cells during an inflammatory response elicits increased capillary permeability, resulting in an excess accumulation of tissue fluid and thus gross swelling (edema).

Obesity
There are two types of obesity—hypertrophic obesity, which occurs when adipose cells increase in size from storing fat (adult onset), and hyperplastic obesity, which is characterized by an increase in the number of adipose cells resulting from overfeeding a newborn for a few weeks after birth. This type of obesity is usually life-long.

Systemic Lupus Erythematosus
Systemic lupus erythematosus is an autoimmune connective tissue disease that results in the inflammation in the connective tissue elements of certain organs as well as of tendons and joints. The symptoms depend on the type and number of antibodies present and can be anywhere from mild to severe and, due to the variety of symptoms, lupus may resemble other conditions such as growing pains, arthritis, epilepsy, and even psychologic diseases. The characteristic symptoms include facial and skin rash, sores in the oral cavity, joint pains and inflammation, kidney malfunction, neurologic conditions, anemia, thrombocytopenia, and fluid on the lungs. For mild cases, the usual choice of treatment is nonsteroidal anti-inflammatory drugs, whereas in severe cases, steroids and immunosuppressants are administered initially.

FIGURE 1 • Loose (areolar) connective tissue. Paraffin section. ×132.

This photomicrograph depicts a whole mount of mesentery, through its entire thickness. The two large **mast cells** (MC) are easily identified, since they are the largest cells in the field and possess a granular cytoplasm. Although their cytoplasms are not visible, it is still possible to recognize two other cell types due to their nuclear morphology. **Fibroblasts** (F) possess oval nuclei that are paler and larger than the nuclei of **macrophages** (M). The semifluid **ground substance** (GS) through which tissue fluid percolates is invisible, since it was extracted during the preparation of the tissues. However, two types of fibers, the thicker, wavy, ribbon-like, interlacing **collagen fibers** (CF) and the thin, straight, branching **elastic fibers** (EF), are well demonstrated.

FIGURE 3 • Mucous connective tissue. Umbilical cord. Human. Paraffin section. ×132.

This example of mucous connective tissue (Wharton's jelly) was derived from the umbilical cord of a fetus. Observe the obvious differences between the two embryonic tissues. The matrix of mesenchymal connective tissue (Fig. 2) contains no collagenous fibers, whereas this connective tissue displays a loose network of haphazardly arranged **collagen fibers** (CF). The cells are no longer mesenchymal cells; instead, they are **fibroblasts** (F), although morphologically they resemble each other. The empty-looking spaces (*arrows*) are areas where the ground substance was extracted during specimen preparation. *Inset.* **Fibroblast. Umbilical cord. Human. Paraffin section. × 270**. Note the centrally placed **nucleus** (N) and the fusiform shape of the **cytoplasm** (c) of this fibroblast.

FIGURE 2 • Mesenchymal connective tissue. Fetal pig. Paraffin section. ×540.

Mesenchymal connective tissue of the fetus is very immature and cellular. The **mesenchymal cells** (MeC) are stellate-shaped to fusiform cells, whose **cytoplasm** (c) can be distinguished from the surrounding matrix. The **nuclei** (N) are pale and centrally located. The ground substance is semifluid in consistency and contains slender reticular fibers. The vascularity of this tissue is evidenced by the presence of **blood vessels** (BV).

FIGURE 4 • Reticular connective tissue. Silver stain. Paraffin section. ×270.

Silver stain, used in the preparation of this specimen, was deposited on the carbohydrate coating of the **reticular fibers** (RF). Note that these fibers are thin, long, branching structures that ramify throughout the field. Note that in this photomicrograph of a lymph node, the reticular fibers in the lower right-hand corner are oriented in a circular fashion. These form the structural framework of a cortical **lymphatic nodule** (LN). The small round cells are probably **lymphoid cells** (LC), whereas the larger cells, closely associated with the reticular fibers, may be **reticular cells** (RC), although definite identification is not possible with this stain. It should be noted that reticular connective tissue is characteristically associated with lymphatic tissue.

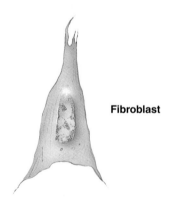

Fibroblast

KEY					
BV	blood vessel	GS	ground substance	MeC	mesenchymal cell
C	cytoplasm	LC	lymphoid cell	N	nucleus
CF	collagen fiber	LN	lymphatic nodule	RC	reticular cell
EF	elastic fiber	M	macrophage	RF	reticular fiber
F	fibroblast	MC	mast cell		

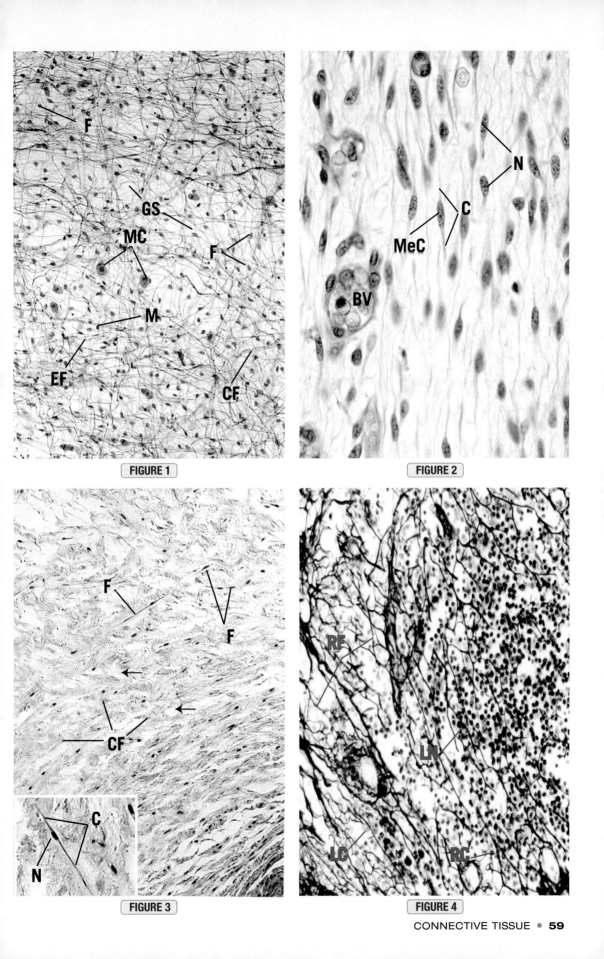

FIGURE 1

FIGURE 2

FIGURE 3

FIGURE 4

FIGURE 1 ● Adipose tissue. Hypodermis. Monkey. Plastic section. ×132.

This photomicrograph of adipose tissue is from monkey hypodermis. The **adipocytes** (A), or fat cells, appear empty due to tissue processing that dissolves fatty material. The **cytoplasm** (c) of these cells appears as a peripheral rim, and the **nucleus** (N) is also pressed to the side by the single, large **fat droplet** (FD) within the cytoplasm. Fat is subdivided into lobules by **septa** (S) of connective tissue conducting **vascular elements** (BV) to the adipocytes. Fibroblast nuclei (*arrows*) are clearly evident in the connective tissue septa. Note the presence of the secretory portions of a **sweat gland** (SG) in the upper aspect of this photomicrograph.

FIGURE 3 ● Dense regular collagenous connective tissue. l.s. Tendon. Monkey. Plastic section. ×270.

Tendons and ligaments present the most vivid examples of dense regular collagenous connective tissue. This connective tissue type is composed of regularly oriented parallel **bundles of collagen fibers** (CF), where individual bundles are demarcated by parallel rows of **fibroblasts** (F). Nuclei of these cells are clearly evident as thin, dark lines, whereas their **cytoplasm** (c) is only somewhat discernible. With hematoxylin and eosin, the collagen bundles stain a more or less light shade of pink with parallel rows of dark blue nuclei of fibroblasts interspersed among them.

FIGURE 2 ● Dense irregular collagenous connective tissue. Palmar skin. Monkey. Plastic section. ×132.

The dermis of the skin provides a good representation of dense irregular collagenous connective tissue. The thick, coarse, intertwined bundles of **collagen fibers** (CF) are arranged in a haphazard fashion. Although this tissue has numerous **blood vessels** (BV) and **nerve fibers** (NF) branching through it, it is not a very vascular tissue. Dense irregular connective tissue is only sparsely supplied with cells, mostly fibroblasts and macrophages, whose **nuclei** (N) appear as dark dots scattered throughout the field. At this magnification, it is not possible to identify the cell types with any degree of accuracy. The large epithelial structure in the upper center of the field is the **duct** (d) of a sweat gland. At higher magnification (*Inset*, × 540), the coarse bundles of collagen fibers are composed of a conglomeration of **collagen fibrils** (Cf) intertwined around each other. The three cells, whose **nuclei** (N) are clearly evident, cannot be identified with any degree of certainty, even though the **cytoplasm** (c) of the two on the left-hand side is visible. It is possible that they are macrophages, but without employing special staining techniques, the possibility of their being fibroblasts cannot be ruled out.

FIGURE 4 ● Dense regular collagenous connective tissue. x.s. Tendon. Paraffin section. ×270.

Transverse sections of tendon present a typical appearance. Tendon is organized into fascicles that are separated from each other by the **peritendineum** (P) surrounding each fascicle. **Blood vessels** (BV) may be observed in the peritendineum. Collagen bundles within the fascicles are regularly arranged; however, shrinkage due to preparation causes an artifactual layering (*arrows*), although in some preparations swelling of the tissue results in a homogenous appearance. The nuclei of **fibroblasts** (F) appear to be strewn about in a haphazard manner.

Adipocyte

KEY					
A	adipocyte	d	duct	NF	nerve fiber
BV	blood vessel	F	fibroblast	P	peritendineum
C	cytoplasm	FD	fat droplet	S	septum
Cf	collagen fibril	N	nucleus	SG	sweat gland
CF	bundle of collagen fibers				

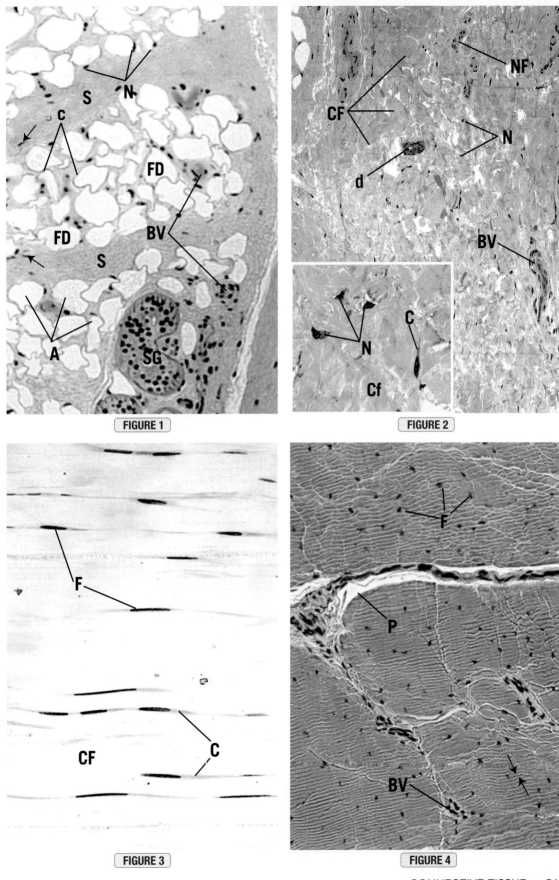

FIGURE 1

FIGURE 2

FIGURE 3

FIGURE 4

FIGURE 1 ● Dense regular elastic connective tissue. l.s. Paraffin section. ×132.

This longitudinal section of dense regular elastic tissue demonstrates that the **elastic fibers** (EF) are arranged in parallel arrays. However, the fibers are short and are curled at their ends (*arrows*). The white spaces among the fibers represent the loose connective tissue elements that remain unstained. The cellular elements are composed of parallel rows of flattened fibroblasts. These cells are also unstained and cannot be distinguished in this preparation.

FIGURE 3 ● Elastic laminae (membranes). Aorta. Paraffin section. ×132.

The wall of the aorta is composed of thick, concentrically arranged **elastic membranes** (EM). Since these sheetlike membranes wrap around within the wall of the aorta, in transverse sections they present discontinuous, concentric circles, which in this photomicrograph are represented by more or less parallel, wavy, dark lines (*arrows*). The connective tissue material between membranes is composed of ground substance, **collagen fibers** (CF), and reticular fibers. Also present are fibroblasts and smooth muscle cells, whose nuclei may be discerned.

FIGURE 2 ● Dense regular elastic connective tissue. x.s. Paraffin section. ×132.

A transverse section of dense regular elastic connective tissue displays a characteristic appearance. In some areas the fibers present precise cross-sectional profiles as dark dots of various diameters (*arrows*). Other areas present oblique sections of these fibers, represented by short linear profiles (*arrowhead*). As in the previous figure, the white spaces represent the unstained loose connective tissue elements. The large clear area (*middle left*) is also composed of loose connective tissue surrounding **blood vessels** (BV).

FIGURE 4 ● Mast cells, plasma cells, macrophages.

Mast cells (MC) are conspicuous components of connective tissue proper, **Figure 4a** (Tendon. Monkey. Plastic section. × 540), although they are only infrequently encountered. Note the round to oval nucleus and numerous small granules in the cytoplasm. Observe also, among the bundles of **collagen fibers** (CF), the nuclei of several fibroblasts. **Mast cells** are very common components of the subepithelial connective tissue (lamina propria) of the digestive tract, **Figure 4b** (Jejunum. Monkey. Plastic section. × 540). Note the **basal membrane** (BM) separating the connective tissue from the **simple columnar epithelium** (E), whose nuclei are oval in shape. The denser, more amorphous nuclei (*arrows*) belong to lymphoid cells, migrating from the connective tissue into the intestinal lumen. The lamina propria also houses numerous **plasma cells** (PC), as evidenced in **Figure 4c** (Jejunum. Monkey. Plastic section. × 540). Plasma cells are characterized by clockface ("cartwheel") nuclei, as well as by a clear paranuclear Golgi zone (*arrowhead*). **Figure 4d** (Macrophage. Liver, injected. Paraffin section. × 270) is a photomicrograph of liver that was injected with india ink. This material is preferentially phagocytosed by macrophages of the liver, known as **Kupffer cells** (KC). These cells appear as dense, black structures in the liver sinusoids; vascular channels are represented by clear areas (*arrow*). An individual Kupffer cell (*Inset*. Paraffin section. × 540) displays the **nucleus** (N) as well as the granules of india ink (*arrowhead*) in its cytoplasm.

 Mast cell

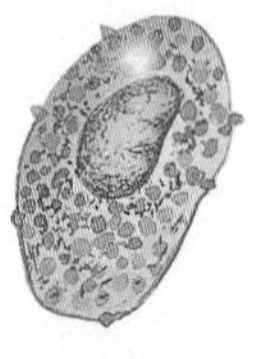

 Plasma cell

KEY							
BM	basal membrane	EF	elastic fiber	KC	Kupffer cell
BV	blood vessel	EM	elastic membrane	N	nucleus
CF	collagen fiber	MC	mast cell	PC	plasma cell

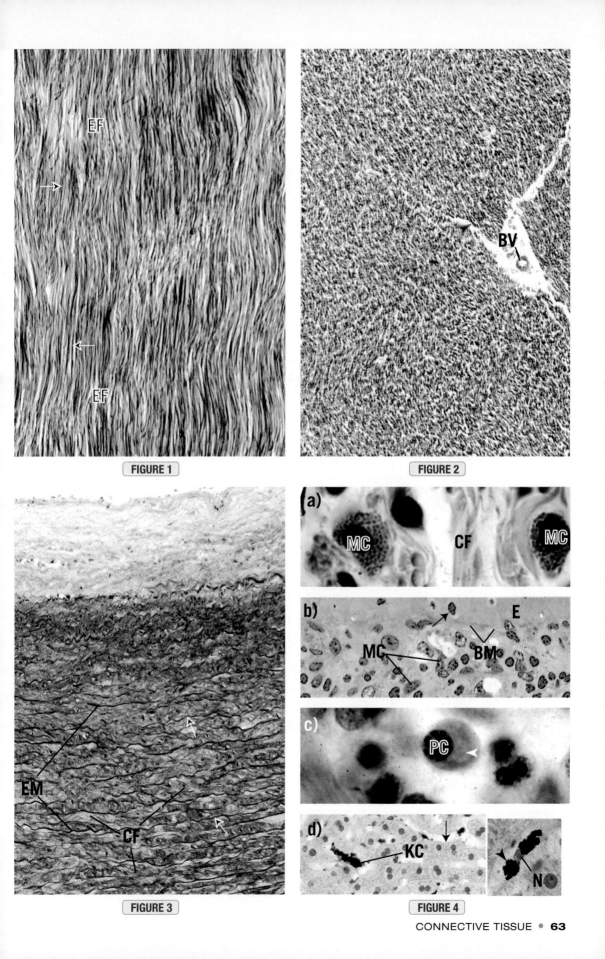

FIGURE 1

FIGURE 2

FIGURE 3

FIGURE 4

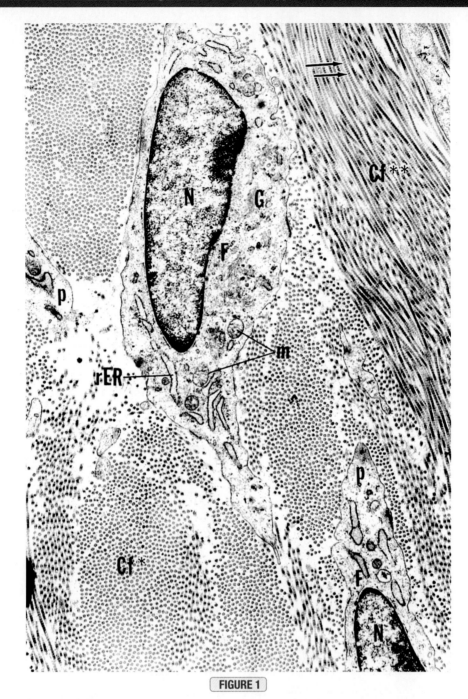

FIGURE 1

FIGURE 1 • Fibroblast. Baboon. Electron microscopy. ×11,070.

This electron micrograph of **fibroblasts** (F) demonstrates that they are long, fusiform cells whose **processes** (p) extend into the surrounding area, between bundles of collagen fibrils. These cells manufacture collagen, reticular and elastic fibers, and the ground substance of connective tissue. Therefore, they are rich in organelles, such as **Golgi apparatus** (G), **rough endoplasmic reticulum** (rER), and **mitochondria** (m); however, in the quiescent stage, as in tendons, where they no longer actively synthesize the intercellular elements of connective tissue, the organelle population of fibroblasts is reduced in number, and the plump, euchromatic **nucleus** (N) becomes flattened and heterochromatic. Note that the bundles of **collagen fibrils** (Cf) are sectioned both transversely (*asterisk*) and longitudinally (*double asterisks*). Individual fibrils display alternating transverse dark and light banding (*arrows*) along their length. The specific banding results from the ordered arrangement of the tropocollagen molecules constituting the collagen fibrils. (From Simpson D, Avery B. J Periodontol 1974;45:500–510.)

PLATE 3-5 Mast Cell, Electron Microscopy

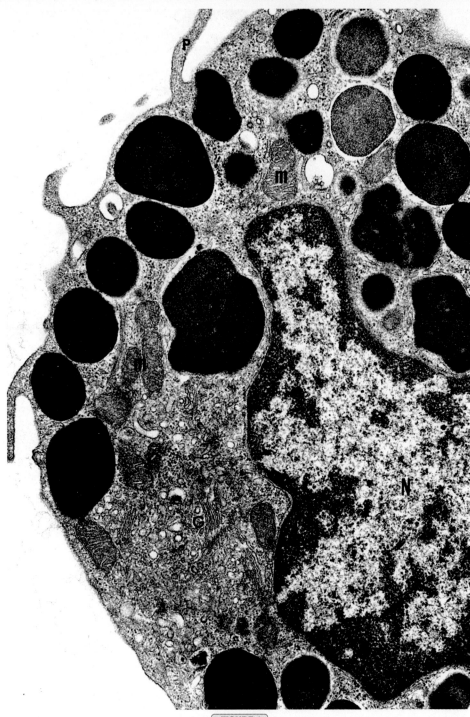

FIGURE 1

FIGURE 1 • Mast cell. Rat. Electron microscopy. ×14,400.

This electron micrograph of a rat peritoneal mast cell displays characteristics of this cell. Note that the **nucleus** (N) is not lobulated, and the cell contains organelles, such as **mitochondria** (m) and **Golgi apparatus** (G). Numerous **processes** (p) extend from the cell. Observe that the most characteristic component of this cell is that it is filled with numerous membrane-bound **granules** (Gr) of more or less uniform density. These granules contain heparin, histamine, and serotonin (although human mast cells do not contain serotonin). Additionally, mast cells release a number of unstored substances that act in allergic reactions. (From Lagunoff D. Contributions of electron microscopy to the study of mast cells. J Invest Dermatol 1972;58:296–311.)

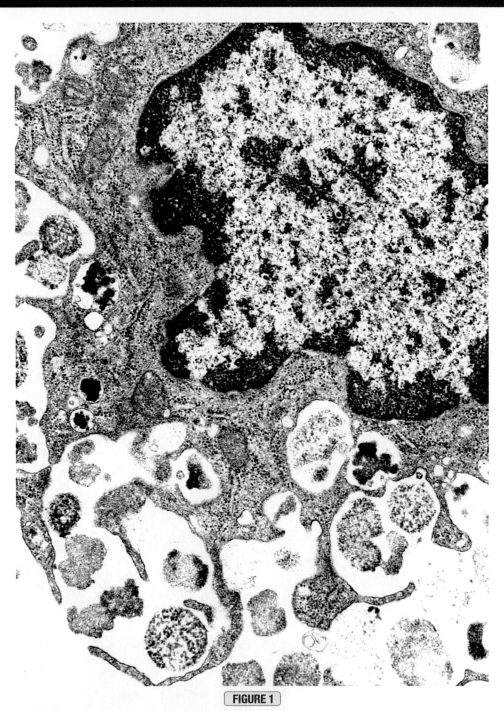

FIGURE 1

FIGURE 1 • Mast cell degranulation. Rat. Electron microscopy. ×20,250.

Mast cells possess receptor molecules on their plasma membrane, which are specific for the constant region of IgE antibody molecules. These molecules attach to the mast cell surface and, as the cell comes in contact with those specific antigens to which it was sensitized, the antigen binds with the active regions of the IgE antibody. Such antibody-antigen binding on the mast cell surface causes degranulation, i.e., the release of granules, as well as the release of the unstored substances that act in allergic reactions. Degranulation occurs very quickly but requires both ATP and calcium. Granules at the periphery of the cell are released by fusion with the cell membrane, whereas granules deeper in the cytoplasm fuse with each other, forming convoluted intracellular canaliculi that connect to the extracellular space. Such a canaliculus may be noted in the bottom left-hand corner of this electron micrograph. (From Lagunoff D. Contributions of electron microscopy to the study of mast cells. J Invest Dermatol 1972;58:296–311.)

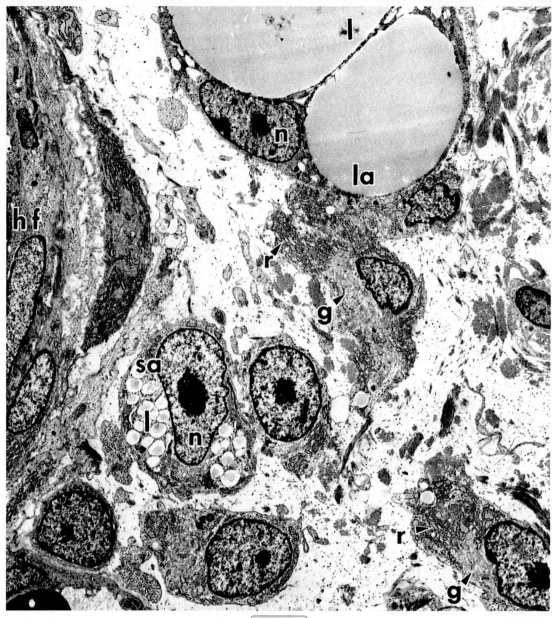

FIGURE 1

FIGURE 1 • Developing fat cell. Rat. Electron microscopy.
×3060.

This electron micrograph from the developing rat hypodermis displays a region of the developing **hair follicle** (hf). The peripheral aspect of the hair follicle presents a **small adipocyte** (sa) whose **nucleus** (n) and nucleolus are clearly visible. Although white adipose cells are unilocular, in that the cytoplasm of the cell contains a single, large droplet of lipid, during development lipid begins to accumulate as small **droplets** (l) in the cytoplasm of the small adipocyte. As the fat cell matures to become a **large adipocyte** (la), its **nucleus** (n) is displaced peripherally, and the lipid **droplets** (l) fuse to form several large droplets, which will eventually

coalesce to form a single, central fat deposit. The nucleus displays some alterations during the transformation from small to large adipocytes, in that the nucleolus becomes smaller and less prominent. Immature adipocytes are distinguishable, since they possess a well-developed **Golgi apparatus** (g) that is actively functioning in the biosynthesis of lipids. Moreover, the **rough endoplasmic reticulum** (r) presents dilated cisternae, indicative of protein synthetic activity. Note the capillary, whose lumen displays a red blood cell in the lower left-hand corner of this photomicrograph. (From Hausman G, Campion D, Richardson R, Martin R. Adipocyte development in the rat hypodermis. Am J Anat 1981;161:85–100.)

Summary of Histological Organization

I. EMBRYONIC CONNECTIVE TISSUE

A. Mesenchymal Connective Tissue

1. Cells
Stellate to spindle-shaped **mesenchymal cells** have processes that touch one another. Pale, scanty cytoplasm with large clear nuclei. Indistinct cell membrane.

2. Extracellular Materials
Delicate, empty-looking matrix, containing fine **reticular fibers**. Small blood vessels are evident.

B. Mucous Connective Tissue

1. Cells
Fibroblasts, with their numerous flattened processes and oval nuclei, constitute the major cellular component. In section, these cells frequently appear spindle-shaped and resemble or are identical to mesenchymal cells when viewed with a light microscope.

2. Extracellular Materials
When compared with mesenchymal connective tissue, the intercellular space is filled with coarse **collagen bundles**, irregularly arranged, in a matrix of precipitated jelly-like material.

II. CONNECTIVE TISSUE PROPER

A. Loose (Areolar) Connective Tissue

1. Cells
The most common cell types are **fibroblasts**, whose spindle-shaped morphology closely resembles the next most numerous cells, the **macrophages**. The oval nuclei of macrophages are smaller, darker, and denser than those of fibroblasts. **Mast cells**, located in the vicinity of blood vessels, may be recognized by their size, the numerous small granules in their cytoplasm, and their large, round, centrally located nuclei. Occasional **fat cells** resembling round, empty spaces bordered by a thin rim of cytoplasm may also be present. When sectioned through its peripherally squeezed, flattened nucleus, a fat cell has a ringlike appearance.

Additionally, in certain regions such as the subepithelial connective tissue (lamina propria) of the intestines, plasma cells and leukocytes are commonly found. **Plasma cells** are small, round cells with round, acentric nuclei, whose chromatin network presents a clockface (cartwheel) appearance. These cells also display a clear, paranuclear Golgi zone. **Lymphocytes**, **neutrophils**, and occasional **eosinophils** also contribute to the cellularity of loose connective tissue.

2. Extracellular Materials
Slender bundles of long, ribbon-like bands of **collagen fibers** are intertwined by numerous thin, straight, long, branching **elastic fibers** embedded in a watery matrix of **ground substance**, most of which is extracted by dehydration procedures during preparation. **Reticular fibers**, also present, are usually not visible in sections stained with hematoxylin and eosin.

B. Reticular Connective Tissue

1. Cells
Reticular cells are found only in reticular connective tissue. They are stellate in shape and envelop the reticular fibers, which they also manufacture. They possess large, oval, pale nuclei, and their cytoplasm is not easily visible with the light microscope. The other cells in the interstitial spaces are **lymphocytes**, **macrophages,** and other **lymphoid cells**.

2. Extracellular Materials
Reticular fibers constitute the major portion of the intercellular matrix. With the use of a silver stain, they are evident as dark, thin, branching fibers.

C. Adipose Tissue

1. Cells
Unlike other connective tissues, adipose tissue is composed of adipose cells so closely packed together that the normal spherical morphology of these cells becomes distorted. Groups of fat cells are subdivided into lobules by thin sheaths of loose connective tissue septa housing **mast cells, endothelial cells** of blood vessels, and other components of **neurovascular elements.**

2. Extracellular Materials
Each fat cell is invested by **reticular fibers**, which, in turn, are anchored to the **collagen fibers** of the connective tissue septa.

D. Dense Irregular Connective Tissue

1. Cells
Fibroblasts, **macrophages**, and cells associated with **neurovascular bundles** constitute the chief cellular elements.

2. Extracellular Materials
Haphazardly oriented thick, wavy bundles of **collagen fibers**, as well as occasional **elastic** and **reticular fibers**, are found in dense irregular connective tissue.

E. Dense Regular Collagenous Connective Tissue

1. Cells
Parallel rows of flattened **fibroblasts** are essentially the only cells found here. Even these are few in number.

2. Extracellular Materials
Parallel fibers of densely packed **collagen** are regularly arranged in dense regular collagenous connective tissue.

F. Dense Regular Elastic Connective Tissue

1. Cells
Parallel rows of flattened fibroblasts are usually difficult to distinguish in preparations that use stains specific for elastic fibers.

2. Extracellular Materials
Parallel bundles of thick **elastic fibers,** surrounded by slender elements of loose connective tissue, comprise the intercellular components of dense regular elastic connective tissue.

Cartilage and Bone

Cartilage and bone form the supporting tissues of the body. In these specialized connective tissues, as in other connective tissues, the extracellular elements dominate their microscopic appearance.

● CARTILAGE

Cartilage forms the supporting framework of certain organs, the articulating surfaces of bones, and the greater part of the fetal skeleton, although most of that will be replaced by bone (see Graphic 4-2).

There are three types of cartilage in the body, namely, hyaline cartilage, elastic cartilage, and fibrocartilage. **Hyaline cartilage** is present at the articulating surfaces of most bones; the C rings of the trachea; and the laryngeal, costal, and nasal cartilages, among others. **Elastic cartilage**, as its name implies, possesses a great deal of elasticity, which is due to the elastic fibers embedded in its matrix. This cartilage is located in areas such as the epiglottis, external ear and ear canal, and some of the smaller laryngeal cartilages. **Fibrocartilage** is present in only a few places, namely, in some symphyses, the eustachian tube, intervertebral (and some articular) disks, and certain areas where tendons insert into bone (Table 4-1).

Cartilage is a nonvascular, strong, and somewhat pliable structure composed of a firm matrix of **proteoglycans** whose main **glycosaminoglycans** are hyaluronic acid, chondroitin-4-sulfate and chondroitin-6-sulfate. The fibrous and cellular components of cartilage are embedded in this matrix. The fibers are either solely collagenous or a combination of elastic and collagenous, depending on the cartilage type. The cellular components are the **chondrocytes**, which are housed in small spaces known as **lacunae**, interspersed within the matrix, as well as **chondroblasts** and **chondrogenic cells**, both of which are located in the **perichondrium**.

Most cartilage is surrounded by a dense irregular collagenous connective tissue membrane, the perichondrium, which has an outer fibrous layer and an inner chondrogenic layer. The **fibrous layer**, although poor in cells, is composed mostly of fibroblasts and collagen fibers. The inner cellular or chondrogenic layer is composed of chondroblasts and chondrogenic cells. The latter give rise to chondroblasts, cells that are responsible for secreting the **cartilage matrix**. It is from this layer that the cartilage may grow **appositionally**.

As the chondroblasts secrete matrix and fibers around themselves, they become incarcerated in their own secretions and are then termed chondrocytes. The space that they occupy within the matrix is known as a lacuna. These **chondrocytes**, at least in young cartilage, possess the capacity to undergo cell division, thus contributing to the growth of the cartilage from within (**interstitial growth**). When this occurs, each lacuna may house several chondrocytes and is referred to as a cell nest (**isogenous group**).

Hyaline cartilage is surrounded by a well-defined **perichondrium**. The type II collagen fibers of the matrix of this cartilage are mostly very fine and are therefore fairly well masked by the surrounding **glycosaminoglycans**, giving the matrix a smooth, glassy appearance.

Elastic cartilage also possesses a perichondrium. The matrix, in addition to the type II collagen fibers, contains a wealth of coarse elastic fibers that impart to it a characteristic appearance.

Fibrocartilage differs from elastic and hyaline cartilage in that it has no perichondrium. Additionally, the chondrocytes are smaller and are usually oriented in parallel longitudinal rows. The matrix of this cartilage contains a large number of thick type I collagen fiber bundles between the rows of chondrocytes (Table 4-1).

● BONE

Bone has many functions, including support, protection, mineral storage, and hemopoiesis. At the specialized cartilage-covered ends, it permits articulation or movement. Bone, a vascular connective tissue consisting of cells and calcified extracellular materials, may be dense (compact) or spongelike (cancellous). Cancellous bone, like that present inside the epiphyses (heads) of long bones, is always surrounded by compact bone. **Cancellous bone** has large, open spaces surrounded by thin,

TABLE 4-1 • Cartilage Types, Characteristics, and Locations

Type	Characteristics	Perichondrium	Locations (Major Samples)
Hyaline	Chondrocytes arranged in groups within a basophilic matrix containing Type II collagen	Usually present except at articular surfaces	Articular ends of long bones, ventral rib cartilage, templates for endochondral bone formation
Elastic	Chondrocytes compacted in matrix containing Type II collagen and elastic fibers	Present	Pinna of ear, auditory canal, laryngeal cartilages
Fibrocartilage	Chondrocytes arranged in rows in an acidophilic matrix containing Type I collagen bundles in rows	Absent	Intervertebral discs, pubic symphysis

anastomosing plates of bone. The large spaces are **marrow spaces**, and the plates of bones are **trabeculae**, composed of several layers or **lamellae.** Compact bone is much more dense than cancellous bone. Its spaces are much reduced in size, and its lamellar organization is much more precise and thicker. The calcified matrix is composed of 50% minerals (mostly **calcium hydroxyapatite**) and 50% organic matter (**collagen**, **proteoglycans**, and **protein-associated glycosaminoglycans**) and bound water.

Bone is always covered and lined by soft connective tissues. The marrow cavity is lined by an **endosteum** composed of **osteoprogenitor cells** (previously known as osteogenic cells), **osteoblasts**, and occasional **osteoclasts**. The periosteum covering the bone surface is composed of an outer fibrous layer consisting mainly of collagen fibers and populated by fibroblasts. The inner osteogenic layer consists of some collagen fibers and mostly osteoprogenitor cells and their progeny, the osteoblasts. The periosteum is affixed to bone via **Sharpey's fibers**, collagenous bundles trapped in the calcified bone matrix during ossification.

Bone matrix is produced by osteoblasts, cells derived from their less differentiated precursors, the **osteoprogenitor cells**. As osteoblasts elaborate bone matrix, they become trapped, and as the matrix calcifies, the trapped osteoblasts become known as **osteocytes**. Osteocytes, occupying lenticular-shaped spaces known as **lacunae**, possess long processes that are housed in tiny canals or tunnels known as **canaliculi**. Since bone, unlike cartilage, is a vascular hard tissue whose blood vessels penetrate and perforate it, canaliculi eventually open into channels known as **haversian canals**, housing the blood vessels. Each haversian canal with its surrounding lamellae of bone containing canaliculi radiating to it from the osteocytes trapped in the lacunae is known as an **osteon** or **haversian canal system**.

The canaliculi of the osteon extend to the haversian canal to exchange cellular waste material for nutrients and oxygen. Haversian canals, which more or less parallel the longitudinal axis of long bones, are connected to each other by **Volkmann's canals**.

The bony lamellae of compact bone are organized into four lamellar systems: **external (outer)** and **internal (inner) circumferential lamellae**, **interstitial lamellae**, and the **osteons** (see Graphic 4-1).

Osteogenesis

Histogenesis of bone occurs via either **intramembranous** or **endochondral ossification**. The former arises in a richly vascularized mesenchymal membrane where **mesenchymal cells** differentiate into osteoblasts (possibly via osteprogenitor cells), which begin to elaborate bone matrix, thus forming trabeculae of bone. As more and more trabeculae form in the same vicinity, they will become interconnected. As they fuse with each other, they form **cancellous bone**, the peripheral regions of which will be remodeled to form **compact bone**. The surfaces of these trabeculae are populated with osteoblasts. Frequently, an additional cell type, the **osteoclast**, may be present. These large, multinucleated cells derived from **monocyte precursors** are found in shallow depressions on the trabecular surface (**Howship's lacunae**) and function to resorb bone. It is through the integrated interactions of these cells and osteoblasts that bone is remodeled. The region of the mesenchymal membrane that does not participate in the ossification process will remain the soft tissue component of bone (i.e., periosteum, endosteum).

Newly formed bone is called **primary** or **woven bone**, since the arrangement of collagen fibers lacks the precise orientation present in older bone. The integrated interaction between osteoblasts and osteoclasts will act to replace the woven bone with **secondary** or **mature bone**.

Endochondral ossification, responsible for the formation of long and short bones, relies on the presence of a hyaline cartilage model that is used as a template on and within which bone is made (see Graphic 4-2). However, it must be appreciated that cartilage does not become bone. Instead, a **bony subperiosteal collar** is formed (via intramembranous ossification) around the midriff of the cartilaginous template. This collar increases in width and length. The chondrocytes in the center of the template hypertrophy and resorb some of their matrix, thus enlarging their lacunae so much that some lacunae become confluent. The **hypertrophied chondrocytes**, subsequent to assisting in calcification of the cartilage, degenerate and die. The newly formed spaces are invaded by the **periosteal bud** (composed of blood vessels, mesenchymal cells, and osteoprogenitor cells). Osteoprogenitor cells differentiate into osteoblasts, and these cells elaborate a bony matrix on the surface of the calcified cartilage. As the subperiosteal bone collar increases in thickness and length, osteoclasts resorb the calcified cartilage-calcified bone complex, leaving an enlarged space, the future marrow cavity (which will be populated by marrow cells). The entire process of ossification will spread away from this primary ossification center, and eventually most of the cartilage template will be replaced by bone, forming the **diaphysis** of a long bone. The formation of the **bony epiphyses** (secondary ossification center) occurs in a modified fashion so that a cartilaginous covering may be maintained at the articular surface. The growth in length of a long bone is due to the presence of epiphyseal plates of cartilage located between the epiphysis and the diaphysis.

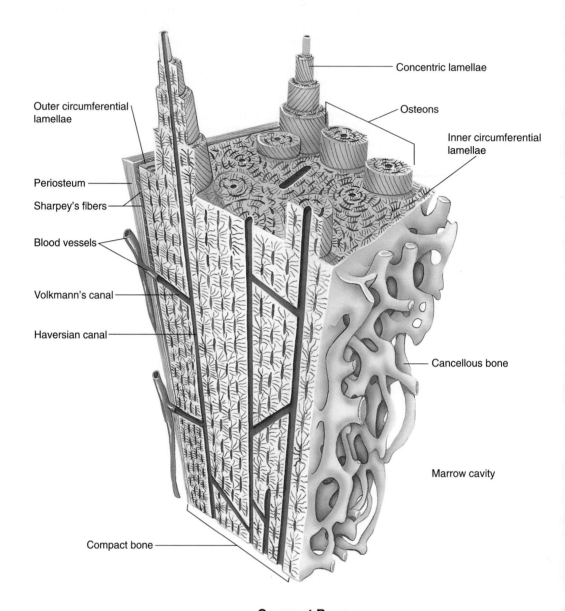

Concentric lamellae

Osteons

Inner circumferential lamellae

Outer circumferential lamellae

Periosteum

Sharpey's fibers

Blood vessels

Volkmann's canal

Haversian canal

Cancellous bone

Marrow cavity

Compact bone

Compact Bone

Compact bone is surrounded by dense irregular collagenous connective tissue, the **periosteum**, which is attached to the **outer circumferential lamellae** by **Sharpey's fibers**. Blood vessels of the periosteum enter the bone via larger nutrient canals or small **Volkmann's canals**, which not only convey blood vessels to the **Haversian canals** of **osteons** but also interconnect adjacent Haversian canals. Each osteon is composed of concentric lamellae of bone whose collagen fibers are arranged so that they are perpendicular to those of contiguous lamellae. The **inner circumferential lamellae** are lined by endosteal lined cancellous bone that protrudes into the marrow cavity.

A

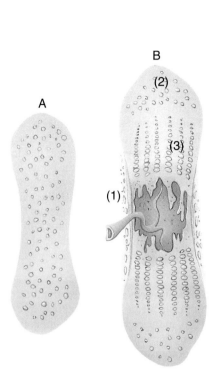

B

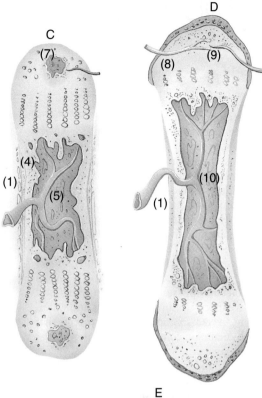

C

D

E

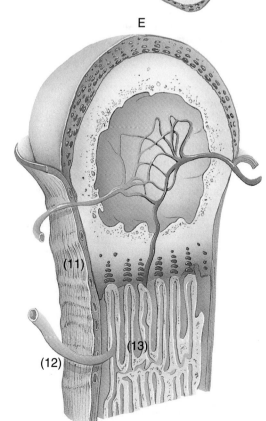

Endochondral Bone Formation

A. Endochondral bone formation requires the presence of a hyaline cartilage model.

B. Vascularization of the diaphysis perichondrium (2) results in the transformation of chondrogenic cells to osteogenic cells, resulting in the formation of a **subperiosteal bone collar** (1) (via intramembranous bone formation), which quickly becomes perforated by osteoclastic activity. Chondrocytes in the center of the cartilage hypertrophy (3), and their lacunae become confluent.

C. The subperiosteal bone collar (1) increased in length and width, the confluent lacunae are invaded by the **periosteal bud** (4), and osteoclastic activity forms a primitive marrow cavity (5) whose walls are composed of calcified cartilage-calcified bone complex. The epiphyses display the beginning of **secondary ossification centers** (7).

D and E. The subperiosteal bond collar (1) has become sufficiently large to support the developing long bone, so that much of the cartilage has been resorbed, with the exception of the **epiphyseal plate** (8) and the covering of the epiphyses (9). Ossification in the epiphyses occurs from the center (10), thus the vascular periosteum (11) does not cover the cartilaginous surface. Blood vessels (12) enter the **epiphyses**, without vascularizing the cartilage, to constitute the vascular network (13) around which spongy bone will be formed.

Histophysiology

I. CARTILAGE

A. Cartilage Matrix

Hyaline cartilage is an avascular connective tissue whose pliable matrix provides a conduit for nutrients and waste products to and from its perichondrium and its chondrocytes. The matrix consists of **type II collagen** embedded in an amorphous ground substance composed of the glycosaminoglycan, **hyaluronic acid**, to which proteoglycans are bound. The glycosaminoglycan components of the proteoglycans are mainly **chondroitin-4-sulfate** and **chondroitin-6-sulfate**. The acidic nature of the proteoglycans, combined with the enormous size of the proteoglycan–hyaluronic acid complex, results in these molecules possessing huge **domains** and tremendous capacity for binding cations and water. Additionally, the matrix contains **glycoproteins** that help the cells maintain contact with the intercellular matrix.

Elastic cartilage is similar to hyaline cartilage, but it also possesses **elastic fibers**. **Fibrocartilage** possesses no perichondrium, only a limited amount of acidophilic matrix, and an abundance of **type I collagen** arranged in parallel rows.

B. Chondrocytes

The **chondrocytes** of hyaline and elastic cartilage resemble each other, in that they may be arranged individually in their **lacunae** or in **cell nests** (in young cartilage). Peripherally located chondrocytes are lenticular in shape, whereas those located centrally are round. The cells completely fill their lacunae. They possess an abundance of glycogen, frequent large lipid droplets, and a well-developed protein synthetic machinery (rough endoplasmic reticulum, Golgi apparatus, *trans*-Golgi network), as well as mitochondria, since these cells continuously turn over the cartilage matrix. For these cells to manufacture type II collagen and the other components of the cartilage matrix, these cells need **Sox9**, a transcription factor.

II. BONE

A. Bone Matrix

Bone is a **calcified**, vascular connective tissue. Its cells are located in the surrounding periosteum, in the endosteal lining, or within lenticular cavities called **lacunae**. Tiny channels known as **canaliculi**, housing slender processes of osteocytes, convey nutrients, hormones, and other necessary substances.

The organic matrix of bone is composed mainly of **type I collagen**, sulfated **glycoproteins**, and some **proteoglycans**. The matrix of collagen is calcified with **calcium hydroxyapatite** crystals, making bone one of the hardest substances in the body. The presence of these crystals makes bone the body's storehouse of calcium, phosphate, and other inorganic ions. Thus, bone is in a dynamic state of flux, continuously gaining and losing inorganic ions to maintain the body's calcium and phosphate homeostasis.

B. Cells of Bone

Osteoprogenitor cells are flattened, undifferentiated-appearing cells located in the cellular layer of the periosteum, in the endosteum, and lining the haversian canals. They give rise to osteoblasts under the influence of transforming growth factor-β and bone morphogenic protein (BMP). However, under hypoxic conditions, osteoprogenitor cells become chondrogenic cells; therefore, these two cells are really the same cell that express different factors under differring oxygen tension.

Osteoblasts are cuboidal to low-columnar cells responsible for the synthesis of bone matrix. As they elaborate bone matrix, they become surrounded by the matrix and then become osteocytes. The bone matrix is calcified due to the seeding of the matrix via **matrix vesicles** derived from osteoblasts. When osteoblasts are quiescent, they lose much of their protein synthetic machinery and resemble osteoprogenitor cells. Osteoblasts function in the control of bone matrix mineralization and are also responsible for the formation, recruitment, and maintenance of osteoclasts as well as for the intiation of bone resorption. Osteoblasts possess **parathyroid receptors** on their cell membrane, and in the presence of **parathormone** they release **macrophage-colony stimulating factor**, which induces the formation of osteoclast precursors. Additionally, osteoblasts have expressed on their cell surface **RANKL (receptor for activation of nuclear factor kappa B)**, a molecule that when contacted by the preosteoclast's surface-bound **RANK** induces preosteoclasts to differentiate into osteoclasts. **Osteoclast-stimulating factor,** also released by osteoblasts, activate osteoclasts to begin resorbing bone. For the osteoclast to attach to bone in a secure fashion, they form a sealing zone on the bone surface and the formation of this tight adherence is facilitated by another osteoblast-derived factor, **osteopontin**. Before the osteoclast can adhere to the bone surface, however, the ostelasts must resorb the noncalcified bone matrix that covers the bone surface and then the osteoblast must leave to provide an available bone surface for the osteoclasts.

Osteocytes are flattened, discoid cells located in **lacunae**; they are responsible for the maintenance of bone. Their cytoplasmic processes contact and form **gap junctions** with processes of other osteocytes within canaliculi; thus, these cells sustain a communication network, so that a large population of osteocytes are able to respond to blood calcium levels as well as to **calcitonin** and **parathormone**, released by the thyroid and parathyroid glands, respectively. Thus, these cells are responsible for the short-term calcium and phosphate homeostasis of the body. Osteocytes are derived from osteoblasts that have surrounded themselves with the bone matrix that they produced. Two transcription factors have been implicated in the transformation of osteoblats to osteocytes, namely, **Cbfa1/Runx2** and **osterix**. Both of these factors are essential for the normal development of mammalian skeleton. As the differentiation occurs, the membrane-bound alkaline phosphatase is no longer expressed.

Osteoclasts, large, multinucleated cells derived from monocyte precursors, are responsible for the resorption of bone. As they remove bone, they appear to occupy a shallow cavity, **Howship's lacuna**. Osteoclasts have four regions, the **basal zone**, housing nuclei and organelles of the cell; the **ruffled border**, composed of finger-like processes that are suspended in the subosteoclastic compartment where the resorption of bone is actively proceeding; the **vesicular zone**, housing numerous vesicles that ferry material out of the cell and into the cell from the subosteoclastic compartment; and the **clear zone**, where the osteoclast forms a seal with the bone, isolating the subosteoclastic compartment from the external milieu. The ruffled border possesses many **proton pumps** that deliver hydrogen ions from the osteoclast into the subosteoclastic compartment. Additionally, **aquapores** and **chloride channels** permit the delivery of water and chloride ions, respectively, forming a concentrated solution of HCl in the subosteoclastic compartment, thus decalcifying bone. Enzymes are delivered via vesicles into the subosteoclastic compartment to degrade the organic components of bone. The byproducts of degradation are endocytosed by endocytic vesicles and are used by the osteoclast or are exocytosed into the extracellular space, where they enter vascular system for distribution to the rest of the body. Osteoclast cell membrane also possesses **calcitonin receptors**; when calcitonin is bound to the receptors, these cells become inhibited, they stop bone resorption, leave the bone surface, and dissociate into individual cells or disintegrate and are eliminated by macrophages.

Cooperation between osteoclasts and osteoblasts is responsible not only for the formation, remodeling, and repair of bone but also for the long-term maintenance of calcium and phosphate homeostasis of the body.

Cartilage Degeneration

Hyaline cartilage begins to degenerate when the chondrocytes hypertrophy and die, a natural process but one that accelerates with aging. This results in decreasing mobility and joint pain.

Vitamin Deficiency

Deficiency in Vitamin A inhibits proper bone formation and growth, whereas an excess accelerates ossification of the epiphyseal plates, producing small stature. Deficiency in vitamin D, which is essential for absorption of calcium from the intestine, results in poorly calcified (soft) bone—rickets in children and osteomalacia in adults. When in excess, bone is resorbed. Deficiency in Vitamin C, which is necessary for collagen formation, produces scurvy, resulting in poor bone growth and repair.

Hormonal Influences on Bone

Calcitonin inhibits bone-matrix resorption by altering osteoclast function, thus preventing calcium release. Parathyroid hormone activates osteoblasts to secrete osteoclast-stimulating factor, thus activating osteoclasts to increase bone resorption, resulting in increased blood calcium levels. If in excess, bones become brittle and are susceptible to fracture.

Paget's Disease of Bone

Paget's disease of bone is a generalized skeletal disease that usually affects older people. Often, the disease has a familial component and its results are thickened but softer bones of the skull and extremities. It is usually asymptomatic and is frequently discovered after radiographic examination prescribed for other reasons or as a result of blood chemistry showing elevated alkaline phosphatase levels. Calcitonin treatment may be used to slow the progression of the disease.

Osteoporosis

Osteoporosis is a decrease in bone mass arising from lack of bone formation or from increased bone resorption. It occurs commonly in old age because of decreased growth hormone and in postmenopausal women because of decreased estrogen secretion. In the latter, estrogen binding to receptors on osteoblasts stimulates the secretion of bone matrix. Without sufficient estrogen, osteoclastic activity reduces bone mass without the concomitant formation of bone, therefore making the bones more liable to fracture.

Osteopetrosis

Osteopetrosis is a constellation of heritable disorders that result in denser bones with possible skeletal malformations. The disease may be the early onset type or the delayed onset type. The early onset type may begin in infancy and can result in early death due to anemia, uncontrollable bleeding, and rampant infection. The delayed onset type of osteopetrosis may be quite mild, exhibiting no clinical symptoms, but thickening of the bones and slight facial deformities may be evident. As the bones become thicker the diameters of the foramina become smaller, and nerves passing through those constricted openings may become compressed and cause considerable pain. Surgical widening of the foramina may help in alleviating the pain.

PLATE 4-1 Embryonic and Hyaline Cartilages

FIGURE 1 • Embryonic hyaline cartilage. Pig. Paraffin section. ×132.

The developing hyaline cartilage is surrounded by **embryonic connective tissue** (ECT). Mesenchymal cells have participated in the formation of this cartilage. Note that the developing **perichondrium** (P), investing the cartilage, merges both with the embryonic connective tissue and with the cartilage. The chondrocytes in their lacunae are round, small cells packed closely together (*arrow*), with little intervening homogeneously staining matrix (*arrowheads*).

FIGURE 3 • Hyaline cartilage. Rabbit. Paraffin section. ×270.

The perichondrium is composed of **fibrous** (F) and **chondrogenic** (CG) layers. The former is composed of mostly collagenous fibers with a few fibroblasts, whereas the latter is more cellular, consisting of **chondroblasts** and **chondrogenic cells** (*arrows*). As chondroblasts secrete matrix they become surrounded by the intercellular substance and are consequently known as **chondrocytes** (C). Note that chondrocytes at the periphery of the cartilage are small and elongated, whereas those at the center are large and ovoid to round (*arrowhead*). Frequently they are found in **isogenous groups** (IG).

FIGURE 2 • Hyaline cartilage. Trachea. Monkey. Paraffin section. ×132.

The trachea is lined by **a pseudostratified ciliated columnar epithelium** (Ep). Deep to the epithelium, observe the large, blood-filled **vein** (V). The lower half of the photomicrograph presents hyaline cartilage whose **chondrocytes** (C) are disposed in **isogenous groups** (IG) indicative of interstitial growth. Chondrocytes are housed in spaces known as lacunae. Note that the territorial matrix (*arrow*) in the vicinity of the lacunae stains darker than the interterritorial matrix (*asterisk*). The entire cartilage is surrounded by **a perichondrium** (P).

FIGURE 4 • Hyaline cartilage. Trachea. Monkey. Plastic section. ×270.

The pseudostratified ciliated columnar epithelium displays numerous goblet cells (*arrows*). The cilia, appearing at the free border of the epithelium, are clearly evident. Note how the subepithelial **connective tissue** (CT) merges with the **fibrous perichondrium** (F). The **chondrogenic layer** of the perichondrium (Cg) houses chondrogenic cells and chondroblasts. As chondroblasts surround themselves with matrix, they become trapped in lacunae and are referred to as **chondrocytes** (C). At the periphery of the cartilage, the chondrocytes are flattened, whereas toward the interior they are round to oval. Due to the various histologic procedures, some of the chondrocytes fall out of their lacunae, which then appear as empty spaces. Although the **matrix** (M) contains many collagen fibrils, they are masked by the glycosaminoglycans; hence, the matrix appears homogeneous and smooth. The proteoglycan-rich lining of the lacunae is responsible for the more intense staining of the territorial matrix, which is particularly evident in Figures 2 and 3.

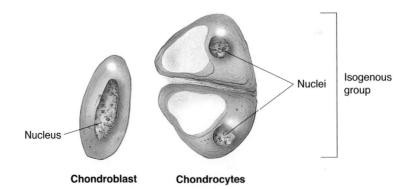

Chondroblast   Chondrocytes

Nucleus

Nuclei   Isogenous group

KEY					
C	chondrocyte	Ep	pseudostratified ciliated columnar epithelium	IG	isogenous group
Cg	chondrogenic perichondrium			M	matrix
CT	connective tissue	F	fibrous perichondrium	P	perichondrium
ECT	embryonic connective tissue			V	vein

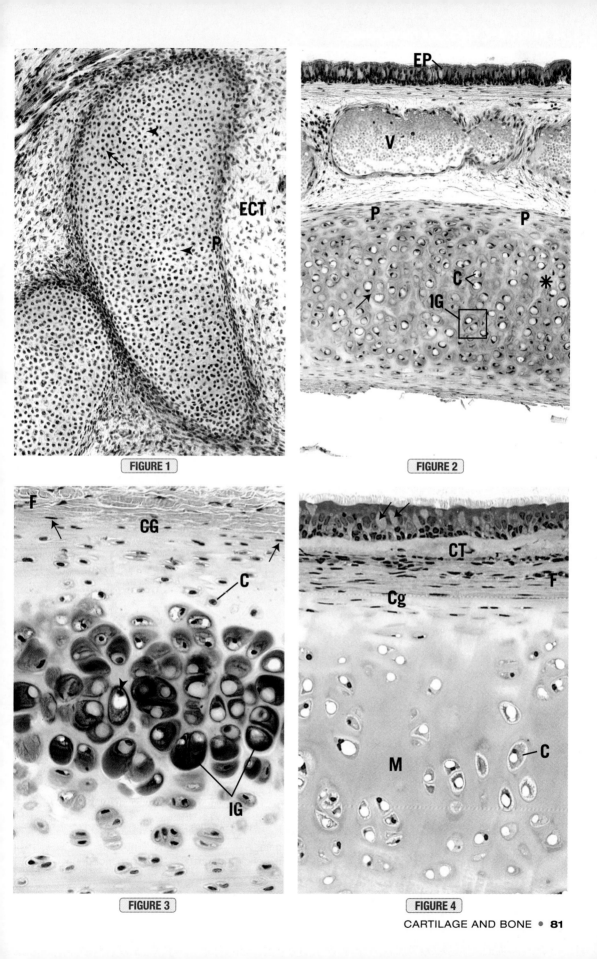

FIGURE 1

FIGURE 2

FIGURE 3

FIGURE 4

CARTILAGE AND BONE • **81**

Elastic cartilage, like hyaline cartilage, is enveloped by a **perichondrium** (P). **Chondrocytes** (C), which are housed in lacunae (*arrow*), have shrunk away from the walls, giving the appearance of empty spaces. Occasional lacunae display two chondrocytes (*asterisk*), indicative of interstitial growth. The matrix has a rich **elastic fiber** (E) component that gives elastic cartilage its characteristic appearance as well as contributing to its elasticity. The *boxed area* appears at a higher magnification in Figure 3.

This is a high magnification of the *boxed area* in Figure 1. The **chondrocytes** (C) are large, oval to round cells with acentric **nuclei** (N). The cells accumulate lipids in their cytoplasm, often in the form of lipid droplets, thus imparting to the cell a "vacuolated" appearance. Note that the **elastic fibers** (E) mask the matrix in some areas and that the fibers are of various thicknesses, especially evident in cross-sections (*arrows*).

This higher magnification of the perichondrial region of Figure 1 displays the outer **fibrous** (F) and inner **chondrogenic** (CG) regions of the perichondrium. Note that the chondrocytes (*arrow*) immediately deep to the chondrogenic layer are more or less flattened and smaller than those deeper in the cartilage. Additionally, the amount and coarseness of the elastic fibers increase adjacent to the large cells.

The **chondrocytes** (C) of fibrocartilage are aligned in parallel rows, lying singly in individual lacunae. The nuclei of these chondrocytes are easily observed, whereas their cytoplasm is not as evident (*arrow*). The matrix contains thick bundles of **collagen fibers** (CF), which are arranged in a more or less regular fashion between the rows of cartilage cells. Unlike elastic and hyaline cartilages, fibrocartilage is not enveloped by a perichondrium.

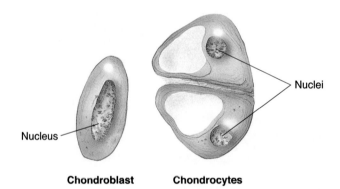

Nuclei

Nucleus

Chondroblast   Chondrocytes

KEY					
C	chondrocyte	E	elastic fiber	N	nucleus
CF	collagen fiber	F	fibrous perichondrium	P	perichondrium
Cg	chondrogenic perichondrium				

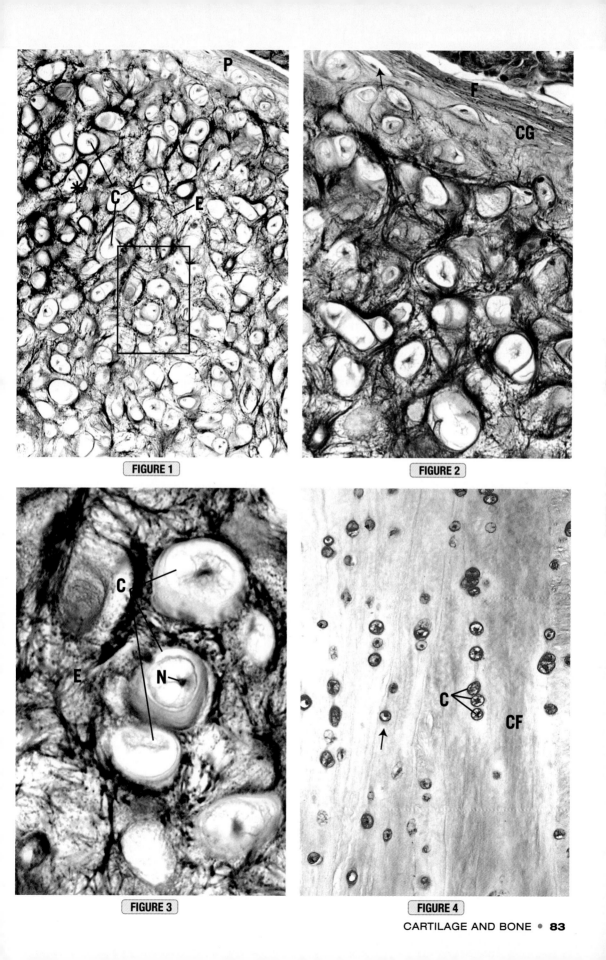

FIGURE 1

FIGURE 2

FIGURE 3

FIGURE 4

PLATE 4-3 Compact Bone

FIGURE 1 • Decalcified compact bone. Human. Paraffin section. ×132.

Cross-section of decalcified bone, displaying **skeletal muscle** (SM) fibers that will insert a short distance from this site. The outer **fibrous periosteum** (FP) and the inner **osteogenic periosteum** (OP) are distinguishable due to the fibrous component of the former and the cellularity of the latter. Note the presence of the **inner circumferential** (IC) **lamellae, osteons** (Os), and interstitial lamellae (*asterisk*). Also observe the **marrow** (M) occupying the marrow cavity, as well as the endosteal lining (*arrow*).

FIGURE 2 • Decalcified compact bone. Human. Paraffin section. ×132.

This is a cross-section of decalcified compact bone, displaying **osteons** or **haversian canal systems** (Os) as well as **interstitial lamellae** (IL). Each osteon possesses a central **haversian canal** (HC), surrounded by several **lamellae** (L) of bone. The boundary of each osteon is visible and is referred to as a cementing line (*arrowheads*). Neighboring haversian canals are connected to each other by **Volkmann's canals** (VC), through which blood vessels of osteons are interconnected to each other.

FIGURE 3 • Decalcified compact bone. Human. Paraffin section. ×540.

A small osteon is delineated by its surrounding cementing line (*arrowheads*). The lenticular-shaped **osteocytes** (Oc) occupy flattened spaces, known as lacunae. The lacunae are lined by uncalcified osteoid matrix. *Inset.* **Decalcified compact bone. Human. Paraffin section. × 540.** A haversian canal of an osteon is shown to contain a small **blood vessel** (BV) supported by slender connective tissue elements. The canal is lined by flattened **osteoblasts** (Ob) and, perhaps, **osteogenic cells** (Op).

FIGURE 4 • Undecalcified ground compact bone. x.s. Human. Paraffin section. ×132.

This specimen was treated with india ink to accentuate some of the salient features of compact bone. The **haversian canals** (HC) as well as the lacunae (*arrows*) appear black in the figure. Note the connection between two osteons at top center, known as **Volkmann's canal** (VC). The canaliculi appear as fine, narrow lines leading to the haversian canal as they anastomose with each other and with lacunae of other osteocytes of the same osteon.

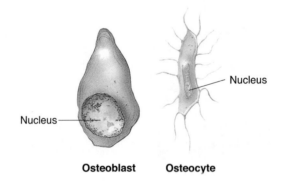

Nucleus

Nucleus

Osteoblast   **Osteocyte**

KEY					
BV	blood vessel	IL	interstitial lamella	Op	osteogenic cell
FP	fibrous periosteum	L	lamella	OP	osteogenic periosteum
HC	haversian canal	M	marrow	Os	osteon
IC	inner circumferential lamella	Ob	osteoblast	SM	skeletal muscle fiber
		Oc	osteocyte	VC	Volkmann's canal

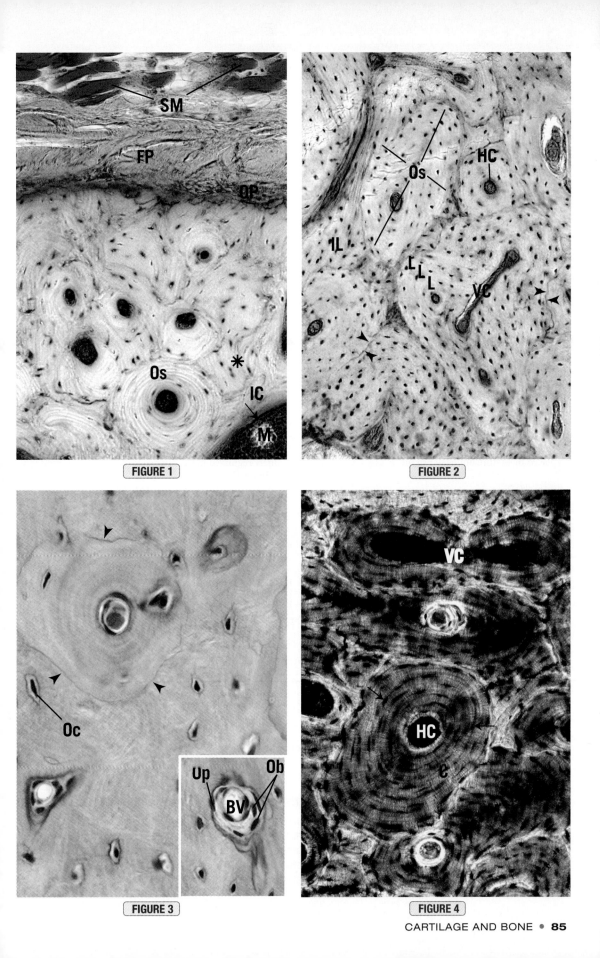

FIGURE 1

FIGURE 2

FIGURE 3

FIGURE 4

CARTILAGE AND BONE • **85**

FIGURE 1 • Undecalcified ground bone. x.s. Human. Paraffin section. ×270.

This transverse section of an osteon clearly displays the **lamellae** (L) of bone surrounding the **haversian canal** (HC). The cementing line acts to delineate the periphery of the osteon. Note that the **canaliculi** (C) arising from the peripheral-most lacunae usually do not extend toward other osteons. Instead, they lead toward the haversian canal. Canaliculi, which appear to anastomose with each other and with lacunae, house long osteocytic processes in the living bone.

FIGURE 2 • Intramembranous ossification. Pig skull. Paraffin section. ×132.

The anastomosing **trabeculae** (T) of forming bone appear darkly stained in a background of **embryonic connective tissue** (ECT). Observe that this connective tissue is highly vascular and that the bony trabeculae are forming primitive **osteons** (Os) surrounding large, primitive **haversian canals** (HC), whose center is occupied by **blood vessels** (BV). Observe that the **osteocytes** (Oc) are arranged somewhat haphazardly. Every trabecula is covered by **osteoblasts** (Ob).

FIGURE 3 • Intramembranous ossification. Pig skull. Paraffin section. ×270.

This photomicrograph of intramenbranous ossification is taken from the periphery of the bone-forming region. Note the developing **periosteum** (P) in the upper right-hand corner. Just deep to this primitive periosteum, **osteoblasts** (Ob) are differentiating and are elaborating **osteoid** (Ot), as yet uncalcified bone matrix. As the osteoblasts surround themselves with bone matrix, they become trapped in their lacunae and are known as **osteocytes** (Oc). These osteocytes are more numerous, larger, and more ovoid than those of mature bone, and the organization of the collagen fibers of the bony matrix is less precise than that of mature bone. Hence, this bone is referred to as immature (primary) bone, and it will be replaced by mature bone later in life.

FIGURE 4 • Intramembranous ossification. Pig skull. Paraffin section. ×540.

This photomicrograph is taken from an area similar to those of Figures 2 and 3. This trabecula demonstrates several points, namely that **osteoblasts** (Ob) cover the entire surface and that **osteoid** (Ot) is interposed between calcified bone and the cells of bone and appears lighter in color. Additionally, note that the osteoblast marked with the *asterisk* is apparently trapping itself in the matrix it is elaborating. Finally, note the large, multinuclear cells, **osteoclasts** (Ocl), which are in the process of resorbing bone. The activity of these large cells results in the formation of Howship's lacunae (*arrowheads*), which are shallow depressions on the bone surface. The interactions between osteoclasts and osteoblasts are very finely regulated in the normal formation and remodeling of bone.

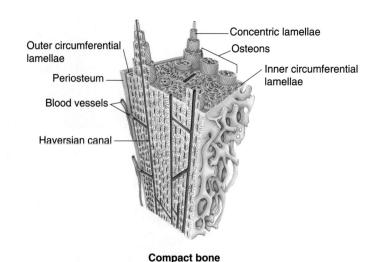

Outer circumferential lamellae

Periosteum

Blood vessels

Haversian canal

Concentric lamellae

Osteons

Inner circumferential lamellae

Compact bone

KEY					
BV	blood vessel	L	lamella	Ot	osteoid
C	canaliculus	Ob	osteoblast	P	periosteum
ECT	embryonic connective tissue	Oc	osteocyte	T	trabecula
		Ocl	osteoclast		
HC	haversian canal	Os	osteon		

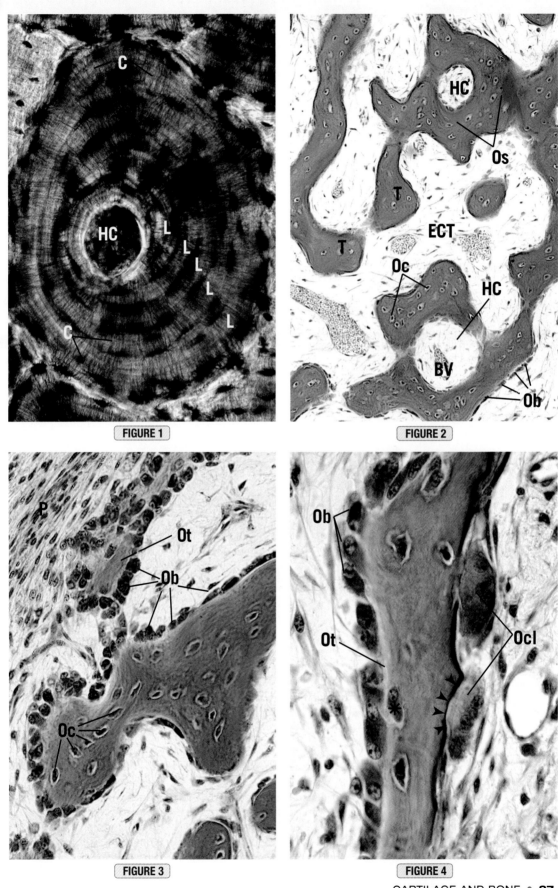

FIGURE 1

FIGURE 2

FIGURE 3

FIGURE 4

FIGURE 1 • Epiphyseal ossification center. Monkey. Paraffin section. ×14.

Most long bones are formed by the endochondral method of ossification, which involves the replacement of a cartilage model by bone. In this low power photomicrograph, the **diaphysis** (D) of the lower phalanx has been replaced by bone, and the medullary cavity is filled with **marrow** (M). The **epiphysis** (E) of the same phalanx is undergoing ossification and is the **secondary center of ossification** (2°), thereby establishing the **epiphyseal plate** (ED). The **trabeculae** (T) are clearly evident on the diaphyseal side of the epiphyseal plate.

FIGURE 2 • Endochondral ossification. l.s. Monkey. Paraffin section. ×14.

Much of the cartilage has been replaced in the diaphysis of this forming bone. Note the numerous **trabeculae** (T) and the developing **bone marrow** (M) of the medullary cavity. Ossification is advancing toward the **epiphysis** (E), in which the secondary center of ossification has not yet appeared. Observe the **periosteum** (P), which appears as a definite line between the subperiosteal bone collar and the surrounding connective tissue. The *boxed area* is represented in Figure 3.

FIGURE 3 • Endochondral ossification. Monkey. Paraffin section. ×132.

This montage is a higher magnification of the *boxed area* of Figure 2. The region where the periosteum and perichondrium meet is evident (*arrowheads*). Deep to the periosteum is the **subperiosteal bone collar** (BC), which was formed via intramembranous ossification. Endochondral ossification is evident within the cartilage template. Starting at the top of the montage, note how the chondrocytes are lined up in long columns (*arrows*), indicative of their intense mitotic activity at the future epiphyseal plate region. In the epiphyseal plate this will be the **zone of cell proliferation** (ZP). The chondrocytes increase in size in the **zone of cell maturation and hypertrophy** (ZH) and resorb some of their lacunar walls, enlarging them to such an extent that some of the lacunae become confluent. The chondrocytes die in the **zone of calcifying cartilage** (ZC). The presumptive medullary cavity is being populated by bone marrow, osteoclastic and osteogenic cells, and blood vessels. The osteogenic cells are actively differentiating into osteoblasts, which are elaborating bone on the calcified walls of the confluent lacunae. At the bottom of the photomicrograph observe the bone-covered trabeculae of calcified cartilage (*asterisks*).

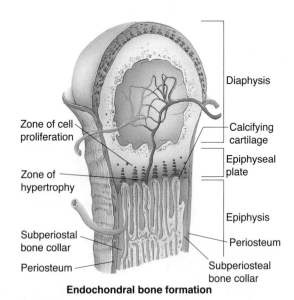

Diaphysis

Zone of cell proliferation

Calcifying cartilage

Epiphyseal plate

Zone of hypertrophy

Epiphysis

Subperiostal bone collar

Periosteum

Subperiosteal bone collar

Endochondral bone formation

KEY					
BC	subperiosteal bone collar	P	periosteum	ZC	zone of calcifying cartilage
D	diaphysis	2°	secondary center of ossification		
E	epiphysis			ZH	zone of cell maturation and hypertrophy
ED	epiphyseal plate	T	trabecula		
M	marrow			ZP	zone of proliferation

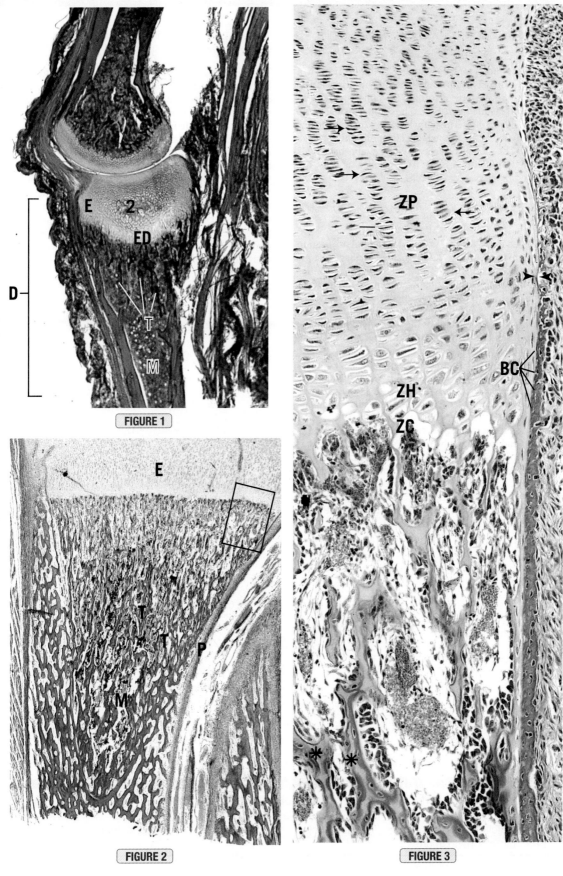

FIGURE 1 • Endochondral ossification. Monkey. Paraffin section. ×132.

This photomicrograph is a higher magnification of a region of Plate 4.5, Figure 3. Observe the multinucleated osteoclast (*arrowheads*) resorbing the bone-covered trabeculae of calcified cartilage. The **subperiosteal bone collar** (BC) and the **periosteum** (P) are clearly evident, as is the junction between the bone collar and the cartilage (*arrows*). The medullary cavity is being established and is populated by **blood vessels** (BV), osteogenic cells, osteoblasts, and hematopoietic cells.

FIGURE 3 • Endochondral ossification. x.s. Monkey. Paraffin section. ×196.

A cross-section of the region of endochondral ossification presents many round spaces in calcified cartilage that are lined with bone (*asterisks*). These spaces represent confluent lacunae in the cartilage template, where the chondrocytes have hypertrophied and died. Subsequently, the cartilage calcified and the invading osteogenic cells have differentiated into osteoblasts (*arrowheads*) and lined the calcified cartilage with bone. Since neighboring spaces were separated from each other by calcified cartilage walls, bone was elaborated on the sides of the walls. Therefore, these trabeculae, which in longitudinal section appear to be stalactite-like structures of bone with a calcified cartilaginous core, are, in fact, spaces in the cartilage template that are lined with bone. The walls between the spaces are the remnants of cartilage between lacunae that became calcified and form the substructure upon which bone was elaborated. Observe the forming **medullary cavity** (MC), housing **blood vessels** (BV), **hematopoietic tissue** (HT), osteogenic cells, and osteoblasts (*arrowheads*). The **subperiosteal bone collar** (BC) is evident and is covered by a **periosteum,** whose two layers, **fibrous** (FP) and **osteogenic** (Og), are clearly discernible.

FIGURE 2 • Endochondral ossification. Monkey. Paraffin section. ×270.

This photomicrograph is a higher magnification of the *boxed area* in Figure 1. Note that the trabeculae of calcified cartilage are covered by a thin layer of bone. The darker staining bone (*arrow*) contains osteocytes, whereas the lighter staining **calcified cartilage** (CC) is acellular, since the chondrocytes of this region have died, leaving behind empty lacunae that are confluent with each other. Observe that **osteoblasts** (Ob) line the trabecular complexes and that they are separated from the calcified bone by thin intervening **osteoid** (Ot). As the subperiosteal bone collar increases in thickness, the trabeculae of bone-covered calcified cartilage will be resorbed so that the cartilage template will be replaced by bone. The only cartilage that will remain will be the epiphyseal plate and the articular covering of the epiphysis.

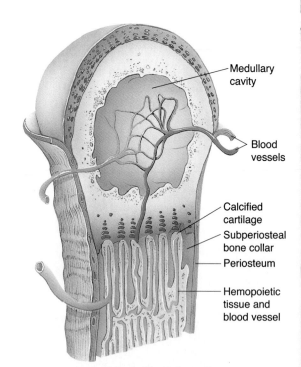

Medullary cavity

Blood vessels

Calcified cartilage

Subperiosteal bone collar

Periosteum

Hemopoietic tissue and blood vessel

Endochondral bone formation

KEY					
BC	subperiosteal bone collar	HT	hematopoietic tissue	Og	osteogenic periosteum
BV	blood vessel	MC	medullary cavity	Ot	osteoid
CC	calcified cartilage	Ob	osteoblast	P	periosteum
FP	fibrous periosteum				

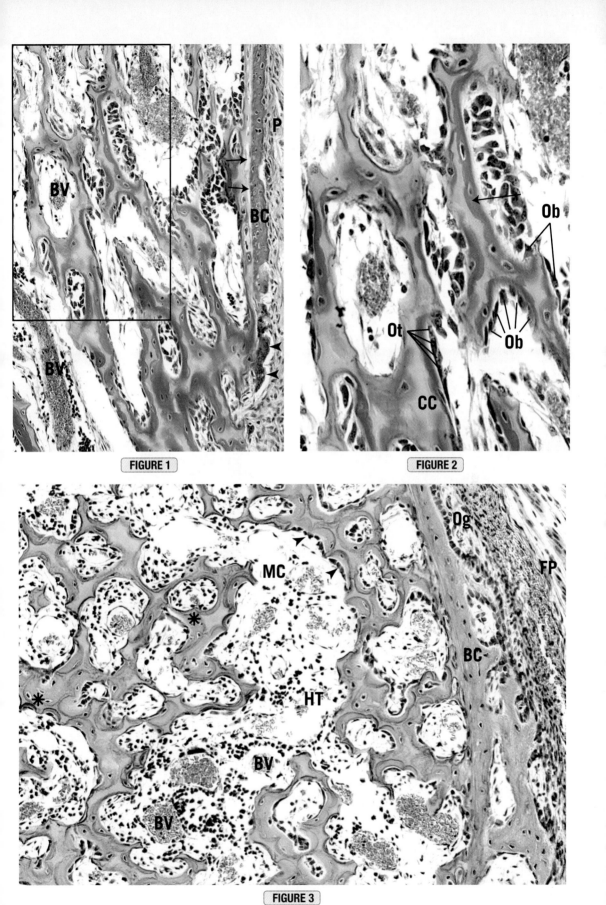

FIGURE 1

FIGURE 2

FIGURE 3

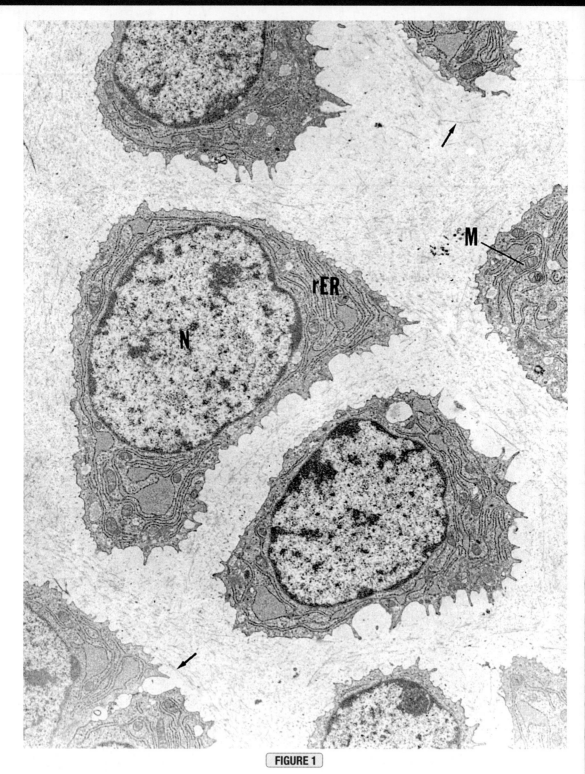

FIGURE 1

FIGURE 1 • Hyaline cartilage. Mouse. Electron microscopy. ×6120.

The hyaline cartilage of a neonatal mouse trachea presents chondrocytes, whose centrally positioned **nuclei** (N) are surrounded with a rich **rough endoplasmic reticulum** (rER) and numerous **mitochondria** (M). The matrix displays fine collagen fibrils (*arrows*). (From Seegmiller R, Ferguson C, Sheldon H. Studies on cartilage, VI: a genetically determined defect in tracheal cartilage. J Ultrastruct Res 1972;38:288–301.)

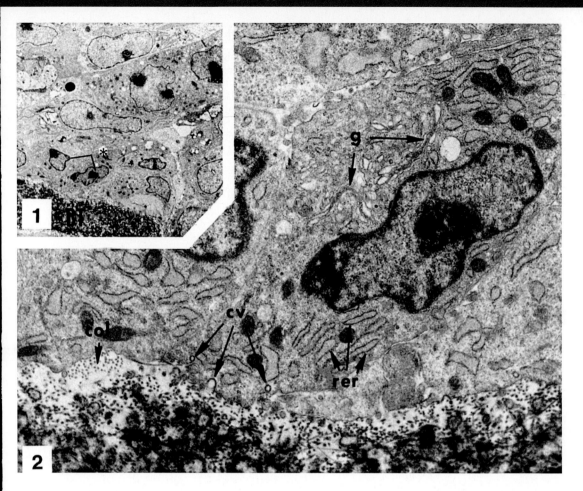

FIGURE 1 ● Osteoblasts from long bone. Rat. Electron microscopy. ×1350.

This low magnification electron micrograph displays numerous fibroblasts and osteoblasts in the vicinity of a **bony trabecula** (BT). The osteoblasts (*asterisk*) are presented at a higher magnification in Figure 2. (From Ryder M, Jenkins S, Horton J. The adherence to bone by cytoplasmic elements of osteoclast. J Dent Res 1981;60:1349–1355.)

FIGURE 2 ● Osteoblasts. Rat. Electron microscopy. ×9450.

Osteoblasts, at higher magnification, present well-developed **Golgi apparatus** (g), extensive **rough endoplasmic reticulum** (rer), and several **coated vacuoles** (cv) at the basal cell membrane. Observe the cross-sections of **collagen fibers** (col) in the bone matrix. (From Ryder M, Jenkins S, Horton J. The adherence to bone by cytoplasmic elements of osteoclast. J Dent Res 1981;60:1349–1355.)

FIGURE 1a • Osteoclast from long bone. Rat. Electron microscopy. ×1800.

Two nuclei of an osteoclast are evident in this section. Observe that the cell is surrounding a bony surface (*asterisk*). The region of the nucleus marked by an *arrowhead* is presented at a higher magnification in Figure 1B.

FIGURE 2 • Osteoclasts. Human. Paraffin section. ×600.

The nuclei (N) of these multinuclear cells are located in their **basal region** (BR), away from **Howship's lacunae** (HL). Note that the **ruffled border** (*arrowheads*) is in intimate contact with Howship's lacunae. (Courtesy of Dr. J. Hollinger.)

FIGURE 1b • Osteoclast. Rat. Electron microscopy. ×10,800.

This is a higher magnification of a region of Figure 1A. Note the presence of the **nucleus** (N) and its **nucleolus** (n), as well as the **ruffled border** (RB) and **clear zone** (CZ) of the osteoclast. Numerous **vacuoles** (v) of various size may be observed throughout the cytoplasm. (From Ryder M, Jenkins S, Horton J. The adherence to bone by cytoplasmic elements of osteoclast. J Dent Res 1981;60:1349–1355.)

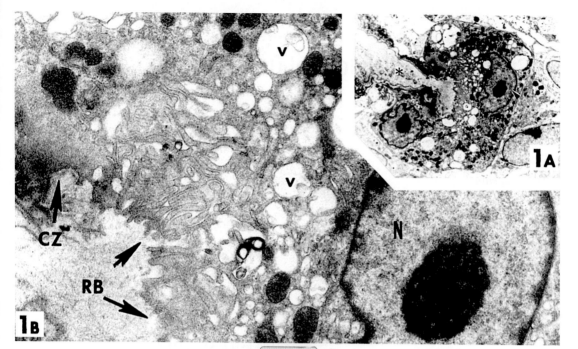

FIGURE 1

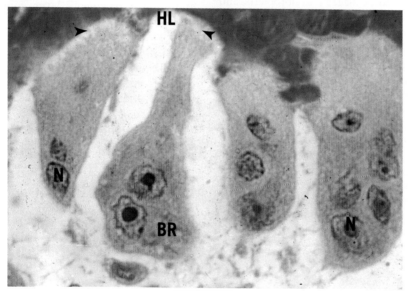

FIGURE 2

Summary of Histological Organization

I. CARTILAGE

A. Embryonic Cartilage

1. Perichondrium
The **perichondrium** is very thin and cellular.

2. Matrix
The **matrix** is scanty and smooth in appearance.

3. Cells
Numerous, small, round **chondrocytes** are housed in small spaces in the matrix. These spaces are known as **lacunae.**

B. Hyaline Cartilage

1. Perichondrium
The perichondrium has two layers, an outer **fibrous layer**, which contains collagen and fibroblasts, and an inner **chondrogenic layer,** which contains **chondrogenic cells** and **chondroblasts.**

2. Matrix
The **matrix** is smooth and basophilic in appearance. It has two regions, the **territorial (capsular) matrix,** which is darker and surrounds **lacunae,** and the **interterritorial (intercapsular) matrix,** which is lighter in color. The collagen fibrils are masked by the ground substance.

3. Cells
Either **chondrocytes** are found individually in **lacunae** or there may be two or more chondrocytes (**isogenous group**) in a lacuna. The latter case signifies **interstitial growth. Appositional growth** occurs just deep to the perichondrium and is attributed to chondroblasts.

C. Elastic Cartilage

1. Perichondrium
The perichondrium is the same in elastic cartilage as in hyaline cartilage.

2. Matrix
The **matrix** contains numerous dark **elastic fibers** in addition to the **collagen fibrils.**

3. Cells
The cells are **chondrocytes, chondroblasts,** and **chondrogenic cells,** as in hyaline cartilage.

D. Fibrocartilage

1. Perichondrium
The perichondrium is usually absent.

2. Matrix
The **ground substance** of matrix is very scanty. Many thick collagen bundles are located between parallel rows of chondrocytes.

3. Cells
The **chondrocytes** in fibrocartilage are smaller than those in hyaline or elastic cartilage, and they are arranged in parallel longitudinal rows between bundles of thick collagen fibers.

II. BONE

A. Decalcified Compact Bone

1. Periosteum
The **periosteum** has two layers, an outer **fibrous layer,** containing **collagen fibers** and **fibroblasts,** and an inner **osteogenic layer,** containing **osteoprogenitor cells** and **osteoblasts.** It is anchored to bone by **Sharpey's fibers.**

2. Lamellar Systems
Lamellar organization consists of **outer** and **inner circumferential lamellae, osteons (haversian canal systems),** and **interstitial lamellae.**

3. Endosteum
The **endosteum** is a thin membrane that lines the **medullary cavity,** which contains **yellow** or **white bone marrow.**

4. Cells
Osteocytes are housed in small spaces called **lacunae. Osteoblasts** and **osteoprogenitor cells** are found in the osteogenic layer of the periosteum, in the endosteum, and lining haversian canals. **Osteoclasts** are located in **Howship's lacunae** along resorptive surfaces of bone. **Osteoid,** noncalcified bone matrix, is interposed between the cells of bone and the calcified tissue.

5. Vascular Supply
Blood vessels are found in the periosteum, in the marrow cavity, and in the haversian canals of osteons. Haversian canals are connected to each other by Volkmann's canals.

B. Undecalcified Compact Ground Bone

1. Lamellar Systems
The lamellar organization is clearly evident as wafer-thin layers or **lamellae** constituting bone. They are then organized as **outer** and **inner circumferential lamellae, osteons,** and **interstitial lamellae.**

Osteons are cylindrical structures composed of concentric lamellae of bone. Their **lacunae** are empty, but in living bone they contain osteocytes. **Canaliculi** radiate from **lacunae** toward the central **haversian canal**, which in living bone houses blood vessels, osteoblasts, and osteogenic cells. **Cementing lines** demarcate the peripheral extent of each osteon. **Volkmann's canals** interconnect neighboring haversian canals.

C. Decalcified Cancellous Bone

1. Lamellar Systems
Lamellar organization consists of **spicules** and **trabeculae** of bone.

2. Cells
Cells are as before, in that **osteocytes** are housed in lacunae. **Osteoblasts** line all trabeculae and spicules. Occasionally, multinuclear, large **osteoclasts** occupy **Howship's lacunae**. **Osteoid**, noncalcified bone matrix, is interposed between the cells of bone and the calcified tissue.

    Bone marrow occupies the spaces among and between **trabeculae**.

D. Intramembranous Ossification

1. Ossification Centers
Centers of ossification are vascularized areas of **mesenchymal connective tissue** where **mesenchymal cells** probably differentiate into **osteoprogenitor cells,** which differentiate into **osteoblasts**.

2. Lamellar Systems
Lamellar organization begins when **spicules** and **trabeculae** form into primitive osteons surrounding blood vessels. The first bone formed is **primary bone (woven bone)**, whose cells are larger and whose fibrillar arrangement is haphazard compared with **secondary (mature) bone**.

3. Cells
The cellular elements of intramembranous ossification are **osteoprogenitor cells, osteoblasts, osteocytes**, and **osteoclasts**. Additionally, mesenchymal and hemopoietic cells are also present.

E. Endochondral Ossification

1. Primary Ossification Center
The **perichondrium** of the **diaphysis** of the cartilage template becomes vascularized, followed by hypertrophy of the centrally located chondrocytes, confluence of contiguous lacunae, calcification of the cartilage remnants, and subsequent **chondrocytic death**. Concomitant with these events, the **chondrogenic cells** of the perichondrium become **osteoprogenitor cells**, which, in turn, differentiate into **osteoblasts**. The osteoblasts form the **subperiosteal bone collar**, thus converting the overlying **perichondrium** into a **periosteum**. A **periosteal bud** invades the diaphysis, entering the confluent **lacunae** left empty by the death of chondrocytes. Osteogenic cells give rise to osteoblasts, which elaborate bone on the **trabeculae of calcified cartilage**. Hemopoiesis begins in the primitive medullary cavity; **osteoclasts** (and, according to some, chondroclasts) develop, which resorb the bone-covered trabeculae of calcified cartilage as the subperiosteal bone collar becomes thicker and elongated.

2. Secondary Ossification Center
The **epiphyseal (secondary) center of ossification** is initiated somewhat after birth. It begins in the center of the epiphysis and proceeds radially from that point, leaving cartilage only at the **articular surface** and at the interface between the epiphysis and the diaphysis, the future **epiphyseal plate**.

3. Epiphyseal Plate
The **epiphyseal plate** is responsible for the future lengthening of a long bone. It is divided into five zones: (1) **zone of reserve cartilage**, a region of haphazardly arranged chondrocytes; (2) **zone of cell proliferation**, where chondrocytes are arranged in rows whose longitudinal axis parallels that of the growing bone; (3) **zone of cell maturation and hypertrophy**, where cells enlarge and the matrix between adjoining cells becomes very thin; (4) **zone of calcifying cartilage**, where lacunae become confluent and the matrix between adjacent rows of chondrocytes becomes calcified, causing subsequent chondrocytic death; and (5) **zone of provisional ossification**, where osteoblasts deposit bone on the calcified cartilage remnants between the adjacent rows. Osteoclasts (and, according to some, chondroclasts) resorb the calcified complex.

Blood and Hemopoiesis

5

The total volume of blood in an average person is approximately 5 liters; it is a **specialized type of connective tissue** composed of cells, cell fragments, and plasma, a fluid extracellular element. Blood circulates throughout the body and is well adapted for its manifold functions in transporting nutrients, oxygen, waste products, carbon dioxide, hormones, cells, and other substances. Moreover, blood also functions in the maintenance of body temperature.

● FORMED ELEMENTS OF BLOOD

The formed elements of blood are red blood cells (erythrocytes), white blood cells (leukocytes), and platelets. **Red blood cells** (**RBC**), the most populous, are anucleated and function entirely within the circulatory system by transporting oxygen and carbon dioxide to and from the tissues of the body. **White blood cells** (**WBC**) perform their functions outside the circulatory system and use the bloodstream as a mode of transportation to reach their destinations. There are two major categories of white blood cells, **agranulocytes** and **granulocytes**. Lymphocytes and monocytes compose the first group, whereas neutrophils, eosinophils, and basophils compose the latter. **Lymphocytes** are the basic cells of the immune system, and, although there are three categories (**T lymphocytes**, **B lymphocytes**, and **null cells**), special immunocytochemical techniques are necessary for their identification. When **monocytes** leave the bloodstream and enter the connective tissue spaces, they become known as **macrophages**, cells that function in phagocytosis of particulate matter as well as in assisting lymphocytes in their immunologic activities. **Granulocytes** are recognizable by their distinctive specific granules, whose coloration provides the classification for these cells. Granules of **neutrophils** possess very limited affinity to stains, whereas those of **eosinophils** stain a reddish-orange color and those of **basophils** stain a dark blue color with dyes used in studying blood preparations. Neutrophils function in **phagocytosis** of bacteria and because of that they are frequently referred to as microphages. Eosinophils participate in antiparasitic activities and phagocytose antigen-antibody complexes. Although the precise function of basophils is unknown, the contents of their granules are similar to those of mast cells and they also release these pharmacologic agents via degranulation. Additionally, basophils also produce and release other pharmacologic agents from the arachidonic acid in their membranes.

Circulating blood also contains cell fragments known as **platelets** (**thrombocytes**). These small, oval-to-round structures, derived from **megakaryocytes** of the bone marrow, function in hemostasis, the clotting mechanism of blood.

● PLASMA

Plasma, the fluid component of blood, comprises approximately 55% of the total blood volume. It contains electrolytes and ions, such as calcium, sodium, potassium, and bicarbonate; larger molecules, namely, **albumins**, **globulins**, and **fibrinogen**; and organic compounds as varied as amino acids, lipids, vitamins, hormones, and cofactors. Subsequent to clotting, a straw-colored **serum** is expressed from blood. This fluid is identical to plasma but contains no fibrinogen or other components necessary for the clotting reaction.

● HEMOPOIESIS

Circulating blood cells have relatively short life spans and must be replaced continuously by newly formed cells. This process of blood cell replacement is known as **hemopoiesis** (hematopoiesis). All blood cells develop from a single pluripotential precursor cell known as the **pluripotential hemopoietic stem cell** (**PHSC**). These cells undergo mitotic activity, whereby they give rise to two types of **multipotential hemopoietic stem cells**, **CFU-GEMM** (Colony-forming unit-granulocyte, erythrocyte, monocyte, megakaryocyte, previously known as CHU-S) and **CFU-Ly** (colony-forming unit-lymphocyte). Most PHSCs and other hemopoietic stem cells of adults are located in the **red bone marrow** of short and flat bones. The marrow of long bones is red in young individuals, but when it becomes infiltrated by fat in the adult, it takes on a yellow appearance and is known as yellow marrow. Although it was once believed that adipose cells accumulated the fat, it is now known that the cells actually responsible for storing fat in the marrow are the **adventitial reticular cells**. Stem cells, in response to various hemopoietic growth factors, undergo cell division and maintain the population of circulating erythrocytes, leukocytes, and platelets.

The nomenclature developed for the cells described below is based on their colorations with Wright or Giemsa's modification of the Romanovsky-type stains as applied to blood and marrow smears used in hematology.

Erythrocytic Series

Erythrocyte development proceeds from **CFU-S**, which, in response to elevated levels of **erythropoietin**, gives rise to cells known as **BFU-E**, which, in response to lower erythropoietin levels, then give rise to CFU-E. Although there are several generations of **CFU-E**, the later ones are recognizable histologically as **proerythroblasts**. These cells give rise to basophilic erythroblasts, which, in turn, undergo cell division to form **polychromatophilic erythroblasts**, which will divide mitotically to form **orthochromatophilic erythroblasts** (**normoblasts**). Cells of this stage no longer divide, will extrude their nuclei, and differentiate into **reticulocytes** (not to be confused with reticular cells of connective tissue), which, in turn, become mature red blood cells. Reticulocytes are stained with methylene blue for manual or thiazole orange for automated counting.

Granulocytic Series

The development of the granulocytic series is initiated from the multipotential **CFU-S**. The first histologically distinguishable member of this series is the **myeloblast**, which gives rise mitotically to **promyelocytes**, which also undergo cell division to yield **myelocytes**. Myelocytes are the first cells of this series to possess specific granules; therefore, neutrophilic, eosinophilic, and basophilic myelocytes may be recognized. The next cells in the series are **metamyelocytes**, which no longer divide but differentiate into **band** (**stab**) cells, the juvenile form, which will become mature granulocytes that enter the bloodstream (Table 5–1).

TABLE 5-1 • Formed Elements of Blood

Element	Diameter (μm) Smear	Section	No./mm³	% of Leukocytes	Granules	Function	Nucleus
Erythrocyte	7–8	6–7	5 × 10⁶ (males) 4.5 × 10⁶ (females)		None	Transport of O_2 and CO_2	None
Lymphocyte	8–10	7–8	1,500–2,500	20–25	Azurophilic only	Immunologic response	Large round acentric
Monocyte	12–15	10–12	200–800	3–8	Azurophilic only	Phagocytosis	Large, kidney-shaped
Neutrophil	9–12	8–9	3,500–7,000	60–70	Azurophilic and small specific (neutrophilic)	Phagocytosis	Polymor-phous
Eosinophil	10–14	9–11	150–400	2–4	Azurophilic, tertiary and large specific (eosinophilic)	Phagocytosis of antigen-antibody complexes and control of parasitic diseases	Bilobed (sausage-shaped)
Basophil	8–10	7–8	50–100	0.5–1	Azurophilic and large specific (basophilic) granules (heparin and histamine)	Perhaps phagocytosis and release of pharmacologic agents	Large, S-shaped
Platelets	2–4	1–3	250,000–400,000		Granulomere	Agglutination and clotting	None

Histophysiology

I. COAGULATION

Coagulation is the result of the exquisitely controlled interaction of a number of plasma proteins and coagulation factors. The regulatory mechanisms are in place so that coagulation typically occurs only if the endothelial lining of the vessel becomes injured. In the intact blood vessel, the endothelium manufactures inhibitors of platelet aggregation (NO and prostacyclins) as well as display agents, thrombomodulin and heparin-like molecule, on their luminal plasmalemmae that block coagulation. However, if the lining of a blood vessel is damaged, the endothelial cells switch from producing and displaying antiaggregation and anticoagulation agents and release **tissue factor** (tissue thromboplastin), **von Willebrand's factor**, and **endothelins**. Tissue factor complexes with **Factor VIIa** to catalyze the conversion of Factor X to its active form, the protease **Factor Xa**; von Willebrand's factor activates platelets, facilitating the adhesion of platelets to the exposed laminin and collagens, and induces them to release ADP and thrombospondin, which encourages their adhesion to each other; and endothelin stimulates the contraction of vascular smooth muscle cells in the region to constrict the damaged blood vessel and thus minimize blood loss. The process of coagulation ensues in one of two convergent pathways, **extrinsic** and **intrinsic**, both of which lead to the final step of converting fibrinogen to fibrin. The extrinsic pathway has a faster onset and depends on the release of tissue factor. The intrinsic pathway is initiated slower, is dependent on contact between vessel wall collagen and platelets (or Factor XII), and requires the presence of von Willebrand's factor and **Factor VIII**. These two factors form a complex that not only binds to exposed collagen but also attaches to receptor sites on the platelet plasmalemma, affecting platelet aggregation and adherence to the vessel wall. The two pathways intersect at the conversion of Factor X to Factor Xa and from that point on the remaining steps of the coagulation pathway are referred to as the **common pathway**.

II. NEUTROPHIL FUNCTION

Neutrophils possess three types of granules: specific granules, azurophilic granules, and tertiary granules. **Specific granules** contain pharmacologic agents and enzymes that permit the neutrophils to perform their antimicrobial roles. **Azurophilic granules** are lysosomes, containing the various lysosomal hydrolases, as well as myeloperoxidase, bacterial permeability increasing protein, lysozyme, and collagenase. **Tertiary granules** contain glycoproteins that are dedicated for insertion into the cell membrane as well as gelatinase and cathepsins. These cells use the contents of the three types of granules to perform their antimicrobial function. When neutrophils arrive at their site of action, they exocytose the contents of their granules. Gelatinase increases the neutrophil's capability of migrating through the basal lamina, and the glycoproteins of the tertiary granules aid in the recognition and phagocytosis of bacteria into phagosomes of the neutrophil. Azurophilic granules and specific granules fuse with and release their hydrolytic enzymes into the phagosomes, thus initiating the enzymatic degradation of the microorganisms. In addition to the enzymatic degradation, microorganisms are also destroyed by the capability of neutrophils to undergo a sudden increase in O_2 utilization known as a respiratory burst. The O_2 is used by the cell to form superoxides, hydrogen peroxide, and hypochlorous acid, highly reactive compounds that destroy bacteria within the phagosomes. Frequently, the avid response of neutrophils results in the release of some of these highly potent compounds into the surrounding connective tissue, precipitating tissue damage. The neutrophils also produce leukotrienes from plasmalemma arachidonic acids to aid in the initiation of an inflammatory response. Subsequent to the performance of these functions, the neutrophils die and become a major component of pus.

III. POSTNATAL HEMOPOIESIS

Hemopoiesis in the adult involves a single type of stem cell, the **pluripotential hemopoietic stem cell** (**PHSC**), which resembles a lymphocyte and is a member of the **null cell** population of lymphocytes. PHSCs are located in large numbers in the bone marrow, but they are also present in circulating blood. These cells have a high mitotic index and form more PHSCs as well as two **multipotential hemopoietic stem cells**, **CFU-GEMM** and **CFU-Ly**. Morphologically, CFU-GEMM and CFU-Ly are identical to PHSCs, but they have a more limited potential. CFU-Ly, known as the **lymphoid stem cell**, will give rise to CFU-LyB and CFU-LyT, the progenitors of B and T lymphocytes, respectively. CFU-GEMM is also referred to as the **myeloid stem cell**, since it will give rise to **BFU-E** (and/or **CFU-E**), the progenitor of erythrocytes; **CFU-Eo**, the progenitor of eosinophils; **CFU-Ba**, the progenitor of basophils; and **CFU-NM**, which will give rise to **CFU-N** and **CFU-M**, the progenitors of neutrophils and monocytes, respectively. **Stem cells** and **progenitor cells** resemble lymphocytes, whereas **precursor cells** can be recognized histologically as members of a cell population that will differentiate into a particular blood cell. Furthermore, stem cells are less committed than are progenitor cells.

Several **hemopoietic growth factors** activate and promote hemopoiesis. These act by binding to plasma membrane receptors of their target cell, controlling their mitotic rate as well as the number of mitotic events. Additionally, they stimulate cell differentiation and enhance the survival of the progenitor cell population. The best known factors are **erythropoietin** (acts on BFU-E and CFU-E), **interleukin–3** (acts on PHSC, CFU-S, and myeloid progenitor cells), **interleukin–7** (acts on CFU-Ly), **granulocyte-macrophage colony-stimulating factor** (acts on granulocyte and monocyte progenitor cells), **granulocyte colony-stimulating factor** (acts on granulocyte progenitor cells), and **macrophage colony-stimulating factor** (acts on monocyte progenitor cells).

IV. LYMPHOCYTES

The three types of lymphocytes—B lymphocytes (B cells), T lymphocytes (T cells), and null cells—are morphologically indistinguishable. It is customary to speak of **T cells** as being responsible for the **cellularly mediated immune response** and **B cells** as functioning in the **humorally mediated immune response**. **Null cells** are few in number, possess no determinants on their cell membrane, and are of two types, **pluripotential hemopoietic stem cells** and **natural killer cells**.

A. T Cells

T cells not only function in the cellularly mediated immune response but also are responsible for the formation of cytokines that facilitate the initiation of the humorally mediated immune response. They are formed in the bone marrow and migrate to the thymic cortex to become immunocompetent cells. They recognize **epitopes** (antigenic determinants) that are displayed by cells possessing **HLA** (human leukocyte antigen; also known as major histocompatibility complex molecules). There are various subtypes of T cells, each possessing a **T-cell receptor** (**TCR**) surface determinant and **cluster of differentiation determinants** (**CD molecules**). The former recognizes the epitope, whereas the latter recognizes the type of HLA on the displaying cell surface.

The various subtypes of T cells are T helper cells (T_H1 and T_H2), cytotoxic T cells (T_C), T regulatory cells (T_{reg}), natural T killer cells, and T memory cells.

B. B Cells

B cells bear HLA type II (also known as MHC II) surface markers and **surface immunoglobulins** (SIG) on their plasmalemma. They are formed in and become immunocompetent in the bone marrow. They are responsible for the humoral response, and, under the direction of T_H2 cells and in response to an antigenic challenge, will differentiate into antibody-manufacturing **plasma cells** and **B memory cells**.

C. Natural Killer (NK) Cells

NK cells belong to the null cell population. They possess F_C receptors but no cell surface determinants and are responsible for **nonspecific cytotoxicity** against virus-infected and tumor cells. They also function in **antibody-dependent cell-mediated cytotoxicity** (**ADCC**).

CLINICAL CONSIDERATIONS

NADPH Oxidase Deficiency

Certain individuals suffer from persistent bacterial infection due to a hereditary NADPH oxidase deficiency. The neutrophils of these individuals are unable to effect a respiratory burst and therefore are incapable of forming the highly reactive compounds such as hypochlorous acid, hydrogen peroxide, and superoxide that assist in the killing of bacteria within their phagosomes.

Multiple Myeloma

Multiple myeloma is a relatively uncommon malignant neoplasm with greater incidence in males than females. Its origin is the bone marrow, and it is characterized by the presence of large numbers of malignant plasma cells that may also be abnormal in morphology. These cells accumulate in the bone marrow of various regions of the skeletal system. Frequently the cell proliferation is so great in the marrow that it places pressure on the walls of the marrow cavity, causing bone pain and even fractures of bones such as the ribs. These cells also produce abnormal proteins such as Bence-Jones proteins, which enter the urine, where they can be detected to provide a diagnosis for multiple myeloma. Treatment includes local radiation therapy, aimed at the bones in which the patient is experiencing pain. Patients with Bence-Jones proteins in their urine are instructed to drink lots of fluids to reduce the chances of dehydration and of kidney failure. Chemotherapy has been shown to be effective in reducing the progression of the disease.

Infectious Mononucleosis

Infection with the Epstein-Barr virus causes infectious mononucleosis, also referred to as the "kissing disease" because it is common among high school and college-aged individuals and is frequently spread by saliva. Patients suffering from infectious mononucleosis have symptoms that include sore throat, swollen and painful lymph nodes, low energy, and an elevated lymphocyte count. The disease can be life-threatening in immunosuppressed individuals.

PLATE 5-1 Circulating Blood

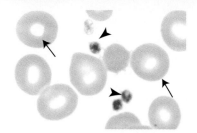

FIGURE 1 • Red Blood Cells. Human. ×1325.

Red blood cells (*arrows*) display a central clear region that represents the thinnest area of the biconcave disc. Note that the platelets (*arrowheads*) possess a central dense region, the granulomere, and a peripheral light region, the hyalomere.

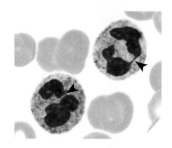

FIGURE 2 • Neutrophils. Human. ×1325.

Neutrophils display a somewhat granular cytoplasm and lobulated (*arrowheads*) nuclei.

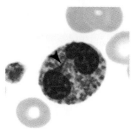

FIGURE 3 • Eosinophils. Human. ×1325.

Eosinophils arc recognized by their large, pink granules and their sausage-shaped nucleus. Observe the slender connecting link (*arrowhead*) between the two lobes of the nucleus.

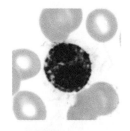

FIGURE 4 • Basophils. Human. ×1325.

Basophils are characterized by their dense, dark, large granules.

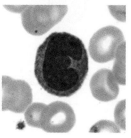

FIGURE 5 • Monocytes. Human. ×1325.

Monocytes are characterized by their large size, acentric, kidney-shaped nucleus, and lack of specific granules.

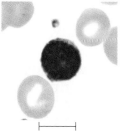

FIGURE 6 • Lymphocytes. Human. ×1325.

Lymphocytes are small cells that possess a single, large, acentrically located nucleus and a narrow rim of light blue cytoplasm.

1 cm = 7.5 µm

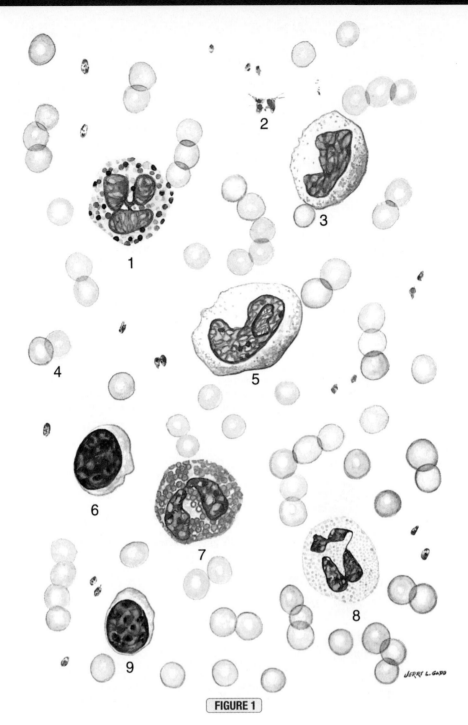

FIGURE 1

KEY

1. Basophil
2. Platelets
3. Monocyte
4. Erythrocytes
5. Monocyte
6. Lymphocyte
7. Eosinophil
8. Neutrophil
9. Lymphocyte

PLATE 5-3 Blood and Hemopoiesis

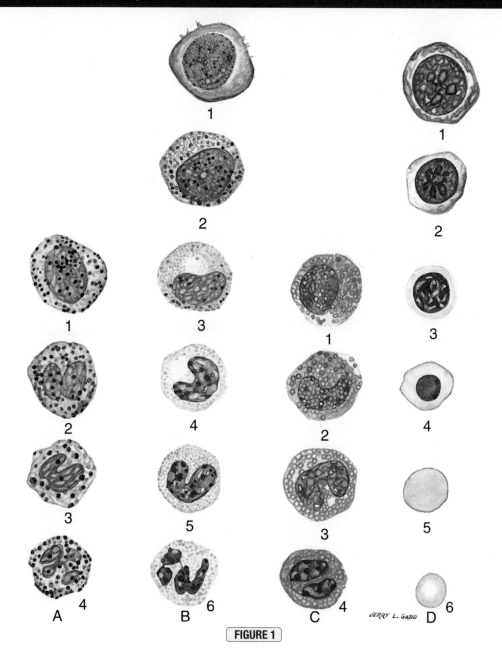

FIGURE 1

KEY

A
1. Basophilic myelocyte
2. Basophilic metamyelocyte
3. Basophil stab cell
4. Basophil

B
1. Myeloblast
2. Promyelocyte
3. Neutrophilic myelocyte
4. Neutrophilic metamyelocyte

5. Neutrophilic stab cell
6. Neutrophil

C
1. Eosinophilic myelocyte
2. Eosinophilic metamyelocyte
3. Eosinophil stab cell
4. Eosinophil

D
1. Proerythroblast
2. Basophilic erythroblast
3. Polychromatophilic erythroblast
4. Orthochromatophilic erythroblast
5. Reticulocyte
6. Erythrocyte

FIGURE 1 • Bone marrow. Human. Paraffin section. ×132.

This transverse section of a decalcified human rib displays the presence of **haversian canals** (H), **Volkmann's canals** (V), **osteocytes** (O) in their lacunae, and the **endosteum** (E). The marrow presents numerous **adventitial reticular cells** (A), blood vessels, and **sinusoids** (S). Moreover, the forming blood elements are also evident as small nuclei (*arrows*). Note the large **megakaryocytes** (M), cells that are the precursors of platelets. The *boxed area* is represented in Figure 2.

FIGURE 3 • Blood smear. Human. Wright stain. ×270

This normal blood smear presents **erythrocytes** (R), **neutrophils** (N), and **platelets** (P). The apparent holes in the centers of the erythrocytes represent the thinnest areas of the biconcave discs. Note that the erythrocytes far outnumber the platelets, and they in turn are much more numerous than the white blood cells. Since neutrophils constitute the highest percentage of white blood cells, they are the ones most frequently encountered of the white blood cell population.

FIGURE 2 • Bone marrow. Human. Paraffin section. ×270.

This photomicrograph is a higher magnification of the *boxed area* of Figure 1. Observe the presence of **osteocytes** (O) in their lacunae as well as the flattened cells of the **endosteum** (E). The endothelial lining of the sinusoids (*arrows*) are clearly evident, as are the numerous cells that are in the process of hemopoiesis. Two large **megakaryocytes** (M) are also discernible.

FIGURE 4 • Bone marrow smear. Human. Wright stain. ×270.

This normal bone marrow smear presents forming blood cells as well as **erythrocytes** (R) and **platelets** (P). In comparison with a normal peripheral blood smear (Figure 3), marrow possesses many more nucleated cells. Some of these are of the erythrocytic series (*arrows*), whereas others are of the granulocytic series (*arrowheads*).

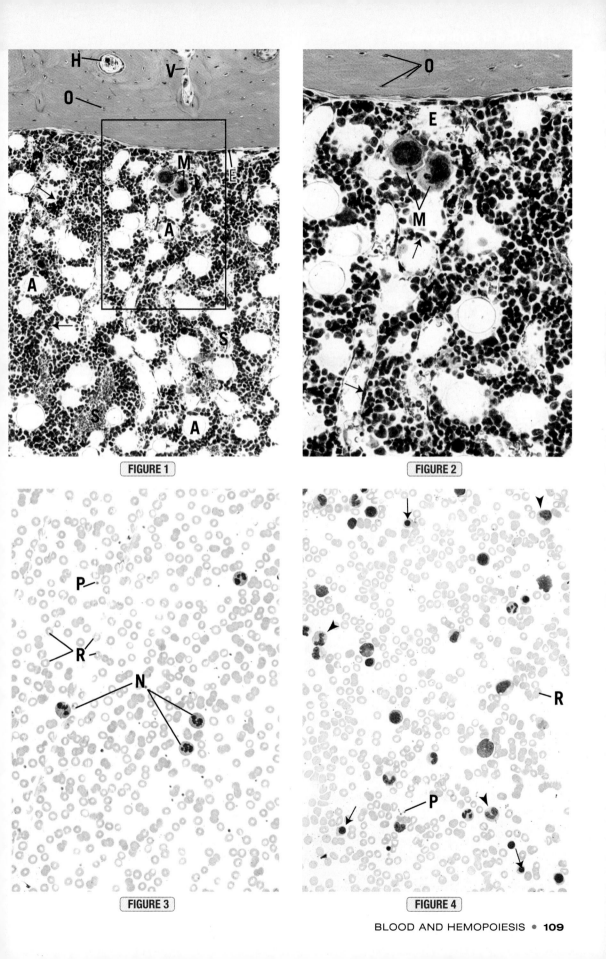

FIGURE 1

FIGURE 2

FIGURE 3

FIGURE 4

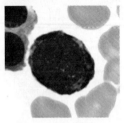

FIGURE 1 • Human marrow smear. ×1325.

Proerythroblast.

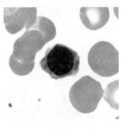

FIGURE 2 • Human marrow smear. ×1325.

Basophilic erythroblast.

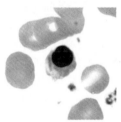

FIGURE 3 • Human marrow smear. ×1325.

Polychromatophilic erythroblast.

FIGURE 4 • Human marrow smear. ×1325.

Orthochromatophilic erythroblast.

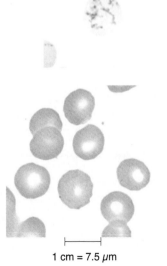

FIGURE 5 • Human marrow smear. Methylene blue stain.
×1325.

Reticulocyte.

FIGURE 6 • Human marrow smear. ×1325.

Erythrocyte.

1 cm = 7.5 µm

PLATE 5-6 Granulocytopoiesis

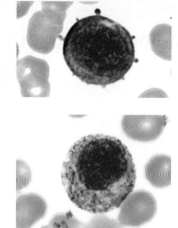

FIGURE 1 • Myeloblast. Human bone marrow smear. ×1325.

FIGURE 2 • Promyelocyte. Human bone marrow smear. ×1325.

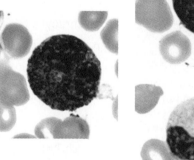

FIGURE 3b • Neutrophilic myelocyte. Human bone marrow smear. ×1325.

FIGURE 3a • Eosinophilic myelocyte. Human bone marrow smear. ×1325.

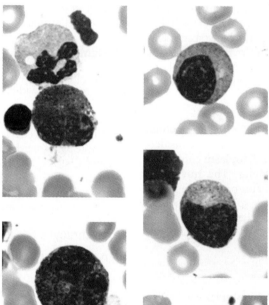

FIGURE 4b • Neutrophilic metamyelocyte. Human bone marrow smear. ×1325.

FIGURE 4a • Eosinophilic metamyelocyte. Human bone marrow smear. ×1325.

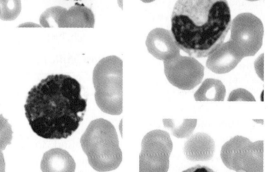

FIGURE 5b • Neutrophilic stab cell. Human bone marrow smear. ×1325.

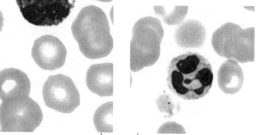

FIGURE 5a • Eosinophilic stab cell. Human bone marrow smear. ×1325.

1 cm = 7.5 μm

FIGURE 6 • Neutrophil. Human bone marrow smear. ×1325.

Summary of Histological Organization

I. CIRCULATING BLOOD*

A. Erythrocytes (RBC)

RBCs are pink, biconcave disks that are 7–8 μm in diameter. They are filled with hemoglobin and possess no nuclei.

B. Agranulocytes

1. Lymphocytes
Histologically, **lymphocytes** may be **small**, **medium**, or **large** (this bears no relationship to T cells, B cells, or null cells). Most lymphocytes are small (8–10 μm in diameter) and possess a dense, blue, acentrically positioned nucleus that occupies most of the cell, leaving a thin rim of light blue, peripheral cytoplasm. Azurophilic granules (lysosomes) may be evident in the cytoplasm.

2. Monocytes
Monocytes are the largest of all circulating blood cells (12–15 μm in diameter). There is a considerable amount of **grayish-blue cytoplasm** containing numerous azurophilic granules. The **nucleus** is acentric and kidney-shaped and possesses a coarse chromatin network with clear spaces. Lobes of the nucleus are superimposed on themselves, and their outlines appear to be distinctly demarcated.

C. Granulocytes

1. **Neutrophils,** the most populous of the leukocytes, are 9–12 mm in diameter and display a light pink cytoplasm housing many azurophilic and smaller specific granules. The specific granules do not stain well, hence the name of these cells. The nucleus is dark blue, coarse, and multilobed, with most being two- to three-lobed with thin connecting strands.

2. **Eosinophils** are 10–14 mm in diameter and possess numerous refractive, spherical, large, reddish-orange specific granules. Azurophilic granules are also present. The nucleus, which is brownish-black, is bilobed, resembling sausage links united by a thin connecting strand.

3. **Basophils,** the least numerous of all leukocytes, are 8–10 mm in diameter. Frequently, their cytoplasm is so filled with dark, large, basophilic-specific granules that they appear to press against the cell membrane, giving it an angular appearance. The specific granules usually mask the azurophilic granules as well as the S-shaped, light blue nucleus.

D. Platelets

Platelets, occasionally called **thrombocytes**, are small, round (2–4 μm in diameter) cell fragments. As such, they possess no nuclei, are frequently clumped together, and present with a dark blue, central granular region, the **granulomere**, and a light blue, peripheral, clear region, the **hyalomere**.

II. HEMOPOIESIS*

During the maturation process, hemopoietic cells undergo clearly evident morphologic alterations. As the cells become more mature, they decrease in size. Their nuclei also become smaller, the chromatin network appears coarser, and their nucleoli (which resemble pale grayish spaces) disappear. The granulocytes first acquire azurophilic and then specific granules, and their nuclei become segmented. Cells of the erythrocytic series never display granules and eventually lose their nuclei.

A. Erythrocytic Series

1. Proerythroblast
a. *Cytoplasm*
Light blue to deep blue clumps in a pale grayish-blue background.

b. *Nucleus*
Round with a fine chromatin network; it is a rich, burgundy red with 3–5 pale gray nucleoli.

2. Basophilic Erythroblast
a. *Cytoplasm*
Bluish clumps in a pale blue cytoplasm with a hint of grayish pink in the background.

b. *Nucleus*
Round, somewhat coarser than the previous stage; burgundy red. A nucleolus may be present.

3. Polychromatophilic Erythroblast
a. *Cytoplasm*
Yellowish pink with bluish tinge.

---

*All of the colors designated in this summary are based on the Wright or Giemsa's modification of the Romanovsky-type stains as applied to blood smears.

b. Nucleus

Small and round with a condensed, coarse chromatin network; dark, reddish black. No nucleoli are present.

4. Orthochromatophilic Erythroblast

a. Cytoplasm

Pinkish with a slight tinge of blue.

b. Nucleus

Dark, condensed, round structure that may be in the process of being extruded from the cell.

5. Reticulocyte

a. Cytoplasm

Appears just like a normal, circulating RBC; if stained with supravital dyes (e.g., methylene blue), however, a bluish reticulum—composed mostly of rough endoplasmic reticulum—is evident.

b. Nucleus

Not present.

B. Granulocytic Series

The first two stages of the granulocytic series, the myeloblast and promyelocyte, possess no specific granules. These make their appearance in the myelocyte stage, when the three types of myelocytes (neutrophilic, eosinophilic, and basophilic) may be distinguished. Since they only differ from each other in their specific granules, only the neutrophilic series is described in this summary, with the understanding that myelocytes, metamyelocytes, and stab (band) cells occur in these three varieties.

1. Myeloblast

a. Cytoplasm

Small blue clumps in a light blue background. No granules. Cytoplasmic blebs extend along the periphery of the cell.

b. Nucleus

Reddish-blue, round nucleus with fine chromatin network. Two or three pale gray nucleoli are evident.

2. Promyelocyte

a. Cytoplasm

The cytoplasm is bluish and displays numerous, small, dark, azurophilic granules.

b. Nucleus

Reddish-blue, round nucleus whose chromatin strands appear more coarse than in the previous stage. A nucleolus is usually present.

3. Neutrophilic Myelocyte

a. Cytoplasm

Pale blue cytoplasm containing dark azurophilic and smaller neutrophilic (specific) granules. A clear, paranuclear Golgi region is evident.

b. Nucleus

Round, usually somewhat flattened, acentric nucleus, with a somewhat coarse chromatin network. Nucleoli are not distinct.

4. Neutrophilic Metamyelocyte

a. Cytoplasm

Similar to the previous stage except that the cytoplasm is paler in color and the Golgi area is nestled in the indentation of the nucleus.

b. Nucleus

Kidney-shaped, acentric nucleus with a dense, dark chromatin network. Nucleoli are not present.

5. Neutrophilic Stab (Band) Cell

a. Cytoplasm

A little more blue than the cytoplasm of a mature neutrophil. Both azurophilic and neutrophilic (specific) granules are present.

b. Nucleus

The nucleus is horseshoe-shaped and dark blue, with a very coarse chromatin network. Nucleoli are not present.

Muscle

6

The ability of animals to move is due to the presence of specific cells that have become highly differentiated, so that they function almost exclusively in contraction. The contractile process has been harnessed by the organism to permit various modes of movement and other activities for its survival. Some of these activities depend on quick contractions of short duration; others depend on long-lasting contractions without the necessity for rapid actions, whereas still others depend on powerful, rhythmic contractions that must be repeated in rapid sequences. These varied needs are accommodated by three types of muscle, namely, skeletal, smooth, and cardiac. There are basic similarities among the three muscle types. They are all **mesodermally derived** and are elongated parallel to their axis of contraction; they possess numerous mitochondria to accommodate their high energy requirements, and all contain **contractile elements** known as **myofilaments**, in the form of **actin** and **myosin**, as well as additional contractile-associated proteins. Myofilaments of skeletal and cardiac muscles are arranged in a specific ordered array that gives rise to a repeated sequence of uniform banding along their length—hence their collective name, **striated muscle**.

Since muscle cells are much longer than they are wide, they are commonly referred to as **muscle fibers**. However, it must be appreciated that these fibers are living entities, unlike the nonliving fibers of connective tissue. Neither are they analogous to nerve fibers, which are living extensions of nerve cells. Often, certain unique terms are used to describe muscle cells; thus, the muscle cell membrane is **sarcolemma** (although earlier use of this term included the attendant basal lamina and reticular fibers), cytoplasm is **sarcoplasm**, mitochondria are **sarcosomes**, and endoplasmic reticulum is **sarcoplasmic reticulum**.

● SKELETAL MUSCLE

Skeletal muscle (see Graphics 6-1 and 6-2) is invested by dense collagenous connective tissue known as the **epimysium**, which penetrates the substance of the gross muscle, separating it into fascicles. Each fascicle is surrounded by **perimysium**, a looser connective tissue. Finally, each individual muscle fiber within a fascicle is enveloped by fine reticular fibers, the **endomysium.** The vascular and nerve supplies of the muscle travel in these interrelated connective tissue compartments. Each skeletal muscle fiber is roughly cylindrical in shape, possessing numerous elongated nuclei located at the periphery of the cell, just deep to the sarcolemma. Longitudinally sectioned muscle fibers display intracellular contractile elements, which are the parallel arrays of longitudinally disposed **myofibrils**. This arrangement produces an overall effect of **crossbanding** of alternating light and dark bands traversing each skeletal muscle cell. The dark bands are **A bands**, and the light bands are **I bands**. Each I band is bisected by a thin, dark **Z disc**, and the region of the myofibril extending from Z disc to Z disc, the **sarcomere**, is the contractile unit of skeletal muscle cell. The A band is bisected by a paler **H zone**, the center of which is marked by the dark **M disc**. During muscle contraction, the various transverse bands behave characteristically, in that the width of the A band remains constant, the two Z discs move closer to each other approaching the A band, and the I band and H zone become extinguished. Electron microscopy has revealed that banding is the result of interdigitation of thick and thin myofilaments. These thin filaments are attached to Z discs by α-actinin. The I band consists solely of thin filaments, whereas the A band, with the exception of its H and M components, consists of both thick and thin filaments. During contraction the thick and thin filaments slide past each other (sliding filament theory of contraction), and the Z discs are brought near the ends of the thick filaments. It should also be noted that the thin filaments are held in register by two molecules of the inelastic protein **nebulin**. Moreover, the thick filaments are affixed to each other at the M disc by **C proteins** and **myomesin** and are connected to the Z disc by elastic proteins called **titin**. Since titin molecules form an elastic lattice around the thick filaments, they facilitate the maintenance of the spatial relationship of these thick filaments to each other as well as to the thin filaments.

Striations of skeletal muscle are resolved into **A bands** and **I bands**. I bands are divided into two equal halves by a **Z disk**, and each A band has a light zone, the **H band**. The center of each H band is a dark **M band**. Adjacent myofibrils are secured to each other by the intermediate filaments desmin and vimentin. The basic contractile unit of the skeletal muscle cell is the **sarcomere**, a precisely ordered collection of **myofilaments** (**thick** and **thin filaments**). Tubular invaginations, **T tubules** (**transverse tubules**), of the muscle cell membrane penetrate deep into the sarcoplasm and surround myofibrils in such a manner that at the junction of each A and I band these tubules become associated with the dilated **terminal cisternae** of the sarcoplasmic reticulum (smooth ER), forming triads.

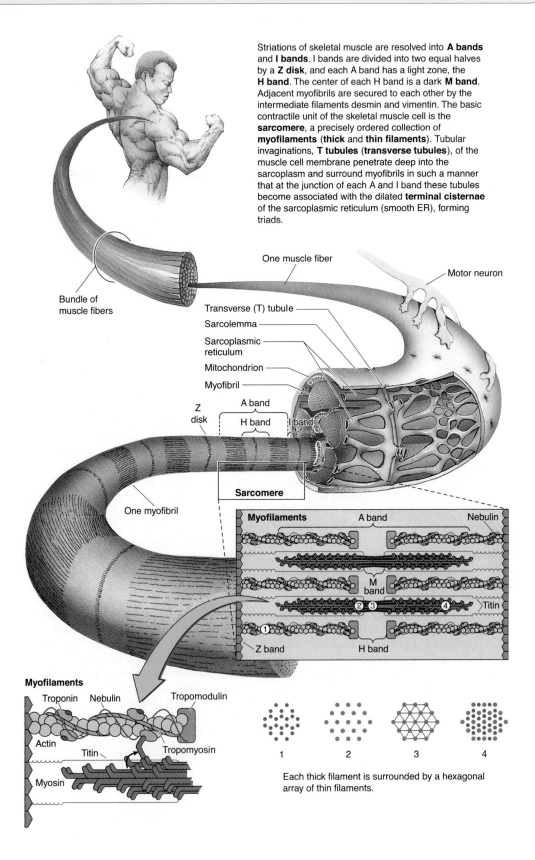

One muscle fiber

Motor neuron

Bundle of muscle fibers

Transverse (T) tubule

Sarcolemma

Sarcoplasmic reticulum

Mitochondrion

Myofibril

Z disk

A band

H band   I band

One myofibril

Sarcomere

Myofilaments   A band   Nebulin

M band

Titin

Z band   H band

Myofilaments

Troponin   Nebulin   Tropomodulin

Actin

Titin   Tropomyosin

Myosin

1   2   3   4

Each thick filament is surrounded by a hexagonal array of thin filaments.

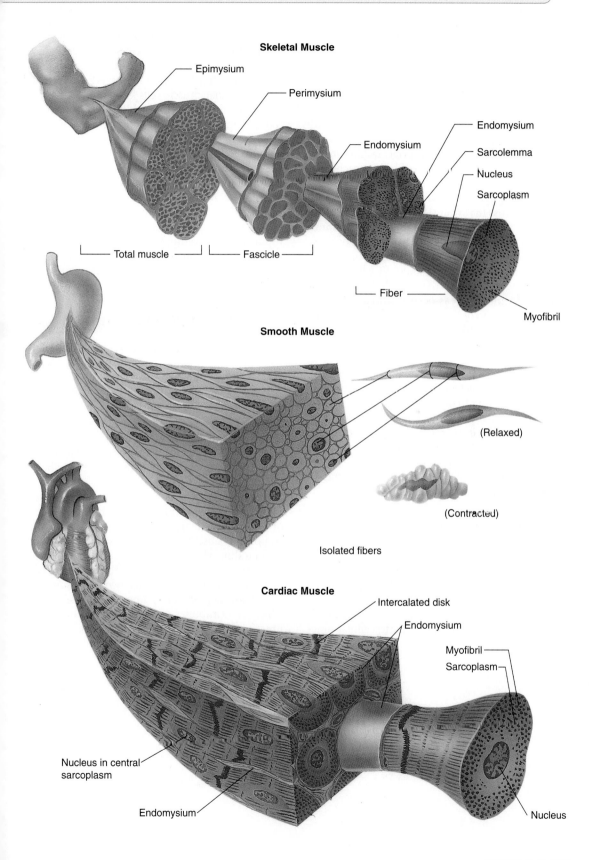

Skeletal Muscle

Epimysium

Perimysium

Endomysium

Endomysium

Sarcolemma

Nucleus

Sarcoplasm

Total muscle

Fascicle

Fiber

Myofibril

Smooth Muscle

(Relaxed)

(Contracted)

Isolated fibers

Cardiac Muscle

Intercalated disk

Endomysium

Myofibril

Sarcoplasm

Nucleus in central sarcoplasm

Endomysium

Nucleus

Moreover, each Z disc is surrounded by intermediate filaments known as **desmin.** The desmin filaments are bound to each other and to the Z discs by **plectin** filaments. Desmin filaments insert into the **costameres,** which are regions of the sarcolemma that are dedicated for the attachment of these intermediate filaments. The heat shock protein αB-crystallin protects the desmin intermediate filaments by binding to them at their contact with the Z disc. The desmin–plectin–αB-crystallin complex, along with the costameres, ensures that the myofibrils of a muscle cell are aligned in the appropriate fashion so that the contraction of all of the myofibrils of each muscle cell occurs in a synchronized fashion.

Nerve impulses, transmitted at the **myoneural junction** across the **synaptic cleft** by **acetylcholine,** cause a wave of depolarization of the sarcolemma, with the eventual result of muscle contraction. This wave of depolarization is distributed throughout the muscle fiber by transverse tubules (**T tubules**), tubular invaginations of the sarcolemma. The T tubules become closely associated with the terminal cisterns of the sarcoplasmic reticulum (SR), so that each T tubule is flanked by two of these elements of the SR, forming a triad. During depolarization the T tubules carry the impulse within the muscle fiber, thus causing the release of calcium ions from the SR. Calcium ions interact with the thin myofilaments to permit contraction to occur.

As a protective mechanism against muscle fiber tears as a result of overstretching and to provide information concerning the position of the body in three-dimensional space, tendons and muscles are equipped with specialized receptors, **Golgi tendon organs** and **muscle spindles**, respectively.

● CARDIAC MUSCLE

Cardiac muscle (see Graphic 6-2) cells are also striated, but each cell usually contains only one centrally placed nucleus. These cells form specialized junctions known as **intercalated discs,** as they interdigitate with each other. These intercalated discs act as Z lines as well as regions of intercellular junctions. Z discs have **transverse portions** that specialize in cell-cell attachments by forming numerous desmosomes and fasciae adherentes and **lateral portions** that are rich in gap junctions, thus permitting cell-to-cell communications to occur. Heart muscle contraction is involuntary, and the cells possess an inherent rhythm. The heart possesses a group of specialized cardiac muscle cells known as the **SA node** (sinoatrial node), which establishes the rate of contraction and initiates contraction of the atrial muscles. The impulse is transmitted to another group of specialized cardiac muscle cells, the **AV node** (atrioventricular node), which holds up the impulse for a few milliseconds; the impulse then travels along the **bundle of His** to the **Purkinje fibers** (both of which are specialized cardiac muscle cells) to cause contraction of the ventricles. The SA node receives input from the sympathetic and parasympathetic components of the autonomic nervous sytem; the former increases and the latter decreases the rate of contraction of the heart.

● SMOOTH MUSCLE

Smooth muscle (see Graphic 6-2) is also involuntary. Each fusiform smooth muscle cell houses a single, centrally placed nucleus, which becomes corkscrew shaped during contraction of the cell. Smooth muscle cells contain an apparently haphazard arrangement of thick and thin filaments, whose interdigitation during contraction is harnessed by an intermediate type of filament. These intermediate filaments, **desmin** and **vimentin**, form dense bodies where they cross each other and at points of attachment to the cytoplasmic aspect of the sarcolemma. It is interesting to note that although the thin filaments of smooth muscle possess F actin and tropomyosin, troponin is absent and its function is assumed by calmodulin, which becomes complexed with calcium. Smooth muscle may be of the **multiunit type,** in which each cell possesses its own nerve supply, or of the **unitary** (visceral) smooth muscle type, in which nerve impulses are transmitted via **nexus** (**gap junctions**) from one muscle cell to its neighbor.

Histophysiology

I. MYOFILAMENTS

Thin filaments (7 nm in diameter and 1 μm in length) are composed of **F actin**, double-helical polymers of **G actin** molecules, resembling a pearl necklace twisted upon itself. Each groove of the helix houses linear **tropomyosin** molecules positioned end to end. Associated with each tropomyosin molecule is a **troponin** molecule composed of three polypeptides: **troponin T (TnT)**, **troponin I (TnI)**, and **troponin C (TnC)**. TnI binds to actin, masking its active site (where it is able to interact with myosin); TnT binds to tropomyosin; and TnC (a molecule similar to **calmodulin**) has a high affinity for calcium ions. The **plus end** of each thin filament is bound to a Z disc by **α-actinin**. Additionally, two **nebulins**, inelastic proteins that ensure that the thin filament is of the proper length, entwine along the entire extent of each thin filament and anchor it to the Z disc. The **negative end** of each thin filament extends to the junction of the A and I bands and is capped by **tropomodulin**.

Thick filaments (15 nm in diameter and 1.5 μm in length) are composed of 200–300 **myosin molecules** arranged in an antiparallel fashion. Each myosin molecule is composed of two pairs of light chains and two identical heavy chains. Each **myosin heavy chain** resembles a golf club, with a linear tail and a globular head, where the tails are wrapped around each other in a helical fashion. Digesting the myosin heavy chain with the enzyme **trypsin** cleaves it into a linear (most of the tail) segment (**light meromyosin**) and a globular segment with the remainder of the tail (**heavy meromyosin**). Another enzyme, papain, cleaves **heavy meromyosin** into a short tail region (**S2 fragment**) and a pair of globular regions (**S1 fragments**). Each pair of **myosin light chains** is associated with one of the S1 fragments. S1 fragments have **ATPase activity** but require the association with actin for this activity to be manifest. Thick filaments are anchored to Z discs by the linear, elastic protein **titin** and are linked to adjacent thick filaments, at the M line, by the proteins **myomesin** and **C protein**.

II. SLIDING FILAMENT MODEL OF SKELETAL MUSCLE CONTRACTION

During **contraction**, the thin filaments slide past the thick filaments, penetrating deeper into the A band; thus, the sarcomere becomes shorter, whereas the myofilaments remain the same length. As a consequence of the sliding of the filaments, the I and H bands disappear, the A band remains the same width (as before contraction), the Z discs are pulled closer to each other, and the entire sarcomere is shortened in length.

Subsequent to the transmission of the impulse across the myoneural junction, the **T tubules** convey the impulse throughout the muscle cell. **Voltage-sensitive** integral proteins, **dihydropyridine-sensitive receptors** (**DHSR**) located in the T tubule membrane, are in contact with **calcium channels** (**ryanodine receptors**) in the terminal cisternae of the **sarcoplasmic reticulum** (**SR**). This complex is visible with the electron microscope and is referred to as **junctional feet**. During depolarization of the skeletal muscle sarcolemma, the DHSRs of the T tubule undergo voltage-induced conformational change, causing the calcium channels of the terminal cisternae to open, permitting the influx of Ca^{2+} ions into the cytosol. **Troponin C** of the thin filament binds the calcium ions and changes its conformation, pressing the **tropomyosin** deeper into the grooves of the F actin filament, thus exposing the **active site** (myosin-binding site) on the **actin** molecule.

ATP, bound to the globular head (**S1 fragment**) of the myosin molecule, is **hydrolyzed**, but both **ADP** and P_i **remain attached** on the S1. The myosin molecule swivels so that the myosin head approximates the active site on the actin molecule. The P_i moiety is released, and in the presence of **calcium**, a link is formed between the **actin** and **myosin**. The bound **ADP** is freed, and the **myosin head** alters its conformation, **moving the thin filament** toward the center of the sarcomere. A new **ATP** attaches to the globular head, and the **myosin dissociates** from the active site of the **actin**. This cycle is repeated 200 to 300 times for complete contraction of the sarcomere.

Relaxation ensues when the **calcium pump** of the **SR** transports calcium from the cytosol into the SR cisterna, where it is bound by **calsequestrin**. The decreased cytosolic Ca^{2+} induces TnC to lose its bound calcium ions, the TnC molecule returns to its previous conformational state, the tropomyosin molecule returns to its original location, and the active site of the actin molecule is once again masked.

III. SMOOTH MUSCLE

A. Contractile Elements

Although the **thick** and **thin filaments** of smooth muscle are not arranged into myofibrils, they are organized so that they are aligned obliquely to the longitudinal axis of the cell. **Myosin molecules** of smooth muscle are unusual, since the **light meromyosin moiety** is folded in such a fashion that its free terminus binds to a "sticky region" of the globular S1 portion. The thin filaments are attached

to **cytoplasmic densities** as well as to **dense bodies** along the cytoplasmic aspect of the sarcolemma, Z disc analogs (containing α-actinin), as are the **intermediate filaments** (**desmin** in multiunit smooth muscle and **vimentin** and **desmin** in unitary smooth muscle cells). The cytosol is rich in **calmodulin** and the enzyme **myosin light-chain kinase**.

B. Contraction

Calcium, released from **caveolae**, binds to calmodulin. The **Ca^{2+}-calmodulin complex** activates myosin light-chain kinase, which **phosphorylates** one of the **myosin light chains**, altering its conformation. This causes the free terminus of the light meromyosin to be released from the S1 moiety. **ATP** binds to the **S1**, and the resultant interaction between actin and myosin is similar to that of skeletal (and cardiac) muscle. As long as calcium and ATP are present, the smooth muscle cell will remain contracted. Smooth muscle contraction lasts longer but develops slower than cardiac or skeletal muscle contraction.

CLINICAL CONSIDERATIONS

Myasthenia Gravis

Myasthenia gravis is an autoimmune disease that is characterized by incremental weakening of skeletal muscles. Antibodies formed against acetylcholine receptors of skeletal muscle fibers bond to and thus block these receptors. The number of sites available for the initiation of depolarization of the muscle sarcolemma is decreased. The gradual weakening affects the most active muscles first (muscles of the face, eyes, and tongue), but eventually the muscles of respiration become compromised and the individual dies of respiratory insufficiency.

Duchenne's Muscular Dystrophy

Duchenne's muscular dystrophy is a muscle degenerative disease that is due to an X-linked genetic defect that strikes 1 in 30,000 males. The defect results in the absence of dystrophin molecules in the muscle cell membrane. Dystrophin is a protein that functions in the interconnection of the cytoskeleton to transmembrane proteins that interact with the extracellu-

lar matrix as well as in providing structural support for the muscle plasmalemma. Individuals afflicted with Duchenne's muscular dystrophy experience muscle weakness by the time they are 7 years of age and are usually wheelchair bound by the time they are 12 years old. It is very unusual to have these patients survive into their early 20s.

Muscle Cramps

A sudden, powerful contraction of a muscle or muscle group is a painful event known as a muscle cramp. It may occur in people of all ages and is usually due to lowered blood flow to the muscle(s), lowered levels of potassium, or vigorous exercise without proper warm-up (stretching). Cramps can also occur at night, and they usually involve the muscles of the lower leg. Cramps can usually be avoided by not exercising after eating (when blood flow is diverted to the digestive tract); avoiding caffeine; and drinking water or (nonalcoholic) potassium-containing beverages after exercising.

FIGURE 1 • Skeletal muscle. l.s. Monkey. Plastic section. ×800.

This photomicrograph displays several of the characteristics of skeletal muscle in longitudinal section. The muscle fibers are extremely long and possess a uniform diameter. Their numerous **nuclei** (N) are peripherally located. The intercellular space is occupied by endomysium, with its occasional flattened **connective tissue cells** (CT) and reticular fibers. Two types of striations are evident: longitudinal and transverse. The longitudinal striations represent **myofibrils** (M) that are arranged in almost precise register with each other. This ordered arrangement is responsible for the dark and light transverse banding that gives this type of muscle its name. Note that the **light band** (I) is bisected by a narrow, dark line, the **Z disc** (Z). The **dark band** (A) is also bisected by the clear **H zone** (H). The center of the H zone is occupied by the M disc, appearing as a faintly discernible dark line in a few regions. The basic contractile unit of skeletal muscle is the **sarcomere** (S), extending from one Z disc to its neighboring Z disc. During muscle contraction the myofilaments of each sarcomere slide past one another, pulling Z discs closer to each other, thus shortening the length of each sarcomere. During this movement, the width of the A band remains constant, whereas the I band and H zone disappear.

FIGURE 2 • Skeletal muscle. x.s. Monkey. Paraffin section. ×132.

Portions of a few fascicles are presented in this photomicrograph. Each fascicle is composed of numerous **muscle fibers** (F) that are surrounded by connective tissue elements known as the **perimysium** (P), which houses nerves and blood vessels supplying the fascicles. The nuclei of endothelial, Schwann, and connective tissue cells are evident as black dots in the perimysium. The peripherally placed **nuclei** (N) of the skeletal muscle fibers appear as black dots; however, they are all within the muscle cell. Nuclei of satellite cells are also present, just external to the muscle fibers, but their identification at low magnification is questionable. The *boxed area* is presented at a higher magnification in Figure 3.

FIGURE 3 • Skeletal muscle. x.s. Monkey. Paraffin section. ×540.

This is a higher magnification of the *boxed area* of Figure 2. Transverse sections of several muscle fibers demonstrate that these cells appear to be polyhedral, that they possess peripherally placed **nuclei** (N), and that their endomysia (E) house numerous **capillaries** (C). Many of the capillaries are difficult to see because they are collapsed in a resting muscle. The pale sarcoplasm occasionally appears granular, due to the transversely sectioned myofibrils. Occasionally, nuclei that appear to belong to **satellite cells** (SC) may be observed, but definite identification cannot be expected. Moreover, the well-defined outline of each fiber was believed to be due to the sarcolemma, but now it is known to be due more to the adherent basal lamina and endomysium.

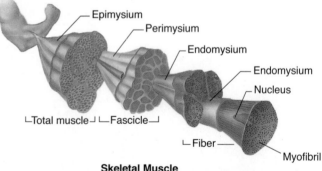

Skeletal Muscle

KEY							
A	A band	F	muscle fiber	P	perimysium
C	capillary	H	H zone	S	sarcomere
CT	connective tissue	I	I band	SC	satellite cell
E	endomysium	N	nucleus	Z	Z disc

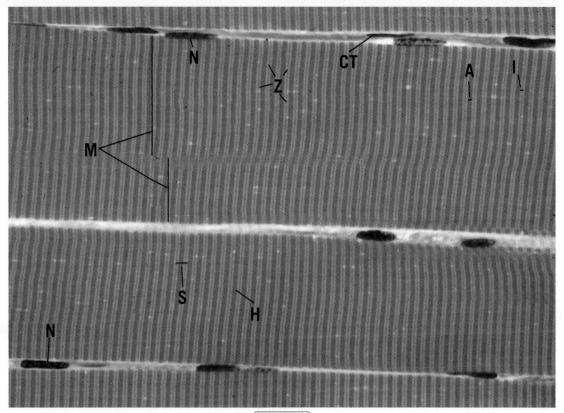

FIGURE 1

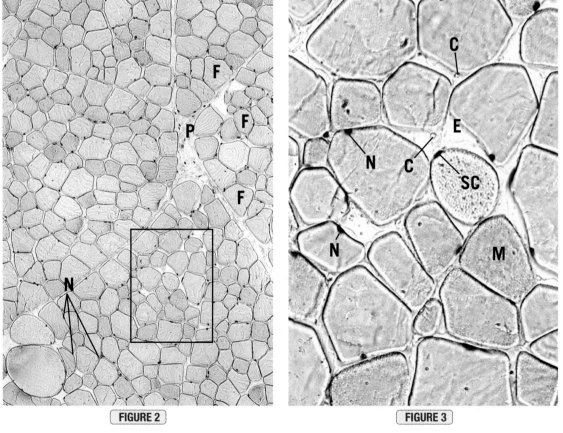

FIGURE 2

FIGURE 3

FIGURE 1 • Skeletal muscle. l.s. Rat. Electron microscopy. ×17,100.

This moderately low power electron micrograph of skeletal muscle was sectioned longitudinally. Perpendicular to its longitudinal axis, note the dark and light crossbandings. The **A band** (A) in this view extends from the upper left-hand corner to the lower right-hand corner and is bordered by an **I band** (I) on either side. Each I band is traversed by a **Z disc** (Z). Observe that the Z disc has the appearance of a dashed line, since individual myofibrils are separated from each other by sarcoplasm. Note that the extent of a **sarcomere** (S) is from Z disc to Z disc and that an almost precise alignment of individual myofibrils ensures the specific orientation of the various bands within the sarcomere. The **H zone** (H) and the **M disc** (MD) are clearly defined in this electron micrograph. Mitochondria are preferentially located in mammalian skeletal muscle, occupying the region at the level of the I band as they wrap around the periphery of the myofibril. Several sarcomeres are presented at a higher magnification in Figure 2. (Courtesy of Dr. J. Strum.)

FIGURE 2 • Skeletal muscle. l.s. Rat. Electron microscopy. ×28,800.

This is a higher power electron micrograph presenting several sarcomeres. Note that the **Z discs** (Z) possess projections (*arrows*) to which the **thin myofilaments** (tM) are attached. The **I band** (I) is composed only of thin filaments. **Thick myofilaments** (TM) interdigitate with the thin filaments from either end of the sarcomere, resulting in the **A band** (A). However, the thin filaments in a relaxed muscle do not extend all the way to the center of the A band; therefore, the **H zone** (H) is composed only of thick filaments. The center of each thick filament appears to be attached to its neighboring thick filament, resulting in localized thickenings, collectively comprising the **M disc** (MD). During muscle contraction, the thick and thin filaments slide past each other, thus pulling the Z discs toward the center of the sarcomere. Due to the resultant overlapping of thick and thin filaments, the I bands and H zones disappear, but the A bands maintain their width. The sarcoplasm houses **mitochondria** (m) preferentially located, glycogen granules (*arrowhead*), as well as a specialized system of sarcoplasmic reticulum and T tubules, forming **triads** (T). In mammalian skeletal muscle, triads are positioned at the junction of the I and A bands. (Courtesy of Dr. J. Strum.)

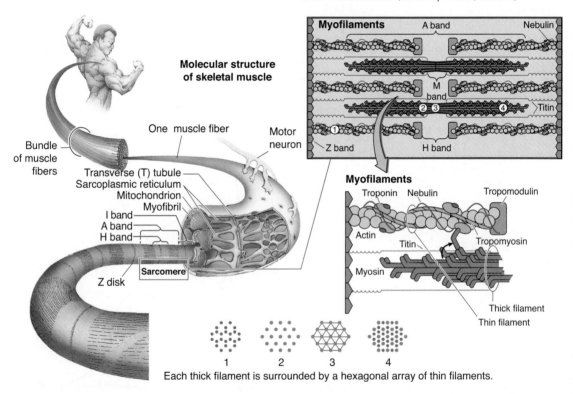

Molecular structure of skeletal muscle

Each thick filament is surrounded by a hexagonal array of thin filaments.

	KEY				
A	A band	MD	M disc	tM	thin myofilament
H	H zone	S	sarcomere	TM	thick myofilament
I	I band	T	triad	Z	Z disc
m	mitochondrion				

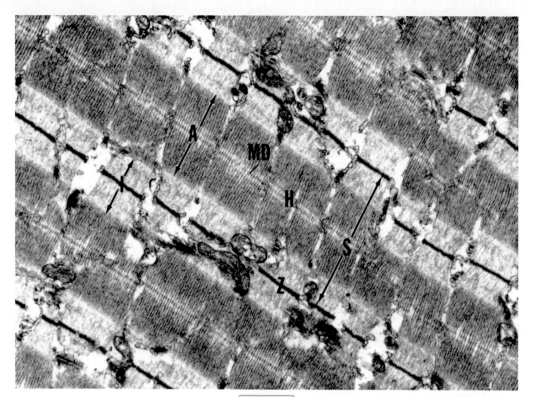

FIGURE 1

FIGURE 2

FIGURE 1 • Myoneural junction. Lateral view. Paraffin section. ×540.

This view of the myoneural junction clearly displays the **myelinated nerve fiber** (MN) approaching the **skeletal muscle fiber** (SM). The **A bands** (A) and **I bands** (I) are well delineated, but the Z discs are not observable in this preparation. As the axon nears the muscle cell, it loses its myelin sheath and continues on as a **nonmyelinated axon** (nMN) but retains its Schwann cell envelope. As the axon reaches the muscle cell, it terminates as a **motor end plate** (MEP), overlying the sarcolemma of the muscle fiber. Although the sarcolemma is not visible in light micrographs, such as this one, its location is clearly approximated due to its associated basal lamina and reticular fibers.

FIGURE 2 • Myoneural junction. Surface view. Paraffin section. ×540.

This view of the myoneural junction demonstrates, as in the previous figure, that as the axon reaches the vicinity of the **skeletal muscle fiber** (SM), it loses its myelin sheath. The axon terminates, forming a **motor end plate** (MEP), composed of a few clusters of numerous small swellings (*arrowhead*) on the sarcolemma of the skeletal muscle fiber. Although it is not apparent in this light micrograph, the motor end plate is located in a slight depression on the skeletal muscle fiber, and the plasma membranes of the two structures do not contact each other. Figure 3 clearly demonstrates the morphology of such a synapse.

FIGURE 3 • Myoneural junction. Rat. Electron microscopy. ×15,353.

This electron micrograph is of a myoneural junction taken from the diaphragm muscle of a rat. Observe that the **axon** (ax) loses its myelin sheath but the **Schwann cell** (sc) continues, providing a protective cover for the nonsynaptic surface of the **end foot** or **nerve terminal** (nt). The myelinated sheath ends in typical paranodal loops at the terminal heminode. The nerve terminal possesses **mitochondria** (m) and numerous clear synaptic vesicles. The margins of the 50-nm primary synaptic cleft are indicated by *arrowheads*. Postsynaptically, the **junctional folds** (j), many **mitochondria** (m), and portions of a **nucleus** (n) and **sarcomere** (s) are apparent in the skeletal muscle fiber. (Courtesy of Dr. C. S. Hudson.)

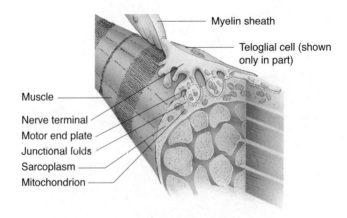

Myelin sheath

Teloglial cell (shown only in part)

Muscle

Nerve terminal

Motor end plate

Junctional folds

Sarcoplasm

Mitochondrion

Myoneural junction

KEY					
A	A band	MEP	motor end plate	nt	nerve terminal
ax	Axon	MN	myelinated nerve fiber	s	sarcomere
I	I band	n	nucleus	sc	Schwann cell
j	junctional fold	nMN	nonmyelinated axon	SM	skeletal muscle fiber
m	mitochondria				

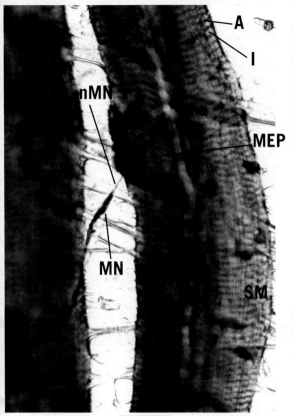

FIGURE 1

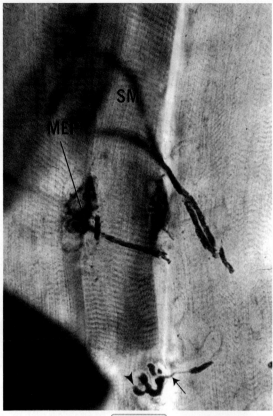

FIGURE 2

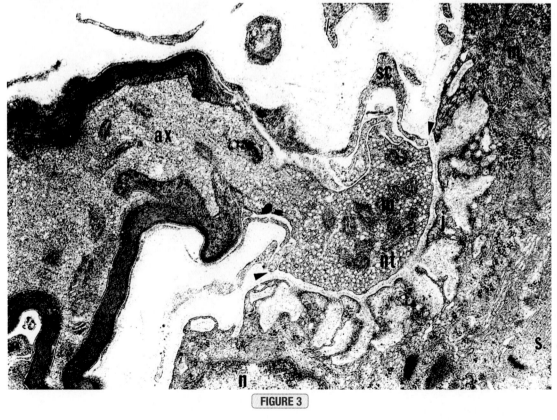

FIGURE 3

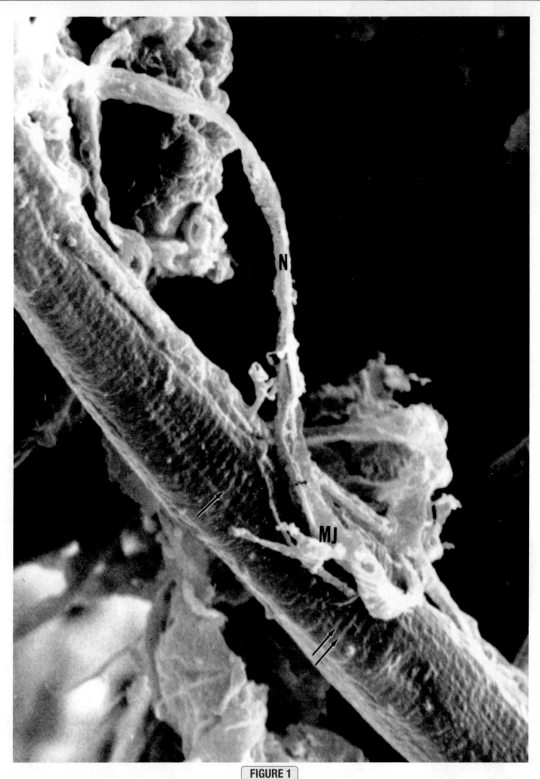

FIGURE 1

FIGURE 1 • Myoneural junction. Tongue. Cat. Scanning electron microscopy. ×2610.

The striations (*arrows*) of an isolated skeletal muscle fiber are clearly evident in this scanning electron micrograph.

Note the **nerve** "twig" (N), which loops up and makes contact with the muscle at the **myoneural junction** (MJ). (Courtesy of Dr. L. Litke.)

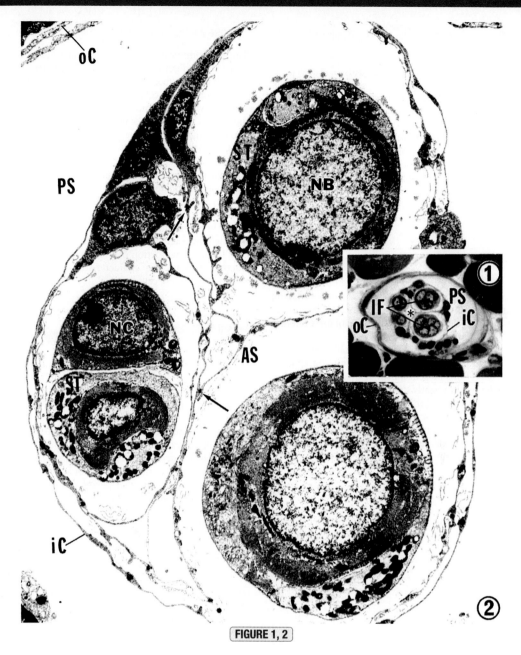

FIGURE 1, 2

FIGURE 1 • Muscle spindle. Mouse. Plastic section. ×436.

Observe that the **outer** (oC) and **inner** (iC) **capsules** of the muscle spindle define the outer **peraxial space** (PS) and the inner **axial space** (*asterisk*). The inner capsule forms an envelope around the **intrafusal fibers** (IF). (From Ovalle W, Dow P. Comparative ultrastructure of the inner capsule of the muscle spindle and the tendon organ. Am J Anat 1983;166:343–357.)

FIGURE 2 • Muscle spindle. Mouse. Electron microscopy. ×6,300.

Parts of the **outer capsule** (oC) may be observed at the corners of this electron micrograph. The **periaxial space** (PS) surrounds the slender **inner capsule** (iC), whose component cells form attenuated branches, subdividing the **axial space** (AS) into several compartments for the **nuclear chain** (NC) and **nuclear bag** (NB) intrafusal fibers and their corresponding **sensory terminals** (ST). Note that the attenuated processes of the inner capsule cells establish contact with each other (*arrows*). (From Ovalle W, Dow P. Comparative ultrastructure of the inner capsule of the muscle spindle and the tendon organ. Am J Anat 1983;166:343–357.)

FIGURE 1 ● Smooth muscle. l.s. Monkey. Plastic section. ×270.

The longitudinal section of smooth muscle in this photomicrograph displays long fusiform **smooth muscle cells** (sM) with centrally located, elongated **nuclei** (N). Since the muscle fibers are arranged in staggered arrays, they can be packed very closely, with only a limited amount of intervening **connective tissue** (CT). Using hematoxylin and eosin, the nuclei appear bluish, whereas the cytoplasm stains a light pink. Each smooth muscle cell is surrounded by a basal lamina and reticular fibers, neither of which is evident in this figure. Capillaries are housed in the connective tissue separating bundles of smooth muscle fibers. The *boxed area* is presented at a higher magnification in Figure 2.

FIGURE 3 ● Smooth muscle. Uterine myometrium. x.s. Monkey. Plastic section. ×270.

The myometrium of the uterus consists of interlacing bundles of smooth muscle fibers, surrounded by **connective tissue** (CT) elements. Note that some of these bundles are cut in longitudinal section (1), others are sectioned transversely (2), and still others are cut obliquely (3). At low magnifications, such as in this photomicrograph, the transverse sections present a haphazard arrangement of dark **nuclei** (N) in a lightly staining region. With practice, it will become apparent that these nuclei are intracellular and that the pale circular regions represent smooth muscle fibers sectioned transversely. Note the numerous **blood vessels** (BV) traveling in the connective tissue between the smooth muscle bundles.

FIGURE 2 ● Smooth muscle. l.s. Monkey. Plastic section. ×540.

This photomicrograph is a higher magnification of the *boxed area* of Figure 1. Observe that the **nuclei** (N) of the smooth muscle fibers are long, tapered structures located in the center of the cell. The widest girth of the nucleus is almost as wide as the muscle fiber. However, the length of the fiber is much greater than that of the nucleus. Note also that any line drawn perpendicular to the direction of the fibers will intersect only a few of the nuclei. Observe the difference between the **connective tissue** (CT) and **smooth muscle** (sM). The smooth muscle cytoplasm stains darker and appears smooth relative to the paleness and rough-appearing texture of the connective tissue. Observe **capillaries** (C) located in the connective tissue elements between bundles of muscle fibers. *Inset.* **Smooth muscle. Contracted. l.s. Monkey. Plastic section.** × 540. This longitudinal section of smooth muscle during contraction displays the characteristic corkscrew-shaped **nuclei** (N) of these cells.

FIGURE 4a ● Smooth muscle. x.s. Monkey. Plastic section. ×540.

To understand the three-dimensional morphology of smooth muscle as it appears in two dimensions, refer to Figure 2 directly above this photomicrograph. Once again note that the muscle fibers are much longer than their nuclei and that both structures are spindle-shaped, being tapered at both ends. Recall also that at its greatest girth, the nucleus is almost as wide as the cell. In transverse section this would appear as a round nucleus surrounded by a rim of cytoplasm (*asterisk*). If the nucleus is sectioned at its tapered end, merely a small dot of it would be present in the center of a large muscle fiber (*double asterisks*). Sectioned anywhere between these two points, the nucleus would have varied diameters in the center of a large muscle cell. Additionally, the cell may be sectioned in a region away from its nucleus, where only the sarcoplasm of the large muscle cell would be evident (*triple asterisks*). Moreover, if the cell is sectioned at its tapered end, only a small circular profile of sarcoplasm is distinguishable (*arrowhead*). Therefore, in transverse sections of smooth muscle, one would expect to find only few cells containing nuclei of various diameters. Most of the field will be closely packed profiles of sarcoplasm containing no nuclei.

FIGURE 4b ● Smooth muscle. Duodenum. Monkey. Plastic section. ×132.

This photomicrograph of the duodenum demonstrates the **glandular portion** (G) with its underlying **connective tissue** (CT). Deep to the connective tissue, note the two smooth muscle layers, one of which is sectioned longitudinally (1) and the other transversely (2).

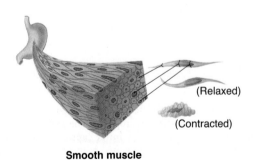

(Relaxed)

(Contracted)

Smooth muscle

KEY					
BV	blood vessel	CT	connective tissue	N	nucleus
C	capillary	G	glandular portion	sM	smooth muscle cell

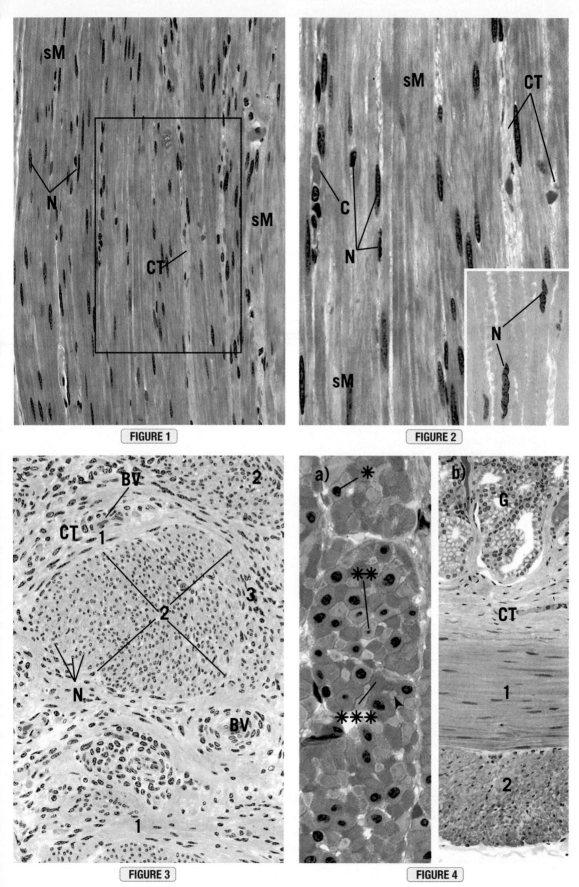

FIGURE 1

FIGURE 2

FIGURE 3

FIGURE 4

PLATE 6-7 Smooth Muscle, Electron Microscopy

FIGURE 1 • Smooth muscle. l.s. Mouse. Electron microscopy. ×15,120.

Smooth muscle does not display cross-bandings, transverse tubular systems, or the regularly arranged array of myofilaments characteristic of striated muscle. However, smooth muscle does possess myofilaments that, along with a system of intermediate filaments, are responsible for its contractile capabilities. Moreover, the plasma membrane appears to possess the functional, if not the structural, aspects of the T tubule. Observe that each smooth muscle is surrounded by an **external lamina** (EL), which is similar in appearance to basal lamina of epithelial cells. The **sarcolemma** (SL) displays the presence of numerous pinocytotic-like invaginations, the **caveolae** (Ca), which are believed to act as T tubules of striated muscles in conducting impulses into the interior of the fiber. Some suggest

that they may also act in concert with the sarcoplasmic reticulum in modulating the availability of calcium ions. The cytoplasmic aspect of the sarcolemma also displays the presence of **dense bodies** (DB), which are indicative of the attachment of **intermediate microfilaments** (IM) at that point. Dense bodies, composed of β-actinin (Z disc protein found in striated muscle), are also present in the sarcoplasm (*arrows*). The **nucleus** (N) is centrally located and, at its pole, **mitochondria** (m) are evident. Actin and myosin are also present in smooth muscle but cannot be identified with certainty in longitudinal sections. Parts of a second smooth muscle fiber may be observed to the left of the cell described. A small **capillary** (C) is evident in the lower right-hand corner. Note the **adherens junctions** (AJ) between the two epithelial cells, one of which presents a part of its **nucleus** (N).

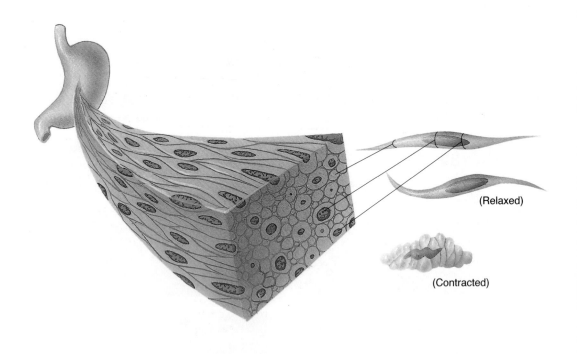

(Relaxed)

(Contracted)

Smooth muscle

KEY							
AJ	adherens junction	DB	dense body	m	mitochondrion
C	capillary	EL	external lamina	N	nucleus
Ca	caveola	IM	intermediate filament	SL	sarcolemma

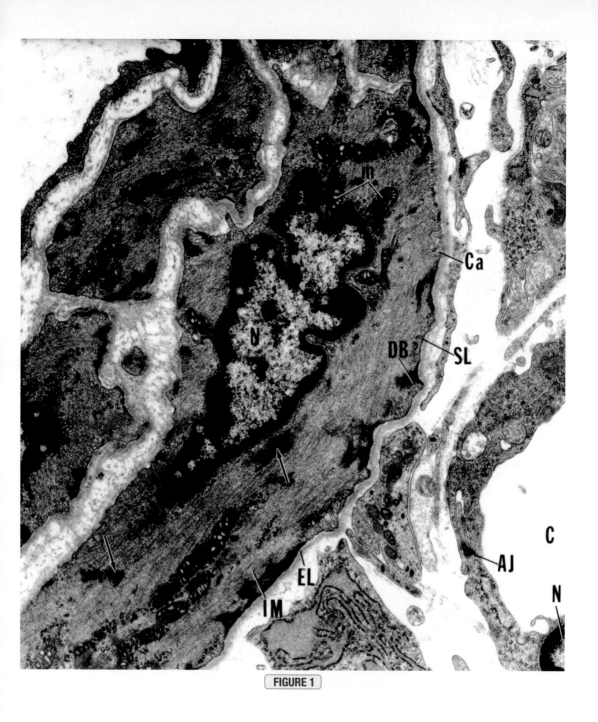

FIGURE 1

FIGURE 1 • Cardiac muscle. l.s. Human. Plastic section. ×270.

This low magnification of longitudinally sectioned cardiac muscle displays many of the characteristics of this muscle type. The branching (*arrow*) of the fibers is readily apparent, as are the dark and light bands (*arrowheads*) running transversely along the length of the fibers. Each muscle cell possesses a large, centrally located, oval **nucleus** (N), although occasional muscle cells may possess two nuclei. The **intercalated discs** (ID), indicating intercellular junctions between two cardiac muscle cells, clearly delineated in this photomicrograph, are not easily demonstrable in sections stained with hematoxylin and eosin. The intercellular spaces of cardiac muscle are richly endowed by blood vessels, especially capillaries. Recall that, in contrast to cardiac muscle, the long skeletal muscle fibers do not branch, their myofilaments parallel one another, their many nuclei are peripherally located, and they possess no intercalated discs. The *boxed area* appears at a higher magnification in Figure 2.

FIGURE 3 • Cardiac muscle. x.s. Human. Plastic section. ×270.

Cross-sections of cardiac muscle demonstrate polygon-shaped areas of **cardiac muscle fibers** (CM) with relatively large intercellular spaces whose rich **vascular supply** (BV) is readily evident. Note that the **nucleus** (N) of each muscle cell is located in the center, but not all cells display a nucleus. The clear areas in the center of some cells (*arrows*) represent the perinuclear regions at the poles of the nucleus. These regions are rich in sarcoplasmic reticulum, glycogen, lipid droplets, and an occasional Golgi apparatus. The numerous smaller nuclei in the intercellular areas belong to endothelial and connective tissue cells. In contrast to cardiac muscle, cross-sections of skeletal muscle fibers display a homogeneous appearance with peripherally positioned nuclei. The connective tissue spaces between skeletal muscle fibers display numerous (frequently collapsed) capillaries.

FIGURE 2 • Cardiac muscle. l.s. Human. Plastic section. ×540.

This is a higher magnification of the *boxed area* of Figure 1. The branching of the fibers (*arrows*) is evident, and the cross-striations, I and A bands (*arrowheads*), are clearly distinguishable. The presence of **myofibrils** (M) within each cell is well displayed in this photomicrograph, as is the "steplike" appearance of the **intercalated discs** (ID). The oval, centrally located **nucleus** (N) is surrounded by a clear area usually occupied by mitochondria. The intercellular areas are richly supplied by **capillaries** (C) supported by slender connective tissue elements.

FIGURE 4 • Cardiac muscle. x.s. Human. Plastic section. ×540.

At high magnifications of cardiac muscle in cross-section, several aspects of this tissue become apparent. Numerous **capillaries** (C) and larger **blood vessels** (BV) abound in the connective tissue spaces. Note the **endothelial nuclei** (EN) of these vessels as well as the **white blood cells** (WBC) within the venule in the upper right-hand corner. **Nuclei** (N) of the muscle cells are centrally located, and the perinuclear clear areas (*arrow*) housing mitochondria are evident. The central clear zones at the nuclear poles are denoted by *asterisks*. Cross-sections of myofibrils (*arrowheads*) are recognizable as numerous small dots of varying diameters within the sarcoplasm.

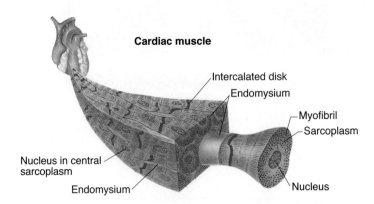

Cardiac muscle

Intercalated disk
Endomysium
Myofibril
Sarcoplasm
Nucleus in central sarcoplasm
Endomysium
Nucleus

KEY					
BV	blood vessel	EN	endothelial nucleus	N	nucleus
C	capillary	ID	intercalated disc	WBC	white blood cell
CM	cardiac muscle fiber	M	myofibril		

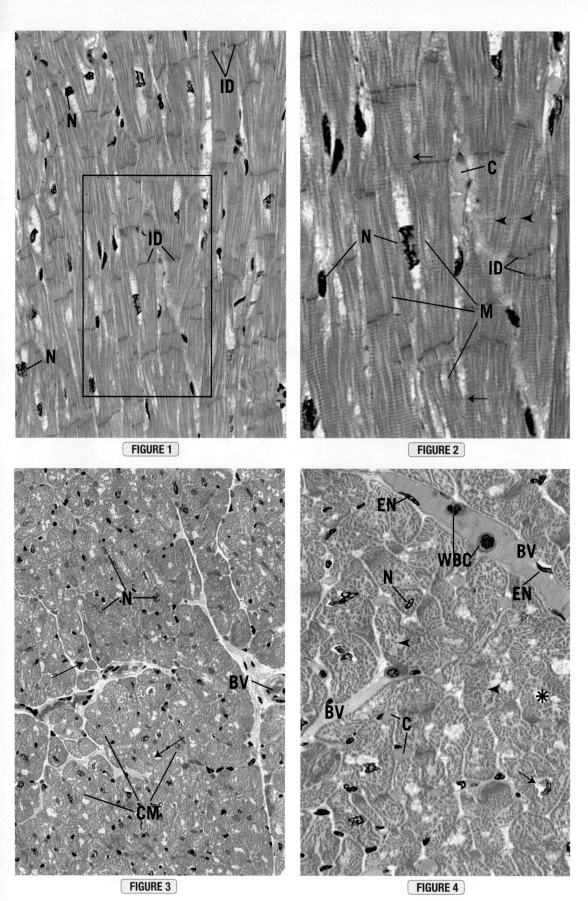

FIGURE 1

FIGURE 2

FIGURE 3

FIGURE 4

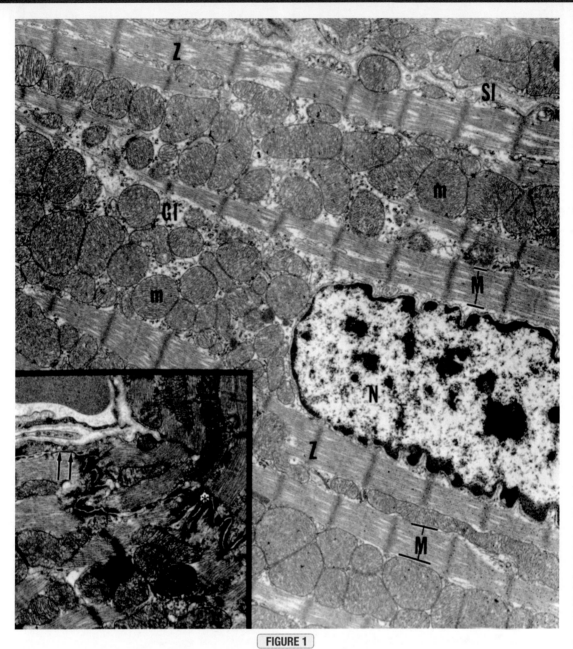

FIGURE 1

FIGURE 1 • Cardiac muscle, l.s. Mouse. Electron microscopy. ×11,700.

The **nucleus** (N) of cardiac muscle cells is located in the center of the cell, as is evident from the location of the **sarcolemma** (Sl) in the upper part of the photomicrograph. The sarcoplasm is well endowed with **mitochondria** (m) and **glycogen** (Gl) deposits. Since this muscle cell is contracted, the I bands are not visible. However, the **Z discs** (**Z**) are clearly evident, as are the individual **myofibrils** (**M**). *Inset.* **Cardiac muscle. l.s. Mouse. Electron microscopy.** × 20,700. An intercalated disc is presented in this electron micrograph. Note that this intercellular junction has two zones, the transverse portion (*asterisk*), composed mostly of desmosome-like junctions, and a longitudinal portion that displays extensive gap junctions (*arrows*).

Summary of Histological Organization

I. SKELETAL MUSCLE

A. Longitudinal Section

1. Connective tissue elements of **perimysium** contain nerves, blood vessels, collagen, fibroblasts, and occasionally other cell types. **Endomysium** is composed of fine reticular fibers and basal lamina, neither of which are normally evident with the light microscope.

2. **Skeletal muscle cells** appear as long, parallel, cylindrical fibers of almost uniform diameter. Nuclei are numerous and peripherally located. **Satellite cell** nuclei may be evident. Cross-striations, **A**, **I**, and **Z**, should be clearly noted at higher magnifications, and with oil immersion (or even high dry), the **H zone** and **M disc** may be distinguished in good preparations.

B. Transverse Section

1. Connective tissue elements may be noted, especially **nuclei of fibroblasts**, cross-sections of **capillaries**, other small **blood vessels**, and **nerves**.

2. Muscle cells appear as irregular polygon-shaped sections of fibers of more or less uniform size. **Myofibrils** present a stippled appearance inside the fiber, frequently clustered into distinct but artifactual groups known as Cohnheim's fields. Peripherally, a **nucleus** or two may be noted in many fibers. Fasciculi are closely packed, but the delicate **endomysium** clearly outlines each cell.

II. CARDIAC MUSCLE

A. Longitudinal Section

1. Connective tissue elements are clearly identifiable because of the presence of **nuclei** that are considerably smaller than those of cardiac muscle cells. The connective tissue is rich in vascular components, especially **capillaries**. The **endomysium** is present but indistinct.

2. **Cardiac muscle cells** form long, branching, and anastomosing **muscle fibers**. Bluntly oval **nuclei** are large, are centrally located within the cell, and appear somewhat vesicular. **A** and **I bands** are present but are not as clearly defined as in skeletal muscle. **Intercalated discs**, marking the boundaries of contiguous cardiac muscle cells, may be indistinct unless special staining techniques are used. **Purkinje fibers** are occasionally evident.

B. Transverse Section

1. Connective tissue elements separating muscle fibers from each other are obvious, since **nuclei** of these cells are much smaller than those of cardiac muscle cells.

2. Cross-sectional profiles of **muscle fibers** are irregularly shaped and vary in size. **Nuclei** are infrequent but are large and located in the center of the cell. **Myofibrils** are clumped as Cohnheim's fields (an artifact of fixation) in a radial arrangement. Occasionally, **Purkinje fibers** are noted, but they are present only in the subendocardium of the ventricles.

III. SMOOTH MUSCLE

A. Longitudinal Section

1. Connective tissue elements between individual muscle fibers are scant and consist of fine **reticular fibers**. Larger bundles or sheets of muscle fibers are separated by loose connective tissue housing blood vessels and nerves.

2. **Smooth muscle cells** are tightly packed, staggered, fusiform structures whose centrally located nuclei are oblong in shape. When the muscle fibers contract, their nuclei assume a characteristic corkscrew shape.

B. Transverse Section

1. A very limited amount of connective tissue, mostly **reticular fibers**, may be noted in the intercellular spaces. Sheets and bundles of smooth muscle are separated from each other by loose connective tissue in which neurovascular elements are evident.

2. Since **smooth muscle cells** are tightly packed, staggered, fusiform structures, transverse sections produce circular, homogeneous-appearing profiles of various diameters. Only the widest profiles contain **nuclei**; therefore, in transverse section only a limited number of nuclei will be present.

Nervous Tissue

7

Nervous tissue is one of the four basic tissues of the body, and it specializes in receiving information from the external and internal milieu. The information is processed, integrated, and compared with stored experiences and/or predetermined (reflex) responses to select and effect an appropriate reaction. The reception of information is the function of the sensory component of the **peripheral nervous system** (**PNS**). The processes of integration, analysis, and response are performed by the brain and spinal cord comprising the **central nervous system** (**CNS**) with its gray matter and white matter. The transmission of the response to the effector organ is relegated to the motor component of the PNS. Therefore, it should be appreciated that the PNS is merely a physical extension of the CNS, and the separation of the two should not imply a strict dichotomy.

The nervous system may also be divided functionally into somatic and autonomic nervous systems. The **somatic nervous system** exercises conscious control over voluntary functions, whereas the **autonomic nervous system** controls involuntary functions. The autonomic nervous system is a motor system, acting on smooth muscle, cardiac muscle, and some glands. Its three components, **sympathetic**, **parasympathetic**, and **enteric nervous systems**, usually act in concert to maintain homeostasis. The sympathetic nervous system prepares the body for action as in a "fight or flight" mode, whereas the parasympathetic system functions to calm the body and provides secretomotor innervation to most exocrine glands; the enteric nervous system is more or less a stand-alone system that is responsible for the process of digestion. It is interesting to note that the enteric nervous system is very large; it has about the same number of neurons as those located in the spinal cord. The actions of the enteric nervous system are modulated by the sympathetic and parasympathetic components of the autonomic nervous system.

The CNS is protected by a bony housing, consisting of the skull and vertebral column, and the **meninges**, a triple-layered connective tissue sheath. The outermost meninx is the thick, fibrous **dura mater**. Deep to the dura mater is the **arachnoid**, a nonvascular connective tissue membrane. The innermost, vascular **pia mater** is the most intimate investment of the CNS. Located between the arachnoid and the pia mater is the **cerebrospinal fluid** (**CSF**).

● NEURONS AND SUPPORTING CELLS

The structural and functional unit of the nervous system is the **neuron**, a cell that is highly specialized to perform its two major functions of irritability and conductivity. Each neuron is composed of a **cell body** (**soma**, **perikaryon**) and processes of varied lengths known as **axons** and **dendrites**, usually located on opposite sides of the cell body (see Graphic 7-2). A neuron possesses only a single axon. However, depending on the number of dendrites a neuron possesses, it may be **unipolar** (a single process but no dendrites—rare in vertebrates, but see below), **bipolar** (an axon and one dendrite), or the more common **multipolar** (an axon and several dendrites). An additional category exists in which the single dendrite and the axon fuse during embryonic development, giving the false appearance of a unipolar neuron; therefore, it is known as a **pseudounipolar neuron**, although recently neuroanatomists began to refer to this neuron type as a **unipolar neuron**.

Neurons also may be classified according to their function. **Sensory neurons** receive stimuli from either the internal or external environment then transmit these impulses toward the CNS for processing. **Interneurons** act as connectors between neurons in a chain or typically between sensory and motor neurons within the CNS. **Motor neurons** conduct impulses from the CNS to the targets cells (muscles, glands, and other neurons).

Information is transferred from one neuron to another across an intercellular space or gap, the **synapse**. Depending on the regions of the neurons participating in the formation of the synapse, it could be axodendritic, axosomatic, axoaxonic, or dendrodendritic. Most synapses are axodendritic and involve one of many **neurotransmitter substances** (such as **acetylcholine**) that is released by the axon of the first neuron into the synaptic cleft. The chemical momentarily destabilizes the plasma

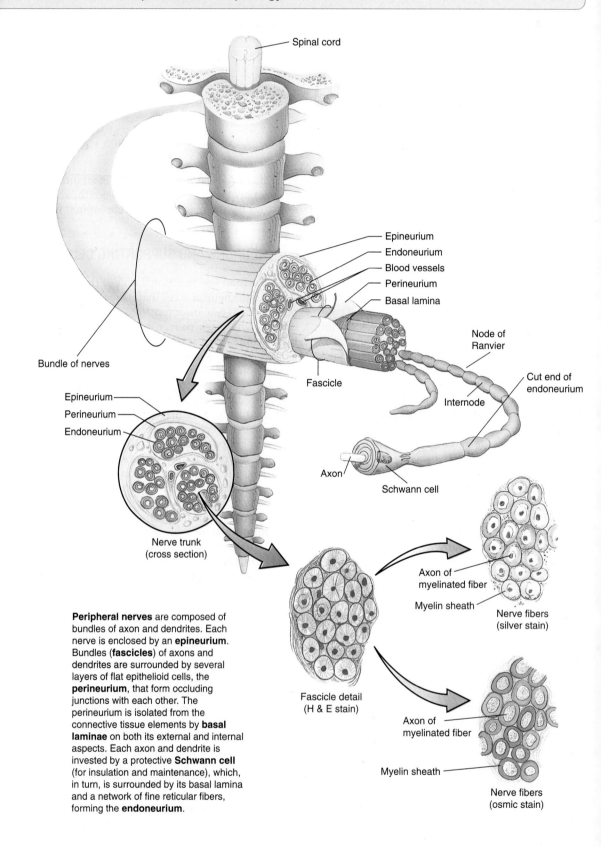

Spinal cord

Epineurium
Endoneurium
Blood vessels
Perineurium
Basal lamina

Node of Ranvier

Cut end of endoneurium

Bundle of nerves

Fascicle

Internode

Epineurium
Perineurium
Endoneurium

Axon

Schwann cell

Nerve trunk
(cross section)

Axon of
myelinated fiber

Myelin sheath

Nerve fibers
(silver stain)

Peripheral nerves are composed of bundles of axon and dendrites. Each nerve is enclosed by an **epineurium**. Bundles (**fascicles**) of axons and dendrites are surrounded by several layers of flat epithelioid cells, the **perineurium**, that form occluding junctions with each other. The perineurium is isolated from the connective tissue elements by **basal laminae** on both its external and internal aspects. Each axon and dendrite is invested by a protective **Schwann cell** (for insulation and maintenance), which, in turn, is surrounded by its basal lamina and a network of fine reticular fibers, forming the **endoneurium**.

Fascicle detail
(H & E stain)

Axon of
myelinated fiber

Myelin sheath

Nerve fibers
(osmic stain)

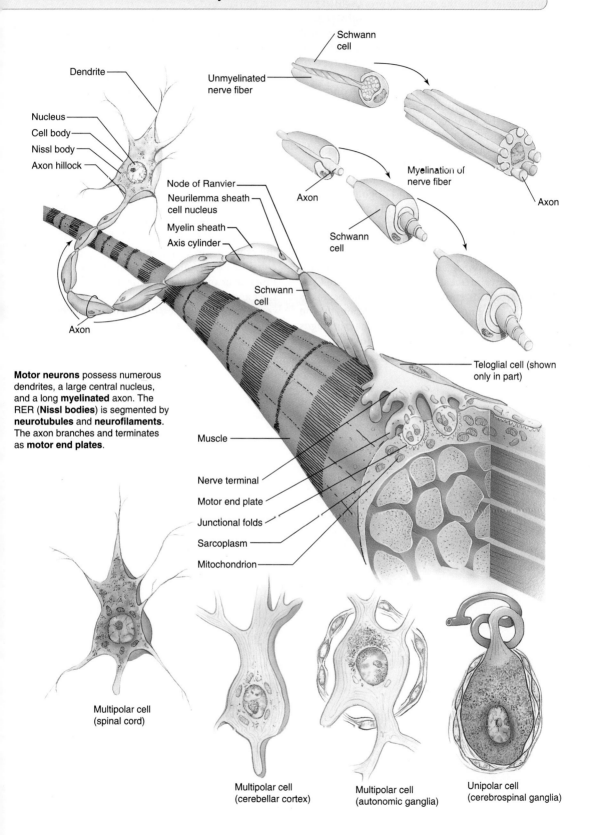

Dendrite

Nucleus

Cell body

Nissl body

Axon hillock

Schwann cell

Unmyelinated nerve fiber

Myelination of nerve fiber

Axon

Axon

Node of Ranvier

Neurilemma sheath cell nucleus

Myelin sheath

Axis cylinder

Schwann cell

Schwann cell

Axon

Teloglial cell (shown only in part)

Motor neurons possess numerous dendrites, a large central nucleus, and a long **myelinated** axon. The RER (**Nissl bodies**) is segmented by **neurotubules** and **neurofilaments**. The axon branches and terminates as **motor end plates**.

Muscle

Nerve terminal

Motor end plate

Junctional folds

Sarcoplasm

Mitochondrion

Multipolar cell (spinal cord)

Multipolar cell (cerebellar cortex)

Multipolar cell (autonomic ganglia)

Unipolar cell (cerebrospinal ganglia)

membrane of the dendrite, and a wave of depolarization passes along the second neuron, which will cause the release of a neurotransmitter substance at the terminus of its axon. This type of a chemical synapse is an **excitatory synapse**, which results in the transmission of an impulse. Another type of synapse may stop the transmission of an impulse by stabilizing the plasma membrane of the second neuron; it is called an **inhibitory synapse**.

Neuroglial cells function in the metabolism and the support of neurons. To prevent spontaneous or accidental depolarization of the neuron's cell membrane, specialized neuroglial cells provide a physical covering over its entire surface. In the CNS these cells are known as **astrocytes** and **oligodendroglia**, whereas in the PNS they are **capsule** and **Schwann cells**. Oligodendroglia and Schwann cells have the capability of forming **myelin sheaths** around axons (Graphic 7-2), which increases the conduction velocity of the impulse along the axon. The region where the myelin sheath of one Schwann cell (or oligodendroglion) ends and the next one begins is referred to as the **node of Ranvier**. Additionally, the CNS possesses **microglia**, which are **macrophages** derived from monocytes, and **ependymal cells**, which line brain ventricles and the central canal of the spinal cord.

Certain terms must be defined to facilitate understanding of the nervous system. A **ganglion** is a collection of nerve cell bodies in the PNS, whereas a similar collection of soma in the CNS is called a **nucleus**. A bundle of axons traveling together in the CNS is known as a **tract** (or **fasciculus** or **column**), whereas a similar bundle in the PNS is known as a **peripheral nerve** (nerve).

● PERIPHERAL NERVES

Peripheral nerves are composed of numerous nerve fibers collected into several fascicles (bundles). These bundles possess a thick connective tissue sheath, the **epineurium** (see Graphic 7-1). Each fascicle within the epineurium is surrounded by a **perineurium**, consisting of an outer connective tissue layer and an inner layer of flattened epithelioid cells. Each nerve fiber and associated Schwann cell has its own slender connective tissue sheath, the **endoneurium**, whose components include fibroblasts, an occasional macrophage, and collagenous and reticular fibers.

Histophysiology

I. MEMBRANE RESTING POTENTIAL

The normal concentration of K^+ is about 20 times greater inside the cell than outside, whereas the concentration of Na^+ is 10 times greater outside the cell than inside. The **resting potential** across the neuron cell membrane is maintained by the presence of **potassium leak channels** in the plasmalemma. These potassium leak channels are always open, and it is through these channels that K^+ ions diffuse from inside the cell to the outside, thus establishing a **positive charge on the outer** aspect and a **negative (less positive) charge on the internal** aspect of the cell membrane, with a total differential of about 40 to 100 mV. It should be noted that Na^+ ions can also traverse this channel but at a 100-fold slower rate than potassium ions. Although the majority of the establishment of the membrane potential is due to the potassium leak channel, the action of the Na^+-K^+ **pump** does contribute to it to a certain extent.

II. ACTION POTENTIAL

The **action potential** is an electrical activity in which charges move along the membrane surface. It is an **all-or-none response** whose duration and amplitude are constant. Some axons are capable of sustaining up to 1,000 impulses/sec.

Generation of an action potential begins when a region of the plasma membrane is **depolarized**. As the resting potential diminishes, a **threshold level** is reached, voltage-gated Na^+ channels open, Na^+ rushes into the cell, and at that point the **resting potential is reversed**, so that the inside becomes positive with respect to the outside. In response to this reversal of the resting potential, the Na^+ channel closes and for the next 1–2 msec cannot be opened (the **refractory period**). Depolarization also causes the **opening** of voltage-gated K^+ channels (note that these are different from the potassium leak channels) through which potassium ions exit the cell, thus repolarizing the membrane and ending not only the refractory period of the Na^+ channel but also the closure of the voltage-gated potassium channel.

The movement of Na^+ ions that enter the cell causes depolarization of the cell membrane toward the axon terminal (**orthodromic spread**). Although sodium ions also move away from the axon terminal (**antidromic spread**), they are unable to affect sodium channels in the antidromic direction, since those channels are in their refractory period.

III. MYONEURAL JUNCTION

Mitochondria, synaptic vesicles, and elements of smooth endoplasmic reticulum are present in the axon terminal. The axolemma involved in the formation of the synapse is known as the **presynaptic membrane**, whereas the sarcolemmal counterpart is known as the **postsynaptic membrane**. The presynaptic membrane has **sodium channels**, **voltage-gated calcium channels**, and **carrier proteins** for the cotransport of Na^+ and choline. The postsynaptic membrane has **acetylcholine receptors** as well as slight invaginations known as **junctional folds**. A basal lamina containing the enzyme **acetylcholinesterase** is also associated with the postsynaptic membrane. As the impulse reaches the end-foot, sodium channels open, and the presynaptic membrane becomes depolarized, resulting in the opening of the voltage-gated calcium channels and the influx of Ca^+ into the end-foot. The high intracellular calcium concentration causes the synaptic vesicles, containing **acetylcholine**, proteoglycans, and ATP, to fuse with the presynaptic membrane and release their contents into the synaptic cleft. The process of fusion depends on receptor molecules in both vesicles and the presynaptic membranes. These receptor molecules are known as **vesicular docking proteins** and **presynaptic membrane docking proteins**. After the contents of the synaptic vesicle is released the presynaptic membrane is larger than prior to fusion, and this excess membrane will be recycled via the formation of clathrin-coated vesicles, thus maintaining the morphology and requisite surface area of the presynaptic membrane. The released acetylcholine binds to **acetylcholine receptors** of the sarcolemma, thus opening **sodium channels**, resulting in sodium influx into the muscle cell, depolarization of the postsynaptic membrane, and the subsequent generation of an action potential and muscle cell contraction. **Acetylcholinesterase** of the basal lamina cleaves acetylcholine into **choline** and acetate, ensuring that a single release of the neurotransmitter substance will not continue to generate excess action potentials. The choline is returned to the end-foot via carrier proteins that are powered by a sodium gradient, where it is combined with activated acetate (derived from mitochondria), a reaction catalyzed by **acetylcholine transferase**, to form acetylcholine. The newly formed acetylcholine is transported into forming synaptic vesicles by a proton pump-driven, antiport carrier protein.

IV. NEUROTRANSMITTER SUBSTANCES

Neurotransmitter substances are signaling molecules (chemical messengers) that are released at the presynaptic membrane and effect a response by binding to receptor molecules (integral proteins) of the postsynaptic membrane. Neurotransmitter substances are varied in chemical composition and are categorized according to their chemical construction as cholinergic, monoaminergic, peptidergic, nonpeptidergic, GABAergic, glutamatergic, and glycinergic.

V. BLOOD-BRAIN BARRIER

The selective barrier that exists between the neural tissues of the CNS and many blood-borne substances is termed the **blood-brain barrier**. This barrier is formed by the fasciae occludentes of contiguous endothelial cells lining the continuous capillaries that course through the neural tissues. Certain substances (i.e., O_2, H_2O, CO_2, and selected small lipid-soluble substances and some drugs) can penetrate the barrier. However, others, including glucose, certain vitamins, amino acids, and drugs, among others, access passage only by **receptor-mediated transport** and/or **facilitated diffusion**. Certain ions are also transported via **active transport**. It is also believed that some of the perivascular neuroglia may play a minor role in the maintenance of the blood-brain barrier.

CLINICAL CONSIDERATIONS

Neuroglial Tumors
Almost 50% of the intracranial tumors are due to proliferation of neuroglial cells. Some of the neuroglial tumors, such as **oligodenroglioma**, are of mild severity, whereas others, such as **glioblastoma**, which are neoplastic cells derived from astrocytes, are higly invasive and usually fatal.

Huntington's Chorea
Huntington's chorea is a hereditary condition that becomes evident in the third and fourth decades of life. Initially, this condition affects only the joints but later is responsible for motor dysfunction and dementia. It is thought to be caused by the loss of neurons of the CNS that produce the neurotransmitter **GABA**. The advent of dementia is thought to be related to the loss of acetylcholine-secreting cells.

Parkinson's Disease
Parkinson's disease is related to the loss of the neurotransmitter **dopamine** in the brain. This crippling disease causes muscular rigidity, tremor, slow movement, and progressively difficult voluntary movement. L-dopa can be administered, but its beneficial effects are only temporary. Transplanted fetal adrenal gland tissue provides some relief, but it is also of short duration.

Therapeutic Circumvention of the Blood-Brain Barrier
The selective nature of the blood-brain barrier prevents certain therapeutic drugs and neurotransmitters conveyed by the bloodstream from entering the CNS. For example, the perfusion of **mannitol** into the bloodstream changes the capillary permeability by altering the tight junctions, thus permitting administration of therapeutic drugs. Other therapeutic drugs can be attached to antibodies developed against **transferrin receptors** located on the luminal aspect of the plasma membranes of these endothelial cells that will permit transport into the CNS.

Guillain-Barré Syndrome
Guillain-Barré Syndrome is a form of immune-mediated condition resulting in rapidly progressing weakness with possible paralysis of the extremities and occasionally even of the respiratory and facial muscles. This demyelinating disease is often associated with a recent respiratory or gastrointestinal infection; the muscle weakness reaches its greatest point within 3 weeks of the initial symptoms, and 5% of the afflicted individuals die of the disease. Early recognition of the disease is imperative for complete (or nearly complete) recovery. Treatment includes immediate hospitalization and monitoring for need for respirator therapy. Monitoring for bedsores and physical therapy are also indicated. Plasmapheresis and administration of autoimmune globulin are treatments of choice.

FIGURE 1 • Spinal cord. x.s. Cat. Silver stain. Paraffin section. ×21.

The spinal cord is invested by a protective coating, the three-layered meninges. Its outermost fibrous layer, the **dura mater** (DM), is surrounded by epidural fat, not present in this photomicrograph. Deep to the dura is the **arachnoid** (A) with its **subarachnoid space** (SS), which is closely applied to the most intimate layer of the meninges, the vascular **pia mater** (PM). The spinal cord itself is organized into **white matter** (W) and **gray matter** (G). The former, which is peripherally located and does not contain nerve cell bodies, is composed of nerve fibers, most of which are myelinated, that travel up and down the cord. It is cellular, however, since it houses various types of glial cells. The centrally positioned gray matter contains the cell bodies of the neurons as well as the initial and terminal ends of their processes, many of which are not usually myelinated. These nerve cell processes and those of the numerous glial cells form an intertwined network of fibers that is referred to as the neuropil. The gray matter is subdivided into regions, namely, the **dorsal horn** (DH), the **ventral horn** (VH), and the **gray commissure** (Gc). The **central canal** (CC) of the spinal cord passes through the gray commissure, dividing it into dorsal and ventral components. Processes of neurons leave and enter the spinal cord as **ventral** (VR) and **dorsal** (DR) **roots**, respectively. A region similar to the *boxed area* is represented in Figure 2.

FIGURE 2 • Spinal cord. x.s. White and gray matter. Human. Paraffin section. ×132.

This photomicrograph represents the *boxed region* of Figure 1. Observe that the interface between **white matter** (W) and **gray matter** (G) is readily evident (*asterisks*). The numerous nuclei (*arrowheads*) present in white matter belong to the various neuroglia, which support the axons and dendrites traveling up and down the spinal cord. The large **nerve cell bodies** (CB) in the ventral horn of the gray matter possess vesicular-appearing nuclei with dense, dark nucleoli. **Blood vessels** (BV), which penetrate deep into the gray matter, are surrounded by processes of neuroglial cells, forming the blood-brain barrier, not visible in this photomicrograph. Small nuclei (*arrows*) in gray matter belong to the neuroglial cells, whose cytoplasm and cellular processes are not evident.

FIGURE 3 • Spinal cord. x.s. Ventral horn. Human. Paraffin section. ×270.

The multipolar neurons and their various processes (*arrows*) are clearly evident in this photomicrograph of the ventral horn. Note the large **nucleus** (N) and dense **nucleolus** (n), both of which are characteristic of neurons. Observe the clumps of basophilic material, **Nissl bodies** (NB), that electron microscopy has demonstrated to be rough endoplasmic reticulum. The small nuclei belong to the various **neuroglial cells** (Ng), which, along with their processes and processes of the neurons, compose the **neuropil** (Np), the matted-appearing background substance of gray matter. The white spaces (*asterisks*) surrounding the soma and blood vessels are due to shrinkage artifacts.

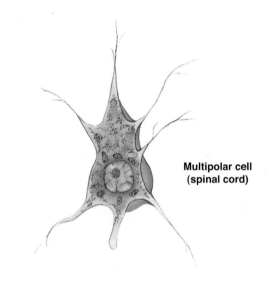

Multipolar cell
(spinal cord)

KEY							
A	arachnoid	G	gray matter	PM	pia mater
BV	blood vessel	Gc	gray commissure	SS	subarachnoid space
CB	nerve cell body	N	nucleus	VH	ventral horn
CC	central canal	n	nucleolus	VR	ventral root
DH	dorsal horn	NB	Nissl body	W	white matter
DM	dura mater	Ng	neuroglial cell		
DR	dorsal root	Np	neuropil		

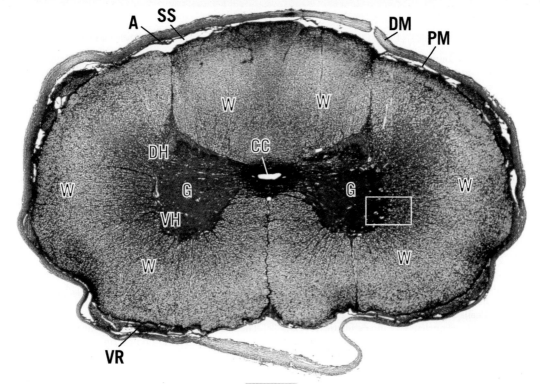

FIGURE 1

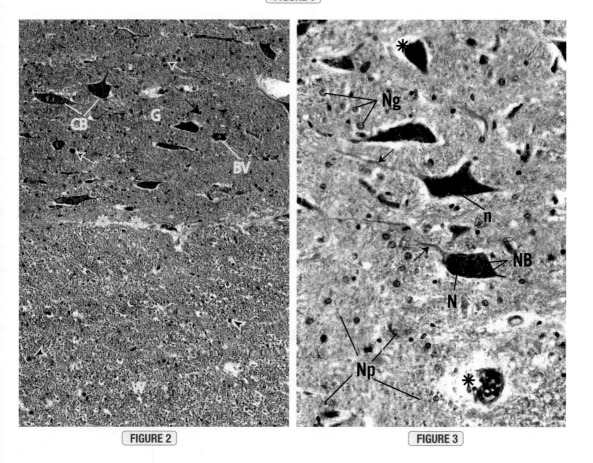

FIGURE 2

FIGURE 3

FIGURE 1 • Cerebellum. Human. Paraffin section. ×14.

The cerebellum, in contrast to the spinal cord, consists of a core of **white matter** (W) and the superficially located **gray matter** (G). Although it is difficult to tell from this low-magnification photomicrograph, the gray matter is subdivided into three layers, the outer **molecular layer** (ML), a middle **Purkinje cell layer** (PL), and the inner **granular layer** (GL). The less dense appearance of the molecular layer is due to the sparse arrangement of nerve cell bodies, whereas the darker appearance of the granular layer is a function of the great number of darkly staining nuclei packed closely together. A region similar to the *boxed area* is represented in Figure 2.

FIGURE 3 • Purkinje cell. Human cerebellum. Paraffin section. ×540.

This is a higher magnification of the *boxed area* of Figure 2. The **granular layer** (GL) of the cerebellum is composed of two cell types, the smaller **granule cells** (GC) and larger **Golgi type II cells** (G2). The flask-shaped **Purkinje cell** (PC) displays its large **nucleus** (N) and **dendritic tree** (D). Nuclei of numerous **basket cells** (BC) of the **molecular layer** (ML) as well as the **unmyelinated fibers** (UF) of the granule cells are well defined in this photomicrograph. These fibers make synaptic contact (*arrows*) with the dendritic processes of the Purkinje cells. **Inset. Astrocyte. Human cerebellum. Golgi stain. Paraffin section.** × 132. Note the numerous processes of this **fibrous astrocyte** (A) in the white matter of the cerebellum.

FIGURE 2 • Cerebellum. Human. Paraffin section. ×132.

This photomicrograph is taken from a region similar to the *boxed area* in Figure 1. The **granular layer** (GL) is composed of closely packed **granule cells** (GC), which, at first glance, resemble lymphocytes due to their dark, round nuclei. Interspersed among these cells are clear spaces called glomeruli or **cerebellar islands** (CI), where synapses occur between axons entering the cerebellum from outside and dendrites of granule cells. The **Purkinje cells** (PC) send their axons into the granular layer; their dendrites arborize in the **molecular layer** (ML). This layer also contains unmyelinated fibers from the granular layer as well as two types of cells, **basket cells** (BC) and the more superficially located **stellate cells** (SC). The surface of the cerebellum is invested by **pia matter** (PM), just barely evident in this photomicrograph. The *boxed area* is presented at a higher magnification in Figure 3.

FIGURE 4 • Synapse. Afferent terminals. Electron microscopy. ×16,200.

The lateral descending nucleus of the fifth cranial nerve displays a **primary afferent terminal** (AT) that is forming multiple synapses with **dendrites** (D) and **axons** (Ax). Observe the presence of **synaptic vesicles** (SV) in the postsynaptic axon terminals as well as the thickening of the membrane of the primary afferent terminal (*arrows*). This terminal also houses **mitochondria** (m) and **cisternae** (Ci) for the synaptic vesicles. (From Meszler RM. Fine structure and organization of the infrared receptor relays: lateral descending nucleus of V in Boidae and nucleus reticularis caloris in the rattlesnake. J Comp Neurol 1983;220:299–309.)

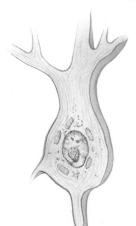

Multipolar cell
(cerebellar cortex)

KEY						
A	fibrous astrocyte	G	gray matter	PC	Purkinje cell
AT	primary afferent terminal	G2	Golgi type II cell	PL	Purkinje cell layer
Ax	axons	GC	granule cell	PM	pia mater
BC	basket cell	GL	granular layer	SC	stellate cell
CI	cerebellar island	m	mitochondrion	SV	synaptic vesicle
Ci	cistern	ML	molecular layer	UF	unmyelinated fiber
D	dendrite	N	nucleus	W	white matter

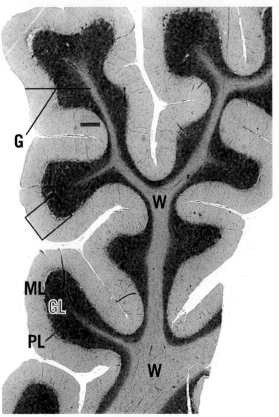

FIGURE 1

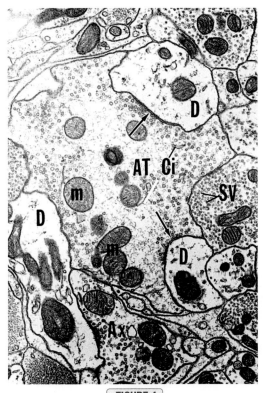

FIGURE 2

FIGURE 3

FIGURE 4

These figures represent a montage of the entire human cerebral cortex and some of the underlying **white matter** (W) at a low magnification. Observe that the numerous **blood vessels** (BV) that penetrate the entire cortex are surrounded by a clear area (*arrow*), which is due to shrinkage artifact. The six layers of the cortex are not clearly defined but are approximated by brackets. The **pia mater** (PM), covering the surface of the cortex, is a vascular tissue that provides larger blood vessels as well as **capillaries** (Ca) that penetrate the brain tissue. Layer one of the cortex is known as the **molecular layer** (1), which contains numerous fibers and only a few neuron cell bodies. It is difficult to distinguish these soma from the neuroglial cells at this magnification. The second, **external granular layer** (2) is composed of small **granule cells** (GC) as well as many **neuroglial cells** (Ng). The third layer is known as the **external pyramidal layer** (3), which is the thickest layer in this section of the cerebral cortex. It consists of **pyramidal cells**

(Py) and some **granule cells** (GC) as well as numerous **neuroglia** (Ng) interspersed among the soma and fibers. The fourth layer, the **internal granular layer** (4), is a relatively narrow band whose cell population consists mostly of small and a few large **granule cells** (GC) and the ever-present **neuroglial cells** (Ng). The **internal pyramidal layer** (5) houses medium and large **pyramidal cells** (Py) as well as the ubiquitous **neuroglia** (Ng), whose nuclei appear as small dots. Although not evident in this preparation, nerve fibers of the internal band of Baillarger pass horizontally through this layer, whereas those of the external band of Baillarger traverse the internal granular layer. The deepest layer of the cerebral cortex is the **multiform layer** (6), which contains cells of various shapes, many of which are fusiform in morphology. Neuroglial cells and Martinotti cells are also present in this layer but cannot be distinguished from each other at this magnification. The **white matter** (W) appears very cellular, due to the nuclei of the numerous neuroglial cells supporting the cell processes derived from and traveling to the cortex.

This photomicrograph of the white matter of the cerebrum presents a matted appearance due to the interweaving of various nerve cell and glial cell processes. Note also the presence of two **blood vessels** (BV) passing horizontally across the field. The long processes of the **fibrous astrocytes** (FA) approach the blood vessels (*arrows*) and assist in the formation of the blood-brain barrier.

This photomicrograph is of a section of the cerebral cortex, demonstrating **nuclei** (N) of nerve cells as well as the presence of **microglia** (Mi). Note that microglia are very small and possess a dense **nucleus** (N) as well as numerous cell processes (*arrows*).

KEY							
BV	blood vessel	Ng	neurological cell	3	external pyramidal layer
Ca	capillary	PM	pia mater	4	internal granular layer
FA	fibrous astrocyte	Py	pyramidal cell	5	internal pyramidal layer
GC	granule cell	W	white matter	6	multiform layer
Mi	microglia	1	molecular layer		
N	nucleus	2	external granular layer		

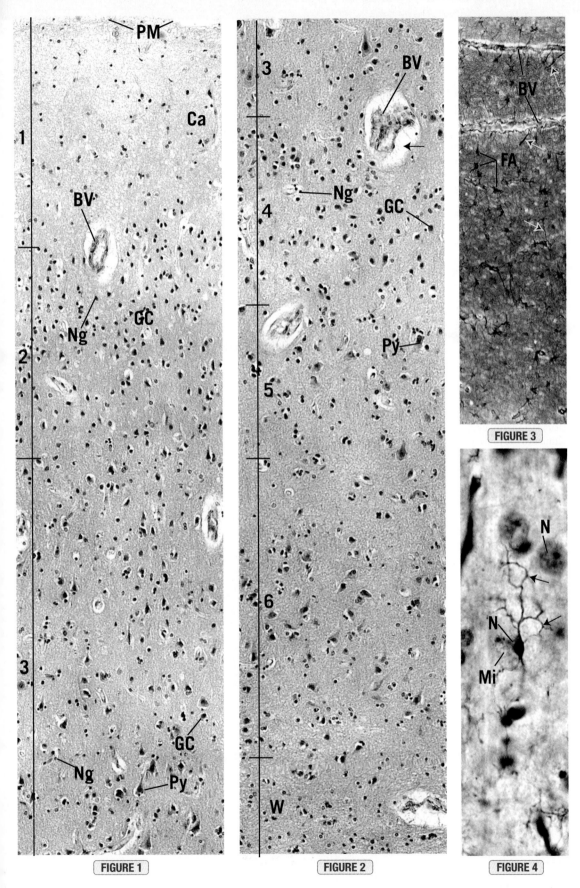

FIGURE 1

FIGURE 2

FIGURE 3

FIGURE 4

PLATE 7-4 Sympathetic Ganglia, Sensory Ganglia

FIGURE 1 • Sympathetic ganglion. l.s. Paraffin section. ×132.

Sympathetic ganglia are structures that receive axons of presynaptic cells, whose soma are within the CNS. Located within the ganglion are soma of postsynaptic neurons upon which the presynaptic cell axons synapse. These ganglia are enveloped by a collagenous connective tissue **capsule** (C), which sends **septa** (S) containing **blood vessels** (BV) within the substance of the ganglion. The arrangement of the cell bodies of the **multipolar neurons** (MN) within the ganglion appears to be haphazard. This very vascular structure contains numerous nuclei that belong to **endothelial cells** (E), intravascular **leukocytes** (L), **fibroblasts** (F), **Schwann cells** (ScC), and those of the **supporting cells** (SS) surrounding the nerve cell bodies. A region similar to the *boxed area* is presented in Figure 2.

FIGURE 3 • Sensory ganglion. l.s. Human. Paraffin section. ×132.

The dorsal root ganglion provides a good representative example of a sensory ganglion. It possesses a **vascular** (BV) connective tissue **capsule** (C), which also envelops its sensory root. The neurons of the dorsal root ganglion are pseudounipolar in morphology; therefore, their **somata** (So) appear spherical in shape. The **fibers** (f), many of which are myelinated, alternate with rows of cell bodies. Note that some somata are large (*arrow*), whereas others are small (*arrowhead*). Each soma is surrounded by neuroectodermally derived **capsule cells** (Cc). A region similar to the *boxed area* is presented at a high magnification in Figure 4.

FIGURE 2 • Sympathetic ganglion. l.s. Paraffin section. ×540.

This photomicrograph presents a higher magnification of a region similar to the *boxed area* of Figure 1. Although neurons of the sympathetic ganglion are multipolar, their processes are not evident in this specimen stained with hematoxylin and eosin. The **nucleus** (N), with its prominent **nucleolus** (n), is clearly visible. The cytoplasm contains **lipofuscin** (Li), a yellowish pigment that is prevalent in neurons of older individuals. The clear space between the soma and the **supporting cells** (SS) is a shrinkage artifact. Note the numerous **blood vessels** (BV) containing red blood cells (*arrows*) and a **neutrophil** (Ne).

FIGURE 4 • Sensory ganglion. l.s. Human. Paraffin section. ×270.

This photomicrograph is a higher magnification of a region similar to the *boxed area* of Figure 3. The spherical cell bodies display their centrally located **nuclei** (N) and **nucleoli** (n). Observe that both small (*arrowheads*) and large (*arrows*) somata are present in the field and that the nuclei are not always in the plane of section. Hematoxylin and eosin stains the somata a more or less homogeneous pink, so that organelles such as Nissl substance are not visible. However, the nuclei and cytoplasm of **capsule cells** (Cc) are clearly evident. Moreover, the small, elongated, densely staining nuclei of **fibroblasts** (F) are also noted to surround somata, just peripheral to the capsule cells. **Axons** (Ax) of myelinated nerve fibers belong to the large pseudounipolar neurons.

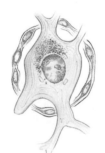

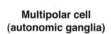

Multipolar cell
(autonomic ganglia)

Unipolar cell
(pseudounipolar
cell from dorsal
root ganglion)

KEY					
Ax	axon	f	nerve fiber	Ne	neutrophil
BV	blood vessel	L	leukocyte	S	septum
C	capsule	Li	lipofuscin	ScC	Schwann cell
Cc	capsule cell	n	nucleolus	So	soma
E	endothelial cell	MN	multipolar neuron	SS	supporting cell
F	fibroblast	N	nucleus		

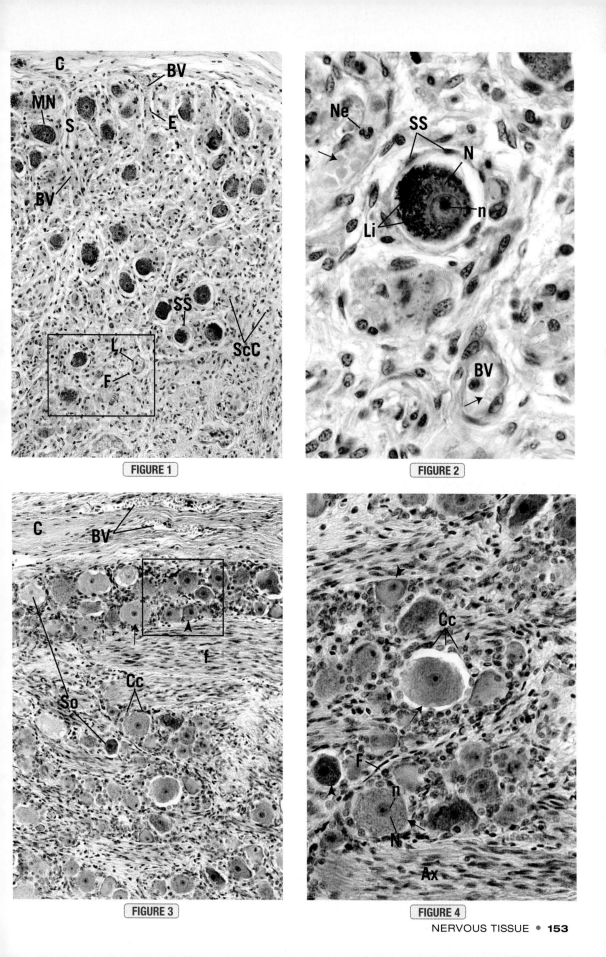

FIGURE 1

FIGURE 2

FIGURE 3

FIGURE 4

FIGURE 1a • Peripheral nerve. l.s. Monkey. Plastic section. ×132.

The longitudinal section of the peripheral nerve fascicle presented in this photomicrograph is enveloped by its **perineurium** (P), composed of an outer **connective tissue layer** (CT) and an inner layer of flattened **epithelioid cells** (E). The perineurium conducts small **blood vessels** (BV), which are branches of larger vessels traveling in the surrounding epineurium, a structure composed of loose connective tissue with numerous fat cells. The peripheral nerve is composed of numerous nonmyelinated and myelinated nerve fibers, an example of which is presented in Figure 1b. The dense nuclei (*arrows*) within the nerve fascicle belong to Schwann cells and endoneurial cells. A region similar to the *boxed area* is presented in Figure 2.

FIGURE 1b • Teased, myelinated nerve fiber. Paraffin section. l.s. ×540.

This longitudinal section of a single myelinated nerve fiber displays its **axon** (Ax) and the neurokeratin network, the remnants of the dissolved **myelin** (M). Note the **node of Ranvier** (NR), a region where two Schwann cells meet. It is here, where the axon is not covered by myelin, that saltatory conduction of impulses occur. Observe that **Schmidt-Lanterman incisures** (SL) are clearly evident. These are regions where the cytoplasm of Schwann cells is trapped in the myelin sheath.

FIGURE 3 • Peripheral nerve. x.s. Paraffin section. ×132.

This transverse section presents portions of two fascicles, each surrounded by **perineurium** (P). The intervening loose connective tissue of the **epineurium** (Ep) with its **blood vessels** (BV) is clearly evident. The perineurium forms a **septum** (S), which subdivides this fascicle into two compartments. Note that the **axons** (Ax) are in the center of the **myelin sheath** (MS) and occasionally a crescent-shaped nucleus of a **Schwann cell** (ScC) is evident. The denser, smaller nuclei (*arrows*) belong to endoneurial cells. *Inset.* **Peripheral nerve. x.s. Silver stain. Paraffin section.** × 540. Silver-stained sections of myelinated nerve fibers have the large, clear spaces (*arrow*) that indicate the dissolved myelin. The **axons** (Ax) stain well as dark, dense structures, and the delicate **endoneurium** (En) is also evident.

FIGURE 2 • Peripheral nerve. l.s. Paraffin section. ×270.

This is a higher magnification of a region similar to the boxed area of Figure 1a. A distinguishing characteristic of longitudinal sections of peripheral nerves is that they appear to follow a zizzag course, particularly evident in this photomicrograph. The sinuous course of these fibers is accentuated by the presence of nuclei of **Schwann cells** (ScC), **fibroblasts** (F), and endothelial cells of capillaries belonging to the endoneurium. Many of these nerve fibers are **myelinated** (M) as corroborated by the presence of the **nodes of Ranvier** (NR) and neurokeratin around the **axons** (Ax).

FIGURE 4 • Choroid plexus. Paraffin section. ×270.

The choroid plexus, located within the ventricles of the brain, is responsible for the formation of cerebrospinal fluid. This structure is composed of tufts of **capillaries** (Ca) whose tortuous course is followed by **villi** (Vi) of the simple cuboidal **choroid plexus epithelium** (cp). The **connective tissue core** (CT) of the choroid plexus is contributed by pia-arachnoid, whereas the simple cuboidal epithelium is modified ependymal lining of the ventricle. The clear spaces surrounding the choroid plexus belong to the ventricle of the brain.

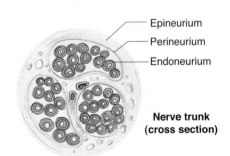

Epineurium

Perineurium

Endoneurium

Nerve trunk (cross section)

KEY					
Ax	axon	En	endoneurium	P	perineurium
BV	blood vessel	Ep	epineurium	S	septum
Ca	capillary	F	fibroblast	ScC	Schwann cell
cp	choroid plexus epithelium	M	myelin	SL	Schmidt-Lanterman incisure
CT	connective tissue	MS	myelin sheath	Vi	villus
E	epithelioid cell	NR	node of Ranvier		

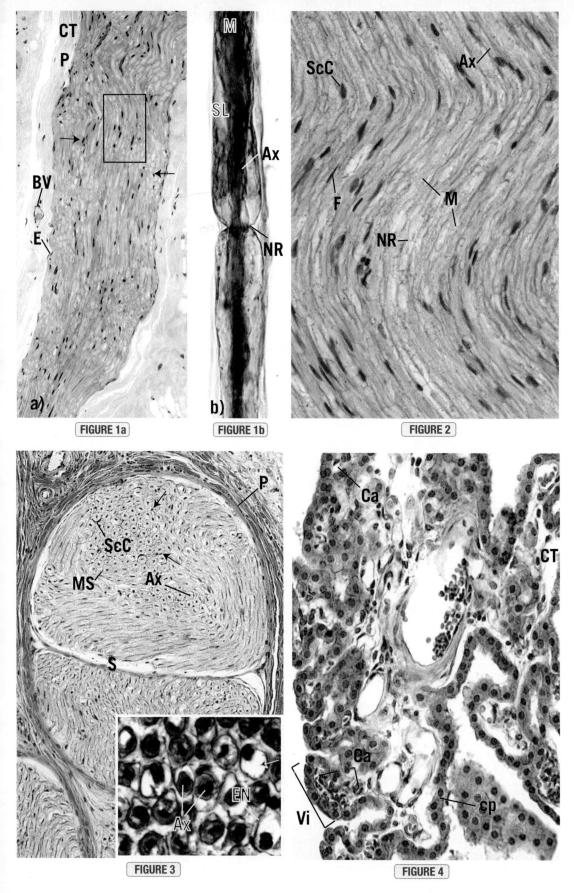

FIGURE 1a

FIGURE 1b

FIGURE 2

FIGURE 3

FIGURE 4

FIGURE 1 • Peripheral nerve. x.s. Mouse. Electron microscopy. ×33,300.

This electron micrograph presents a cross-section of three myelinated and several unmyelinated nerve fibers. Note that the **axons** (Ax) (although they may be the afferent fibers of pseudounipolar neurons) are surrounded by a thick **myelin sheath** (MS), peripheral to which is the bulk of the **Schwann cell cytoplasm** (ScC) housing **mitochondria** (m), **rough endoplasmic reticulum** (rER), and **pinocytotic vesicles** (PV). The Schwann cell is surrounded by a **basal lamina** (BL) isolating this cell from the **endoneurial connective tissue** (CT). The myelin sheath is derived from the plasma membrane of the Schwann cell, which presumably wraps spirally around the axon, resulting in the formation of an **external** (EM) and **internal** (IM) **mesaxon**. The **axolemma** (Al) is separated from the Schwann cell membrane by a narrow cleft,

the periaxonal space. The axoplasm houses **mitochondria** (m) as well as **neurofilaments** (Nf) and **neurotubules** (Nt). Occasionally, the myelin wrapping is surrounded by Schwann cell cytoplasm on its outer and inner aspects, as in the nerve fiber in the upper right-hand corner. The **unmyelinated nerve fibers** (f) in the top of this electron micrograph display their relationship to the **Schwann cell** (ScC). The fibers are positioned in such a fashion that each lies in a complicated membrane-lined groove within the Schwann cell. Some fibers are situated superficially, whereas others are positioned more deeply within the grooves. However, a periaxonal (or peridendritic) space (*arrows*) is always present. **Mitochondria** (m), **neurofilaments** (Nf), and **neurotubules** (Nt) are also present. Note that the entire structure is surrounded by a **basal lamina** (BL), which covers but does not extend into the grooves (*arrowheads*) housing the nerve fibers. (Courtesy of Dr. J. Strum.)

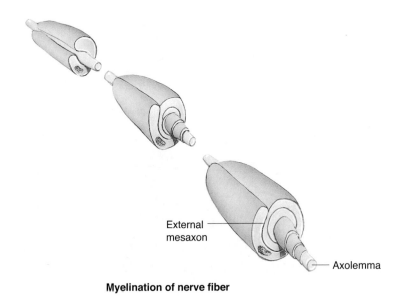

External mesaxon

Axolemma

Myelination of nerve fiber

	KEY						
Al	axolemma		f	nerve fiber	Nt	neurotubule
Ax	axon		IM	internal mesaxon	PV	pinocytotic vesicle
BL	basal lamina		m	mitochondrion	rER	rough ER
CT	endoneurial connective tissue	MS	myelin sheath	ScC	Schwann cell cytoplasm
EM	external mesaxon		Nf	neurofilament		

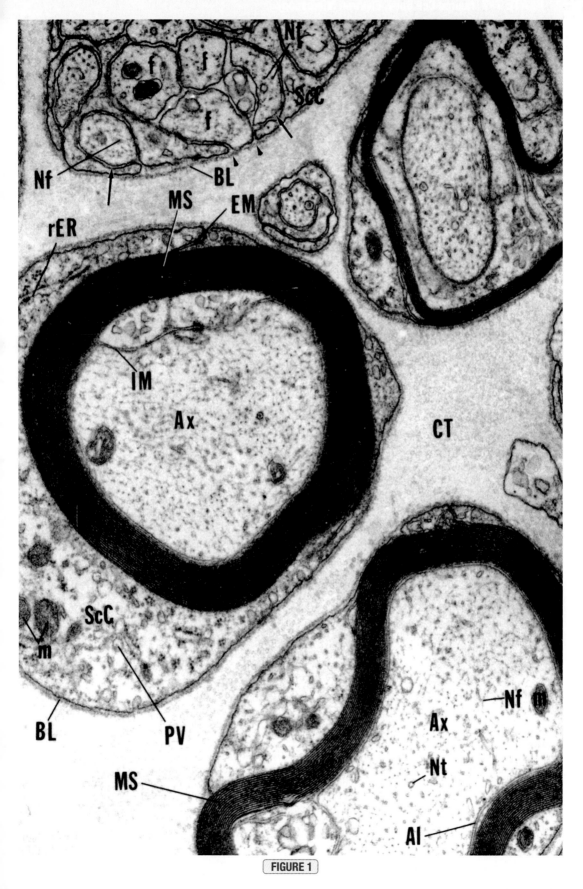

FIGURE 1

NERVOUS TISSUE • **157**

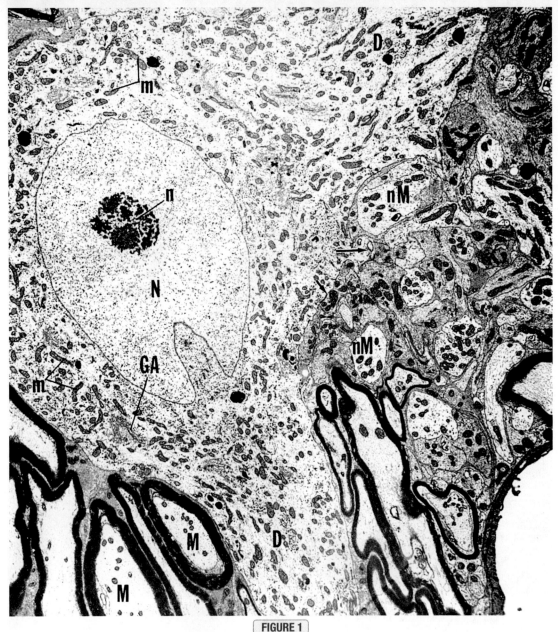

FIGURE 1

FIGURE 1 • Neuron. Lateral descending nucleus. Electron microscopy. ×3589.

The soma of this neuron presents a typical appearance. Note the large **nucleus** (N) and **nucleolus** (n) surrounded by a considerable amount of cytoplasm rich in organelles. Observe the extensive **Golgi apparatus** (GA), numerous **mitochondria** (m), and elements of rough endoplasmic reticulum, which extend into the **dendrites** (D). **Myelinated** (M) and **nonmyelinated** (nM) fibers are also present, as are synapses (*arrows*) along the cell surface. (From Meszler R, Auker C, Carpenter D. Fine structure and organization of the infrared receptor relay, the lateral descending nucleus of the trigeminal nerve in pit vipers. J Comp Neurol 1981;196:571–584.)

Summary of Histological Organization

I. SPINAL CORD

A. Gray Matter

The **gray matter**, centrally located and more or less in the shape of an H, has two **dorsal horns** and two **ventral horns**. Ventral horns display numerous **multipolar (motor) cell bodies.** The perikaryon possesses a large, clear **nucleus** and a dense **nucleolus.** Its cytoplasm is filled with clumps of basophilic **Nissl substance** (rough endoplasmic reticulum) that extends into **dendrites** but not into the **axon**. The origin of the axon is indicated by the **axon hillock** of the **soma**. Numerous small nuclei abound in the gray matter; they belong to the various **neuroglia**. The nerve fibers and neuroglial processes in the gray matter are referred to as the **neuropil**. The right and left halves of the gray matter are connected to each other by the **gray commissure**, which houses the **central canal** lined by simple cuboidal **ependymal cells.**

B. White Matter

The **white matter** of the spinal cord is peripherally located and consists of **ascending** and **descending fibers**. These fibers are mostly **myelinated** (by **oligodendroglia**), accounting for the coloration in live tissue. **Nuclei** noted in white matter belong to the various **neuroglia**.

C. Meninges

The **meninges** of the spinal cord form three layers. The most intimate layer is the **pia mater**, surrounded by the **arachnoid**, which, in turn, is invested by the thick, collagenous **dura mater**.

II. CEREBELLUM

A. Cortex

The **cortex** of the cerebellum consists of an outer **molecular layer** and an inner **granular layer** with a single layer of **Purkinje cells** interposed between them. The **perikaryons** of the molecular layer are small and relatively few in number. Most of the fibers are unmyelinated. **Purkinje cells** are easily distinguished by their location, large size, and extensive **dendritic arborization**. The **granular layer** displays crowded arrays of nuclei belonging to **granule cells** and intervening clear regions known as glomeruli (or **cerebellar islands**). These mainly represent areas of synapses on granule cell dendrites.

B. Medullary Substance

The **medullary substance** (internal white mass) is the region of **white matter** deep to the granular layer of the cerebellum, composed mostly of myelinated fibers and associated **neuroglial cells**.

III. CEREBRUM

A. Cortex

The **cerebral cortex** is composed of **gray matter**, mostly subdivided into six layers, with each housing neurons whose morphology is characteristic of that particular layer. The major neuronal types are **pyramidal cells, stellate (granule) cells, horizontal cells**, and **inverted (Martinotti) cells**. The following description refers to the **neocortex** and is presented from superficial to deep order. The first layer is just deep to the pia mater, whereas the sixth level is the deepest cortical layer, bordering the central white matter of the cerebrum.

1. Molecular Layer
Composed of **horizontal cells** and cell processes.

2. External Granular Layer
Consists mostly of **granule (stellate) cells**, tightly packed.

3. External Pyramidal Layer
Large **pyramidal cells** and **granule (stellate) cells**.

4. Internal Granular Layer
Closely packed **granule (stellate) cells**, most of which are small, although some are larger.

5. Internal Pyramidal Layer
Medium and large **pyramidal cells** constitute this layer.

6. Multiform Layer
Consisting of various cell shapes, many of which are fusiform. This layer also houses **Martinotti cells**.

B. White Matter

Deep to the cerebral cortex is the **subcortical white matter**, composed mostly of myelinated fibers and associated **neuroglial cells**.

IV. CHOROID PLEXUS

The **choroid plexus** consists of tufts of small vascular elements (derived from the pia-arachnoid) that are covered by **modified ependymal cells** (simple cuboidal in shape). These structures, located in the ventricles of the brain, are responsible for the formation of the **cerebrospinal fluid** (CSF).

V. DORSAL ROOT GANGLION (DRG)

A. Neurons

The **somata** of these cells are **pseudounipolar**, with large nuclei and nucleoli. Surrounding each soma are **capsule cells**, recognized by their small, round nuclei. **Fibroblasts** (satellite cells) are also evident. Synapses do not occur in the DRG.

B. Fibers

Fibers are mostly myelinated and travel in bundles through the DRG.

C. Connective Tissue

The DRG is surrounded by collagenous **connective tissue**, whose septa penetrate the substance of the ganglion.

VI. PERIPHERAL NERVE

A. Longitudinal Section

The parallel fibers stain a pale pink with hematoxylin and eosin, although **Schwann cells** and occasional **fibroblast nuclei** are clearly evident. The most characteristic feature is the apparent wavy, zigzag course of the nerve fibers. At low magnification the **perineurium** is clearly distinguishable, whereas at high magnification the **nodes of Ranvier** may be recognizable.

B. Transverse Section

The most characteristic feature of transverse sections of nerve fibers is the numerous, small, irregular circles with a centrally located dot. Thin spokes appear to traverse the empty-looking space between the dot and the circumference of the circle. These represent the **neurolemma**, the extracted **myelin** (**neurokeratin**), and the central **axon**. Occasionally, crescent-shaped nuclei hug the myelin; these belong to **Schwann cells**. The **endoneurium** may show evidence of **nuclei** of **fibroblasts** also. At lower magnification the **perineuria** of several fascicles of nerve fibers are clearly distinguishable. When stained with OsO_4, the **myelin sheath** stands out as dark, round structures with lightly staining centers.

Circulatory System

The circulatory system is composed of two separate but connected components: the blood vascular system (cardiovascular system) that transports blood and the lymphatic vascular system that collects and returns excess extracellular fluid (lymph) to the blood vascular system. Lymphoid tissue is presented in Chapter 9.

● BLOOD VASCULAR SYSTEM

The **blood vascular system**, consisting of the heart and blood vessels, functions in propelling and transporting blood and its various constituents throughout the body. The heart, acting as a pump, forces blood at high pressure into large, elastic arteries that carry the blood away from the heart. These arteries give way to increasingly smaller muscular arteries. Eventually, blood reaches extremely thin-walled vessels, capillaries, and small venules, where exchange of materials occurs. It is mostly here that certain cells, oxygen, nutrients, hormones, certain proteins, and additional materials leave the bloodstream, whereas carbon dioxide, waste products, certain cells, and various secretory products enter the bloodstream. **Capillary beds**, except those of the glomerulus, which are drained by arterioles, are drained by the venous components of the circulatory system, which return blood to the heart. The blood vascular system is subdivided into the pulmonary and systemic circuits, which originate from the right and left sides of the heart, respectively. The **pulmonary circuit** takes oxygen-poor blood to the lungs to become oxygenated and returns it to the left side of the heart. The oxygen-rich blood is propelled via the **systemic circuit** to the remainder of the body to be returned to the right side of the heart, completing the cycle.

● HEART

The heart is a four-chambered organ composed of two atria and two ventricles. The atria, subsequent to receiving blood from the pulmonary veins, venae cavae, and coronary sinus, discharge it into the ventricles. Contractions of the ventricles then propel the blood either from the right ventricle into the pulmonary trunk for distribution to the lungs or from the left ventricle into the aorta for distribution to the remainder of the body. Although the walls of the ventricles are thicker than those of the atria, these chambers possess common characteristics in that they are composed of three layers: epicardium, myocardium, and endocardium. **Epicardium**, the outermost layer, is covered by a simple squamous mesothelium deep to which is a fibroelastic connective tissue. The deepest aspect of the epicardium is composed of adipose tissue that houses nerves and the coronary vessels. Most of the wall of the heart is composed of **myocardium**, consisting of bundles of cardiac muscle that are attached to the thick collagenous connective tissue skeleton of the heart. The **endocardium** forms the lining of the atria and ventricles and is composed of a simple squamous endothelium as well as a subendothelial fibroelastic connective tissue. The endocardium participates in the formation of the heart valves, which control the direction of blood flow through the heart. Additionally, some cardiac muscle fibers are modified and specialized to regulate the sequence of atrial and ventricular contractions. These are the sinoatrial and atrioventricular nodes and the bundle of His and Purkinje fibers. The **sinoatrial node** (**SA node**), the pacemaker of the heart, is located at the junction of the superior vena cava and the right atrium. Impulses generated at this point are conducted to the **atrioventricular node** (**AV node**), which is located on the medial wall of the right ventricle near the tricuspid valve, as well as to the atrial myocardium. Arising from the AV node is the **bundle of His**, which bifurcates in the septum membranaceum to serve both ventricles. As these fibers reach the subendocardium, they ramify and are known as **Purkinje fibers**, which eventually merge with and become indistinguishable from cells of the myocardium. The inherent rhythm of the SA node is modulated by the autonomic nervous system, in that parasympathetic fibers derived from the vagus nerve decrease the rate of the heart beat, whereas fibers derived from sympathetic ganglia increase it.

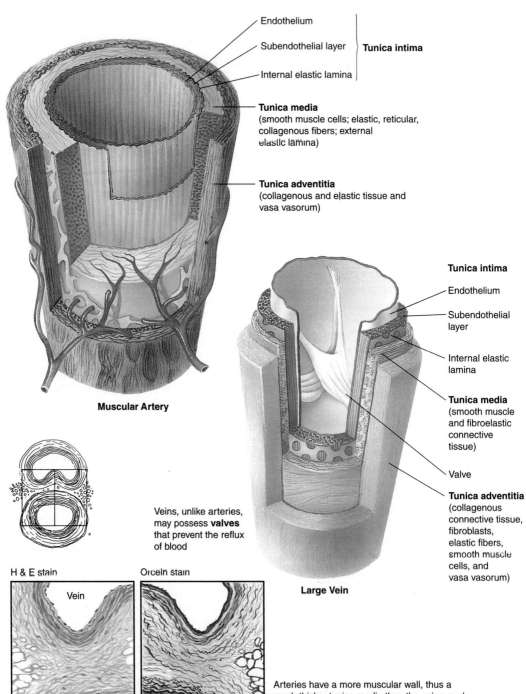

Endothelium
Subendothelial layer
Internal elastic lamina
Tunica intima

Tunica media
(smooth muscle cells; elastic, reticular, collagenous fibers; external elastic lamina)

Tunica adventitia
(collagenous and elastic tissue and vasa vasorum)

Muscular Artery

Tunica intima
Endothelium
Subendothelial layer
Internal elastic lamina

Tunica media
(smooth muscle and fibroelastic connective tissue)

Valve

Tunica adventitia
(collagenous connective tissue, fibroblasts, elastic fibers, smooth muscle cells, and vasa vasorum)

Large Vein

Veins, unlike arteries, may possess **valves** that prevent the reflux of blood

H & E stain

Vein

Orcein stain

Artery

Arteries have a more muscular wall, thus a much thicker tunica media than the veins, and they have a greater amount of elastic tissue. Conversely, the tunica adventitia of veins are much thicker than those of the arteries.

The outermost layer is the **tunica adventitia**, composed of fibroelastic connective tissue, whose vessels, the **vasa vasorum**, penetrate the outer regions of the tunica media, supplying its cells with nutrients.

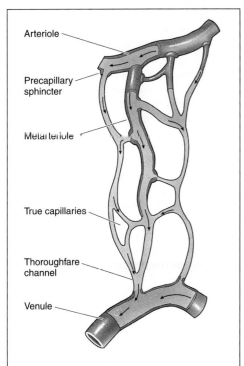

Arteriole

Precapillary sphincter

Metarteriole

True capillaries

Thoroughfare channel

Venule

Some capillary beds, such as those of the skin, are designed so that they may be bypassed under certain circumstances. One method whereby blood flow may be controlled is the use of **central channels** that convey blood from and arteriole to a venule. The proximal half of the central channel is a **metarteriole**, a vessel with an incomplete smooth muscle coat. Flow of blood into each capillary that arises from the metarteriole is controlled by a smooth muscle cell, the **precapillary sphincter**. The distal half of the central channel is the **thoroughfare channel**, which possesses no smooth muscle cells and accepts blood from the capillary bed. If the capillary bed is to be bypassed, the precapillary sphincters contract, preventing blood flow into the capillary bed, and the blood goes directly into the venule.

Capillaries consists of a simple squamous epithelium rolled into a narrow cylinder 8–10 μm in diameter. **Continuous (somatic) capillaries** have no fenestrae; material transverses the endothelial cell in either direction via **pinocytotic vesicles. Fenestrated (visceral) capillaries** are characterized by the presence of perforations, **fenestrae**, 60–80 μm in diameter, which may or may not be bridged by a diaphragm. **Sinusoidal capillaries** have a large lumen (30–40 μm in diameter), possess numerous fenestrae, have discontinuous basal lamina, and lack pinocytotic vesicles. Frequently, adjacent endothelial cells of sinusoidal capillaries overlap one another in an incomplete fashion.

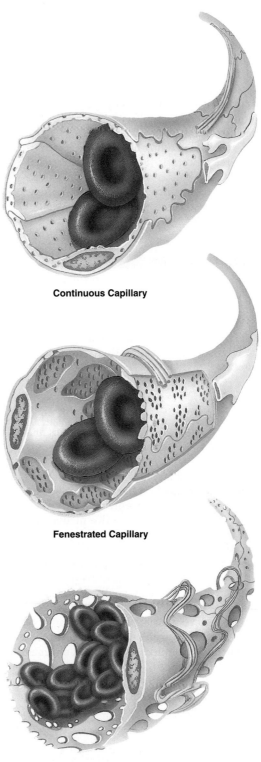

Continuous Capillary

Fenestrated Capillary

Sinusoidal (Discontinuous) Capillary

● ARTERIES

Arteries, by definition, conduct blood away from the heart and may be classified into three categories: elastic (also known as conducting or large), muscular (also known as distributing or medium), and arterioles (see Graphic 8-1). **Elastic arteries**, such as the aorta, receive blood directly from the heart and consequently are the largest of the arteries. **Muscular arteries** distribute blood to various organs, whereas **arterioles** regulate blood pressure and the distribution of blood to capillary beds via vasoconstriction and vasodilatation of vessel walls.

Blood vessels, including all arteries, are composed of three concentric layers: tunica intima, tunica media, and tunica adventitia. The **tunica intima** is composed of a continuous sheet of simple squamous endothelial cells lining the lumen and of various amounts of subendothelial connective tissue. The **tunica media**, usually the thickest of the three layers, is composed of circularly arranged smooth muscle cells and fibroelastic connective tissue, whose elastic content increases greatly with the size of the vessel. The **tunica adventitia** is the outermost layer of the vessel wall, consisting of fibroelastic connective tissue. In larger vessels, the tunica adventitia houses **vasa vasorum**, small blood vessels that supply the tunica adventitia and media of that vessel.

● VEINS

Veins conduct blood away from body tissues and back to the heart (see Graphic 8-1). Generally, the diameters of veins are larger than those of corresponding arteries; however, veins are thinner walled, since they do not bear high blood pressures. Veins also possess three concentric, more or less definite layers: **tunica intima**, **tunica media**, and **tunica adventitia**. Furthermore, veins have fewer layers of smooth muscle cells in their tunica media than do arteries. Finally, many veins possess valves that act to prevent regurgitation of blood. Three categories of veins exist: **small**, **medium**, and **large**. The smallest veins, frequently referred to as **venules**, are also responsible for the exchange of materials. Moreover, **vasodilator substances**, such as **serotonin** and **histamine**, appear to act on small venules, causing them to become "leaky" by increasing the intercellular distances between the membranes of contiguous endothelial cells. Most such intercellular gaps occur in small venules rather than in capillaries.

● CAPILLARIES

Capillaries usually form thin-walled networks that are supplied by arterioles and metarterioles and drained by venules (see Graphic 8-2). Frequently, capillary networks may be circumvented by specialized vessels called **arteriovenous anastomoses**, interposed between the arterial and venous systems. Capillaries are composed of highly attenuated **endothelial cells** that form narrow vascular channels 8–10 μm in diameter and are usually less than 1 mm long. Associated with capillaries are **basal laminae** and **pericytes**, but the capillary possesses no smooth muscle cells. Therefore, capillaries do not exhibit vasomotor activities. Control of blood flow into a capillary bed is established at the sites where individual capillaries arise from **terminal arterioles** or metarterioles and is accomplished by smooth muscle cells known as **precapillary sphincters**. The presence of **metarterioles** and **thoroughfare channels** permits the maintenance of an adequate blood supply during reduced flow through a capillary bed. Based on fine structural characteristics, three types of capillaries are recognized: fenestrated, continuous, and discontinuous. **Fenestrated capillaries** possess numerous pores, usually bridged by diaphragms, through which material may enter or leave the capillary lumen. **Continuous capillaries** are devoid of pores, and material must traverse the endothelial cell either via pinocytotic vesicles or between endothelial cell junctions. In certain areas of the body (brain, thymus, testes), however, fasciae occludentes formed by contiguous endothelial cells prevent the escape or entry of material through intercellular spaces. **Discontinuous capillaries** (**sinusoids**) are tortuous and possess large lumina. Their endothelial cells present large fenestrae and intercellular spaces. Moreover, their basal lamina is not continuous. Frequently, macrophages are associated with discontinuous capillaries. Some authors recognize sinusoids, venous sinusoids, and sinusoidal capillaries in place of discontinuous capillaries.

● LYMPH VASCULAR SYSTEM

Excess extracellular fluid, which does not enter the venous return system at the level of the capillary bed or venule, gains entry into **lymphatic capillaries**, blindly ending thin vessels of the lymph vascular system. Subsequent to passing through chains of lymph nodes and larger lymph vessels, the fluid known as lymph enters the blood vascular system at the root of the neck.

Histophysiology

I. BLOOD VASCULAR SYSTEM

A. Heart

The **heart** is a muscular pump that propels blood at high pressure, via elastic arteries, to the lungs (**pulmonary circuit**) for oxygenation and via the aorta (**systemic circuit**) for distribution of oxygenated blood to the tissues of the body. The cardiac muscle cells of the heart possess gap junctions at the intercalated discs that, permit the movement of ions and very small molecules from one cell to the next. It is important to realize that the cardiac muscle cells of the atria do not come into contact with the cardiac muscle cells of the ventricles but are separated from one another by fibrous connective tissue elements.

1. Generation and Conduction of Impulse
The **sinoatrial node** (**SA node**) of the heart generates impulses that result in the contraction of the atrial muscles; blood from the atria then enters the ventricles. The impulse is then transmitted to the **atrioventricular node** (**AV node**) via the atrioventricular bundle.

The **atrioventricular bundle** (**of His**) arises from the AV node and travels in the interventricular septum, where it subdivides to form the Purkinje fibers. The **Purkinje fibers** deliver the impulse to the cardiac muscle cells of the ventricles that contract to pump the blood from the right ventricle into the pulmonary trunk and from the left ventricle into the aorta.

This arrangement of the cardiac myocytes as well as the atrioventricular bundle permit the contraction of the atria first, followed after a time lag, by contraction of the ventricles. In this fashion, blood from the atria can enter the ventricles and, once the ventricles are filled, they contract and propel the blood into the systemic and pulmonary circuits.

2. Valves
Atrioventricular valves between the atria and ventricles prevent regurgitation of blood into the atria. Similarly, **semilunar valves** located in the pulmonary trunk and the aorta prevent regurgitation of blood from these vessels back into their respective ventricles. The closing of these valves is responsible for the sounds associated with the heartbeat.

B. Arteries

Arteries are classified into three types: elastic, muscular, and arterioles. Capillaries, whose walls do not have a smooth muscle tunic, arise from the terminal ends of arterioles.

1. Elastic Arteries
Elastic arteries are the largest of the arteries. Since they arise directly from the heart, they are subject to cyclic changes of blood pressure, high as the ventricles pump blood into their lumina and low between the emptying of these chambers. To compensate for these intermittent pressure alterations, an abundance of elastic fibers are located in the walls of these vessels. These elastic fibers not only provide structural stability and permit distention of the elastic arteries but they also assist in the maintenance of blood pressure in between heartbeats.

2. Muscular Arteries
Muscular arteries comprise most of the named arteries of the body. Their tunica media is composed mostly of many layers of smooth muscle cells. Both elastic and muscular arteries are supplied by **vasa vasorum** and nerve fibers.

3. Arterioles
Arterioles are the smallest arteries and are responsible for regulating blood pressure. **Metarterioles** are the terminal ends of the arterioles, and they are characterized by the presence of incomplete rings of smooth muscle cells (**precapillary sphincters**) that encircle the origins of the capillaries. Metarterioles form the arterial (proximal) end of a **central channel**, and they are responsible for delivering blood into the capillary bed. The venous (distal) end of the central channel, known as a **thoroughfare channel**, is responsible for draining blood from the capillary bed and delivering it into venules. Contraction of precapillary sphincters of the metarteriole shunts the blood into the **thoroughfare channel** and from there into the venule; this way, the blood bypasses the capillary bed (see Graphic 8-2). **Arteriovenous anastomoses** are direct connections between arteries and venules and they also function in having blood bypass the capillary bed. These shunts function in **thermoregulation** and blood pressure control.

a. Endothelial Cell Functions
Endothelial cells function in formation of a selectively permeable membrane, vasoconstriction, vasodilation, initiation of coagulation, facilitation of transepithelial migration of inflammatory cells, angiogenesis, synthesis of growth factors, modifying Angiotensin I, and oxidation of lipoproteins.

Vasoconstriction is due not only to the action of sympathetic nerve fibers that act on the smooth muscles of the tunica media but also to the pharmacologic agent **Endothelin 1**, produced and released by endothelial cells of blood vessels.

Vasodilation is accomplished by parasympathetic nerve fibers in an indirect fashion. Instead of acting on smooth muscle cells, acetylcholine, released by the nerve end-foot, is bound to receptors on the endothelial cells, inducing them to release **nitric oxide** (**NO**), previously known as endothelial-derived releasing factor (EDRF). Nitric oxide acts on the cGMP system of the smooth muscle cells, causing their relaxation. Additionally, endothelial cells can produce **prostacyclins**, pharmacologic agents that induce the cAMP second messenger pathway in smooth muscle cells, effecting their relaxation.

Endothelial cells also release **tissue factor** (also known as **thromboplastin**), an agent that facilitates entry into the common pathway of **blood coagulation**, and **von Willebrand's factor**, which activates and facilitates the adhesion of platelets to the exposed laminin and collagens and induces them to release ADP and thrombospondin, which encourages their adhesion to each other

When inflammatory cells have to leave the blood stream to enter the connective tissue spaces, endothelial cells express on their luminal plasma membranes **E-selectins**. These signaling molecules are recognized by carbohydrate ligands on the surface of the inflammatory cells, triggering their **epithelial transmigration**.

Angiogenesis occurs in adult tissues in response to repair of damaged vessels, establishment of new vessels in repairing injuries, formation of new vessels subsequent to menstruation, formation of the corpus luteum, as well as in response to tumor formation. New vessels arise from existing vessels due to the interactions of various signaling molecules, such as Angiopoietins 1 and 2, with specific receptors on endothelial cells that induce mitotic activity in preexisting endothelial cells and recruit smooth muscle cells to form the tunica media of the developing vessels.

Endothelial cells also **synthesize growth factors** such as various colony-stimulating factors, which induce cells of blood lineage to undergo mitosis and produce various blood cells, and growth inhibitors, such as transforming growth

factor B. Additionally, endothelial cells convert Angiotensin I to Angiotensin II, a powerful smooth muscle contractant and inducer of aldosterone release by the suprarenal cortex. Endothelial cells also oxidize high cholesterol containing low density lipoproteins and very low density lipoproteins, so that the oxidized byproduct can be phagoytosed by macrophages.

C. Capillaries

Capillaries are very small vessels that consist of a single layer of endothelial cells surrounded by a basal lamina and occasional **pericytes**. These vessels exhibit **selective permeability** and they, along with venules, are responsible for the exchange of gases, metabolites, and other substances between the blood stream and the tissues of the body. There are three types of capillaries: continuous, fenestrated, and sinusoidal.

1. Capillary Types

Continuous capillaries lack fenestrae, display only occasional pinocytotic vesicles, and possess a continuous basal lamina. They are present in regions such as peripheral nerve fibers, skeletal muscle, lungs, and thymus.

Fenestrated capillaries are penetrated by relatively large diaphragm-covered pores. These cells also possess pinocytic vesicles and are enveloped by a continuous basal lamina. Fenestrated capillaries are located in endocrine glands, pancreas, and lamina propria of the intestines, and they also constitute the glomeruli of the kidneys, although their fenestrae are not covered by a diaphragm.

Sinusoidal capillaries are much larger than their fenestrated or continuous counterparts. They are enveloped by a discontinuous basal lamina, and their endothelial cells do not possess pinocytic vesicles. The intercellular junctions of their endothelial cells display gaps, thus permitting leakage of material into and out of these vessels. Sinusoidal capillaries are located in the liver, spleen, lymph nodes, bone marrow, and the suprarenal cortex.

2. Capillary Permeability

Capillary permeability is dependent not only on the endothelial cells comprising the capillary but also on the [physico]-chemical characteristics, such as size, charge, and shape, of the traversing substance. Some molecules, such as H_2O, diffuse through, whereas others are actively transported by carrier proteins across the endothelial cell plasma membrane.

Still others move through fenestrae or through gaps in the intercellular junctions. Certain pharmacological agents, such as **bradykinin** and **histamine**, have the ability to alter capillary permeability.

Leukocytes leave the bloodstream by passing through intercellular junctions of the endothelial cells (**diapedesis**) to enter the extracellular spaces of tissues and organs.

D. Veins

Veins, unlike arteries, are low pressure vessels that conduct blood from the tissues of the body back to the heart. Generally, they have larger lumina and thinner walls with fewer layers of smooth muscle cells than their companion arteries. Also, many veins contain valves in the lumen that prevent retrograde blood flow.

II. LYMPHATIC VASCULAR SYSTEM

Lymphatic capillaries begin as blind-ending vessels. Excess extracellular fluid enters these capillaries and becomes known as lymph; this fluid is delivered into lymphatic vessels of larger and larger diameters. Interspersed among these vessels are a series of lymph nodes that filter the lymph. The lymphatic vessels eventually deliver their contents into the **thoracic** and **right lymphatic ducts** that empty the lymph into large veins in the root of the neck. Large lymphatic vessels are similar in structure to small veins except that they possess valves, have larger lumina, and have thinner walls.

CLINICAL CONSIDERATIONS

Valve Defects
Children who have had rheumatic fever may develop valve defects. These valve defects may be related to improper closing (**incompetency**) or improper opening (**stenosis**). Fortunately, most of these defects can be repaired surgically.

Aneurysm
A damaged vessel wall may, over time, become weakened and begin to enlarge and form a bulging defect known as an aneurysm. This condition occurs most often in large vessels such as the aorta. If undetected or left untreated, it may rupture without warning and cause internal bleeding with fatal consequences. Surgical repair is possible, depending on the health of the individual.

Atherosclerosis
Atherosclerosis, the deposition of plaque within the walls of large- and medium-sized arteries, results in reduced blood flow within that vessel. If this condition involves the coronary arteries, the decreased blood flow to the myocardium causes coronary heart disease. The consequences of this disease may be angina pectoris, myocardial infarct, chronic ischemic cardiopathy, or sudden death.

Raynaud's Disease
Raynaud's disease is an idiopathic condition in which the arterioles of the fingers and toes go into sudden spasms lasting minutes to hours, cutting off blood supply to the digits with a resultant cyanosis and loss of sensation. This condition, affecting mostly younger women, is believed to be due to exposure to cold as well as to the patient's emotional state. Other causes include atherosclerosis, scleroderma, injury, and reaction to certain medications. The treatment of choice is limiting exposure to cold, prescribing mild sedatives, and discontinuing the use of tobacco products. Occasionally, the practicing of relaxation therapy may also control the condition.

Von Willebrand's Disease
Von Willebrand's disease is a genetic disorder in which the individual is either incapable of producing a normal quantity of von Willebrand Factor or the Factor that they produce is deficient. Most indiviuals have a mild form of the condition that is not life threathening. These individuals have problems with the process of blood clotting and display symptoms such as bruising easily, longer bleeding time, excessive bleeding from tooth extraction, excessive menstrual bleeding, and bloody mucous membranes.

Stroke
Stroke is a condition in which blood flow to a part of the brain is interrupted either due to a blockage of blood vessels or because of hemorrhage of blood vessels. The lack of blood causes anoxia of the affected region with a consequent death of the neurons of that region, resulting in weakness, paralysis, sensory loss, or the inability to speak. If stroke victims can reach a health facility equipped with dealing with the problem, and, depending on the extent of the injury, they can be rehabilitated to recover some or all of the lost function.

PLATE 8-1 Elastic Artery

FIGURE 1 • Elastic Artery. l.s. Aorta. Monkey. Plastic Section. ×132.

This low magnification photomicrograph displays almost the entire thickness of the wall of the aorta, the largest artery of the body. The **tunica intima** (TI) is lined by a simple squamous epithelium whose nuclei (*arrowheads*) bulge into the lumen of the vessel. The lines, which appear pale at this magnification, are elastic fibers and laminae, whereas the nuclei belong to smooth muscle cells and connective tissue cells. The internal elastic lamina is not readily identifiable because the intima is rich in elastic fibers. The **tunica media** (TM) is composed of smooth muscle cells whose **nuclei** (N) are clearly evident. These smooth muscle cells lie in the spaces between the concentrically layered **fenestrated membranes** (FM), composed of elastic tissue. The **external elastic lamina** (xEL) is that portion of the media that adjoins the adventitia. The outermost coat of the aorta, the **tunica adventitia** (TA), is composed of collagenous and elastic fibers interspersed with connective tissue cells and blood vessels, the **vasa vasorum** (VV). Regions similar to the *boxed areas* are presented in Figures 2 and 3.

FIGURE 3 • Elastic artery. x.s. Monkey. Plastic section. ×540.

This is a higher magnification of the tunica adventitia similar to the *boxed region* of Figure 1. The outermost region of the **tunica media** (TM) is demarcated by the **external elastic lamina** (xEL). The **tunica adventitia** (TA) is composed of thick bundles of **collagen fibers** (CF) interspersed with elastic fibers. Observe the nuclei of **fibroblasts** (F) located in the interstitial spaces among the collagen fiber bundles. Since the vessel wall is very thick, nutrients diffusing from the lumen cannot serve the entire vessel; therefore, the adventitia is supplied by small vessels known as **vasa vasorum** (VV). Vasa vasorum provide circulation not only for the tunica adventitia but also for the outer portion of the tunica media. Moreover, lymphatic vessels (not observed here) are also present in the adventitia.

FIGURE 2 • Elastic artery. x.s. Monkey. Plastic section. ×540.

This is a higher magnification of a region of the tunica intima, similar to the *boxed area* of Figure 1. The endothelial lining of the blood vessel presents **nuclei** (*arrowhead*), which bulge into the **lumen** (L). The numerous **elastic fibers** (EF) form an incomplete elastic lamina. Note that the interstices of the tunica intima house many **smooth muscle cells** (SM), whose nuclei are corkscrew-shaped (*arrows*), indicative of muscle contraction. Although most of the cellular elements are smooth muscle cells, it has been suggested that fibroblasts and macrophages may also be present; however, it is believed that the elastic fibers and the amorphous intercellular substances are synthesized by the smooth muscle cells.

FIGURE 4 • Elastic artery. x.s. Human. Elastic stain. Paraffin section. ×132.

The use of a special stain to demonstrate the presence of concentric elastic sheets, known as **fenestrated membranes** (FM), displays the highly elastic quality of the aorta. The number of fenestrated membranes, as well as the thickness of each membrane, increase with age, so that the adult will possess almost twice as many of these structures as an infant. These membranes are called fenestrated, since they possess spaces (*arrows*) through which nutrients and waste materials diffuse. The interstices between the fenestrated membranes are occupied by smooth muscle cells, whose **nuclei** (N) are evident, as well as amorphous intercellular materials, collagen, and fine elastic fibers. The **tunica adventitia** (TA) is composed mostly of **collagenous fiber bundles** (CF) and some **elastic fibers** (EF). Numerous **fibroblasts** (F) and other connective tissue cells occupy the adventitia.

KEY					
CF	collagen fiber	L	lumen	TI	tunica intima
EF	elastic fiber	N	nucleus	TM	tunica media
F	fibroblast	SM	smooth muscle cell	VV	vasa vasorum
FM	fenestrated membrane	TA	tunica adventitia	xEL	external elastic lamina

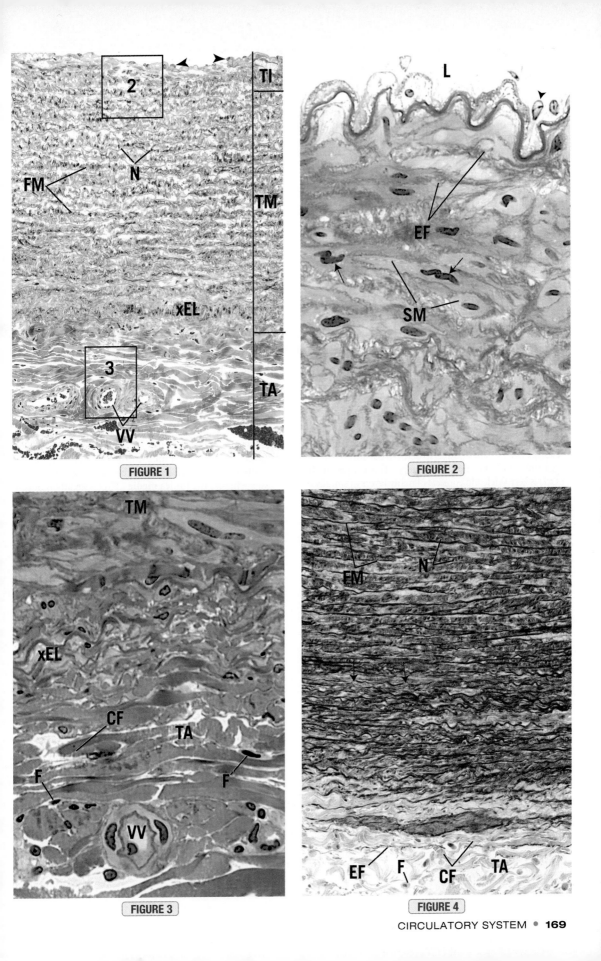

FIGURE 1

FIGURE 2

FIGURE 3

FIGURE 4

PLATE 8-2 Muscular Artery, Vein

FIGURE 1 • Artery and vein. x.s. Monkey. Plastic section. ×132.

This low magnification photomicrograph presents a **muscular artery** (MA) and corresponding **vein** (V). Observe that the wall of the artery is much thicker than that of the vein and contains considerably more muscle fibers. The three concentric tunicae of the artery are evident. The **tunica intima** (TI), with its **endothelial layer** (En) and **internal elastic lamina** (iEL), is readily apparent. The thick **tunica media** (TM) is identified by the circularly or spirally displayed **smooth muscle cells** (SM) that are embedded in an elastic type of intercellular material. These elastic fibers, as well as the external elastic lamina—the outermost layer of the tunica media—are not apparent with hematoxylin and eosin stain. The **tunica adventitia** (TA), almost as thick as the media, contains no smooth muscle cells. It is composed chiefly of **collagen** (CF) and **elastic** (EF) fibers as well as fibroblasts and other connective tissue cells. The wall of the companion vein presents the same three tunicae: **intima** (TI), **media** (TM), and **adventitia** (TA); however, all three (but especially the media) are reduced in thickness.

FIGURE 3 • Artery. x.s. Elastic stain. Paraffin section. ×132.

This photomicrograph is a higher magnification of a region similar to the *boxed area* of Figure 2. The **endothelium** (En), subendothelial connective tissue (*arrow*), and the highly contracted **internal elastic lamina** (iEL) are readily evident. These three structures constitute the tunica intima of the muscular artery. The **tunica media** (TM) is very thick and consists of many layers of spirally or circularly disposed **smooth muscle cells** (SM), whose **nuclei** (N) are readily identifiable with this stain. Numerous **elastic fibers** (EF) ramify through the intercellular spaces between smooth muscle cells. The **external elastic lamina** (xEL), which comprises the outermost layer of the tunica media, is seen to advantage in this preparation. Finally, note the **collagenous** (CF) and **elastic** (EF) fibers of the **tunica adventitia** (TA), as well as the nuclei (*arrowhead*) of the various connective tissue cells.

FIGURE 2 • Artery and vein. x.s. Elastic stain. Paraffin section. ×132.

The elastic stain used in this transverse section of a **muscular artery** (MA) and corresponding **vein** (V) clearly demonstrates the differences between arteries and veins. The **tunica intima** (TI) of the artery stains dark, due to the thick internal elastic lamina, whereas that of the vein does not stain nearly as intensely. The thick **tunica media** (TM) of the artery is composed of numerous layers of circularly or spirally disposed **smooth muscle cells** (SM) with many elastic fibers ramifying through this tunic. The **tunica media** (TM) of the vein has only a few smooth muscle cell layers with little intervening elastic fibers. The **external elastic lamina** (xEL) of the artery is much better developed than that of the vein. Finally, the **tunica adventitia** (TA) constitutes the bulk of the wall of the vein and is composed of **collagenous** (CF) and **elastic** (EF) fibers. The **tunica adventitia** (TA) of the artery is also thick, but it comprises only about half the thickness of its wall. It is also composed of collagenous and elastic fibers. Both vessels possess their own **vasa vasorum** (VV) in their tunicae adventitia. A region similar to the *boxed area* is presented at a higher magnification in Figure 3.

FIGURE 4 • Large vein. x.s. Human. Paraffin section. ×270.

Large veins, as the inferior vena cava in this photomicrograph, are very different from the medium-sized veins of Figures 1 and 2. The **tunica intima** (TI) is composed of **endothelium** (EN) and some subendothelial connective tissue, whereas the **tunica media** (TM) is greatly reduced in thickness and contains only occasional smooth muscle cells. The bulk of the wall of the vena cava is composed of the greatly thickened **tunica adventitia** (TA), consisting of three concentric regions. The innermost layer (1) displays thick collagen bundles (*arrows*) arrayed in a spiral configuration, which permits it to become elongated or shortened, with respiratory excursion of the diaphragm. The middle layer (2) presents smooth muscle (or cardiac muscle) cells, longitudinally disposed. The outer layer (3) is characterized by thick bundles of **collagen fibers** (CF) interspersed with elastic fibers. This region contains **vasa vasorum** (VV), which supply nourishment to the wall of the vena cava.

KEY						
CF	collagen fiber	N	nucleus	M	tunica media
EF	elastic fiber	SM	smooth muscle cell	V	vein
En	endothelial layer	TA	tunica adventitia	VV	vasa vasorum
iEL	internal elastic lamina	TI	tunica intima	xEL	external elastic lamina
MA	muscular artery				

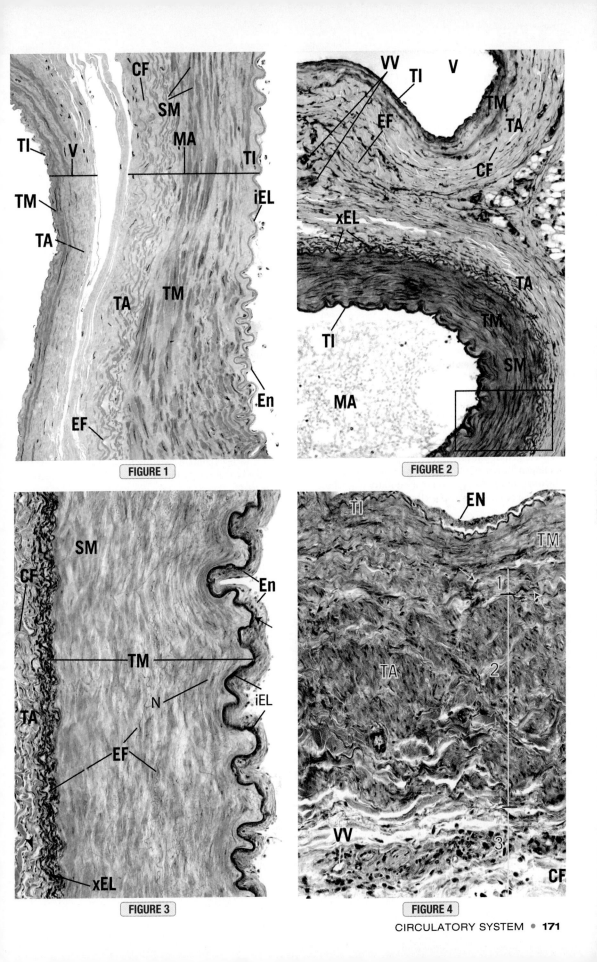

FIGURE 1

FIGURE 2

FIGURE 3

FIGURE 4

FIGURE 1 ● Arteriole and venule. l.s. Monkey. Plastic section. ×270.

This longitudinal section of a large **arteriole** (A) and companion **venule** (Ve) from the connective tissue septum of a monkey submandibular gland displays a **duct** (D) of the gland between the two vessels. Observe that the thickness of the arteriole wall approximates the diameter of the **lumen** (L). The endothelial cell **nuclei** (N) are readily evident in both vessels, as are the **smooth muscle cells** (SM) of the tunica media. The arteriole also presents an **internal elastic lamina** (iEL) between the tunica media and the endothelial cells. The **tunica adventitia** (TA) of the arteriole displays nuclei of fibroblasts, whereas those of the venule merge imperceptibly with the surrounding connective tissue. Glandular acini are evident in this field as are **serous units** (SU) and **serous demilunes** (SD).

FIGURE 3 ● Capillary. l.s. Monkey. Plastic section. ×540.

In this photomicrograph of the monkey cerebellum, the molecular layer displays longitudinal sections of a capillary. Note that the endothelial cell **nuclei** (N) are occasionally in the field of view. The **cytoplasm** (Cy) of the highly attenuated endothelial cells is visible as thin, dark lines, bordering the **lumina** (L) of the capillary. Red blood cells (*arrows*) are noted to be distorted as they pass through the narrow lumina of the vessel. *Inset.* **Capillary. x.s. Monkey. Plastic section.** × 540. The connective tissue represented in this photomicrograph displays bundles of **collagen fibers** (CF), nuclei of connective tissue cells (*arrow*), and a cross section of a **capillary** (C), whose endothelial cell **nucleus** (N) is clearly evident.

FIGURE 2 ● Arteriole and venule. x.s. Monkey. Plastic section. ×540.

This small **arteriole** (A) and its companion **venule** (Ve) are from the submucosa of the fundic region of a monkey stomach. Observe the obvious difference between the diameters of the **lumina** (L) of the two vessels as well as the thickness of their walls. Due to the greater muscularity of the **tunica media** (TM) of the arteriole, the **nuclei** (N) of its endothelial cells bulge into its round lumen. The **tunica media** (TM) of the venule is much reduced, whereas the **tunica adventitia** (TA) is well developed and is composed of **collagenous connective tissue** (CT) interspersed with elastic fibers (not evident in this hematoxylin and eosin section).

FIGURE 4 ● Lymphatic vessel. l.s. Monkey. Plastic section. ×270.

This photomicrograph presents a villus from monkey duodenum. Note the simple columnar **epithelium** (E) interspersed with occasional **goblet cells** (GC). The connective tissue lamina propria displays numerous **plasma cells** (PC), **mast cells** (MC), **lymphocytes** (Ly), and **smooth muscle fibers** (SM). The longitudinal section of the **lumen** (L) lined with **endothelium** (En) is a lacteal, a blindly ending lymphatic channel. Since lymph vessels do not transport red blood cells, the lacteal appears to be empty, but in fact it contains lymph. Subsequent to a fatty meal, lacteals contain chylomicrons. Observe that the wall of the lacteal is very flimsy in relation to the diameter of the vessel.

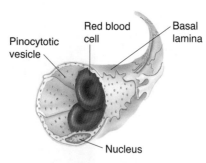

Pinocytotic vesicle

Red blood cell

Basal lamina

Nucleus

Continuous capillary

KEY					
A	arteriole	En	endothelium	PC	plasma cell
C	capillary	GC	goblet cell	SD	serous demilune
CF	collagen fiber	iEL	internal elastic lamina	SM	smooth muscle cell
CT	collagenous connective tissue	L	lumen	SU	serous unit
Cy	cytoplasm	Ly	lymphocyte	TA	tunica adventitia
D	duct	MC	mast cell	TM	tunica media
E	epithelium	N	nucleus	Ve	venule

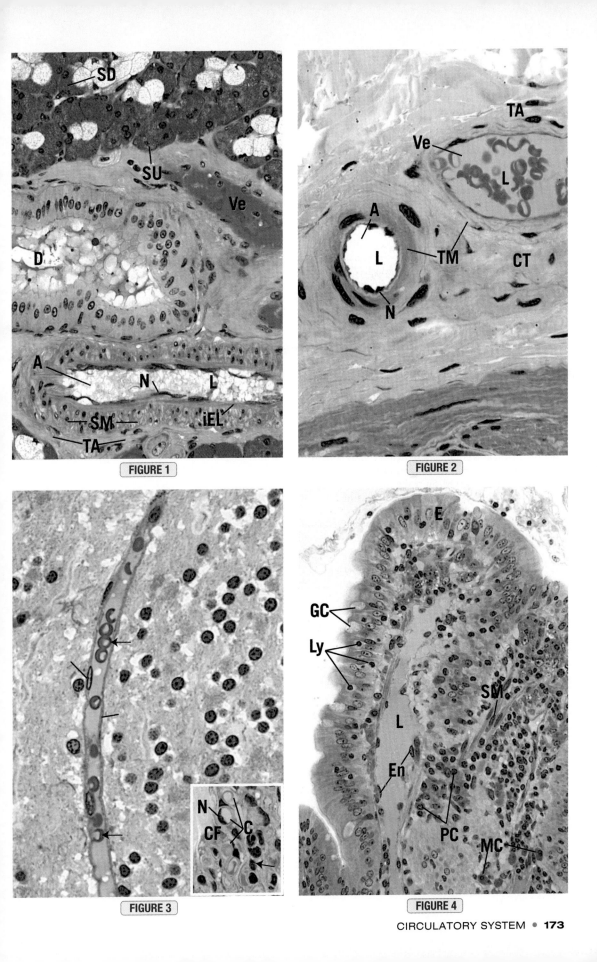

FIGURE 1

FIGURE 2

FIGURE 3

FIGURE 4

CIRCULATORY SYSTEM • **173**

FIGURE 1 • Endocardium. Human. Paraffin section. ×132.

The endocardium, the innermost layer of the heart, is lined by a simple squamous epithelium that is continuous with the endothelial of the various blood vessels entering or exiting the heart. The endocardium is composed of three layers, the innermost of which consists of the **endothelium** (En) and the subendothelial **connective tissue** (CT), whose collagenous fibers and connective tissue cell **nuclei** (N) are readily evident. The middle layer of the endocardium, although composed of dense collagenous and elastic fibers and some smooth muscle cells, is occupied in this photomicrograph by branches of the conducting system of the heart, the **Purkinje fibers** (PF). The third layer of the endocardium borders the thick **myocardium** (My) and is composed of looser connective tissue elements housing blood vessels, occasional adipocytes, and additional connective tissue cells.

FIGURE 3 • Heart valve. l.s. Paraffin section. ×132.

This figure is a montage, displaying a **valve leaflet** (Le) as well as the **endocardium** (EC) of the heart. The leaflet is in the **lumen** (L) of the ventricle, as evidenced by the numerous trapped **red blood cells** (RBC). The **endothelial** (En) lining of the endocardium is continuous with the endothelial lining of the leaflet. The three layers of the endocardium are clearly evident, as are the occasional **smooth muscle cells** (SM) and **blood vessels** (BV). The core of the leaflet is composed of dense collagenous and elastic connective tissue, housing numerous cells whose nuclei are readily observed. Since the core of these leaflets is devoid of blood vessels, the connective tissue cells receive their nutrients directly from the blood in the lumen of the heart via simple diffusion. The connective tissue core of the leaflet is continuous with the skeleton of the heart, which forms a fibrous ring around the opening of the valves.

FIGURE 2 • Purkinje fibers. Iron hematoxylin. Paraffin section. ×132.

The stain utilized in preparing this section of the ventricular myocardium intensively stains **red blood cells** (RBC) and **cardiac muscle cells** (CM). Therefore, the thick bundle of **Purkinje fibers** (PF) is shown to advantage, due to its less dense staining quality. The **connective tissue** (CT) surrounding these fibers is highly vascularized, as evidenced by the red blood cell–filled capillaries. Purkinje fibers are composed of individual cells, each with a centrally placed single **nucleus** (N). These fibers form numerous gap junctions with each other and with cardiac muscle cells. The *boxed area* is presented at a higher magnification in the inset. *Inset.* **Purkinje fibers. Iron hematoxylin. Paraffin section.** × 270. Individual cells of Purkinje fibers are much larger than cardiac muscle cells. However, the presence of peripherally displaced **myofibrils** (m) displaying A and I bands (*arrow*) clearly demonstrates that they are modified cardiac muscle cells. The **nucleus** (N) is surrounded by a clear area, housing glycogen and mitochondria.

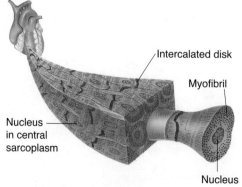

Intercalated disk

Myofibril

Nucleus in central sarcoplasm

Nucleus

Cardiac muscle

KEY					
BV	blood vessel	En	endothelium	My	myocardium
CM	cardiac muscle cell	L	lumen	N	nucleus
CT	connective tissue	Le	valve leaflet	PF	Purkinje fiber
EC	endocardium	m	myofibril	RBC	red blood cell

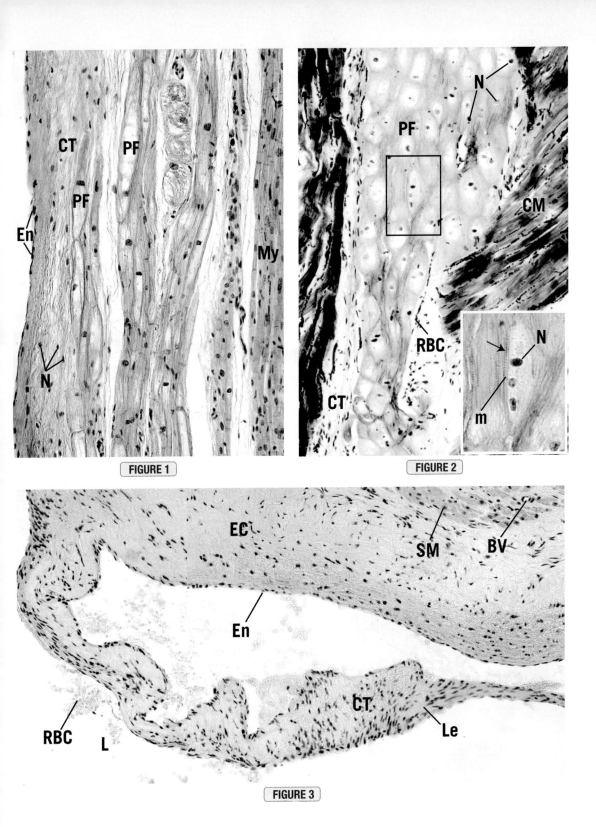

PLATE 8-5 Capillary, Electron Microscopy

FIGURE 1 • Continuous capillary. x.s. Cardiac muscle. Mouse. Electron microscopy. ×29,330.

This electron micrograph of a continuous capillary in cross section was taken from mouse heart tissue. Observe that the section passes through the **nucleus** (N) of one of the endothelial cells constituting the wall of the vessel and that the lumen contains **red blood cells** (RBC). Note that the endothelial cells are highly attenuated and that they form tight junctions (*arrows*) with each other. *Arrowheads* point to pinocytotic vesicles that traverse the endothelial cell. The **lamina densa** (LD) and **lamina lucida** (LL) of the basal lamina are clearly evident.

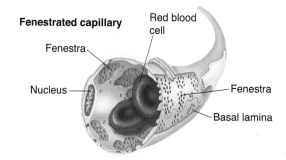

Fenestrated capillary

Fenestra

Nucleus

Red blood cell

Fenestra

Basal lamina

FIGURE 1

FIGURE 1

FIGURE 1 • Fenestrated capillary. Hamster. Electron Microscopy. Freeze fracture. ×205,200.

This electron micrograph is a representative example of fenestrated capillaries from the hamster adrenal cortex, as revealed by the freeze-fracture replica technique. The parallel lines (*arrows*) running diagonally across the field represent the line of junction between two endothelial cells, which are presented in a surface view. Note that the numerous **fenestrae** (F), whose diameters range from 57–166 nm, are arranged in tracts, with the regions between tracts nonfenestrated. Occasional **caveolae** (Ca) are also present. (From Ryan U, Ryan J, Smith D, Winkler H. Fenestrated endothelium of the adrenal gland: freeze-fracture studies. Tissue Cell 1975;7:181–190.)

Summary of Histological Organization

I. ELASTIC ARTERY (CONDUCTING ARTERY)

Among these are the **aorta**, **common carotid**, and **subclavian arteries**.

A. Tunica Intima

Lined by short, polygonal **endothelial cells**. The **subendothelial connective tissue** is fibroelastic and houses some longitudinally disposed smooth muscle cells. **Internal elastic lamina** is not clearly defined.

B. Tunica Media

Characterized by numerous **fenestrated membranes** (spiral to concentric sheets of fenestrated elastic membranes). Enmeshed among the elastic material are circularly disposed **smooth muscle cells** and associated **collagenous**, **reticular**, and **elastic fibers**.

C. Tunica Adventitia

Thin, **collagenous connective tissue** containing some **elastic fibers** and a few longitudinally oriented **smooth muscle cells**. **Vasa vasorum** (vessels of vessels) are also present.

II. MUSCULAR ARTERY (DISTRIBUTING ARTERY)

Among these are the named arteries, with the exception of the elastic arteries.

A. Tunica Intima

These are lined by polygonal-shaped, flattened **endothelial cells** that bulge into the lumen during vasoconstriction. The **subendothelial connective tissue** houses fine **collagenous fibers** and few longitudinally disposed **smooth muscle cells**. The **internal elastic lamina**, clearly evident, is frequently split into two membranes.

B. Tunica Media

Characterized by many layers of circularly disposed **smooth muscle cells**, with some **elastic**, **reticular**, and **collagenous fibers** among the muscle cells. The **external elastic lamina** is well defined.

C. Tunica Adventitia

Usually a very thick **collagenous** and **elastic tissue**, with some longitudinally oriented **smooth muscle fibers**. **Vasa vasorum** are also present.

III. ARTERIOLES

These are arterial vessels whose diameter is less than 100 μm.

A. Tunica Intima

Endothelium and a variable amount of **subendothelial connective tissue** are always present. The **internal elastic lamina** is present in larger arterioles but absent in smaller arterioles.

B. Tunica Media

The spirally arranged **smooth muscle fibers** may be up to three layers thick. An **external elastic lamina** is present in larger arterioles but absent in smaller arterioles.

C. Tunica Adventitia

This is composed of **collagenous** and **elastic connective tissues**, whose thickness approaches that of the tunica media.

IV. CAPILLARIES

Most **capillaries** in cross section appear as thin, circular profiles 8–10 μm in diameter. Occasionally, a fortuitous section will display an **endothelial cell nucleus**, a red blood cell, or, very infrequently, a white blood cell. Frequently, capillaries will be collapsed and not evident with the light microscope. **Pericytes** are usually associated with capillaries.

V. VENULES

Venules possess much larger lumina and thinner walls than corresponding arterioles.

A. Tunica Intima

Endothelium lies on a very thin **subendothelial connective tissue** layer, which increases with the size of the vessel. **Pericytes** are frequently associated with smaller venules.

B. Tunica Media

Absent in smaller venules, whereas in larger venules one or two layers of **smooth muscle cells** may be observed.

C. Tunica Adventitia

Consists of **collagenous connective tissue** with **fibroblasts** and some **elastic fibers**.

VI. MEDIUM-SIZED VEINS

A. Tunica Intima

The **endothelium** and a scant amount of **subendothelial connective tissue** are always present. Occasionally, a thin **internal elastic lamina** is observed. **Valves** may be evident.

B. Tunica Media

Much thinner than that of the corresponding artery but does possess a few layers of **smooth muscle cells.** Occasionally, some of the muscle fibers, instead of being circularly disposed, are longitudinally disposed. Bundles of **collagen fibers** interspersed with a few **elastic fibers** are also present.

C. Tunica Adventitia

Composed of **collagen** and some **elastic fibers**, which constitute the bulk of the vessel wall. Occasionally, longitudinally oriented **smooth muscle cells** may be present. **Vasa vasorum** are noted to penetrate even the **tunica media**.

VII. LARGE VEINS

A. Tunica Intima

Same as that of medium-sized veins but displays thicker **subendothelial connective tissue**. Some large veins have well-defined **valves**.

B. Tunica Media

Not very well defined, although it may present some **smooth muscle cells** interspersed among **collagenous** and **elastic fibers**.

C. Tunica Adventitia

Thickest of the three layers and accounts for most of the vessel wall. May contain longitudinally oriented **smooth muscle fiber bundles** among the thick layers of **collagen** and **elastic fibers**. **Vasa vasorum** are commonly present.

VIII. HEART

An extremely thick, muscular organ composed of three layers: **endocardium**, **myocardium**, and **epicardium**. The presence of **cardiac muscle** is characteristic of this organ. Additional structural parameters may include **Purkinje fibers**, thick **valves**, **atrioventricular** and **sinoatrial nodes**, as well as the **chordae tendineae** and the thick, connective tissue **cardiac skeleton**.

IX. LYMPHATIC VESSELS

Lymphatic vessels are either collapsed and therefore not discernible, or they are filled with lymph. In the latter case, they present the appearance of a clear, endothelial-lined space resembling a blood vessel. However, the lumina contain no **red blood cells**, though **lymphocytes** may be present. The **endothelium** may display **valves**.

Lymphoid Tissue

Lymphoid tissue forms the basis of the immune system of the body and is organized into diffuse and nodular lymphatic tissues (see Graphic 9-1). The lymphocyte, the principal cell of lymphoid tissue, is a key controller responsible for the proper functioning of the immune system. Although morphologically identical, small lymphocytes may be further identified according to function into three categories: null cells, B lymphocytes, and T lymphocytes. Null cells are composed of two categories of cells, namely stem cells and natural killer (NK) cells (although some immunologists prefer not to use this classification system and avoid the null cell category). Stem cells are undifferentiated cells that will give rise to the various cellular elements of blood cell lineage, whereas NK cells are cytotoxic cells that are responsible for the destruction of certain categories of foreign cells. NK cells resemble cytotoxic T cells but they do not have to enter the thymus to become mature killer cells. B lymphocytes, believed to mature in bone marrow in mammals (bursa of Fabricius in birds), have the capability of transforming into plasma cells; T lymphocytes are potentiated in the thymus. Plasma cells possess the ability to manufacture humoral antibodies specific against a particular antigen. Antibodies, once released, bind to a specific antigen. In some instances, binding inactivates the antigen, whereas in others the attachment of antibodies to antigens may enhance phagocytosis (opsonization) or activate the complement cascade, resulting in chemotaxis of neutrophils and, frequently, lysis of the invader. T lymphocytes do not produce antibodies; instead, they function in the cell-mediated immune response. It is the T lymphocytes that participate in the graft rejection phenomenon and in the elimination of virally transformed cells. Several subgroups of T and B lymphocytes exist, such as memory cells, T helper cells (T_H0, T_H1, and T_H2 cells), T reg cells (regulatory T cells), and T cytotoxic cells (T killer cells); a discussion of these is found later in this chapter. Once a T lymphocyte becomes activated by the presence of an antigen, it releases cytokines, substances that activate macrophages, attract them to the site of antigenic invasion, and enhance their phagocytic capabilities. Frequently, T lymphocytes also assist B lymphocytes to amplify and modulate their immune response.

● DIFFUSE LYMPHOID TISSUE

Diffuse lymphoid tissue occurs throughout the body, especially under moist epithelial membranes, where the loose connective tissue is infiltrated by lymphoid cells, such as lymphocytes, plasma cells, macrophages, and reticular cells. Therefore, these are referred to as **mucosa-associated lymphoid tissue** (**MALT**). MALT is particularly evident in the lamina propria of the digestive tract and in the subepithelial connective tissue of the respiratory tract, where they are known as **gut-associated lymphoid tissue** (**GALT**) and **bronchus-associated lymphoid tissue** (**BALT**), respectively. It may be noted that the lymphoid cells are not arranged in any particular pattern but are scattered in a haphazard manner. Frequently, lymphoid nodules, transitory structures that are a denser aggregation of lymphoid tissue composed mainly of lymphocytes, may be observed. Lymphoid nodules may be primary or secondary, where the secondary lymphoid nodules present the characteristic appearance of a lighter **germinal center** and a darker, peripherally located **corona**, indicating activation by antigen. The germinal centers are sites of plasma cell production, whereas the corona is produced by mitosis from existing B lymphocytes.

● LYMPH NODES

Lymph nodes are ovoid- to kidney-shaped organs through which lymph is filtered by exposure to large numbers of lymphoid cells (see Graphic 9-2). They possess a convex surface, which receives afferent lymph vessels, and a hilum, where blood vessels leave and enter and efferent lymph vessels leave and drain lymph from the organ. Each lymph node has a dense, irregular, collagenous connective tissue **capsule** and septa, derived from the capsule,

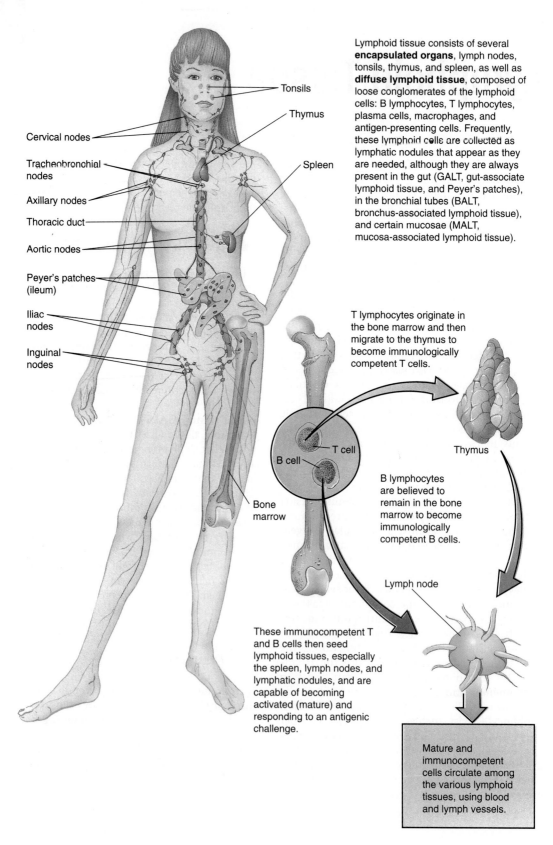

Tonsils

Cervical nodes

Tracheobronchial nodes

Axillary nodes

Thoracic duct

Aortic nodes

Peyer's patches (ileum)

Iliac nodes

Inguinal nodes

Thymus

Spleen

Lymphoid tissue consists of several **encapsulated organs**, lymph nodes, tonsils, thymus, and spleen, as well as **diffuse lymphoid tissue**, composed of loose conglomerates of the lymphoid cells: B lymphocytes, T lymphocytes, plasma cells, macrophages, and antigen-presenting cells. Frequently, these lymphoid cells are collected as lymphatic nodules that appear as they are needed, although they are always present in the gut (GALT, gut-associate lymphoid tissue, and Peyer's patches), in the bronchial tubes (BALT, bronchus-associated lymphoid tissue), and certain mucosae (MALT, mucosa-associated lymphoid tissue).

T lymphocytes originate in the bone marrow and then migrate to the thymus to become immunologically competent T cells.

T cell

B cell

Thymus

Bone marrow

B lymphocytes are believed to remain in the bone marrow to become immunologically competent B cells.

Lymph node

These immunocompetent T and B cells then seed lymphoid tissues, especially the spleen, lymph nodes, and lymphatic nodules, and are capable of becoming activated (mature) and responding to an antigenic challenge.

Mature and immunocompetent cells circulate among the various lymphoid tissues, using blood and lymph vessels.

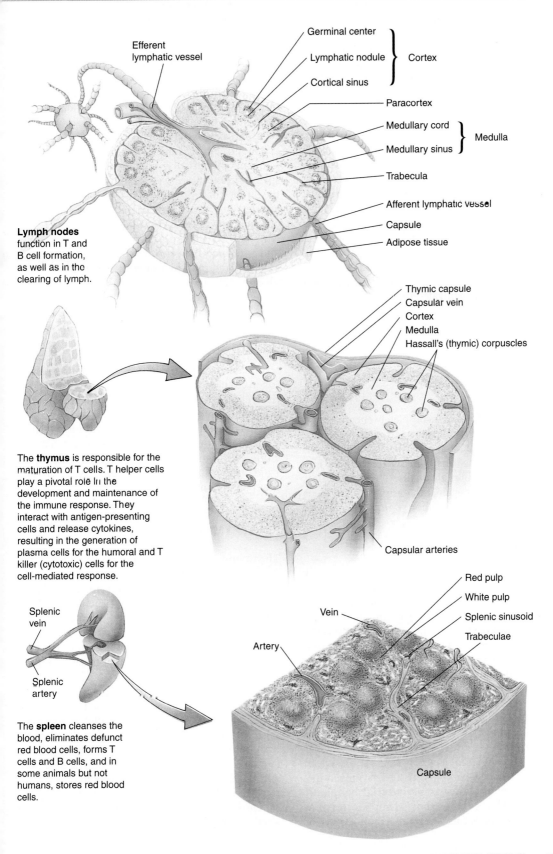

Efferent lymphatic vessel

Germinal center

Lymphatic nodule ⎤ Cortex

Cortical sinus

Paracortex

Medullary cord ⎤ Medulla

Medullary sinus ⎦

Trabecula

Afferent lymphatic vessel

Capsule

Adipose tissue

Lymph nodes function in T and B cell formation, as well as in the clearing of lymph.

Thymic capsule
Capsular vein
Cortex
Medulla
Hassall's (thymic) corpuscles

Capsular arteries

The **thymus** is responsible for the maturation of T cells. T helper cells play a pivotal role in the development and maintenance of the immune response. They interact with antigen-presenting cells and release cytokines, resulting in the generation of plasma cells for the humoral and T killer (cytotoxic) cells for the cell-mediated response.

Splenic vein

Splenic artery

The **spleen** cleanses the blood, eliminates defunct red blood cells, forms T cells and B cells, and in some animals but not humans, stores red blood cells.

Red pulp
White pulp
Vein
Splenic sinusoid
Trabeculae
Artery
Capsule

subdividing the cortex into incomplete compartments. Attached to the septa and the internal aspect of the capsule is a network of reticular tissue and associated reticular cells that act as a framework for housing the numerous free and migratory cells, mostly lymphocytes, antigen presenting cells, and macrophages, occupying the organ. The **cortex** of the lymph node houses the capsular and cortical sinuses, as well as lymphoid nodules, composed mainly of **B lymphocytes** and **reticular cells**. Between the cortex and the medulla is the **paracortex**, populated by **T lymphocytes**. The **medulla** consists of medullary **sinusoids** and **medullary cords**. The medullary sinusoids are continuous with the capsular and cortical sinuses, whereas the **medullary cords** are composed mainly of lymphoid cells. Additional cell components of lymph nodes are **macrophages**, **antigen-presenting cells**, and some **granulocytes**. Aside from functioning in the maintenance and production of immunocompetent cells, lymph nodes also filter lymph. The filtering process is facilitated by the elongated processes of reticular cells that span the sinuses of the node and thus disturb and retard lymph flow, providing more time for the resident macrophages to phagocytose antigens and other debris.

● TONSILS

Tonsils are aggregates of incompletely **encapsulated lymphoid tissue** situated at the entrances to the oral pharynx and to the nasal pharynx. Participating in the formation of the **tonsillar ring** are the **palatine**, **pharyngeal**, and **lingual tonsils**. These structures produce antibodies against the numerous antigens and microorganisms that abound in their vicinity.

● SPLEEN

The **spleen** is the largest lymphoid organ of the body (see Graphic 9-2). Its principal functions are to filter blood, phagocytose senescent red blood cells and invading microorganisms, supply immunocompetent **T and B lymphocytes**, and manufacture **antibodies**. Unlike lymph nodes, the spleen is not divided into cortical and medullary regions, nor is it supplied by afferent lymphatic vessels. Blood vessels enter and leave the spleen at its hilum and travel within the parenchyma via trabeculae derived from its connective tissue capsule. The spleen is subdivided into **red** and **white pulps**; the former consists of **pulp cords** (**of Billroth**) interposed between sinusoids, whereas the latter is composed of lymphoid tissue associated with arteries. This lymphoid tissue is arranged in a specific fashion, either as **periarterial lymphatic sheaths** (**PALS**) composed of T lymphocytes or as **lymphoid nodules** consisting of B lymphocytes. The

region between the red and white pulps is known as the **marginal zone** and is rich in arterial vessels and avidly phagocytic macrophages. The **red pulp** is composed of a spongy network of sinusoids lined by unusual elongated endothelial cells displaying large intercellular spaces, supported by a thick, discontinuous, hooplike basement membrane. Reticular cells and reticular fibers associated with these sinusoids extend into the pulp cords to contribute to the cell population that consists of **macrophages**, **plasma cells**, and extravasated blood cells.

Understanding splenic organization depends on knowing the vascular supply of the spleen. The splenic artery entering at the hilum is distributed to the interior of the organ via trabeculae as trabecular arteries. On leaving a trabecula, the vessel enters the parenchyma to be surrounded by the periarterial lymphatic sheath and occasional lymphoid nodules and is termed the central artery. **Central arteries** enter the red pulp by losing their periarterial lymphatic sheath and subdivide into numerous straight vessels known as **penicillar arteries**. These small vessels possess three regions: **pulp arterioles**, **sheathed arterioles**, and **terminal arterial capillaries**. Whether these terminal arterial capillaries drain directly into the sinusoids (closed circulation) or terminate as open-ended vessels in the pulp cords (open circulation) has not been determined conclusively; however, in humans, the open circulation is believed to predominate. It is during this passage of red blood cells from the splenic cords into the sinusoids that damaged and aging red blood cells are eliminated. Sinusoids are drained by pulp veins, which lead to trabecular veins and eventually join the splenic vein.

● THYMUS

The **thymus** is a bilobed lymphoid organ located in the mediastinum, overlying the great vessels of the heart (see Graphic 9-2). Its major functions are the formation, potentiation, and destruction of T lymphocytes. Immunoincompetent (immature) T lymphocytes enter the thymus, where they become immunocompetent and are released into the general circulation with the caveat that those T lymphocytes that would recognize and attack the self are not released but are destroyed in the cortex. The thin connective tissue capsule of the thymus sends septa deep into the organ, incompletely subdividing it into lobules. The thymus, unlike the previous lymphoid structures, is of endodermal origin and later becomes infiltrated by lymphocytes. Additionally, the thymus possesses no lymphoid nodules; instead, it is divided into an outer **cortex**, composed of **epithelial reticular cells**, **macrophages**, and **small T lymphocytes** (**thymocytes**), and an inner, lighter staining **medulla** consisting of **epithelial reticular cells**, **large T lymphocytes**, and **thymic (Hassall's) corpuscles**. Blood vessels gain entrance to the medulla by traveling in the connective tissue septa, which they exit at the corticomedullary junction, where they provide capillary loops to the cortex. The capillaries that enter the cortex are the continuous type and are surrounded by epithelial reticular cells that isolate them from the cortical lymphocytes, thus establishing a **blood-thymus barrier**, providing an antigen-free environment for the potentiation of the immunocompetent T lymphocytes. The blood vessels of the medulla are not unusual and present no blood-thymus barrier. The thymus is drained by venules in the medulla, which also receives blood from the cortical capillaries. Epithelial reticular cells form a specialized barrier between the cortex and medulla to prevent medullary material from gaining access to the cortex. The thymus attains its greatest development shortly after birth, but subsequent to puberty it begins to **involute** and becomes infiltrated by adipose tissue; however, even in the adult the thymus retains its ability to form a reduced number of T lymphocytes.

Histophysiology

I. THE IMMUNE RESPONSE

The immune system relies on the interactions of its primary cell components, lymphocytes and antigen-presenting cells, to effect an immune response. These responses are meticulously controlled and directed, but a complete description of the mechanisms of their actions is beyond the purposes of this *Atlas*. Therefore, only the salient features of the mechanisms of the immune process will be described.

A. Cells of the Immune System

The cells of the immune system may be subdivided into four major categories: clones of T lymphocytes and clones of B lymphocytes, NK cells, and antigen-presenting cells. A **clone** is a small population of identical cells, each of which is capable of recognizing and responding to one specific (or very closely related) **epitope** (antigenic determinant). Resting T and B cells become activated if they come in contact with the specific epitope and certain cytokines. These activated cells proliferate and differentiate into **effector cells**. **Antigen-presenting cells**, such as macrophages, participate in the immune process by phagocytosing foreign substances, breaking them down to epitopes. They present these epitopes on their cell surface in conjunction with **major histocompatibility complex molecules** (MHC molecules) and other membrane-associated markers. It should be noted that in humans MHC molecules are also referred to as human leukocyte antigen molecules (HLA molecules).

1. T Lymphocytes

T lymphocytes (T cells) are immunoincompetent until they enter the cortex of the thymus. Here, under the influence of the cortical environment, they express their T cell receptors and **cluster of differentiation markers** (CD2, CD3, CD4, CD8, and CD28) and become immunocompetent. Once immunocompetent, the T cells enter the medulla of the thymus or are killed if they are committed against the self. In the medulla they will lose either their CD4 or their CD8 markers and thus develop into **CD8$^+$** or **CD4$^+$** cells, respectively. These cells enter into blood vessels of the medulla to become members of the circulating population of lymphocytes.

T cells encompass several categories of cells that are responsible not only for the **cell-mediated immune response** but also for facilitating the **humorally mediated response** of B cells to **thymic-dependent antigens**. To be able to perform their functions, T cells possess characteristic integral membrane proteins on their cell surfaces. One of these is the **T cell receptor** (TCR), which has the capability of recognizing that particular epitope for which the cell is genetically programmed; however, T cells can recognize only those epitopes that are bound to MHC molecules present on the surface of antigen presenting cells. Thus, T cells are said to be **MHC restricted**. There are three general categories of T cells: naïve T cells, memory T cells, and effector T cells.

a. **Naïve T cells** are immunologically competent and possess CD45RA molecules on their plasma membrane, but they have to become activated before they can function as T cells. Activation involves the interaction of the naïve T cell's T cell receptor–CD3 complex with the MHC-epitope complex of antigen-presenting cells, as well as the interaction of the T cell's CD28 molecule with the antigen-presenting cell's B7 molecule. The activated naïve T cell enters the cell cycle and forms memory T cells and effector T cells.

b. **Memory T cells** are immunocompetent cells that are the progeny of activated T cells that undergo mitotic activity during an antigenic challenge. These cells are long lived, circulating cells that are added to and increase the number of cells of the original clone. It is this increase in the size of the clone that is responsible for the **anamnestic response** (a more rapid and more intense secondary response) against another encounter with the same antigen.

c. **Effector T cells**. The categories of effector T cells are T helper cells (T_H cells), cytotoxic T lymphocytes (CTLs, T killer cells), regulatory T cells (T reg cells), and natural T killer cells.

1. **T Helper cells** are subdivided into three categories: T_H0, T_H1, and T_H2 cells, and they are all CD4$^+$ cells. T_H0 cells enter the cell cycle and can give rise to T_H1 and T_H2 cells. T_H1 cells produce and release the cytokines interleukin 2, interferon-γ, and tumor necrosis factor-α. T_H1 cells have an essential role in the initiation of the cell-mediated immune response and in the destruction of intracellular pathogens. T_H2 cells produce and release interleukins 4, 5, 6, 9, 10, and 13, which, among other roles, induce B cells to proliferate and differentiate into **plasma cells**

that produce antibodies. Additionally, T_H2 cells initiate the reaction against parasites and mucosal infections.

2. **Cytotoxic T lymphocytes** are $CD8^+$ cells. Upon contacting the proper MHC-epitope complex displayed by antigen-presenting cells and having been activated by interleukin 2, these cells undergo mitosis to form numerous **cytotoxic T lymphocytes** (CTLs). These newly formed cells kill foreign and virally transformed self cells by secreting **perforins** and **fragmentins** and by expressing CD95L (the death ligand) on their plasmalemma, which activates CD95 (death receptor) on the target cell's plasma membrane, which drives the target cell into apoptosis.

3. **T Reg cells** are $CD4^+$ cells that function in the suppression of the immune response. There are two types of T regulatory cells: **natural T reg cells**, whose TCR binds to antigen-presenting cells and thus suppresses the immune response, and the **inducible T reg cells** that release cytokines that inhibit the formation of T_H1 cells.

4. **Natural T killer** cells are similar to NK cells, but they have to enter the cortex of the thymus to be immunocompetent. They are unusual because they have the ability to recognize lipid antigens.

2. B Lymphocytes

B lymphocyte (B cells) are formed and become immunocompetent in the bone marrow. They enter the general circulation, establish clones whose members seed various lymphoid organs, and are responsible for the **humoral immune response**. As the B cell is becoming immunocompetent, it manufactures IgM or IgD and places them on their cell membrane in such a fashion that the epitope binding sites are located in the extracellular space and the Fc moiety of the surface immunoglobulins (SIGs) is embedded in the plasmalemma in association with two pairs of integral proteins, **Igβ** and **Igα**. The SIGs of a particular B cell target the same epitope. Unlike T cells, B cells have the capability of acting as antigen-presenting cells and present their MHC II-epitope complex to T_H1 cells.

When the newly formed B cell binds to its epitope, the Igβ and Igα transduce the information with the resultant activation of the B cell. Once activated, B cells manufacture and release IL-12, a cytokine that promotes the formation of T_H1 cells. B cells proliferate during a humoral immune response to form plasma cells and B memory cells.

a. **Plasma cells** are differentiated cells that do not possess surface immunoglobulins but are "antibody factories" that synthesize and release an enormous number of identical copies of the same antibody that is specific against a particular epitope (although it may cross-react with similar epitopes).

b. **B memory cells** are similar to T memory cells in that they are long-lived, circulating cells that are added to and increase the number of cells of the original clone. They possess surface immunoglobulins so that they can be activated by an appropriate antigen during a secondary immune response. Thus, it is this increase in the size of the clone that is responsible for the **anamnestic response** against a subsequent encounter with the same antigen.

3. Natural Killer Cells

Natural killer cells (NK cells) are members of the **null cell** division of lymphocytes. NK cells do not have the cell surface determinants typical of T or B cells and they are immunocompetent as soon as they are formed in the bone marrow. These cells kill virally altered cells and tumor cells in a **nonspecific** manner and they are not MHC restricted. NK cells also recognize and become activated by the Fc portions of those antibodies that are bound to cell surface epitopes. Once activated, NK cells release perforins and fragmentins to kill these decorated cells by a procedure known as **antibody-dependent cell-mediated cytotoxicity** (ADCC). Perforins assemble as pores within the plasmalemma of target cells, contributing to **necrotic cell death**, whereas fragmentins drive the target cell into apoptosis, **directed cell death**. NK cells also possess integral proteins known as **killer activating receptors** that have an affinity to specific proteins on the cell membranes of nucleated cells. To protect self cells from this response, NK cells also possess additional transmembrane proteins, known as **killer-inhibitor receptors**, that avoid the killing of healthy cells by recognizing MHC I molecules on the cell surface of these cells.

4. Antigen-Presenting Cells

Antigen-presenting cells (APCs), macrophages, and B lymphocytes possess class II major histocompatibility complex molecules (**MHC II molecules**), whereas all other nucleated cells possess **MHC I molecules**.

APCs phagocytose and degrade antigens into **epitopes**, small highly antigenic peptides 7 to 11 amino acids long. Each epitope is attached to an MHC II molecule, and this complex is placed on the external aspect of its cell membrane. The MHC II-epitope complex is recognized by the T cell receptor (**TCR**) in conjunction with the **CD4 molecule** of the T_H1 or T_H2 cells, a process known as **MHC II restriction**.

Antigen-presenting cells and, specifically, macrophages, produce and release a variety of cytokines that modulate the immune response. These include **interleukin 1**, which stimulates T helper cells and self-activated macrophages as well as **prostaglandin E$_2$**, which attenuates some immune responses. Cytokines, such as **interferon-γ**, released by other lymphoid cells as well as by macrophages, enhance the phagocytic and cytolytic avidity of macrophages.

II. LYMPH NODES

The convex aspect of lymph nodes receives **afferent lymph vessels** that deliver their contents into the subcapsular sinuses. Paratrabecular (cortical) sinuses drain subcapsular sinuses and convey their lymph to the sinusoids of the medulla, which are drained by **efferent lymph vessels** at the hilum. The **cortex** is subdivided into several incomplete compartments, with each housing a lymphatic nodule rich in B cells as well as APCs and macrophages. The region of the lymph node between the cortex and medulla, the **paracortex**, houses mostly T cells, APCs, and macrophages. Cells that arise in the cortex or paracortex migrate into the medulla, where they form **medullary cords** composed of T cells, B cells, and plasma cells. T cells and B cells enter the sinusoids and leave the lymph node via efferent lymph vessels. Lymphocytes also enter lymph nodes via arterioles that penetrate the lymph node at the hilum, travel to the paracortex within connective tissue trabeculae, and form **high endothelial vessels** (postcapillary venules).

III. SPLEEN

Branches of the splenic artery, the trabecular arteries, enter the **white pulp** by leaving their trabeculae and, as they become surrounded by sheaths of T cells, the **periarterial lymphatic sheath** (**PALS**), are known as central arteries. Along the path of the central arteries are occasional lymphatic nodules composed mostly of B cells but still surrounded by the PALS. As central arteries lose their lymphatic sheath, they branch repeatedly, forming straight vessels, penicillar arteries, that possess three regions: pulp arterioles, macrophage-sheathed arterioles, and terminal arterial capillaries. The terminal arterial capillaries terminate either in the splenic

sinusoids (**closed circulation**) or freely in the red pulp (**open circulation**). In humans, it is believed that the open circulation predominates. The **red pulp** is composed of the sinusoids, the reticular fiber network, and the cells of the splenic cords. A region of smaller sinusoids forms the interface between the white and red pulps, and this interface is known as the marginal zone. Capillaries arising from the central arteries deliver their blood to sinusoids of the **marginal zone**. APCs of the marginal zone monitor this blood for the presence of antigens and foreign substances.

IV. THYMUS

The thymic cortex is completely isolated from all vascular and connective tissue elements by **reticular epithelial cells**. Additionally, within the cortex, these cells form a three-dimensional meshwork in whose interstices clusters of T cells become mature. Although there are six different types of epithelial reticular cells (three in the cortex and three in the medulla), they all present the same appearance as large, pale cells with large, ovoid nuclei and are, therefore, not easily differentiated in normal histological preaparations. These cells are derived from the third pharyngeal pouch and migrate into the developing thymus. They manufacture the hormones **thymosin, serum thymic factor**, and **thymopoietin**, all of which facilitate the transformation of immature T cells into immunocompetent T cells. During the transformation, which occurs in the thymic **cortex**, the immature T cells (**thymocytes**) undergo **gene rearrangement**, in that they express on their cell membrane T cell receptors (**TCRs**) and cluster of differentiation (**CD**) markers (especially CD2, CD3, CD4, and CD8).

Most of the T cells die as they migrate from the cortex to the medulla; their remnants are phagocytosed by macrophages. It is believed that the cells that were killed were genetically programmed to recognize self-proteins as antigens. In the thymic **medulla**, T cells lose either their CD4 or CD8 markers and develop into CD8$^+$ and CD4$^+$ cells, respectively.

CLINICAL CONSIDERATIONS

Hodgkin's Disease
Hodgkin's disease is a neoplastic transformation of lymphocytes that is prevalent mostly in young males. Its clinical signs are asymptomatic initially because the swelling of the liver, spleen, and lymph nodes are not accompanied by pain. Other manifestations include the loss of weight, elevated temperature, diminished appetite, and generalized weakness. Histopathologic characteristics include the presence of Reed-Sternberg cells, easily recognizable by their large size, and the presence of two large, pale, oval nuclei in each cell.

Wiskott-Aldrich Syndrome
Wiskott-Aldrich syndrome is an immunodeficiency disorder occurring only in boys and is characterized by eczema (dermatitis), lowered platelet count, and lymphocytopenia (abnormally low levels of lymphocytes, both B and T cell populations). The immunosuppressed state of these children leads to recurring bacterial infections, hemorrhage, and death at an early age. Most children who survive the first decade of life are stricken with leukemia or lymphoma.

DiGeorge's Syndrome
DiGeorge's syndrome is the name of the congenital disorder when the thymus fails to develop and the patient is unable to produce T lymphocytes. These patients cannot mount a cellularly mediated immune response, and some of their humorally mediated responses are also disabled or curtailed. Most individuals with this syndrome die in early childhood as a result of uncontrollable infections.

Lymph Nodes During Infection
In a healthy patient with a normal amount of adipose tissue, the lymph nodes are small, soft structures that cannot be palpated easily. However, during an infection the regional lymph nodes become enlarged and hard to the touch due to the large number of lymphocytes that are being formed within the node.

FIGURE 1 • Lymphatic infiltration. Monkey duodenum. Plastic section. ×540.

The **connective tissue** (CT) deep to moist epithelia is usually infiltrated by loosely aggregated **lymphocytes** (Ly) and **plasma cells** (PC), evident from their clock-face nuclei. Observe that the simple columnar **epithelium** (E) contains not only the **nuclei** (N) of epithelial cells but also dark, dense nuclei of lymphocytes (*arrows*), some of which are in the process of migrating from the lamina propria (connective tissue) into the lumen of the duodenum. Note also the presence of a **lacteal** (La), a blindly ending, lymph-filled lymphatic channel unique to the small intestine. These vessels can be recognized by the absence of red blood cells, although nucleated white blood cells may frequently occupy their lumen.

FIGURE 3 • Lymphatic nodule. Monkey. Plastic section. ×270.

This is a higher magnification of a lymphatic nodule from Peyer's patches in the monkey ileum. Note that the lighter staining **germinal center** (Gc) is surrounded by the **corona** (Co) of darker staining cells possessing only a limited amount of cytoplasm around a dense nucleus. These cells are small **lymphocytes** (Ly). Germinal centers form in response to an antigenic challenge and are composed of lymphoblasts and plasmablasts, whose nuclei stain much lighter than those of small lymphocytes. The *boxed area* is presented at a higher magnification in the following figure.

FIGURE 2 • Lymphatic nodule. Monkey. Plastic section. ×132.

The gut-associated lymphatic nodule in this photomicrograph is part of a cluster of nodules known as **Peyer's patches** (PP) and is taken from the monkey ileum. The **lumen** (L) of the small intestine is lined by a simple columnar **epithelium** (E) with numerous **goblet cells** (GC). However, note that the epithelium is modified over the lymphoid tissue into a **follicle-associated epithelium** (FAE), whose cells are shorter, infiltrated by lymphocytes, and display no goblet cells. Observe that this particular lymphatic nodule presents no germinal center but is composed of several cell types, as recognized by nuclei of various sizes and densities. These will be described in Figures 3 and 4. Although this lymphatic nodule is unencapsulated, the **connective tissue** (CT) between the **smooth muscle** (SM) and the lymphatic nodule is free of infiltrate.

FIGURE 4 • Lymphatic nodule. Monkey. Plastic section. ×540.

This is a higher magnification of the *boxed area* of the previous figure. Observe the **small lymphocytes** (Ly) at the periphery of the **germinal center** (Gc). The activity of this center is evidenced by the presence of mitotic figures (*arrows*) as well as the **lymphoblasts** (LB) and **plasmablasts** (PB). The germinal center is the site of production of small lymphocytes that then migrate to the periphery of the lymphatic nodule to form the corona.

KEY					
Co	corona	GC	goblet cell	PB	plasmablast
CT	connective tissue	L	lumen	PC	plasma cell
E	epithelium	La	lacteal	PP	Peyer's patch
FAE	follicle-associated epithelium	LB	lymphoblast	SM	smooth muscle
		Ly	small lymphocyte		
Gc	germinal center	N	nucleus		

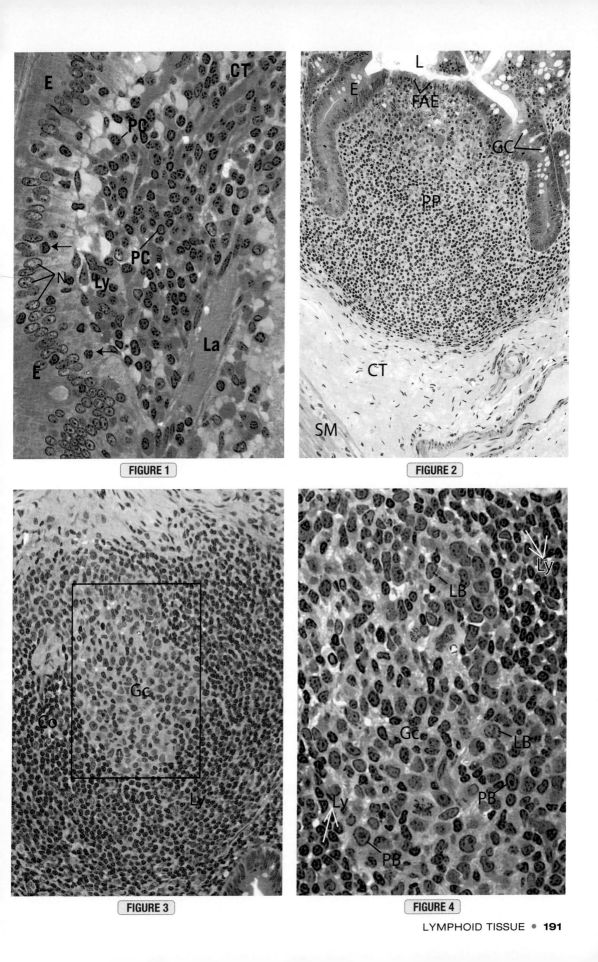

FIGURE 1

FIGURE 2

FIGURE 3

FIGURE 4

FIGURE 1 • Lymph node. Paraffin section. ×14.

Lymph nodes are kidney-shaped structures possessing a convex and a concave (hilar) surface. They are invested by a connective tissue **capsule** (Ca) that sends **trabeculae** (T) into the substance of the node, thereby subdividing it into incomplete compartments. The compartmentalization is particularly prominent in the **cortex** (C), the peripheral aspect of the lymph node. The lighter staining central region is the **medulla** (M). The zone between the medulla and cortex is the **paracortex** (PC). Observe that the cortex displays numerous **lymphatic nodules** (LN), many with **germinal centers** (Gc). This is the region of B lymphocytes, whereas the paracortex is particularly rich in T lymphocytes. Note that the medulla is composed of **sinusoids** (S), **trabeculae** (T) of connective tissue conducting blood vessels, and **medullary cords** (MC). The medullary cords are composed of lymphocytes, macrophages, reticular cells, and plasma cells. Lymph enters the lymph node, and as it percolates through sinuses and sinusoids, foreign substances and non-self antigenic elements are removed from it by phagocytic activity of macrophages.

FIGURE 3 • Lymph node. Monkey. Plastic section. ×132.

The cortex of the lymph node is composed of numerous lymphatic nodules, one of which is presented in this photomicrograph. Observe that the lymph node is usually surrounded by **adipose tissue** (AT). The thin connective tissue **capsule** (Ca) sends **trabeculae** (T) into the substance of the lymph node. Observe that the lymphatic nodule possesses a dark staining **corona** (Co), composed mainly of **small lymphocytes** (Ly) whose heterochromatic nuclei are responsible for their staining characteristics. The **germinal center** (Gc) displays numerous cells with lightly staining nuclei, belonging to dendritic reticular cells, plasmablasts, and lymphoblasts.

FIGURE 2 • Lymph node. Monkey. Plastic section. ×270.

Afferent lymphatic vessels (AV) enter the lymph node at its convex surface. These vessels bear **valves** (V) that regulate the direction of flow. Lymph enters the **subcapsular sinus** (SS), which contains numerous **macrophages** (Ma), **lymphocytes** (Ly), and antigen-transporting cells. These sinuses are lined by **endothelial cells** (EC), which also cover the fine collagen fibers that frequently span the sinus to create a turbulence in lymph flow. Lymph from the subcapsular sinus enters the cortical sinus, then moves into the medullary sinusoids. It is here that lymphocytes also migrate into the sinusoids, leaving the lymph node via the efferent lymph vessels eventually to enter the general circulation.

FIGURE 4 • Lymph node. Human. Silver stain. Paraffin section. ×132.

The hilum of the human lymph node displays the collagenous connective tissue **capsule** (Ca), from which numerous **trabeculae** (T) enter into the substance of the lymph node. Observe that the region of the hilum is devoid of lymphatic nodules but is particularly rich in **medullary cords** (MC). Note that the basic framework of these medullary cords, as well as of the lymph node, is composed of thin reticular fibers (*arrows*), which are connected to the collagen fiber bundles of the trabeculae and capsule.

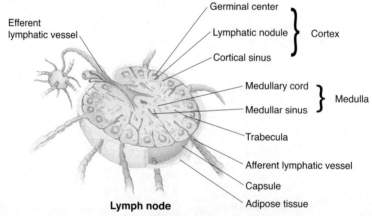

Efferent lymphatic vessel

Germinal center

Lymphatic nodule } Cortex

Cortical sinus

Medullary cord } Medulla

Medullar sinus

Trabecula

Afferent lymphatic vessel

Capsule

Adipose tissue

Lymph node

KEY					
AT	adipose tissue	Gc	germinal center	PC	paracortex
AV	afferent lymphatic vessel	LN	lymphatic nodule	S	sinusoid
C	cortex	Ly	small lymphocyte	SS	subcapsular sinus
Ca	capsule	M	medulla	T	trabeculae
Co	corona	Ma	macrophage	V	valve
EC	endothelial cell	MC	medullary cord		

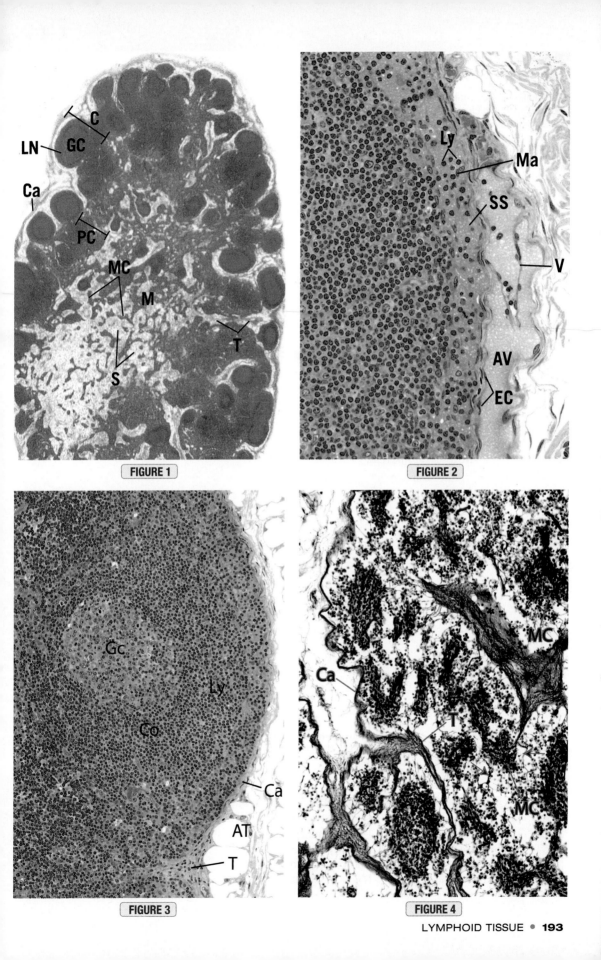

FIGURE 1

FIGURE 2

FIGURE 3

FIGURE 4

FIGURE 1 • Lymph node. Paraffin section. ×132.

The medulla of the lymph node is rich in endothelially lined **sinusoids** (S), which receive lymph from the cortical sinuses. Surrounding the sinusoids are many **medullary cords** (MC), packed with macrophages, small lymphocytes, and plasma cells, whose nuclei (*arrows*) stain intensely. Both T and B lymphocytes populate the medullary cords, since they are in the process of migrating from the paracortex and cortex, respectively. Some of these lymphocytes will leave the lymph node using the sinusoids and efferent lymphatic vessels at the hilum. The medulla also displays connective tissue **trabeculae** (T), connective tissue elements that are conduits for **blood vessels** (BV), which enter and leave the lymph node at the hilum.

FIGURE 3 • Palatine tonsil. Human. Paraffin section. ×14.

The palatine tonsil is an aggregate of **lymphatic nodules** (LN), many of which possess **germinal centers** (Gc). The palatine tonsil is covered by a stratified squamous nonkeratinized **epithelium** (E) that lines the deep **primary crypts** (PCr) that invaginate deeply into the substance of the tonsil. Frequently **secondary crypts** (SCr) are evident, also lined by the same type of epithelium. The crypts frequently contain debris (*arrow*) that consists of decomposing food particles as well as lymphocytes that migrate from the lymphatic nodules through the epithelium to enter the crypts. The deep surface of the palatine tonsil is covered by a thickened connective tissue **capsule** (Ca).

FIGURE 2 • Lymph node. Monkey. Plastic section. ×540.

High magnification of a **sinusoid** (S) and surrounding **medullary cords** (MC) of a lymph node medulla. Note that the medullary cords are populated by macrophages, **plasma cells** (PC), and small **lymphocytes** (Ly). The sinusoids are lined by a discontinuous **endothelium** (EC). The lumen contains lymph, small **lymphocytes** (Ly), and **macrophages** (Ma). The vacuolated appearance of these macrophages is indicative of their active phagocytosis of particulate matter.

FIGURE 4 • Pharyngeal tonsil. Human. Paraffin section. ×132.

The pharyngeal tonsil, located in the nasopharynx, is a loose aggregate of lymphatic nodules, often displaying **germinal centers** (Gc). The **epithelial lining** (E) is pseudostratified ciliated columnar with occasional patches of stratified squamous nonkeratinized epithelium (*asterisk*). The lymphatic nodules are located in a loose, collagenous **connective tissue** (CT) that is infiltrated by small **lymphocytes** (Ly). Note that lymphocytes migrate through the epithelium (*arrows*) to gain access to the nasopharynx.

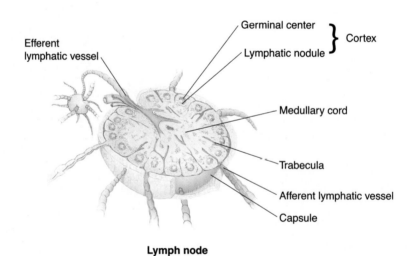

Efferent lymphatic vessel

Germinal center
Lymphatic nodule } Cortex

Medullary cord

Trabecula

Afferent lymphatic vessel

Capsule

Lymph node

KEY							
BV	blood vessel	Gc	germinal center	PC	plasma cell		
Ca	capsule	LN	lymphatic nodule	PCr	primary crypt		
CT	connective tissue	Ly	lymphocyte	S	sinusoid		
E	epithelium	Ma	macrophage	T	trabeculae		
EC	endothelial cell	MC	medullary cord	SCr	secondary crypt		

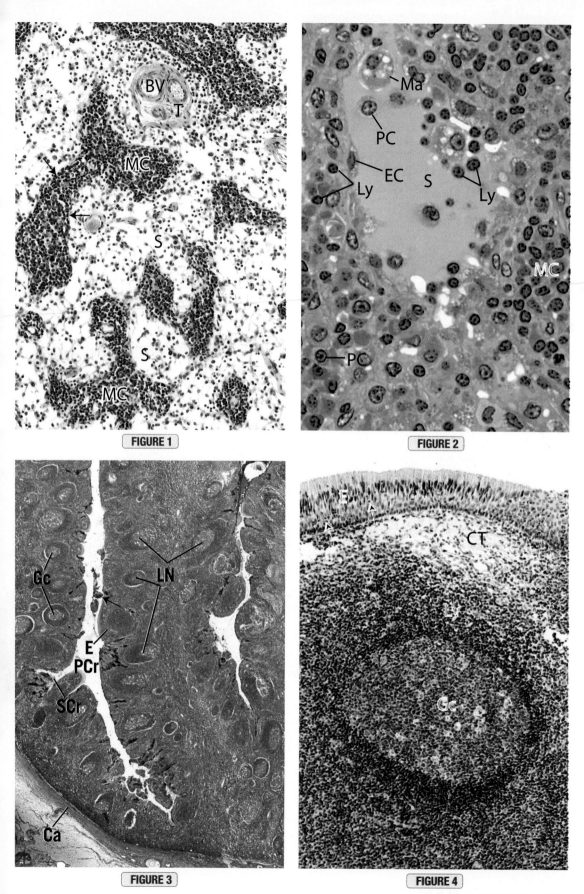

FIGURE 1

FIGURE 2

FIGURE 3

FIGURE 4

FIGURE 1 • Popleteal lymph node. Mouse. Electron microscopy. ×8608.

Electron micrograph of a mouse lymph node. Immediately deep to the **capsule** (Ca) lies the subcapsular sinus occupied by three **lymphocytes**, one of which is labeled (L), as well as the **process** (P) of an antigen-transporting (antigen-presenting) cell, whose cell body (*arrowheads*) and nucleus are in the cortex, deep to the sinus. The process enters the lumen of the subcapsular sinus via a

pore (*arrows*) in the epithelial lining of its floor (FL). It is believed that antigen-transporting cells are nonphagocytic and that they trap antigens at the site of antigenic invasion and transport them to lymphatic nodules of lymph nodes, where they mature to become dendritic reticular cells. (From Szakal A, Homes K, Tew J. Transport of immune complexes from the subcapsular sinus to lymph node follicles on the surface of nonphagocytic cells, including cells with dendritic morphology. J Immunol 1983;131:1714–1717.)

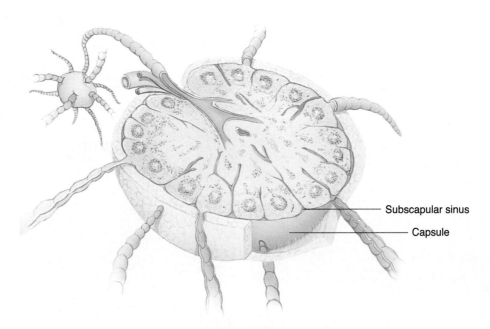

Subscapular sinus

Capsule

Lymph node

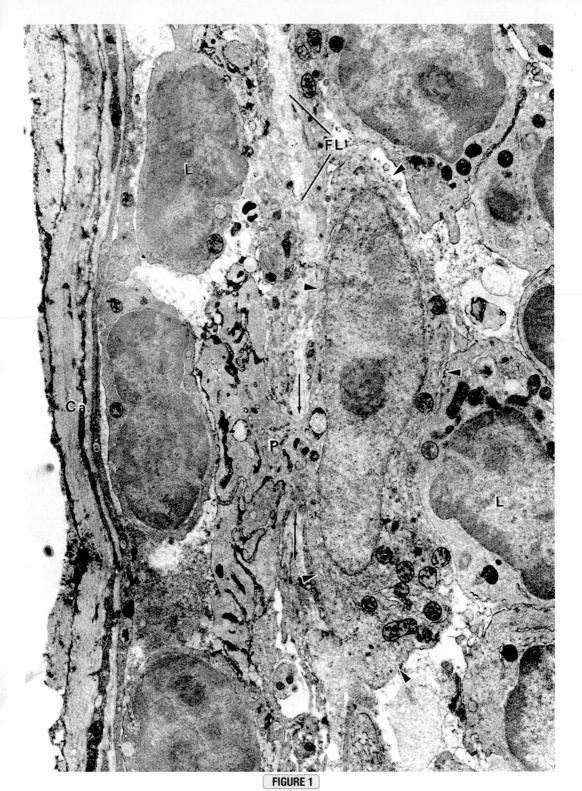

FIGURE 1

FIGURE 1 • Thymus. Human infant. Paraffin section. ×14.

The thymus of a prepubescent individual is a well-developed organ that displays its many characteristics to advantage. This photomicrograph presents a part of one lobe. It is invested by a thin connective tissue **capsule** (Ca) that incompletely subdivides the thymus into **lobules** (Lo) by connective tissue **septa** (Se). Each lobule possesses a darker staining peripheral **cortex** (C) and a lighter staining **medulla** (M). The medulla of one lobule, however, is continuous with that of other lobules. The connective tissue capsule and septa convey blood vessels into the medulla of the thymus. The thymus begins to involute in the postpubescent individual, and the connective tissue septa become infiltrated with adipocytes.

FIGURE 2 • Thymus. Monkey. Plastic section. ×132.

The lobule of the thymus presented in this photomicrograph appears to be completely surrounded by connective tissue **septa** (Se), three-dimensional reconstruction would reveal this lobule to be continuous with surrounding **lobules** (Lo). Observe the numerous **blood vessels** (BV) in the septa as well as the darker staining **cortex** (C) and the lighter staining **medulla** (M). The characteristic light patches of the cortex correspond to the high density of epithelial reticular cells and macrophages (*arrows*). The darker staining structures are nuclei of the T-lymphocyte series. The medulla contains the characteristic **thymic corpuscles** (TC) as well as blood vessels, macrophages, and epithelial reticular cells.

FIGURE 3 • Thymus. Monkey. Plastic section. ×270.

The center of this photomicrograph is occupied by the **medulla** (M) of the thymus, presenting a large **thymic (Hassall's) corpuscle** (TC), composed of concentrically arranged **epithelial reticular cells** (ERC). The function, if any, of this structure is not known. The thymic medulla houses numerous **blood vessels** (BV), macrophages, **lymphocytes** (Ly), and occasional plasma cells.

FIGURE 4 • Thymus. Monkey. Plastic section. ×540.

The cortex of the thymus is bounded externally by collagenous connective tissue **septa** (Se). The substance of the cortex is separated from the septa by a zone of **epithelial reticular cells** (ERC), recognizable by their pale nuclei. Additional ERC form a cellular reticulum, in whose interstices **lymphocytes** (Ly) develop into mature T lymphocytes. Numerous **macrophages** (Ma) are also evident in the cortex. These cells phagocytose lymphocytes destroyed in the thymus.

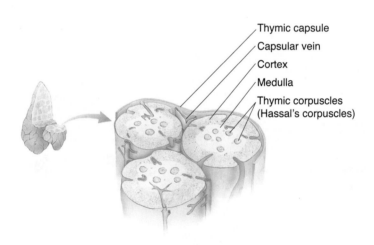

Thymic capsule
Capsular vein
Cortex
Medulla
Thymic corpuscles
(Hassal's corpuscles)

Thymus

KEY					
BV	blood vessel	Lo	lobule	Ma	macrophage
C	cortex	Ly	lymphocyte	Se	septum
Ca	capsule	M	medulla	TC	thymic corpuscle
ERC	epithelial reticular cell				

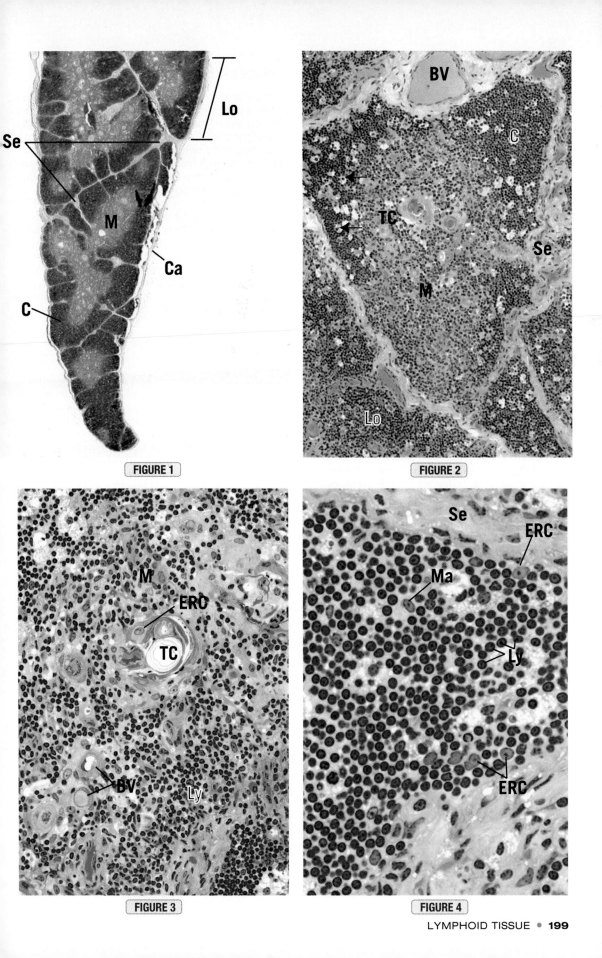

FIGURE 1 • Spleen. Human. Paraffin section. ×132.

The spleen, the largest lymphoid organ, possesses a thick collagenous connective tissue **capsule** (Ca). Since it lies within the abdominal cavity, it is surrounded by a simple squamous **epithelium** (E). Connective tissue **septa** (SE), derived from the capsule, penetrate the substance of the spleen, conveying **blood vessels** (BV) into the interior of the organ. Histologically, the spleen is composed of **white pulp** (WP) and **red pulp** (RP). White pulp is arranged as a cylindrical, multilayered sheath of **lymphocytes** (Ly) surrounding a blood vessel known as the **central artery** (CA). The red pulp consists of **sinusoids** (S) meandering through a cellular tissue known as **pulp cords** (PC). The white pulp of the spleen is found in two different arrangements. The one represented in this photomicrograph is known as a **periarterial lymphatic sheath** (PALS), composed mostly of T lymphocytes. The zone of lymphocytes at the junction of the periarterial lymphatic sheath and the red pulp is known as the **marginal zone** (MZ).

FIGURE 3 • Spleen. Monkey. Plastic section. ×540.

The red pulp of the spleen, presented in this photomicrograph, is composed of **splenic sinusoids** (S) and **pulp cords** (PC). The splenic sinusoids are lined by a discontinuous type of epithelium, surrounded by an unusual arrangement of **basement membrane** (BM) that encircles the sinusoids in a discontinuous fashion. Sinusoids contain numerous **blood cells** (BC). **Nuclei** (N) of the sinusoidal lining cells bulge into the lumen. The regions between sinusoids are occupied by pulp cords, rich in macrophages, reticular cells, and plasma cells. The vascular supply of the red pulp is derived from penicillar arteries, which give rise to **arterioles** (AR), whose **endothelial cells** (EC) and **smooth muscle** (SM) cells are evident in the center of this field.

FIGURE 2 • Spleen. Monkey. Plastic section. ×132.

Lying within the **periarterial lymphatic sheaths** (PALS) of the spleen, a second arrangement of white pulp may be noted, namely **lymphatic nodules** (LN) bearing a **germinal center** (Gc). Lymphatic nodules frequently occur at branching of the **central artery** (CA). Nodules are populated mostly by B lymphocytes (*arrows*), which account for the dark staining of the **corona** (CO). The germinal center is the site of active production of B lymphocytes during an antigenic challenge. The **marginal zone** (MZ), also present around lymphatic nodules, is the region where lymphocytes leave the small capillaries and first enter the connective tissue spaces of the spleen. It is from here that T lymphocytes migrate to the periarterial lymphatic sheaths, whereas B lymphocytes seek out lymphatic nodules. Both the marginal zone and the white pulp are populated with numerous macrophages and antigen-presenting cells (*arrowheads*), in addition to lymphocytes.

FIGURE 4 • Spleen. Human. Silver stain. Paraffin section. ×132.

The connective tissue framework of the spleen is demonstrated by the use of silver stain, which precipitates around reticular fibers. The **capsule** (Ca) of the spleen is pierced by **blood vessels** (BV) that enter the substance of the organ via trabeculae. The **white pulp** (WP) and **red pulp** (RP) are clearly evident. In fact, the lymphatic nodule presents a well-defined **germinal center** (Gc) as well as a **corona** (CO). The **central artery** (CA) is also evident in this preparation. **Reticular fibers** (RF), which form an extensive network throughout the substance of the spleen, are attached to the capsule and to the trabeculae.

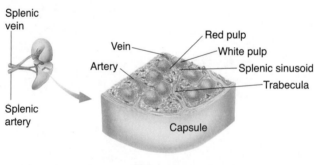

Spleen

KEY					
AR	arteriole	EC	endothelial cell	PC	pulp cord
BC	blood cell	Gc	germinal center	RF	reticular fiber
BM	basement membrane	LN	lymphatic nodule	RP	red pulp
BV	blood vessel	Ly	lymphocyte	S	sinusoid
Ca	capsule	MZ	marginal zone	SE	septum
CA	central artery	N	nucleus	SM	smooth muscle
CO	corona	PALS	periarterial lymphatic	T	trabeculae
E	epithelium		sheath	WP	white pulp

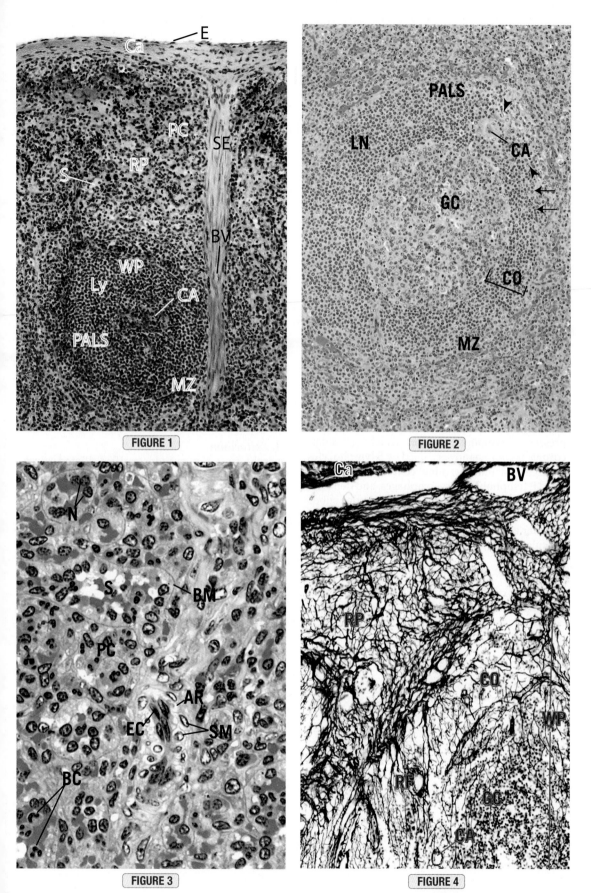

FIGURE 1

FIGURE 2

FIGURE 3

FIGURE 4

Summary of Histological Organization

Lymphoid tissue consists of **diffuse** and **dense lymphoid tissue**. The principal cell of lymphoid tissue is the **lymphocyte**, of which there are two categories: **B lymphocytes** and **T lymphocytes**. Additionally, **macrophages, reticular cells, plasma cells, dendritic cells,** and **antigen-presenting cells** perform important functions in lymphatic tissue.

I. LYMPH NODE

A. Capsule

The **capsule**, usually surrounded by **adipose tissue**, is composed of dense irregular **collagenous connective tissue** containing some **elastic fibers** and **smooth muscle. Afferent lymphatic vessels** enter the convex aspect; **efferent lymphatics** and **blood vessels** pierce the **hilum**.

B. Cortex

The **cortex** of a lymph node is characterized by the presence of **lymphatic nodules**, which have a dark **corona**, predominantly occupied by **B lymphocytes**, and lighter staining **germinal centers,** housing activated **B lymphoblasts, macrophages,** and **dendritic reticular cells**. Connective tissue **trabeculae** subdivide the cortex into incomplete compartments. **Subcapsular** and **cortical sinuses** possess **lymphocytes, reticular cells,** and **macrophages**.

C. Paracortex

The **paracortex** is the zone between the cortex and medulla, composed of **T lymphocytes. Postcapillary venules,** with their characteristic **cuboidal endothelium,** are present.

D. Medulla

The **medulla** displays connective tissue **trabeculae, medullary cords** (composed of macrophages, plasma cells, and lymphocytes), and **medullary sinusoids** lined by discontinuous **endothelial cells. Lymphocytes, plasma cells,** and **macrophages** are the common cell types in the lumina of sinusoids. The region of the **hilum** is distinguished by the thickened capsule and lack of lymphatic nodules.

E. Reticular Fibers

With the use of special stains, such as silver stains, an extensive network of **reticular fibers** may be demonstrated to constitute the framework of lymph nodes.

II. TONSILS

A. Palatine Tonsils

1. Epithelium
Covered by **stratified squamous nonkeratinized epithelium** that extends into the **tonsillar crypts. Lymphocytes** may migrate through the epithelium.

2. Lymphatic Nodules
Surround **crypts** and frequently display **germinal centers**.

3. Capsule
Dense, irregular collagenous connective tissue **capsule** separates the tonsil from the underlying pharyngeal wall musculature. **Septa,** derived from the capsule, extend into the tonsil.

4. Glands
Not present.

B. Pharyngeal Tonsils

1. Epithelium
For the most part, **pseudostratified ciliated columnar epithelium** (infiltrated by lymphocytes) covers the free surface, as well as the folds that resemble crypts.

2. Lymphatic Nodules
Most **lymphatic nodules** possess **germinal centers**.

3. Capsule
The thin **capsule**, situated deep to the tonsil, provides **septa** for the tonsil.

4. Glands
Ducts of the **seromucous glands,** beneath the capsule, pierce the tonsil to open onto the epithelially covered surface.

C. Lingual Tonsils

1. Epithelium
Stratified squamous nonkeratinized epithelium covers the tonsil and extends into the shallow **crypts**.

2. Lymphatic Nodules
Most **lymphatic nodules** present **germinal centers**.

3. Capsule
The **capsule** is thin and ill-defined.

4. Glands
Seromucous glands open into the base of **crypts**.

III. SPLEEN

A. Capsule

The **capsule**, composed predominantly of **dense irregular collagenous connective tissue**, is significantly thickened at the **hilum**. The capsule also possesses a small amount of **elastic fibers** and some **smooth muscle cells**. It is covered by **mesothelium** (simple squamous epithelium) but is not surrounded by adipose tissue. **Trabeculae**, bearing blood vessels, extend from the capsule into the substance of the spleen.

B. White Pulp

White pulp is composed of **periarterial lymphatic sheaths** and **lymphatic nodules** with germinal centers. Both periarterial lymphatic sheaths (predominantly **T lymphocytes**) and lymphatic nodules (predominantly **B lymphocytes**) surround the acentrically located **central artery**.

C. Marginal Zone

A looser accumulation of **lymphocytes, macrophages**, and **plasma cells** are located between white and red pulps. The vascular supply of this zone is provided by **capillary loops** derived from the **central artery**.

D. Red Pulp

Red pulp is composed of **pulp cords** and **sinusoids**. Pulp cords are composed of delicate reticular fibers, stellate-shaped **reticular cells, plasma cells, macrophages**, and **cells** of the **circulating blood**. **Sinusoids** are lined by elongated discontinuous **endothelial cells** surrounded by thickened hoop-like **basement membrane** in association with **reticular fibers**. The various regions of **penicilli** are evident in the red pulp. These are **pulp arterioles, sheathed arterioles**, and **terminal arterial capillaries**. Convincing evidence to determine whether circulation in the red pulp is open or closed is not available, although, in humans, the open circulation is believed to be the most prevalent.

E. Reticular Fibers

With the use of special stains, an extensive network of **reticular fibers**, which constitute the framework of the spleen, can be demonstrated.

IV. THYMUS

A. Capsule

The thin **capsule** is composed of **dense irregular collagenous connective tissue** (with some elastic fibers). **Interlobular trabeculae** extending from the capsule incompletely subdivide the thymus into lobules.

B. Cortex

Typically, the **cortex** is devoid of lymphatic nodules or plasma cells. It is composed of lightly staining **epithelial reticular cells, macrophages**, and densely packed, darkly staining, small **T lymphocytes (thymocytes)** responsible for the dark appearance of the cortex. Epithelial reticular cells also surround **capillaries**, the only blood vessels present in the cortex.

C. Medulla

The lightly staining **medulla** is continuous from lobule to lobule. It is occupied by **plasma cells, lymphocytes, macrophages**, and **epithelial reticular cells**. Moreover, **thymic (Hassall's) corpuscles**, concentrically arranged epithelial reticular cells, are characteristic features of the thymic medulla.

D. Involution

The thymus begins to involute subsequent to puberty. The **cortex** becomes less dense because its population of lymphocytes and epithelial reticular cells is, to some extent, replaced by fat. In the medulla, **thymic corpuscles** increase in number and size.

E. Reticular Fibers and Sinusoids

The thymus possesses neither reticular fibers nor sinusoids.

Endocrine System

The endocrine system, in cooperation with the nervous system, orchestrates homeostasis by influencing, coordinating, and integrating the physiological functions of the body.

The endocrine system consists of several glands, isolated groups of cells within certain organs, and individual cells scattered among parenchymal cells of the body. This chapter considers only that part of the endocrine system that is composed of glands. Islets of Langerhans, interstitial cells of Leydig, cells responsible for ovarian hormone production, and DNES (diffuse neuroendocrine) cells are treated in more appropriate chapters.

The **endocrine glands** to be discussed here are the pituitary, thyroid, parathyroid, and suprarenal glands, as well as the pineal body. All of these glands produce **hormones**, low-molecular-weight molecules that are transported via the bloodstream to their target cells. Therefore, endocrine glands possess an extensive vascular supply that is particularly rich in fenestrated capillaries. Since some hormones are proteins, they do not cross the target cell plasmalemma but attach to specific receptors on the plasma membrane of the target cell, thus activating its intracellular **second messenger system**. Other hormones are lipid soluble and, subsequent to entering the target cell, bind to their intracellular receptors and thus exert their influence. Still other hormones act to modify the electrical potential difference across the plasmalemma of certain cells, such as muscle cells or neurons. Therefore, the activity of the hormone will, to a large extent, depend on the target cell receptors to which it becomes attached. The presence of most hormones also elicits a vascularly mediated negative feedback response, in that subsequent to a desired response, the further production and/or release of that particular hormone is inhibited.

● PITUITARY GLAND

The **pituitary gland** (hypophysis) is composed of several regions, namely, pars anterior (pars distalis), pars tuberalis, infundibular stalk, pars intermedia, and pars nervosa (the last two are known as the pars posterior) (see Graphic 10-1). Since the pituitary gland develops from two separate embryonic origins, the epithelium of the pharyngeal roof and the floor of the diencephalon, it is frequently discussed as being subdivided into two parts: the **adenohypophysis** (**pars anterior, pars tuberalis**, and **pars intermedia**) and the **neurohypophysis** (**pars nervosa** and **infundibular stalk**). The pars nervosa is continuous with the median eminence of the hypothalamus via the thin neural stalk (infundibular stalk).

The pituitary gland receives its **blood supply** from the right and left **superior hypophyseal arteries**, serving the median eminence, pars tuberalis, and the infundibulum, and from the right and left **inferior hypophyseal arteries**, which serve the pars nervosa.

Hypophyseal Portal System: The two superior hypophyseal arteries give rise to the **primary capillary plexus** located in the region of the median eminence. **Hypophyseal portal veins** drain the primary capillary plexus and deliver the blood into the secondary capillary plexus, located in the pars distalis. Both capillary plexuses are composed of fenestrated capillaries.

Pars Anterior

The **pars anterior** is composed of numerous parenchymal cells arranged in thick cords, with large capillaries known as sinusoids, richly vascularizing the intervening regions. The parenchymal cells are classified into two main categories: those whose granules readily take up stain, chromophils, and those cells that do not possess a strong affinity for stains, chromophobes. **Chromophils** are of two types: **acidophils** and **basophils**. Although considerable controversy surrounds the classification of these cells vis-à-vis their function, it is probable that at least six of the seven hormones manufactured by the pars anterior are made by separate cells. Hormones that modulate the secretory functions of the pituitary-dependent endocrine glands are **somatotropin, thyrotropin (TSH), follicle-stimulating hormone (FSH), luteinizing hormone (LH), prolactin, adrenocorticotropin (ACTH)**, and **melanocyte-stimulating hormone (MSH)**. It is believed that two types of acidophils produce somatotropin and prolactin, whereas various populations of basophils produce the

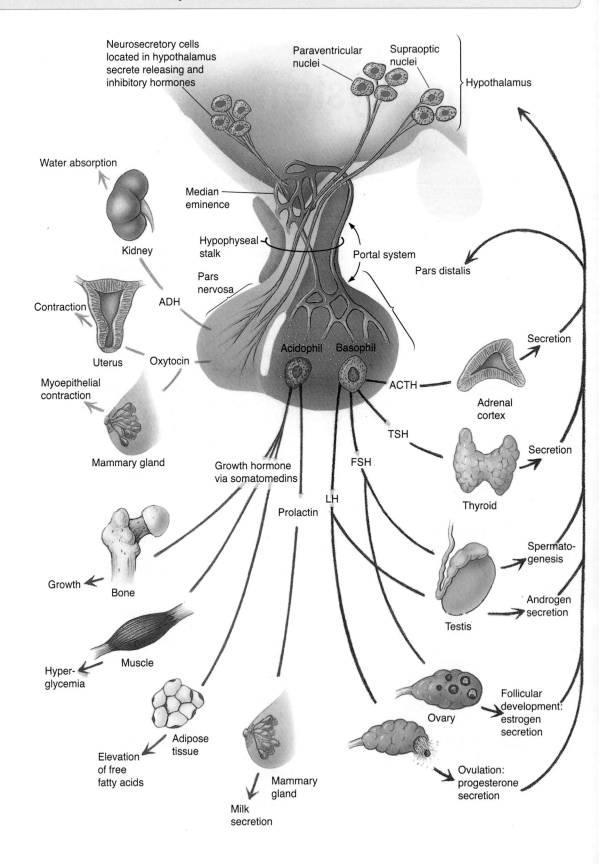

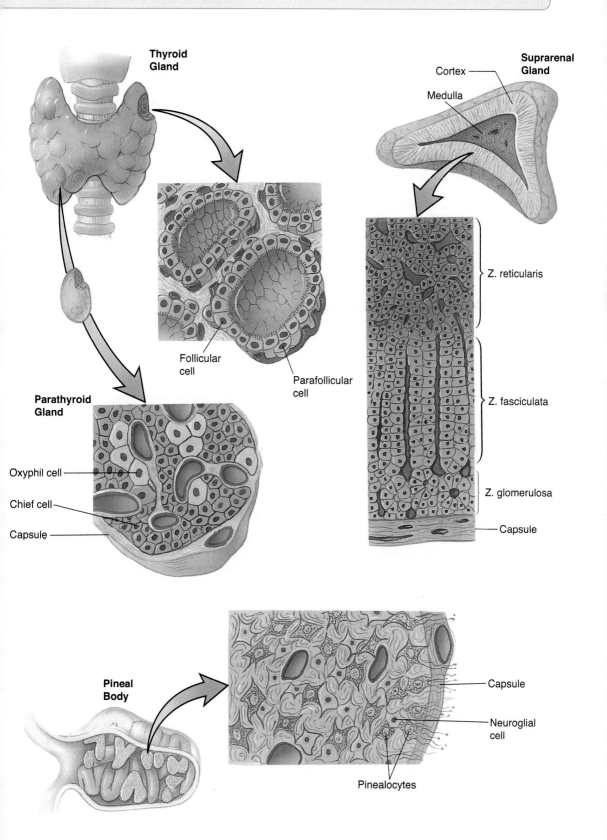

Thyroid Gland

Suprarenal Gland

Cortex

Medulla

Z. reticularis

Z. fasciculata

Follicular cell

Parafollicular cell

Z. glomerulosa

Parathyroid Gland

Capsule

Oxyphil cell

Chief cell

Capsule

Pineal Body

Capsule

Neuroglial cell

Pinealocytes

remaining five hormones. **Chromophobes**, however, probably do not produce hormones. They are believed to be acidophils and basophils that have released their granules.

Control of Anterior Pituitary Hormone Release: The axons of parvicellular, hypophyseotropic neurons whose soma are located in the paraventricular and arcuate nuclei of the hypothalamus terminate at the primary capillary bed. These axons store releasing hormones (somatotropin-releasing hormone, prolactin-releasing hormone, corticotropin-releasing hormone, thyrotropin-releasing hormone, and gonadotropin releasing hormone) and inhibitory hormones (prolactin inhibiting hormone, inhibitin, and somatostatin). The hormones are released by these axons into the primary capillary plexus and are conveyed to the secondary capillary plexus by the hypophyseal portal veins. The hormones then activate (or inhibit) chromophils of the adenohypophysis, causing them to release or prevent them from releasing their hormones.

An additional control is the mechanism of negative feedback, so that the presence of specific plasma levels of the pituitary hormones prevents the chromophils from releasing additional quantities of their hormones.

Pars Intermedia

The **pars intermedia** is not well developed. It is believed that the cell population of this region may have migrated into the pars anterior to produce **melanocyte-stimulating hormone** and **adrenocorticotropin**. It is quite probable that a single basophil can produce both of these hormones.

Pars Nervosa and Infundibular Stalk

The **pars nervosa** does not present a very organized appearance. It is composed of **pituicytes**, cells believed to be neuroglial in nature that may fulfill a supporting function for the numerous unmyelinated axons of the pars nervosa. These axons, whose cell bodies are located in the **supraoptic** and **paraventricular nuclei** of the hypothalamus, enter the pars nervosa via the **hypothalamo-hypophyseal tract**. They possess expanded axon terminals, referred to as **Herring bodies**, within the pars nervosa. Herring bodies contain **oxytocin** and **antidiuretic hormone** (**ADH, vasopressin**), two neurosecretory hormones that are stored in the pars nervosa but are manufactured in the cell bodies in the **hypothalamus**. The release of these neurosecretory hormones (neurosecretion) is mediated by nerve impulses and occurs at the interface between the axon terminals and the fenestrated capillaries. When the axon is ready to release its secretory products, the pituicytes withdraw their processes and permit the secretory product a clear access to the capillaries.

Pars Tuberalis

The **pars tuberalis** is composed of numerous cuboidal cells whose function is not known.

● THYROID GLAND

The **thyroid gland** consists of right and left lobes that are interconnected by a narrow isthmus across the thyroid cartilage and upper trachea (see Graphic 10-2). It is enveloped by a connective tissue capsule whose septa penetrate the substance of the gland, forming not only its supporting framework but also its conduit for its rich vascular supply. The parenchymal cells of the gland are arranged in numerous follicles, composed of a **simple cuboidal epithelium** lining a central **colloid-filled lumen**. The colloid, secreted and resorbed by the **follicular cells**, is composed of the thyroid hormone that is bound to a large protein, and the complex is known as **thyroglobulin**. An additional secretory cell type, **parafollicular cells** (**clear cells**), is present in the thyroid. These cells have no contact with the colloidal material. They manufacture the hormone **calcitonin**, which is released directly into the connective tissue in the immediate vicinity of capillaries. Thyroid hormone is essential for regulating basal metabolism and for influencing growth rate and mental processes and generally stimulates endocrine gland functioning. Calcitonin helps control calcium concentrations in the blood by inhibiting bone resorption by osteoclasts (i.e., when blood calcium levels are high, calcitonin is released).

● PARATHYROID GLANDS

The **parathyroid glands**, usually four in number, are embedded in the fascial sheath of the posterior aspect of the thyroid gland. They possess slender connective tissue capsules from which septa are derived to penetrate the glands and convey a vascular supply to the interior. In the adult, two types of parenchymal cells are present in the parathyroid glands: numerous small **chief cells** and a smaller number of large **acidophilic cells**, the **oxyphils**. Fatty infiltration of the glands is common in older individuals. Although there is no know function of oxyphils, chief cells produce **parathyroid hormone** (**PTH**), the most important "minute to minute" regulator of calcium in the body. If the blood calcium levels drop below normal, calcium-sensing receptors on the chief cells cause them to release PTH, which helps control serum calcium levels by acting directly on osteoblasts to increase osteoclastic activity, reducing calcium loss through the kidneys, and facilitating calcium absorption in the intestines. Lack of parathyroid glands is not compatible with life.

● SUPRARENAL GLANDS

The **suprarenal glands** (adrenal glands in some animals) are invested by a connective tissue capsule (see Graphics 10-2 and 10-3). The glands are derived from two different embryonic origins, namely, **mesodermal epithelium**, which gives rise to the **cortex**, and **neuroectoderm**, from which the **medulla** originates. The rich vascular supply of the gland is conveyed to the interior in connective tissue elements derived from the capsule.

Cortex

The cortex is subdivided into three concentric regions or zones. The outermost region, just beneath the capsule, is the **zona glomerulosa**, where the cells are arranged in arches and spherical clusters with numerous capillaries surrounding them. The second region, the **zona fasciculata**, is the most extensive. Its parenchymal cells, usually known as **spongiocytes**, are arranged in long cords, with numerous capillaries between the cords. The innermost region of the cortex, the **zona reticularis**, is arranged in anastomosing cords of cells with a rich intervening capillary network. Three types of hormones are produced by the suprarenal cortex, namely, **mineralocorticoids** (zona glomerulosa), **glucocorticoids** (zona fasciculata and, to some extent, zona reticularis), and some **androgens** (zona fasciculata and zona reticularis).

Medulla

The cells of the **medulla**, disposed in irregularly arranged short cords surrounded by capillary networks, contain numerous granules that stain intensely when the freshly cut tissue is exposed to chromium salts. This is referred to as the chromaffin reaction, and the cells are called **chromaffin cells**. There are two types of chromaffin cells: one produces **epinephrine** and the other manufactures **norepinephrine**, the two hormones of the suprarenal medulla. Since these cells are innervated by preganglionic sympathetic nerve fibers, chromaffin cells are considered to be related to postganglionic sympathetic neurons (see Graphic 10-3). Additionally, the medulla of the suprarenal gland also houses large, postganglionic sympathetic nerve cell bodies whose function is not known.

● PINEAL BODY

The **pineal body** (**epiphysis**) is a projection of the roof of the diencephalon (see Graphic 10-2). The connective tissue covering of the pineal body is pia mater, which sends trabeculae and septa into the substance of the pineal body, subdividing it into incomplete lobules. Blood vessels, along with postganglionic sympathetic nerve fibers from the superior cervical ganglia, travel in these connective tissue elements. As the nerve fibers enter the pineal body they lose their myelin sheath. The parenchyma of the pineal body is composed of **pinealocytes** and **neuroglial cells**. The pinealocytes form communicating junctions with each other and manufacture **melatonin**, whereas neuroglial cells lend support to pinealocytes. Interestingly, melatonin is manufactured only at night. The pineal body receives indirect input from the retina, which allows the pineal to differentiate between day and night, and, in that manner, assists in the establishment of the circadian rhythm. The intercellular spaces of the pineal body contain calcified granular material known as **brain sand** (**corpora arenacea**), whose significance, if any, is not known.

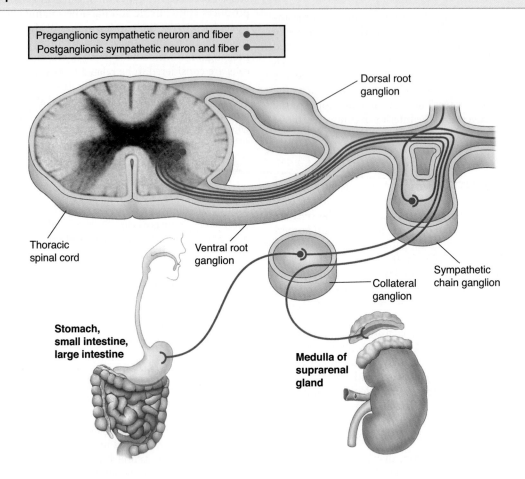

Preganglionic sympathetic neuron and fiber
Postganglionic sympathetic neuron and fiber

Dorsal root ganglion

Thoracic spinal cord

Ventral root ganglion

Sympathetic chain ganglion

Collateral ganglion

Stomach, small intestine, large intestine

Medulla of suprarenal gland

Histophysiology

I. MECHANISM OF HORMONAL ACTION

Hormones are substances secreted by cells of the endocrine system into the connective tissue spaces. Some hormones act in the immediate vicinity of their secretion, whereas other hormones enter the vascular system and find their target cells at a distance from their site of origin.

Some hormones (e.g., **thyroid hormone**) have a generalized effect, in that most cells are affected by them; other hormones (e.g., **aldosterone**) affect only certain cells. **Receptors** located either on the cell membrane or within the cell are specific for a particular hormone. The binding of a hormone initiates a sequence of reactions that results in a particular response. Because of the specificity of the reaction, only a minute quantity of the hormone is required. Some hormones elicit and others inhibit a particular response.

Hormones are of two types, nonsteroid and steroid based. **Nonsteroid-based hormones** may be derivatives of tyrosine (catecholamines and thyroid hormone) and small peptides (ADH and oxytocin) or small proteins (glucagon, insulin, anterior pituitary proteins, and parathormone). **Steroid-based hormones** are cholesterol derivatives (aldosterone, cortisol, estrogen, progesterone, and testosterone).

A. Nonsteroid-Based Hormones

Nonsteroid-based endocrine hormones bind to **receptors** (some are G protein linked, and some are catalytic) located on the target cell membrane, activate them, and thus initiate a sequence of intracellular reactions. These may act by altering the state of an **ion channel** (opening or closing) or by activating (or inhibiting) an **enzyme** or group of enzymes associated with the cytoplasmic aspect of the cell membrane.

Opening or closing an ion channel will permit the particular ion to traverse or inhibit the particular ion from traversing the cell membrane, thus altering the membrane potential. Neurotransmitters and **catecholamines** act on ion channels.

The binding of most hormones to their receptor will have only a single effect, which is the activation of **adenylate cyclase**. This enzyme functions in the transformation of ATP to **cAMP** (**cyclic adenosine monophosphate**), the major **second messenger** of the cell. cAMP then activates a specific sequence of enzymes that are necessary to accomplish the desired result. There are a few hormones that activate a similar compound, **cyclic guanosine monophosphate** (**cGMP**), which functions in a comparable fashion.

Some hormones facilitate the opening of **calcium channels**; calcium enters the cell, and three or four calcium ions bind to the protein **calmodulin**, altering its conformation. The altered calmodulin is a **second messenger** that activates a sequence of enzymes, causing a specific response.

Thyroid hormones are unusual among the nonsteroid-based hormones, in that they directly enter the nucleus, where they bind with **receptor molecules**. The hormone–receptor complexes control the activities of **operators** and/or **promoters**, resulting in mRNA transcription. The newly formed mRNAs enter the cytoplasm, where they are translated into proteins that elevate the cell's metabolic activity.

B. Steroid-Based Hormones

Steroid-based endocrine hormones diffuse into the target cell through the plasma membrane, and, once inside the cell, bind to a **receptor molecule**. The receptor molecule–hormone complex enters the nucleus, seeks out a specific region of the DNA molecule, and initiates the synthesis of mRNA. The newly formed mRNA codes for the formation of specific enzymes that will accomplish the desired result.

II. THYROID HORMONE

A. Synthesis

Iodide from the bloodstream is actively transported into follicular cells at their basal aspect via **iodide pumps**. Iodide is oxidized by **thyroid peroxidase** on the apical cell membrane and is bound to **tyrosine residues** of **thyroglobulin** molecules. Within the colloid the iodinated tyrosine residues become rearranged to form **triiodothyronine (T_3)** and **thyroxine (T_4)**.

B. Release

The binding of **thyroid-stimulating hormone** to receptors on the basal aspect of their plasmalemma induces follicular cells to become tall cuboidal cells. They form **pseudopods** on their apical cell membrane that engulf and endocytose colloid. The colloid-filled vesicles fuse with lysosomes, and T_3 and T_4 residues are removed from thyroglobulin, liberated into the cytosol, and are released at the basal aspect of the cell into the perifollicular capillary network.

III. PARATHYROID HORMONE AND CALCITONIN

Parathyroid hormone (**PTH**), produced by chief cells of the parathyroid gland, is responsible for maintaining proper calcium ion balance. The concentration of calcium ions is extremely important in the normal function of muscle and nerve cells and as a release mechanism for neurotransmitter substance. A drop in blood calcium concentration activates a feedback mechanism that stimulates chief cell secretion. PTH binds to receptors on osteoblasts that release osteoclast-stimulating factor followed by bone resorption and a consequent increase in blood calcium ion concentration. In the kidneys, PTH prevents urinary calcium loss; thus, ions are returned to the bloodstream. PTH also controls calcium uptake in the intestines indirectly by modulating kidney production of vitamin D, which is essential for calcium absorption.

Increased levels of PTH cause an elevation in plasma calcium concentration; however, it takes several hours for this level to peak. The concentration of PTH in the blood is also controlled by plasma calcium levels.

Calcitonin acts as an antagonist to PTH. Unlike PTH, calcitonin is fast acting and, since it binds directly to receptors on osteoclasts, it elicits a peak reduction in blood calcium levels within one hour. Calcitonin inhibits bone resorption, thus reducing calcium ion levels in the blood. High levels of calcium ions in the blood stimulate calcitonin release.

IV. SUPRARENAL GLANDS

The suprarenal parenchyma is divided into an external cortex and an internal medulla.

A. Cortex

Parenchymal cells of the **cortex**, derived from mesoderm, are regionalized into three zones that secrete specific hormones. Control of these hormonal secretions is mostly regulated by ACTH from the pituitary gland.

Cells of the zona glomerulosa secrete **aldosterone**, a mineralocorticoid that acts on cells of the distal convoluted tubules of the kidney to modulate water and electrolyte balance.

Zona fasciculata cells secrete **cortisol** and **corticosterone**. These glucocorticoids regulate carbohydrate metabolism, facilitate the catabolism of fats and proteins, exhibit anti-inflammatory activity, and suppress the immune response.

Zona reticularis cells secrete weak **androgens** that promote masculine characteristics.

B. Medulla

Parenchymal cells of the **medulla** are derived from neural crest material. They consist of two populations of **chromaffin cells** that secrete mainly **epinephrine** (adrenaline) or **norepinephrine** (noradrenaline). Secretion of these two catecholamines is directly regulated by preganglionic fibers of the sympathetic nervous system that impinge on the postganglionic sympathetic neuron-like chromaffin cells. Catecholamine release occurs in physical and psychological stress. Moreover, scattered **sympathetic ganglion cells** in the medulla act on smooth muscle cells of the medullary veins, thus controlling blood flow in the cortex.

V. PINEAL BODY (PINEAL GLAND; EPIPHYSIS)

Pinealocytes, parenchymal cells of the **pineal body**, synthesize melatonin during the night. However, it is unclear how the gland functions in humans but it does exert an affect on the control of the circadiam rhythm. Nonetheless, melatonin is used to treat jet lag and in regulating emotional responses related to shortened daylight during winter, a condition called seasonal affective disorder (SAD).

CLINICAL CONSIDERATIONS

Pituitary Gland

Galactorrhea is a condition in which a male produces breast milk or a woman who is not breast feeding produces breast milk. In men it is often accompanied by impotence, headache, and loss of peripheral vision and in women by hot flashes, vaginal dryness, and an abnormal menstrual cycle. This rather uncommon condition is usually a result of prolactinoma, a tumor of prolactin-producing cells of the pituitary gland. The condition is usually treated by drug intervention or surgery, or both.

Postpartum Pituitary Infarct is a condition due the the pregnancy-induced enlargening of the pituitary gland and its concommitant increase in its vascularity. The high vascularity of the pituitary increases the chances of a vascular accident, such as hemorrhage, which results in the partial destruction of the pituatary gland. The condition may be severe enough to produce Sheehan's syndrome, which is recognized by the lack of milk production, the loss of pubic and axillary hair, and fatigue.

Thyroid Gland

Graves' disease is caused by binding of autoimmune IgG antibodies to TSH receptors thus stimulating increased thyroid hormone production (**hyperthyroidism**). Clinically, the thyroid gland becomes enlarged and there is evidence of exophthalmic goiter (protrusion of the eyeballs).

Parathyroid Gland

Hyperparathyroidism may be due to the presence of a benign tumor causing the excess production of parathyroid hormone. The high levels of circulating PTH cause increased bone resorption with a resultant greatly elevated blood calcium. The excess calcium may become deposited in arterial walls and in the kidneys, creating kidney stones.

Suprarenal Gland

Addison's disease is an autoimmune disease, although it may also be the aftermath of tuberculosis. It is characterized by decreased production of adrenocortical hormones due to the destruction of the suprarenal cortex and without the administration of steroid treatment it may have fatal consequences.

Type 2 polyglandular syndrome, a heridetary disorder, affects the thyroid and suprarenal glands in such a fashion that they are underactive (although the thyroid may become overactive). Frequently, patients with this disorder also develop diabetes.

FIGURE 1 • Pituitary gland. Paraffin section. ×19.

This survey photomicrograph of the pituitary gland demonstrates the relationship of the gland to the **hypothalamus** (H), from which it is suspended by the infundibulum. The infundibulum is composed of a neural portion, the **infundibular stem** (IS) and the surrounding **pars tuberalis** (PT). Note that the **third ventricle** (3V) of the brain is continuous with the **infundibular recess** (IR). The largest portion of the pituitary is the **pars anterior** (PA), which is glandular and secretes numerous hormones. The neural component of the pituitary gland is the **pars nervosa** (PN), which does not manufacture its hormones but stores and releases them. Even at this magnification, its resemblance to the brain tissue and to the substance of the infundibular stalk is readily evident. Between the pars anterior and pars nervosa is the **pars intermedia** (PI), which frequently presents an **intraglandular cleft** (IC), a remnant of Rathke's pouch.

FIGURE 2 • Pituitary gland. Pars anterior. Paraffin section. ×132.

The pars anterior is composed of large cords of cells that branch and anastomose with each other. These cords are surrounded by an extensive capillary network. However, these capillaries are wide, Yendothelially lined vessels known as **sinusoids** (S). The parenchymal cells of the anterior pituitary are divided into two groups: **chromophils** (Ci) and **chromophobes** (Co). With hematoxylin and eosin the distinction between chromophils and chromophobes is obvious. The former stain blue or pink, whereas the latter stain poorly. The *boxed area* is presented at a higher magnification in Figure 3.

FIGURE 3 • Pituitary gland. Pars anterior. Paraffin section. ×270.

This is a higher magnification of the *boxed area* of Figure 2. Note that the **chromophobes** (Co) do not take up the stain well and only their **nuclei** (N) are demonstrable. These cells are small; therefore, chromophobes are easily recognizable since their nuclei appear to be clumped together. The chromophils may be classified into two categories by their affinity to histologic dyes: blue-staining **basophils** (B) and pink-colored **acidophils** (A). The distinction between these two cell types in sections stained with hematoxylin and eosin is not as apparent as with some other stains. Note also the presence of a large **sinusoid** (S).

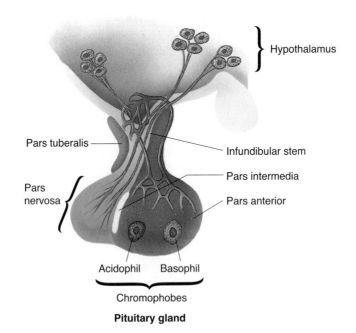

Pars tuberalis
Pars nervosa
Hypothalamus
Infundibular stem
Pars intermedia
Pars anterior
Acidophil   Basophil
Chromophobes
Pituitary gland

KEY					
A	acidophils	IC	intraglandular cleft	PI	pars intermedia
B	basophils	IR	infundibular recess	PN	pars nervosa
Ci	chromophils	IS	infundibular stem	PT	pars tuberalis
Co	chromophobes	N	nucleus	S	sinusoids
H	hypothalamus	PA	pars anterior	3V	third ventricle

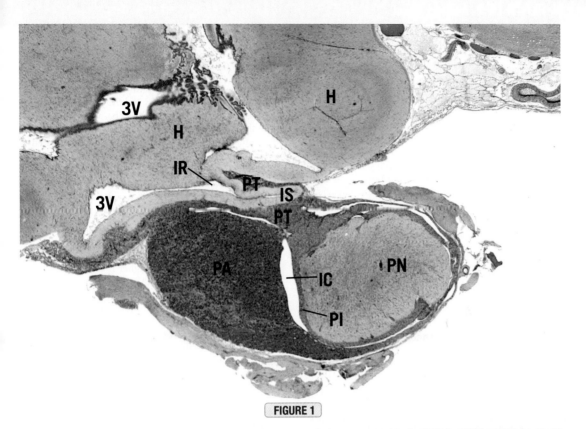

FIGURE 1

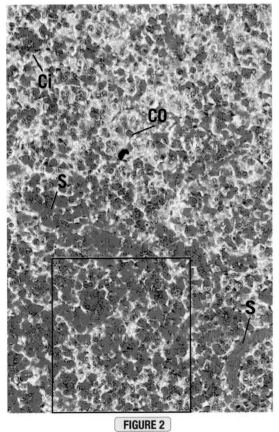

FIGURE 2

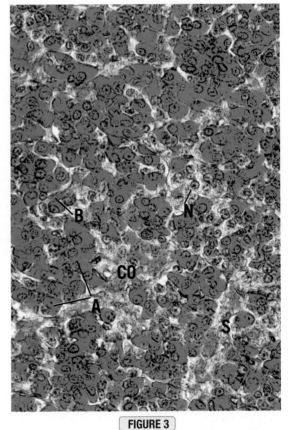

FIGURE 3

FIGURE 1 • Pituitary gland. Paraffin section. ×540.

It is somewhat difficult to discriminate between the **aci-dophils** (A) and **basophils** (B) of the pituitary gland stained with hematoxylin and eosin. Even at high magnification, such as in this photomicrograph, only slight differences are noted. Acidophils stain pinkish and are slightly smaller in size than the basophils, which stain pale blue. In a black and white photomicrograph, basophils appear darker than aci-dophils. **Chromophobes** (Co) are readily recognizable, since their cytoplasm is small and does not take up stain. Moreover, cords of chromophobes present clusters of **nuclei** (N) crowded together.

FIGURE 3 • Pituitary gland. Pars nervosa. Paraffin section. ×132.

The pars nervosa of the pituitary gland is composed of elongated cells with long processes known as **pituicytes** (P), which are thought to be neuroglial in nature. These cells, which possess more or less oval nuclei, appear to support numerous unmyelinated nerve fibers traveling from the hypothalamus via the hypothalamo-hypophy-seal tract. These nerve fibers cannot be distinguished from the cytoplasm of pituicytes in a hematoxylin and eo-sin–stained preparation. Neurosecretory materials pass along these nerve fibers and are stored in expanded re-gions at the termination of the fibers, which are then referred to as **Herring bodies** (HB). Note that the pars nervosa resembles neural tissue. The *boxed area* is pre-sented at a higher magnification in Figure 4.

FIGURE 2 • Pituitary gland. Pars intermedia. Human. Paraffin section. ×270.

The pars intermedia of the pituitary gland is situated be-tween the **pars anterior** (PA) and the **pars nervosa** (PN). It is characterized by **basophils** (B), which are smaller than those of the pars anterior. Additionally, the pars in-termedia contains **colloid** (Cl)-filled follicles, lined by pale, small, low cuboidal shaped cells (*arrows*). Note that some of the basophils extend into the pars nervosa. Nu-merous **blood vessels** (BV) and **pituicytes** (P) are evident in this area of the pars nervosa.

FIGURE 4 • Pituitary gland. Pars nervosa. Paraffin section. ×540.

This photomicrograph is a higher magnification of the *boxed area* of Figure 3. Note the numerous more or less oval **nuclei** (N) of the pituicytes, some of whose processes (*arrows*) are clearly evident at this magnification. The un-myelinated nerve fibers and processes of pituicytes make up the cellular network of the pars nervosa. The expanded terminal regions of the nerve fibers, which house neurose-cretions, are known as **Herring bodies** (HB). Also observe the presence of **blood vessels** (BV) in the pars nervosa.

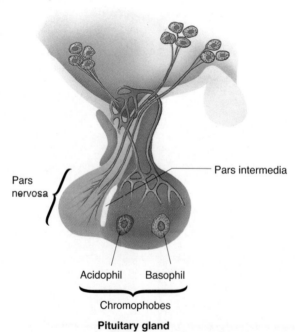

Pars nervosa

Pars intermedia

Acidophil   Basophil

Chromophobes

Pituitary gland

KEY					
A	acidophils	Co	chromophobes	P	pituicytes
B	basophils	HB	Herring bodies	PA	pars anterior
BV	blood vessels	N	nucleus	PN	pars nervosa
Cl	colloid				

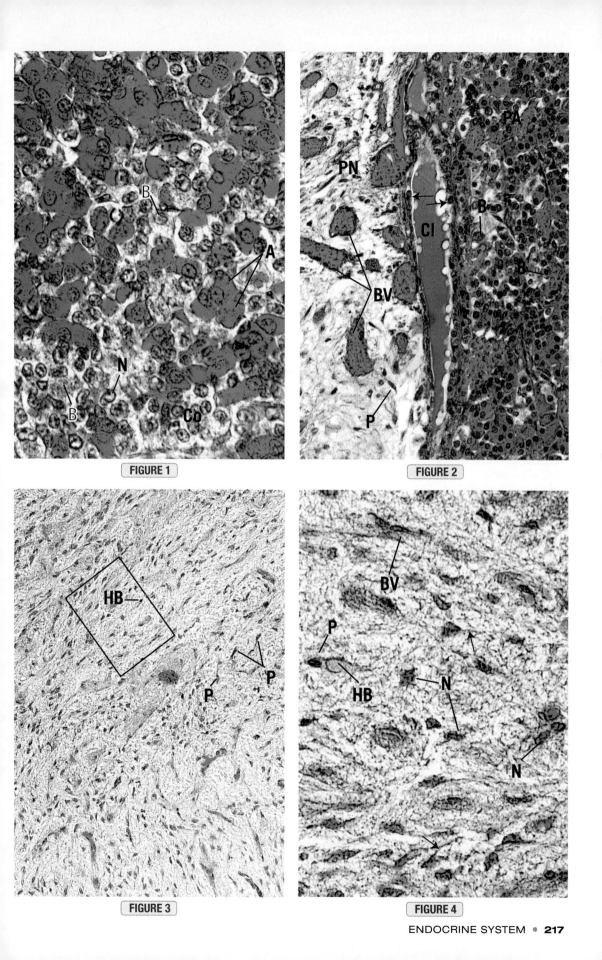

FIGURE 1

FIGURE 2

FIGURE 3

FIGURE 4

FIGURE 1 • Thyroid gland. Monkey. Plastic section. ×132.

The capsule of the thyroid gland sends septa of connective tissue into the substance of the gland, subdividing it into incomplete lobules. This photomicrograph presents part of a lobule displaying many **follicles** (F) of varied sizes. Each follicle is surrounded by slender **connective tissue** (CT), which supports the follicles and brings **blood vessels** (BV) in close approximation. The follicles are composed of **follicular cells** (FC), whose low cuboidal morphology indicates that the cells are not producing secretory product. During the active secretory cycle, these cells become taller in morphology. In addition to the follicular cells, another parenchymal cell type is found in the thyroid gland. These cells do not border the colloid, are located on the periphery of the follicles, and are known as **parafollicular cells** (PF) or C cells. They are large and possess centrally placed round nuclei, and their cytoplasm appears paler.

FIGURE 3 • Thyroid and parathyroid glands. Monkey. Plastic section. ×132.

Although the **parathyroid** (PG) and **thyroid glands** (TG) are separated by their respective **capsules** (Ca), they are extremely close to each other. The capsule of the parathyroid gland sends **trabeculae** (T) of connective tissue carrying **blood vessels** (BV) into the substance of the gland. The parenchyma of the gland consists of two types of cells, namely, **chief cells** (CC), also known as principal cells, and **oxyphil cells** (OC). Chief cells are more numerous and possess darker staining cytoplasm. Oxyphil cells stain lighter and are usually larger than chief cells, and their cell membranes are evident. A region similar to the *boxed area* is presented at a higher magnification in Figure 4.

FIGURE 2 • Thyroid gland. Monkey. Plastic section. ×540.

The thyroid **follicle** (F) presented in this photomicrograph is surrounded by several other follicles and intervening **connective tissue** (CT). **Nuclei** (N) in the connective tissue may belong either to endothelial cells or to connective tissue cells. Since most capillaries are collapsed in excised thyroid tissue, it is often difficult to identify endothelial cells with any degree of certainty. The **follicular cells** (FC) are flattened, indicating that these cells are not actively secreting thyroglobulin. Note that the follicles are filled with a **colloid** (Cl) material. Observe the presence of a **parafollicular cell** (PF), which may be distinguished from the surrounding cells by its pale cytoplasm (*arrow*) and larger nucleus.

FIGURE 4 • Parathyroid gland. Monkey. Plastic section. ×540.

This photomicrograph is a region similar to the *boxed area* of Figure 3. The **chief cells** (CC) of the parathyroid gland form small cords surrounded by slender **connective tissue** (CT) elements and **blood vessels** (BV). The **nuclei** (N) of connective tissue cells may be easily recognized due to their elongated appearance. **Oxyphil cells** (OC) possess a paler cytoplasm and frequently the cell membranes are evident (*arrows*). The glands of older individuals may become infiltrated by adipocytes.

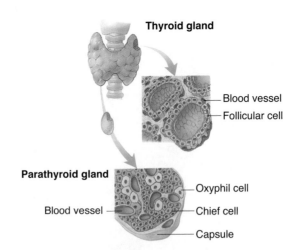

Thyroid gland

Blood vessel
Follicular cell

Parathyroid gland

Blood vessel

Oxyphil cell
Chief cell
Capsule

KEY					
BV	blood vessels	F	follicle	PG	parathyroid gland
Ca	capsule	FC	follicular cells	T	trabeculae
CC	chief cells	N	nucleus	TG	thyroid gland
Cl	colloid	OC	oxyphil cells		
CT	connective tissue	PF	parafollicular cells		

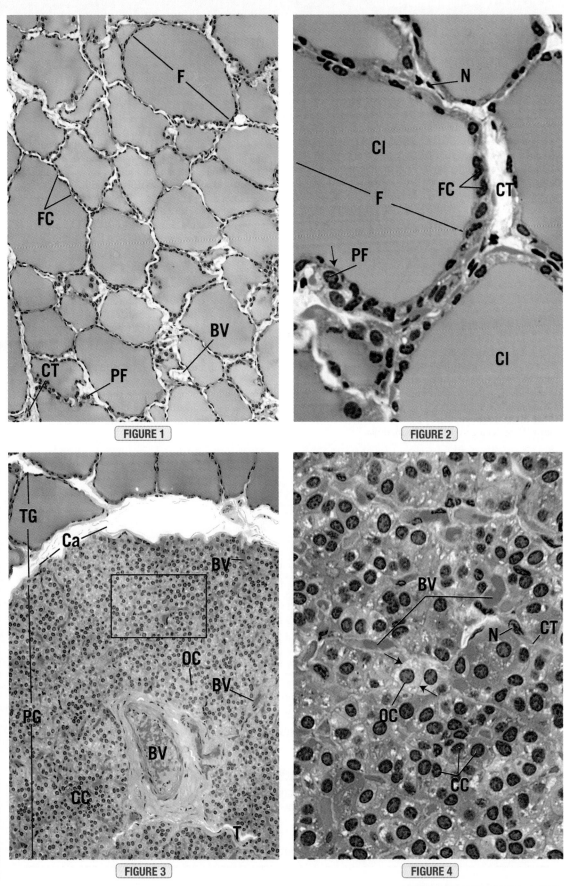

FIGURE 1

FIGURE 2

FIGURE 3

FIGURE 4

ENDOCRINE SYSTEM • **219**

FIGURE 1 • Suprarenal gland. Paraffin section. ×14.

The suprarenal gland, usually embedded in **adipose tissue** (AT), is invested by a collagenous connective tissue **capsule** (Ca) that provides thin connective tissue elements that carry blood vessels and nerves into the substance of the gland. Since the **cortex** (Co) of the suprarenal gland completely surrounds the flattened **medulla** (M), it appears duplicated in any section that completely transects the gland. The cortex is divided into three concentric regions: the outermost **zona glomerulosa** (ZG), middle **zona fasciculata** (ZF), and the innermost **zona reticularis** (ZR). The medulla, which is always bounded by the zona reticularis, possesses several large **veins** (V), which are always accompanied by a considerable amount of connective tissue.

FIGURE 3 • Suprarenal gland. Monkey. Plastic section. ×132.

The columnar arrangement of the cords of the **zona fasciculata** (ZF) is readily evident by viewing the architecture of the blood vessels indicated by the *arrows*. The cells in the deeper region of the zona fasciculata are smaller and appear denser than the more superficially located **spongiocytes** (Sp). Cells of the **zona reticularis** (ZR) are arranged in irregular, anastomosing cords whose interstices contain wide capillaries. The cords of the zona reticularis merge almost imperceptibly with those of the zona fasciculata. This is a relatively narrow region of the cortex. The **medulla** (M) is clearly evident since its cells are much larger than those of the zona reticularis. Moreover, numerous large **veins** (V) are characteristic of the medulla.

FIGURE 2 • Suprarenal gland. Cortex. Monkey. Plastic section. ×132.

The collagenous connective tissue **capsule** (Ca) of the suprarenal gland is surrounded by adipose tissue through which **blood vessels** (BV) and **nerves** (Ne) reach the gland. The parenchymal cells of the cortex, immediately deep to the capsule, are arranged in an irregular array, forming the more or less oval to round clusters or arch-like cords of the **zona glomerulosa** (ZG). The cells of the **zona fasciculata** (ZF) form long, straight columns of cords oriented radially, each being one to two cells in width. These cells are larger than those of the zona glomerulosa. They present a vacuolated appearance due to the numerous lipid droplets that were extracted during processing and are often referred to as **spongiocytes** (Sp). The interstitium is richly vascularized by **blood vessels** (BV).

FIGURE 4 • Suprarenal gland. Monkey. Plastic section. ×540.

The **capsule** (Ca) of the suprarenal gland displays its **collagen fibers** (Cf) and the **nuclei** (N) of the fibroblasts. The **zona glomerulosa** (ZG), which occupies the upper part of the photomicrograph, displays relatively small cells with few vacuoles (*arrows*). The lower part of the photomicrograph demonstrates the **zona fasciculata** (ZF), whose cells are larger and display a more vacuolated (*arrowheads*) appearance. Note the presence of **connective tissue** (CT) elements and **blood vessels** (BV) in the interstitium between cords of parenchymal cells.

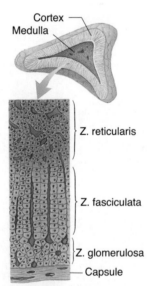

Cortex
Medulla

Z. reticularis

Z. fasciculata

Z. glomerulosa

Capsule

Suprarenal gland

KEY					
AT	adipose tissue	CT	connective tissue	V	veins
BV	blood vessels	M	medulla	ZF	zona fasciculata
Ca	capsule	N	nuclei	ZG	zona glomerulosaP
Cf	collagen fibers	Ne	nerves	ZR	zona reticularis
Co	cortex	Sp	spongiocytes		

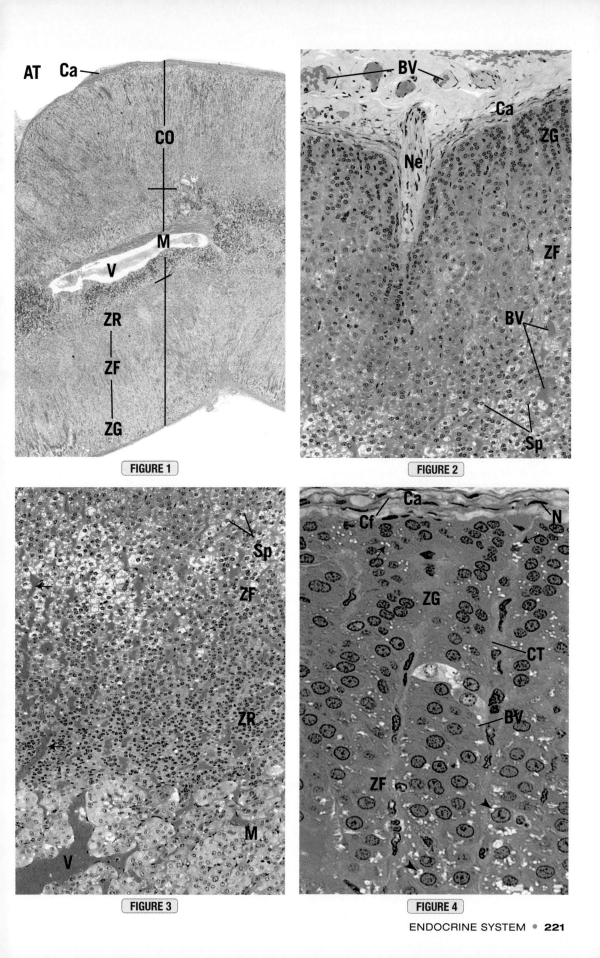

AT Ca

CO

M

V

ZR

ZF

ZG

FIGURE 1

BV

Ca

ZG

Ne

ZF

BV

Sp

FIGURE 2

Sp

ZF

ZR

M

V

FIGURE 3

Ca

Cf

N

ZG

CT

BV

ZF

FIGURE 4

FIGURE 1 • Suprarenal gland. Cortex. Monkey. Plastic section. ×540.

The upper part of this photomicrograph presents the border between the **zona fasciculata** (ZF) and the **zona reticularis** (ZR). Note that the **spongiocytes** (Sp) of the fasciculata are larger and more vacuolated than the cells of the reticularis. The parenchymal cells of the zona reticularis are arranged in haphazardly anastomosing cords. The interstitium of both regions house large capillaries containing **red blood cells** (RBC). *Inset.* **Zona fasciculata. Monkey. Plastic section.** × 540. The **spongiocytes** (Sp) of the zona fasciculata are of two different sizes. Those positioned more superficially in the cortex, as in this inset, are larger and more vacuolated (*arrows*) than spongiocytes close to the zona reticularis.

FIGURE 3 • Pineal body. Human. Paraffin section. ×132.

The pineal body is covered by a capsule of connective tissue derived from the pia mater. From this capsule, connective tissue **trabeculae** (T) enter the substance of the pineal body, subdividing it into numerous incomplete **lobules** (Lo). Nerves and **blood vessels** (BV) travel in the trabeculae to be distributed throughout the pineal, providing it with a rich vascular supply. In addition to endothelial and connective tissue cells, two other types of cells are present in the pineal, namely, the parenchymal cells, known as **pinealocytes** (Pi), and **neuroglial supporting cells** (Ng). A characteristic feature of the pineal body is the deposit of calcified material known as corpora arenacea or **brain sand** (BS). The *boxed area* is presented at a higher magnification in Figure 4.

FIGURE 2 • Suprarenal gland. Medulla. Monkey. Plastic section. ×270.

The cells of the adrenal medulla, often referred to as **chromaffin cells** (ChC), are arranged in round to ovoid clusters or in irregularly arranged short cords. The cells are large and more or less round to polyhedral in shape with a pale **cytoplasm** (Cy) and vesicular appearing **nucleus** (N), displaying a single, large **nucleolus** (n). The interstitium presents large **veins** (V) and an extensive **capillary** (Cp) network. Large ganglion cells are occasionally noted.

FIGURE 4 • Pineal body. Human. Paraffin section. ×540.

This photomicrograph is a higher magnification of the *boxed area* of Figure 3. With the use of hematoxylin and eosin stain, only the nuclei of the two cell types are clearly evident. The larger, paler, more numerous nuclei belong to the **pinealocytes** (Pi). The smaller, denser nuclei are those of the **neuroglial cells** (Ng). The pale background is composed of the long, intertwining processes of these two cell types. The center of the photomicrograph is occupied by **brain sand** (BS). Observe that these concretions increase in size by apposition of layers on the surface of the calcified material, as may be noted at the *arrow.*

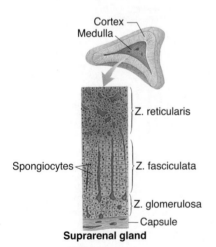

Cortex
Medulla

Z. reticularis

Spongiocytes

Z. fasciculata

Z. glomerulosa

Capsule

Suprarenal gland

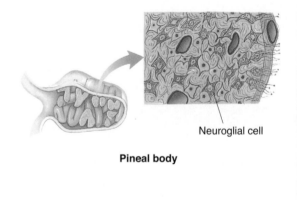

Neuroglial cell

Pineal body

KEY						
BS	brain sand	N	nucleus	T	trabeculate
BV	blood vessels	n	nucleolus	V	veins
ChC	chromaffin cells	Ng	neuroglial cells	ZF	zona fasciculata
Cp	capillaries	Pi	pinealocytes	ZR	zona reticularis
Cy	cytoplasm	RBC	red blood cells		
Lo	lobules	Sp	spongiocytes		

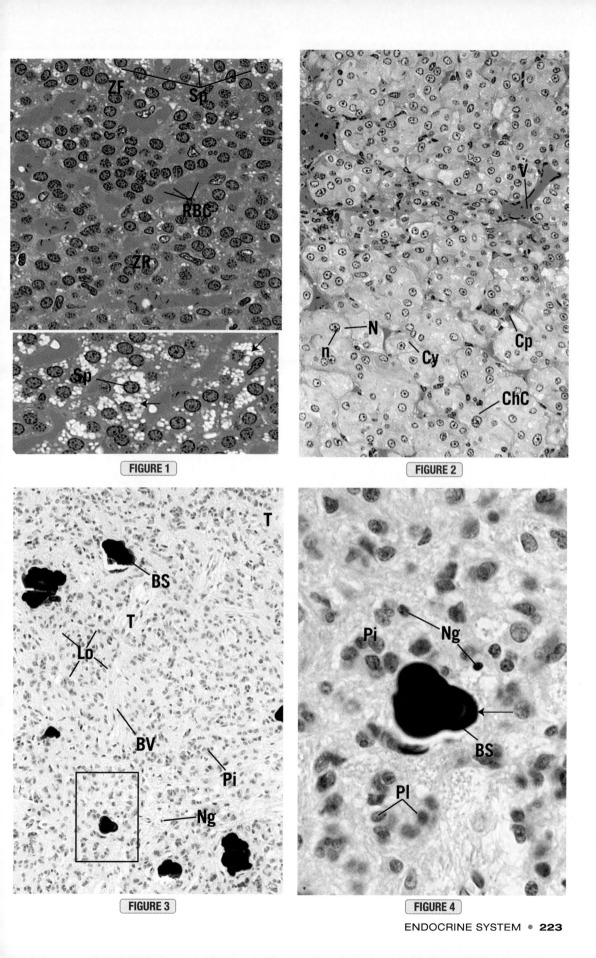

FIGURE 1

FIGURE 2

FIGURE 3

FIGURE 4

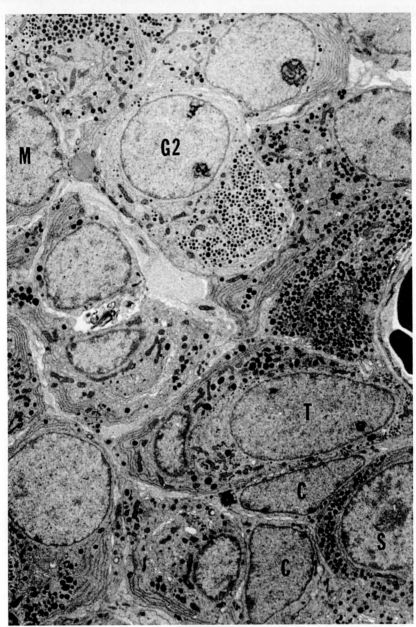

FIGURE 1

FIGURE 1 ● Pituitary gland. Pars anterior. Electron microscopy. ×4,950.

Although considerable controversy surrounds the precise fine structural identification of the cells of the pars anterior, it is reasonably certain that the several cell types presented in this electron micrograph are acidophils, basophils, and chromophobes, as observed by light microscopy. The acidophils are **somatotropes** (S) and **mammotropes** (M), whereas only two types of basophils are included in this electron micrograph, namely, **type II gonadotropes** (G2) and **thyrotropes** (T). The **chromophobes** (C) may be recognized by the absence of secretory granules in their cytoplasm. (From Poole M. Cellular distribution within the rat adenhypophysis: a morphometric study. Anat Rec 1982;204:45–53.)

PLATE 10-7 Pituitary Gland, Electron Microscopy

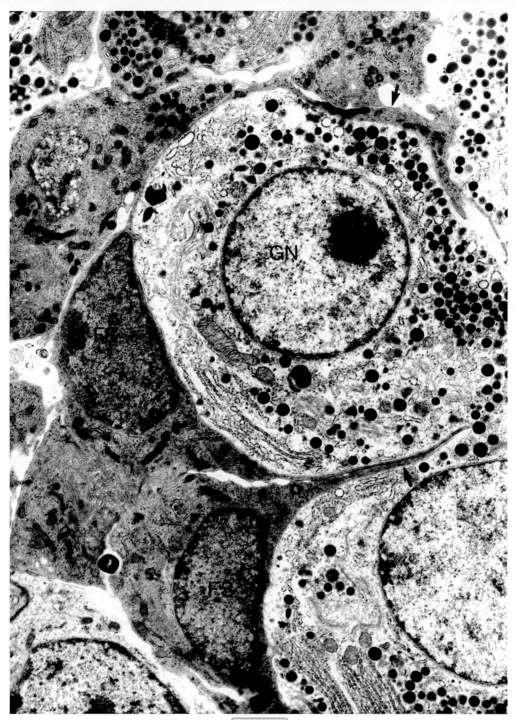

FIGURE 1

FIGURE 1 • Pituitary gland. Rat. Electron microscopy. ×8,936.

The pars distalis of the rat pituitary houses various cell types, two of which are represented here. The granule-containing **gonadotrophs** (GN) are surrounded by nongranular **folliculostellate cells** (FS), whose processes are demarcated by *arrows*. The functions of folliculostellate cells are in question, although some believe them to be supportive, phagocytic, regenerative, or secretory in nature. (From Strokreef JC, Reifel CW, Shin SH. A possible phagocytic role for folliculo-stellate cells of anterior pituitary following estrogen withdrawal from primed male rats. Cell Tissue Res 1986;243:255–261.)

Summary of Histological Organization

Endocrine glands are characterized by the absence of ducts and the presence of a rich vascular network. The parenchymal cells of endocrine glands are usually arranged in short **cords**, **follicles**, or **clusters**, although other arrangements are also common.

I. PITUITARY GLAND

The **pituitary gland** is invested by a **connective tissue capsule**. The gland is subdivided into four component parts.

A. Pars Anterior

1. Cell Types

a. Chromophils
  1. Acidophils

  Stain pink with hematoxylin and eosin. They are found mostly in the center of the pars anterior.
  2. Basophils

  Stain darker than acidophils with hematoxylin and eosin. They are more frequently found at the periphery of the pars anterior.

b. Chromophobes
  Chromophobes are smaller cells whose cytoplasm is not granular and has very little affinity for stain. They may be recognized as clusters of nuclei throughout the pars anterior.

B. Pars Intermedia

The **pars intermedia** is rudimentary in man. Small basophils are present, as well as **colloid**-filled **follicles**.

C. Pars Nervosa and Infundibular Stalk

These have the appearance of nervous tissue. The cells of the **pars nervosa** are **pituicytes**, resembling neuroglial cells. They probably support the **unmyelinated nerve fibers**, whose terminal portions are expanded, since they store **neurosecretions** within the pars nervosa. These expanded terminal regions are known as **Herring bodies**.

D. Pars Tuberalis

The **pars tuberalis** is composed of **cuboidal cells** arranged in cords. They may form small colloid-filled **follicles**.

II. THYROID GLAND

A. Capsule

The **capsule** of the thyroid gland consists of a thin **collagenous connective tissue** from which **septa** extend into the substance of the gland, subdividing it into lobules.

B. Parenchymal Cells

The **parenchymal cells** of the thyroid gland form **colloid**-filled **follicles** composed of
1. Follicular Cells (simple cuboidal epithelium)
2. Parafollicular Cells (clear cells) located at the periphery of the follicles

C. Connective Tissue

Slender connective tissue elements support a rich vascular supply.

III. PARATHYROID GLAND

A. Capsule

The gland is invested by a slender collagenous connective tissue **capsule** from which **septa** arise to penetrate the substance of the gland.

B. Parenchymal Cells

1. Chief Cells
Chief cells are numerous, small cells with large nuclei that form cords.

2. Oxyphils
Oxyphils are larger, acidophilic, and much fewer in number than chief cells.

C. Connective Tissue

Collagenous connective tissue **septa** as well as slender **reticular fibers** support a rich vascular supply. **Fatty infiltration** is common in older individuals.

IV. SUPRARENAL GLAND

The **suprarenal gland** is invested by a collagenous connective tissue **capsule**. The gland is subdivided into a **cortex** and a **medulla**.

A. Cortex

The **cortex** is divided into three concentric zones: **zona glomerulosa**, **zona fasciculata**, and **zona reticularis**.

1. Zona Glomerulosa
The **zona glomerulosa** is immediately deep to the capsule. It consists of columnar cells arranged in arches and spherical clusters.

2. Zona Fasciculata
The thickest zone of the cortex is the **zona fasciculata**. The more or less cuboidal cells (**spongiocytes**) are arranged in long, parallel cords. **Spongiocytes** appear highly vacuolated except for those of the deepest region, which are smaller and much less vacuolated.

3. Zona Reticularis
The innermost zone of the cortex is the **zona reticularis**. It is composed of small, dark cells arranged in irregularly anastomosing cords. The intervening capillaries are enlarged.

B. Medulla
The **medulla** is small in humans and is composed of large, granule-containing **chromaffin cells** arranged in short cords. Additionally, large autonomic ganglion cells are also present. A characteristic of the medulla is the presence of large veins.

V. PINEAL BODY

A. Capsule
The **capsule**, derived from **pia mater**, is thin collagenous connective tissue. **Septa** derived from the capsule divide the pineal body into incomplete lobules.

B. Parenchymal Cells

1. Pinealocytes
Pinealocytes are recognized by the large size of their nuclei.

2. Neuroglial Cells
Neuroglial cells possess smaller, denser nuclei than the pinealocytes.

C. Brain Sand
Characteristic of the pineal body are the calcified accretions in the intercellular spaces, known as **brain sand** or **corpora arenacea**.

Integument

11

The integument, the largest and heaviest organ of the body, is composed of skin and its various derivatives, including sebaceous glands, sweat glands, hair, and nails. The skin covers the entire body and is continuous with the mucous membranes at the lips, at the anus, in the nose, at the leading edges of the eyelids, and at the external orifices of the urogenital system. Some of the many functions of skin include protection against physical, chemical, and biologic assaults; providing a waterproof barrier; absorbing ultraviolet radiation for both vitamin D synthesis and protection; excretion (i.e., sweat) and thermoregulation; monitoring the external milieu via its various nerve endings; and immunologic defense of the body.

● SKIN

Skin is composed of a superficial **stratified squamous keratinized epithelium** known as the **epidermis** and of a deeper connective tissue layer, the **dermis** (see Graphic 11-1). The epidermis and dermis interdigitate with each other by the formation of **epidermal ridges** and **dermal ridges** (**dermal papillae**), where the two are separated by a basement membrane. Frequently a dermal ridge is subdivided into two secondary dermal ridges with an intervening interpapillary peg from the epidermis. The ridges on the fingertips that imprint as fingerprints are evidence of this interdigitation. Interposed between skin and deeper structures is a fascial sheath known as the hypodermis, which is not a part of skin. Skin can be **thick**, as on the sole of the foot and the palm of the hand, or **thin,** as over the remainder of the body. Thick skin has five well-developed layers, whereas in thin skin the stratum granulosum and stratum lucidum are absent as well-defined layers. However, individual cells of the two absent layers are present even in thin skin.

Epidermis

Depending on the thickness of the keratin layer, skin is classified as thick or thin. The **epidermis** of thick skin is described first, since it is composed of all five layers rather than just three or four present in thin skin. The deepest layer, the **stratum basale** (stratum germinativum), is a single layer of cuboidal to columnar cells. These cells are responsible for cell renewal, via mitosis (usually at night), and are pushed surfaceward, giving rise to the thickest layer, the **stratum spinosum**. This layer is quite a few cells thick and is composed of polyhedral **prickle cells** characterized by numerous processes (intercellular bridges) that form desmosomes with processes of surrounding prickle cells. Cells of the stratum spinosum also display mitotic activity (usually at night). These prickle cells also form **membrane-coating granules** (**Odland bodies, lamellar bodies**), whose lipid-rich contents are composed of ceramides, phospholipids, and glycosphingolipids. The stratum granulosum and the stratum spinosum are frequently referred to as the **stratum Malpighii,** and their continued mitotic activity is responsible for the continuous migration of these cells into the next layer, known as the **stratum granulosum**. Cells of this layer accumulate **keratohyalin granules**, which eventually overfill the cells, destroying their nuclei and organelles. The fourth layer, the **stratum lucidum**, is relatively thin and not always evident. Present only in palmar and plantar skin, it usually appears as a thin, translucent region, interposed between the strata granulosum and the corneum. The cells of the stratum lucidum have no nuclei or organelles but contain tonofibrils (densely packed keratin filaments) and contain eleidin, a transformation product of keratohyalin. The surface-most layer is the **stratum corneum**, composed of preferentially arranged stacks of dead hulls known as **squames**. The superficial layers of the stratum corneum are desquamated at the same rate as they are being replaced by the mitotic activity of the strata basale and spinosum.

The epidermis is composed of four cell types: keratinocytes (described above), melanocytes, Langerhans cells, and Merkel cells. **Keratinocytes**, responsible for the production of **keratin**, are the most populous of epidermal cells and are derived from ectoderm. **Melanocytes**, derived from neural crest cells, are responsible for the manufacture of

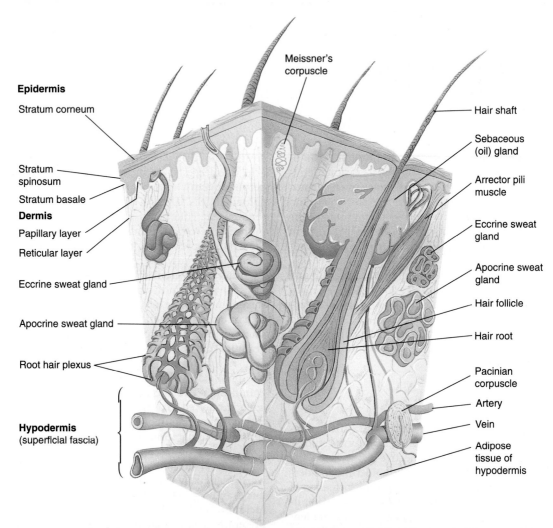

Epidermis

Stratum corneum

Stratum spinosum

Stratum basale

Dermis

Papillary layer

Reticular layer

Eccrine sweat gland

Apocrine sweat gland

Root hair plexus

Hypodermis
(superficial fascia)

Meissner's corpuscle

Hair shaft

Sebaceous (oil) gland

Arrector pili muscle

Eccrine sweat gland

Apocrine sweat gland

Hair follicle

Hair root

Pacinian corpuscle

Artery

Vein

Adipose tissue of hypodermis

Skin and its appendages, **hair**, **sweat glands** (both **eccrine** and **apocrine**), **sebaceous glands**, and **nails**, are known as the **integument**. Skin may be **thick** or **thin**, depending on the thickness of its epidermis. Thick skin epidermis is composed of five distinct layers of **keratinocytes** (strata basale, spinosum, granulosum, lucidum, and corneum) interspersed with three additional cell types, **melanocytes**, **Merkel's cells**, and **Langerhans' cells**. Thin skin epidermis lacks strata granulosum and lucidum, although individual cells that constitute the absent layers are present.

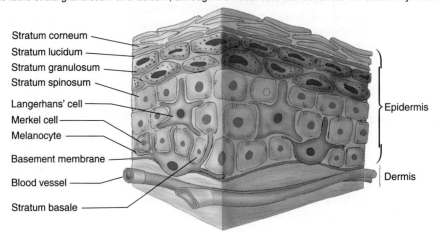

Stratum corneum

Stratum lucidum

Stratum granulosum

Stratum spinosum

Langerhans' cell

Merkel cell

Melanocyte

Basement membrane

Blood vessel

Stratum basale

Epidermis

Dermis

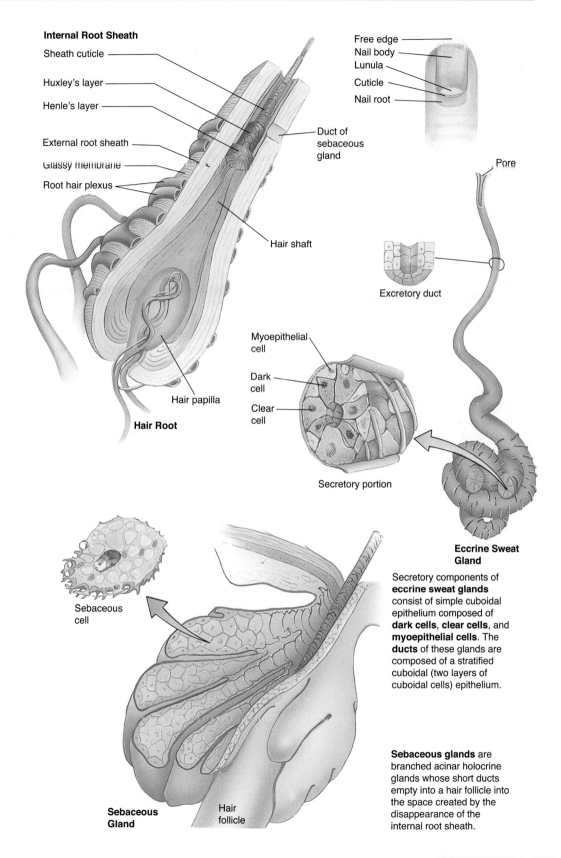

Internal Root Sheath

Sheath cuticle

Huxley's layer

Henle's layer

External root sheath

Glassy membrane

Root hair plexus

Duct of sebaceous gland

Hair shaft

Hair papilla

Hair Root

Free edge

Nail body

Lunula

Cuticle

Nail root

Pore

Excretory duct

Myoepithelial cell

Dark cell

Clear cell

Secretory portion

Eccrine Sweat Gland

Secretory components of **eccrine sweat glands** consist of simple cuboidal epithelium composed of **dark cells**, **clear cells**, and **myoepithelial cells**. The **ducts** of these glands are composed of a stratified cuboidal (two layers of cuboidal cells) epithelium.

Sebaceous cell

Sebaceous glands are branched acinar holocrine glands whose short ducts empty into a hair follicle into the space created by the disappearance of the internal root sheath.

Sebaceous Gland

Hair follicle

melanin, which is synthesized in specialized organelles called **melanosomes**. These melanocytes, the second most populous cell type, are interspersed among the keratinocytes of the stratum basale and are also present in hair follicles and the dermis. They possess long, thin, cytoplasmic processes that extend into the intercellular spaces between cells of the stratum spinosum. **Langerhans cells** (dendritic cells), derived from bone marrow and located mostly in the stratum spinosum, function as antigen-presenting cells in immune responses. **Merkel cells**, whose origin is uncertain, are interspersed among the cells of the stratum basale and are most abundant in the fingertips. Afferent nerve terminals approximate these cells, forming complexes that are believed to function as **mechanoreceptors** (touch receptors). There is some evidence that Merkel cells may also have a neurosecretory function.

Thin skin differs from thick skin in that it has only three or four strata. Stratum lucidum is always absent in thin skin, whereas strata corneum, granulosum, and spinosum are greatly reduced in size. Frequently, only an incomplete layer of stratum granulosum is present.

Dermis

The **dermis** of the skin, lying directly deep to the epidermis, is derived from mesoderm. It is composed of **dense**, **irregular collagenous connective tissue** containing mostly type I collagen and numerous elastic fibers that assist in securing the skin to the underlying **hypodermis**. The dermis is subdivided into a loosely woven **papillary layer** (composed of primary and secondary dermal ridges), a superficial region that interdigitates with the epidermal ridges (and interpapillary pegs) of the epidermis, and a deeper, coarser, and denser **reticular layer**. The interface between the papillary and reticular layers is indistinct. **Dermal ridges** (as well as secondary dermal ridges) display encapsulated nerve endings, such as **Meissner's corpuscles**, as well as capillary loops that bring nourishment to the avascular epidermis.

● DERIVATIVES OF SKIN

Derivatives of skin include hair, sebaceous glands, sweat glands, and nails (see Graphic 11-2). These structures originate from epidermal downgrowths into the dermis and hypodermis, while maintaining their connection to the outside. Each **hair**, composed of a shaft of cornified cells and a root contained within a hair follicle, is associated with a **sebaceous gland** that secretes an oily **sebum** into the neck of the hair follicle. A small bundle of smooth muscle cells, the **arrector pili muscle**, attaches to the hair follicle and, cradling the sebaceous gland, inserts into the superficial aspects of the skin.

Sweat glands do not develop in association with hair follicles. These are simple, coiled, tubular glands whose secretory units produce sweat, which is delivered to the surface of the skin by long ducts. **Myoepithelial cells** surround the secretory portion of these glands.

Nails are cornified structures on the distal phalanx of each finger or toe. These horny plates lie on a nail bed and are bounded laterally by a nail wall. The **cuticle** (**eponychium**) lies over the **lunula**, an opaque, crescent-shaped area of the nail plate. The **hyponychium** is located beneath the free edge of the nail plate.

● Histophysiology

I. KERATINOCYTES AND KERATIN FORMATION

In the superficial layers of the stratum spinosum and in the stratum granulosum, the cells accumulate a histidine-rich protein, **keratohyalin granules**, in which the ends of intermediate filaments are embedded. In the stratum lucidum, the cellular organelles are no longer evident, the keratohyalin granules have lost their identity, and they are now referred to as **eleidin**, a combination of filamentous material embedded in a dense matrix. Cells of the stratum corneum are filled with **keratin**, a scleroprotein composed of 10-nm-thick filaments rich in lysine residues as well as the keratohyalin-associated filaments, **fillagrin** and **trichohyalin**; these two proteins, rich in histidine and cystine, function in the binding of keratohyalin filaments into thicker bundles of **tonofibrils**. Additionally, the cytoplasmic aspects of the cell membranes of the keratinocytes of strata granulosum, lucidum, and corneum are reinforced by **involucrin**, a fibrous protein that forms a cross-linked mat whose individual components are 12 nm in diameter, as well as by the glycine-rich, 25-kD protein **loricrin**. Cells of the strata spinosum and granulosum house membrane-coating granules whose contents, a lipid-rich substance, are released into the extracellular spaces, forming a barrier that is impermeable to aqueous fluids. Moreover, lysosomal enzymes released into the cytosol of cells of the strata granulosum and lucidum digest the cell's organelles, and, by the time the keratinocytes reach the stratum corneum, they are non-living, keratin-filled husks. Keratin of skin is "soft" keratin, whereas keratin of nails is "hard" keratin because that of the nails has many more disulfide bonds.

Recent investigations indicate that keratinocytes produce immunogenic molecules and are probably active in the immune process. Evidence also shows that these cells are capable of producing several interleukins, colony-stimulating factors, interferons, tumor necrosis factors, as well as platelet- and fibroblast-stimulating growth factors.

II. MELANIN FORMATION

Melanin is synthesized by **melanocytes**, cells derived from neural crest cells. Although these cells are located in the stratum basale, they possess long processes that extend into the stratum spinosum. There are two types of melanin, **eumelanin**, a dark brown to black pigment composed of polymers of **hydroxyindole**, and **pheomelanin**, a red to rust-colored compound composed of **cysteinyl dopa** polymers. The former is present in individuals with dark hair and the latter is found in individuals with red and blond hair.

Both types of melanin are derived from the amino acid **tyrosine**, which is transported into specialized **tyrosinase**-containing vesicles derived from the *trans*-Golgi network, known as melanosomes. Within these oval (1.0 by 0.5 μm) melanosomes, tyrosinase converts tyrosine into 3,4-dihydroxyphenylalanine, which is transformed into dopaquinone and, eventually, into melanin.

Melanosomes pass to the tips of the melanocyte processes, which are engulfed and **endocytosed** by keratinocytes of the stratum spinosum. The freed melanosomes migrate to the nucleus of the keratinocyte and form a protective umbrella, shielding the nucleus (and its chromosomes) from the ultraviolet rays of the sun. Soon thereafter, **lysosomes** attack and destroy the melanosomes.

Ultraviolet rays not only increase the rates of darkening of melanin and endocytosis of the tips of melanocytic processes but also enhance tyrosinase activity and thus, melanin production.

Fewer melanocytes are located on the insides of the thighs and undersides of the arms and face. However, skin pigmentation is related to the location of melanin rather than to the numbers of melanocytes. Melanosomes are fewer and congregate around the keratinocyte nucleus in Caucasians, whereas in blacks they are larger and are more dispersed throughout the keratinocyte cytoplasm.

Itching (Pruritis)

The sensation of itching is accompanied by an instinctive, almost irrepressible urge to scratch. There are many different causes of itching, some as simple as a fly walking on one's skin and moving the hair follicles, or as serious as debilitating systemic conditions such as kidney failure or liver disease. If the itching is accompanied by a rash, then the probable cause is not the kidney or the liver. Parasitic infestations (mites, scabies, etc.), insect bites, plant toxins (such as poison oak and poison ivy), and drug allergies are usually accompanied by a rash and require medical intervention. If the itching is long term, the patient should seek the assistance of a physician. Pregnancy and cold, dry weather may also be contributing factors to itching.

Psoriasis

Psoriasis is a condition characterized by patchy lesions on the skin, especially around joints and the scalp. This condition is produced by increased proliferation of keratinocytes and an acceleration of the cell cycle, resulting in an accumulation of cells in the stratum corneum. The condition is cyclic and is of unknown etiology.

Erythema multiforme

Patches of elevated red skin, frequently resembling a target, displaying a symmetrical distribution over the face and extremities, that occurs periodically, indicate the disorder erythema multiforme. It is most frequently due to herpes simplex infection. The condition is not usually accompanied by itching, although painful lesions (blisters) on the lips and buccal cavity are common occurrences. Usually the condition resolves itself, but in more severe cases, medical intervention is indicated.

Warts

Warts are benign epidermal growths on the skin caused by papilloma viral infection of the keratinocytes. Warts are common in young children, in young adults, and in immunosuppressed patients.

Vitiligo

A condition in which the skin has paches of white areas due to the lack of pigmentation is known as vitiligo. The melanocytes of the affected region are destroyed in an autoimmune response. The condition may appear suddenly after a physical injury or as a consequence of sunburn. If the area affected has hair, as the hair grows it will be white. Although there are no physical consequences to vitiligo, there may be psychological sequalae.

Malignancies of Skin

The three most common malignancies of skin are basal cell carcinoma, squamous cell carcinoma, and malignant melanoma.

Basal cell carcinoma, the most common human malignancy, develops in the stratum basale from damage caused by ultraviolet radiation. The most frequent site of basal cell carcinoma is on the nose, occurring as papules or nodules, which eventually craters. Surgery is usually 90% effective with no recurrence.

Squamous cell carcinoma, the second most frequent skin malignancy, is invasive and metastatic. Its probable etiology is environmental factors, such as ultraviolet radiation and x-irradiation, as well as a variety of chemical carcinogens, including arsenic. The carcinoma originates in cells of the stratum spinosum and appears clinically as a hyperkeratotic, scaly plaque with deep invasion of underlying tissues, often accompanied by bleeding. Surgery is the treatment of choice.

Malignant melanoma may be a life-threatening malignancy. It develops in the melanocytes that become mitotically active and invade the dermis, eventually entering the lymphatic and circulatory system to metastasize to other organ systems. The treatment of choice is a combination of surgery and chemotherapy.

FIGURE 1 • Thick skin. Paraffin section. ×132.

Skin is composed of the superficial **epidermis** (E) and the deeper **dermis** (D). The interface of the two tissues is demarcated by **epidermal ridges** (ER) and **dermal ridges** (DR) (dermal papillae). Between successive epidermal ridges are the interpapillary pegs, which divide each dermal ridge into secondary dermal ridges. Note that in thick skin the keratinized layer, **stratum corneum** (SC), is highly developed. Observe also that the **duct** (d) of the sweat gland pierces the base of an epidermal ridge. The dermis of skin is subdivided into two regions, a **papillary layer** (PL), composed of the looser, collagenous connective tissue of the dermal ridges, and the deeper, denser, collagenous connective tissue of the **reticular layer** (RL). **Blood vessels** (BV) from the reticular layer enter the dermal ridges.

FIGURE 3 • Thick skin. Monkey. Plastic section. ×540.

This is a higher magnification of a region similar to the *boxed area* in the previous figure. The **papillary layer** (PL) of the dermis displays **nuclei** (N) of the various connective tissue cells, as well as the interface between the dermis and the **stratum basale** (SB). Observe that these cells are cuboidal to columnar in shape, and interspersed among them are occasional clear cells, probably inactive **melanocytes** (M), although it should be stressed that Merkel cells also appear as clear cells. Cells of the **stratum spinosum** (SS) are polyhedral in shape, possessing numerous intercellular bridges, which interdigitate with those of other cells, accounting for their spiny appearance.

FIGURE 2 • Thick skin. Monkey. Plastic section. ×132.

This photomicrograph of thick skin presents a view similar to that in Figure 1. However, the layers of the **epidermis** (E) are much easier to delineate in this plastic section. Observe that the squames of the **stratum corneum** (SC) appear to lie directly on the **stratum granulosum** (SG), whose cells contain keratohyalin granules. The thickest layer of lining cells in the epidermis is the **stratum spinosum** (SS), whereas the **stratum basale** (SB) is only a single cell layer thick. The stratum lucidum is not evident, although a few transitional cells (*arrows*) may be identified. Note that the **secondary dermal ridges** (SDR), on either side of the **interpapillary peg** (IP), present **capillary loops** (CL). Regions similar to the *boxed areas* are presented in Figures 3 and 4 at higher magnification.

FIGURE 4 • Thick skin. Monkey. Plastic section. ×540.

This is a higher magnification of a region similar to the *boxed area* of Figure 2. Observe that as the cells of the **stratum spinosum** (SS) are being pushed surfaceward, they become somewhat flattened. As the cells reach the **stratum granulosum** (SG) they accumulate keratohyalin granules (*arrows*), which increase in number as the cells progress through this layer. Occasional transitional cells (*arrowheads*) of the poorly defined stratum lucidum may be observed, as well as the **squames** (S) of the **stratum corneum** (SC). *Inset.* **Thick skin. Paraffin section.** × 132. This photomicrograph displays the **stratum lucidum** (SL) to advantage. Note that this layer is between the **stratum granulosum** (SG) and **stratum corneum** (SC). Observe the **duct** (d) of a sweat gland.

KEY					
BV	blood vessel	IP	interpapillary peg	SG	stratum granulosum
CL	capillary loop	M	melanocytes	SB	stratum basale
D	dermis	N	nucleus	SS	stratum spinosum
d	duct	PL	papillary layer	S	squames
DR	dermal ridges	RL	reticular layer	SL	stratum lucidum
E	epidermis	SC	stratum corneum		
ER	epidermal ridges	SDR	secondary dermal ridges		

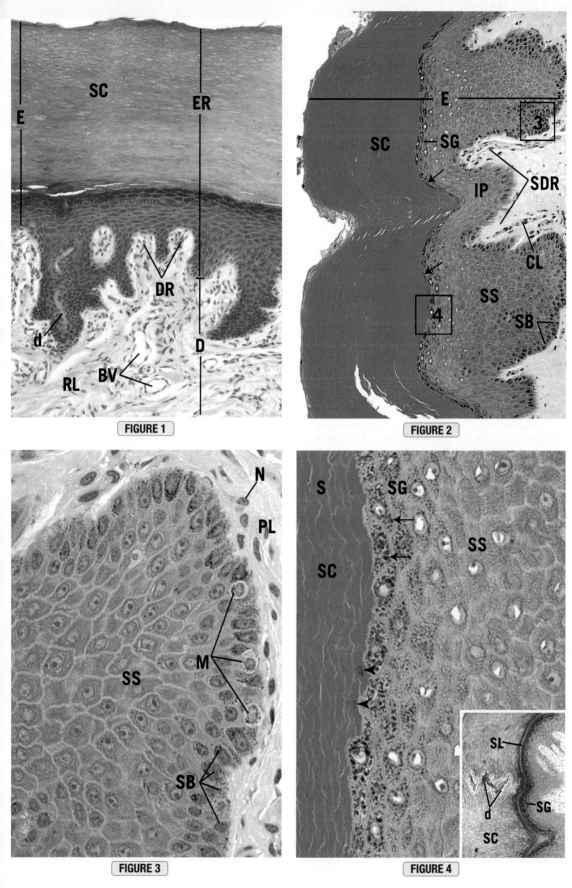

FIGURE 1

FIGURE 2

FIGURE 3

FIGURE 4

FIGURE 1 • Thin skin. Human. Paraffin section. ×19.

Thin skin is composed of a very slender layer of **epidermis** (E) and the underlying **dermis** (D). Although thick skin has no hair follicles and sebaceous glands associated with it, most thin skin is richly endowed with both. Observe the **hair** (H) and the **hair follicles** (HF), whose expanded **bulb** (B) presents the connective tissue **papilla** (P). Much of the follicle is embedded beneath the skin in the superficial fascia, the fatty connective tissue layer known as the **hypodermis** (hD), which is not a part of the integument. **Sebaceous glands** (sG) secrete their sebum into short **ducts** (d), which empty into the lumen of the hair follicle. Smooth muscle bundles, **arrector pili muscle** (AP), cradle these glands, in passing from the hair follicle to the papillary layer of the dermis. **Sweat glands** (swG) are also present in the reticular layer of the dermis. A region similar to the *boxed area* is presented at a higher magnification in Figure 2.

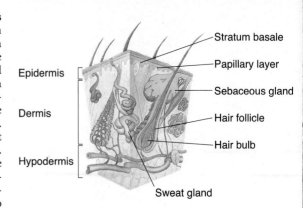

FIGURE 2 • Thin skin. Human. Paraffin section. ×132.

This is a higher magnification of a region similar to the *boxed area* of the previous figure. Observe that the **epidermis** (E) is much thinner than that of thick skin and that the **stratum corneum** (SC) is significantly reduced. The epidermal ridges and **interpapillary pegs** (IP) are well represented in this photomicrograph. Note that the **papillary layer** (PL) of the dermis is composed of much finer bundles of **collagen fibers** (CF) than those of the dense irregular collagenous connective tissue of the **reticular layer** (RL). The dermis is quite vascular, as evidenced by the large number of **blood vessels** (BV) whose cross-sectional profiles are readily observed. The numerous **nuclei** (N) of the various connective tissue cells attest to the cellularity of the dermis. Note also the presence of the **arrector pili muscle** (AP), whose contraction elevates the hair and is responsible for the appearance of "goose bumps." The *boxed area* is presented at a higher magnification in the following figure.

FIGURE 3 • Thin skin. Human. Paraffin section. ×270.

This photomicrograph is a higher magnification of the *boxed area* of Figure 2. Epidermis of thin skin possesses only three of four of the layers found in thick skin. The **stratum basale** (SB) is present as a single layer of cuboidal to columnar cells. Most of the epidermis is composed of the prickle cells of the **stratum spinosum** (SS), whereas stratum granulosum and stratum lucidum are not represented as complete layers. However, individual cells of stratum granulosum (*arrow*) and stratum lucidum are scattered at the interface of the stratum spinosum and **stratum corneum** (SC). The papillary layer of the **dermis** (D) is richly vascularized by **capillary loops** (CL), which penetrate the **secondary dermal ridges** (sDR). Observe that the **collagen fiber** (CF) bundles of the dermis become coarser as the distance from the epidermis increases.

KEY							
AP	arrector pili muscle		H	hair		SC	stratum corneum
B	bulb		hD	hypodermis		sDR	secondary dermal ridges
BV	blood vessels		HF	hair follicles		sG	sebaceous glands
CF	collagen fibers		IP	interpapillary peg		SB	stratum basale
CL	capillary loops		N	nuclei		SS	stratum spinosum
D	dermis		P	papilla		swG	sweat glands
d	ducts		PL	papillary layer			
E	epidermis		RL	reticular layer			

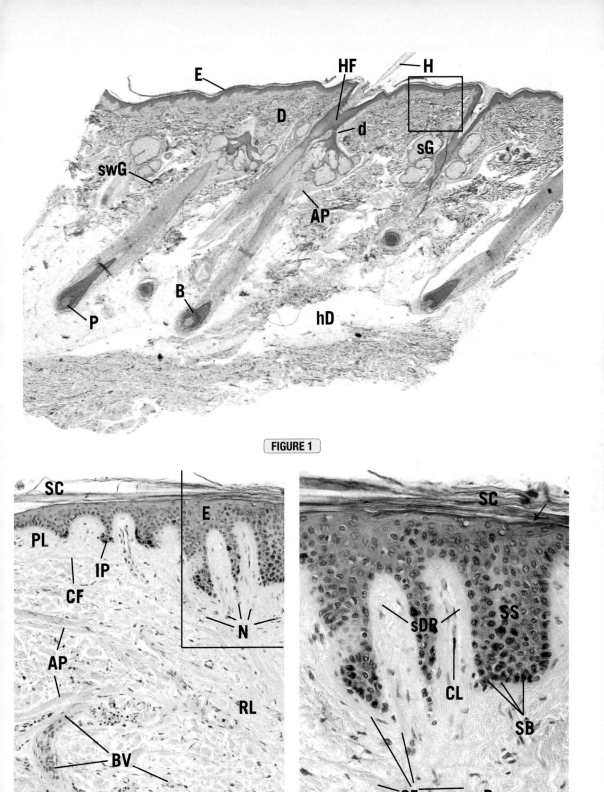

FIGURE 1

FIGURE 2

FIGURE 3

PLATE 11-3 Hair Follicles and Associated Structures, Sweat Glands

FIGURE 1 • Hair follicle. l.s. Human. Paraffin section. ×132.

The terminal expansion of the hair follicle, known as the bulb, is composed of a connective tissue, **papilla** (P), enveloped by epithelially derived cells of the **hair root** (HR). The mitotic activity responsible for the growth of hair occurs in the matrix, from which several concentric sheaths of epithelial cells emerge to be surrounded by a **connective tissue sheath** (CTS). Color of hair is due to the intracellular pigment that accounts for the dark appearance of some cells (*arrow*).

FIGURE 3 • Sebaceous gland. Human. Paraffin section. ×132.

Sebaceous glands (sG) are branched, acinar holocrine glands, which produce an oily sebum. The secretion of these glands is delivered into the lumen of a **hair follicle** (HF), with which sebaceous glands are associated. **Basal cells** (BC), located at the periphery of the gland, undergo mitotic activity to replenish the dead cells, which, in holocrine glands, become the secretory product. Note that as these cells accumulate sebum in their cytoplasm, they degenerate, as evidenced by the gradual pyknosis of their **nuclei** (N). Observe the **arrector pili muscle** (AP), which cradles the sebaceous glands.

FIGURE 2 • Hair follicle. x.s. Human. Paraffin section. ×132.

Many of the layers comprising the growing hair follicle may be observed in these cross-sections. The entire structure is surrounded by a **connective tissue sheath** (CTS), which is separated from the epithelially derived components by a specialized basement membrane, the **inner glassy membrane** (BM). The clear polyhedral cells compose the **external root sheath** (ERS), which surrounds the **internal root sheath** (IRS), whose cells become keratinized. At the neck of the hair follicle, where the ducts of the sebaceous glands enter, the internal root sheath disintegrates, providing a lumen into which sebum and apocrine sweat are discharged. The **cuticle** (Cu) and **cortex** (Co) constitute the highly keratinized components of the hair, whereas the medulla is not visible at this magnification. Note the presence of **arrector pili muscle** (AP).

FIGURE 4 • Sweat gland. Monkey. Plastic section. ×132.

The simple, coiled, tubular eccrine gland is divided into two compartments: a **secretory** portion (s) and a **duct** (d). The secretory portion of the gland consists of a simple cuboidal epithelium, composed of dark and clear secretory cells (which cannot be distinguished from each other unless special procedures are utilized). Intercellular canaliculi are noted between clear cells, which are smaller than the **lumen** (L) of the gland. **Ducts** (d) may be recognized readily since they are darker staining and composed of stratified cuboidal epithelium. *Insets a and b.* **Duct and secretory unit. Monkey. Plastic section.** × 540. The duct is readily evident, since its **lumen** (L) is surrounded by two layers of cuboidal cells. **Secretory cells** (s) of the eccrine sweat gland are surrounded by darker staining **myoepithelial cells** (My). Hair root, eccrine sweat gland, and sebaceous gland.

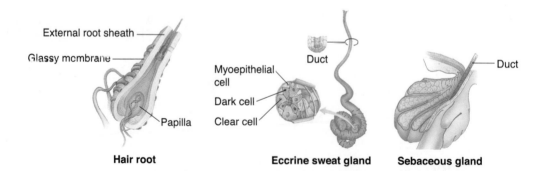

External root sheath

Glassy membrane

Papilla

Hair root

Myoepithelial cell

Dark cell

Clear cell

Duct

Eccrine sweat gland

Duct

Sebaceous gland

KEY							
AP	arrector pili muscle	d	ducts	My	myoepithelial cells
BC	basal cells	ERS	external root sheath	N	nucleus
BM	inner glassy membrane	HF	hair follicle	P	papilla
Co	cortex	HR	hair root	s	secretory
CTS	connective tissue sheath	IRS	internal root sheath	sG	sebaceous glands
Cu	cuticle	L	lumen		

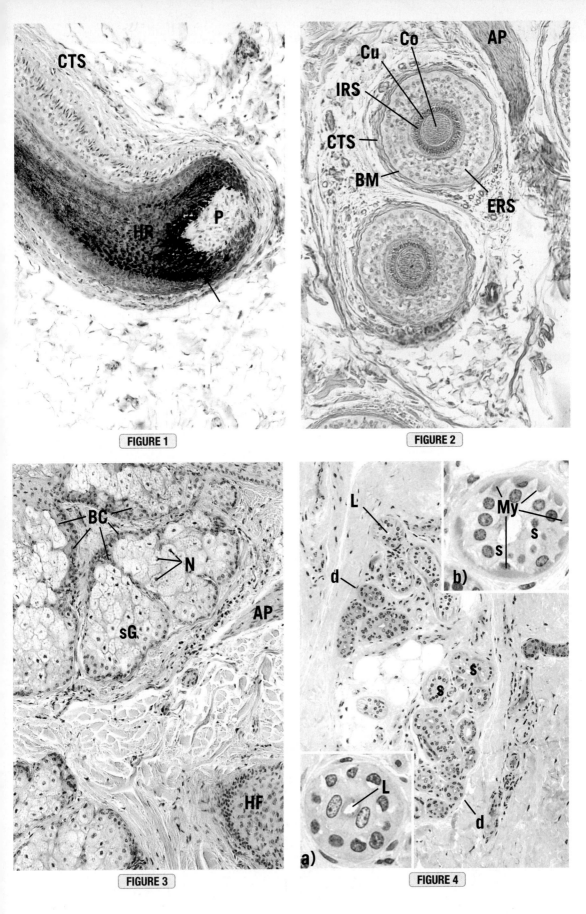

FIGURE 1

FIGURE 2

FIGURE 3

FIGURE 4

FIGURE 1 • Fingernail. l.s. Paraffin section. ×14.

The nail is a highly keratinized structure that is located on the dorsal surface of the **distal phalanx** (Ph) of each finger and toe. The horny **nail plate** (NP) extends deep into the dermis, forming the **nail root** (NR). The epidermis of the distal phalanx forms a continuous fold, resulting in the **eponychium** (Ep), or cuticle, the **nail bed** (NB) underlying the nail plate, and the **hyponychium** (Hy). The epithelium (*arrow*) surrounding the nail root is responsible for the continuous elongation of the nail. The **dermis** (D) between the nail bed and the **bone** (Bo) of the distal phalanx is tightly secured to the **fibrous periosteum** (FP). Note that this is a developing finger, as evidenced by the presence of **hyaline cartilage** (HC) and endochondral osteogenesis (*arrowheads*).

FIGURE 3 • Meissner's corpuscle. Paraffin section. ×540.

Meissner's corpuscles are oval, encapsulated mechanoreceptors lying in dermal ridges just deep to the **stratum basale** (SB). They are especially prominent in the genital areas, lips, fingertips, and soles of the feet. A connective tissue **capsule** (Ca) envelops the corpuscle. The **nuclei** (N) within the corpuscle belong to flattened (probably modified) Schwann cells, which are arranged horizontally in this structure. The afferent **nerve fiber** (NF) pierces the base of Meissner's corpuscle, branches, and follows a tortuous course within the corpuscle.

FIGURE 2 • Fingernail. x.s. Paraffin section. ×14.

The **nail plate** (NP) in cross-section presents a convex appearance. On either side it is bordered by a **nail wall** (NW), and the groove it occupies is referred to as the lateral **nail groove** (NG). The **nail bed** (NB) is analogous to four layers of the epidermis, whereas the nail plate represents the stratum corneum. The **dermis** (D), deep to the nail bed, is firmly attached to the **fibrous periosteum** (FP) of the **bone** (Bo) of the terminal phalanx. Observe that the fingertip is covered by thick skin whose **stratum corneum** (SC) is extremely well developed. The small, darkly staining structures in the dermis are **sweat glands** (swG).

FIGURE 4 • Pacinian corpuscle. Paraffin section. ×132.

Pacinian corpuscles, located in the dermis and hypodermis, are mechanoreceptors. They are composed of a **core** with an **inner** (IC) and an **outer** (OC) region, as well as a **capsule** (Ca) that surrounds the core. The inner core invests the afferent **nerve fiber** (NF), which loses its myelin sheath soon after entering the corpuscle. The core cells are modified Schwann cells, whereas the components of the capsule are continuous with the endoneurium of the afferent nerve fiber. Pacinian corpuscles are readily recognizable in section since they resemble the cut surface of an onion. Observe the presence of an **arrector pili muscle** (AP) and profiles of **ducts** (d) of a sweat gland in the vicinity of, but not associated with, the pacinian corpuscle.

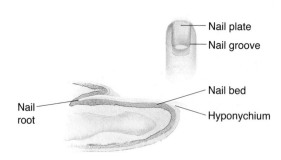

Fingernail

KEY						
AP	arrector pili	Hy	hyponychium	NW	nail wall
Ca	capsule	IC	inner core	OC	outer core
Bo	bone	N	nuclei	Ph	distal phalanx
D	dermis	NB	nail bed	SC	stratum corneum
d	duct	NF	nerve fiber	SB	stratum basale
Ep	eponychium	NG	nail groove	swG	sweat glands
FP	fibrous periosteum	NP	nail plate		
HC	hyaline cartilage	NR	nail root		

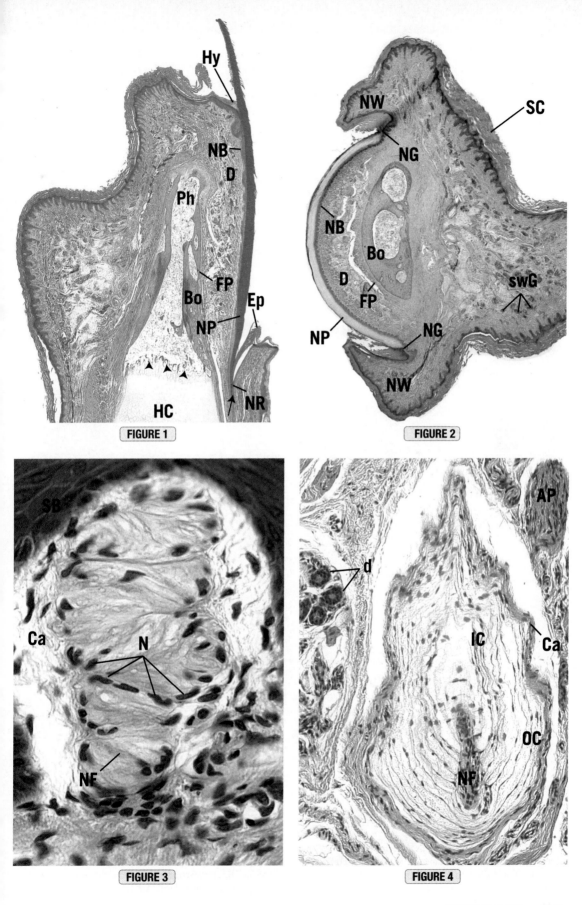

FIGURE 1

FIGURE 2

FIGURE 3

FIGURE 4

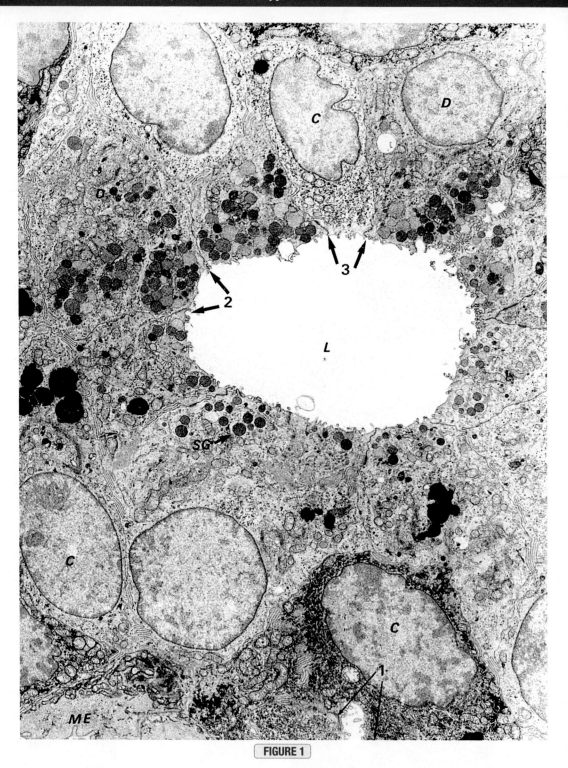

FIGURE 1

FIGURE 1 • Sweat gland. x.s. Human. Electron microscopy. ×5,040.

Tight junctions (*arrows*) occur at three locations in the secretory coil of human sweat glands: (1) between **clear cells** (C) separating the lumen of the intercellular canaliculus (*arrowhead*) and the basolateral intercellular space; (2) between two **dark cells** (D) separating the main lumen and the lateral intercellular space; and (3) between a clear cell and a dark cell, separating the main lumen (L) and intercellular space. Note the presence of **secretory granules** (SG) and **myoepithelial cell** (ME). (From Briggman JV, Bank HL, Bigelow JB, et al. Structure of the tight junctions of the human eccrine sweat gland. Am J Anat 1981;162:357–368.)

Summary of Histological Organization

I. SKIN

A. Epidermis

The **epidermis** constitutes the superficial, epithelially derived region of skin. It is composed of four cell types: **keratinocytes, melanocytes, Langerhans cells,** and **Merkel cells.** The keratinocytes are arranged in five layers, and the remaining three cell types are interspersed among them. The five layers of the epidermis are

1. Stratum Basale
A single layer of cuboidal to columnar cells that stand on the **basement membrane.** This is a region of cell division. It also contains **melanocytes** and **Merkel cells.**

2. Stratum Spinosum
Composed of many layers of polyhedral **prickle cells** bearing **intercellular bridges.** Mitotic activity is also present. It also contains **Langerhans cells** and processes of **melanocytes.**

3. Stratum Granulosum
Cells that are somewhat flattened and contain **keratohyalin granules.** It is absent as a distinct layer in thin skin.

4. Stratum Lucidum
A thin, translucent layer whose cells contain **eleidin.** It is also absent in thin skin.

5. Stratum Corneum
Composed of **squames** packed with **keratin.** Superficial squames are desquamated.

B. Dermis

The **dermis** is a **dense, irregular, collagenous connective tissue** subdivided into two layers: papillary and reticular.

1. Papillary Layer
The **dermal ridges** (dermal papillae) and **secondary dermal ridges** interdigitate with the **epidermal ridges** (and **interpapillary pegs**) of the epidermis. **Collagen fibers** are slender in comparison with those of deeper layers of the dermis. Dermal ridges house **capillary loops** and **Meissner's corpuscles.**

2. Reticular Layer
The **reticular layer** of skin is composed of coarse bundles of collagen fibers. It supports a **vascular plexus** and interdigitates with the underlying **hypodermis.** Frequently, it houses **hair follicles, sebaceous glands,** and **sweat glands. Krause's end bulbs** and **pacinian corpuscles** may also be present.

II. APPENDAGES

A. Hair

Hair is an **epidermal** downgrowth embedded into dermis or hypodermis. It has a free **shaft** surrounded by several layers of cylindrical sheaths of cells. The terminal end of the hair follicle is expanded as the **hair bulb,** composed of connective tissue **papilla** and the **hair root.** The concentric layers of the follicle are

1. Connective Tissue Sheath

2. Glassy Membrane
A modified basement membrane.

3. External Root Sheath
Composed of a few layers of polyhedral cells and a single layer of columnar cells.

4. Internal Root Sheath
Composed of three layers: **Henle's layer, Huxley's layer,** and the **cuticle.** The internal root sheath stops at the neck of the follicle, where sebaceous gland ducts open into the hair follicle, forming a **lumen** into which the sebum is delivered.

5. Cuticle of the Hair
Composed of highly keratinized cells that overlap each other.

6. Cortex
The bulk of the hair, composed of highly keratinized cells.

7. Medulla
A thin core of the hair whose cells contain soft keratin.

B. Sebaceous Glands

Sebaceous glands are in the forms of **saccules** associated with hair follicles. They are **branched alveolar holocrine glands** that produce an oily **sebum.** Secretions are delivered into the neck of the hair follicle via short, wide **ducts. Basal cells** are regenerative cells of sebaceous glands, located at the periphery of the **saccule.**

C. Arrector Pili Muscle

Arrector pili muscles are bundles of smooth muscle cells extending from the **hair follicle** to the **papillary layer** of the dermis. They cradle the **sebaceous gland**. Contractions of these muscle fibers elevate the hair, forming "goose bumps," release heat, and assist in the delivery of sebum from the gland into its duct.

D. Sweat Glands

1. Sweat Glands

Simple, coiled, tubular glands whose **secretory portion** is composed of a simple cuboidal epithelium. **Dark cells** and **light cells** are present with **intercellular canaliculi** between cells. **Myoepithelial cells** surround the secretory portion.

2. Ducts

Composed of a stratified cuboidal (two-cell-thick) epithelium. Cells of the duct are darker and smaller than those of the secretory portions. Ducts pierce the base of the epidermal ridges to deliver sweat to the outside.

E. Nail

The horny **nail plate** sits on the **nail bed**. It is bordered laterally by the **nail wall**, the base of which forms the **lateral nail groove**. The **eponychium** (cuticle) is above the nail plate. The **hyponychium** is located below the free end of the nail plate. The posterior aspect of the nail plate is the **nail root**, which lies above the **matrix**, the area responsible for the growth of the nail.

Respiratory System

12

The respiratory system functions in exchanging carbon dioxide for oxygen, which is then distributed to all of the tissues of the body. To accomplish this function, air must be brought to that portion of the respiratory system where exchange of gases can occur. The respiratory system, therefore, has a **conducting portion** and a **respiratory portion**. Some of the larger conduits of the conducting portion are extrapulmonary, whereas its smaller components are intrapulmonary. The respiratory portions, however, are completely intrapulmonary. The luminal diameters of the various conduits can be modified by the presence of smooth muscle cells along their length (Table 12-1).

● CONDUCTING PORTION OF THE RESPIRATORY SYSTEM

The extrapulmonary region of the conducting portion consists of the nasal cavities, pharynx, larynx, trachea, and bronchi. The intrapulmonary region entails the intrapulmonary bronchi, bronchioles, and terminal bronchioles (see Graphic 12-1).

Extrapulmonary Region

The mucosa of the extrapulmonary region of the conducting portion modifies the inspired air by humidifying, cleansing, and adjusting its temperature. This **mucosa** is composed of **pseudostratified ciliated columnar epithelium** (respiratory epithelium) with numerous **goblet cells** and an underlying connective tissue sheath that is well endowed with **seromucous glands**. Modulation of the temperature of the inspired air is accomplished mostly in the nasal cavity by the rich vascularity of the connective tissue just deep to its respiratory epithelium. In certain areas, the mucosa of the nasal cavity is modified to function in olfaction and is referred to as the **olfactory mucosa**. The glands in the lamina propria of this region produce a thin mucous secretion that dissolves odoriferous substances, and the **olfactory cells** of the pseudostratified columnar olfactory epithelium perceive these sensory stimuli. In addition to the olfactory cells, two other cell types compose the olfactory epithelium, namely, supporting cells and basal cells.

Supporting cells do not possess any sensory function, but they manufacture a yellowish-brown pigment that is responsible for the coloration of the olfactory mucosa; additionally, they insulate and support the olfactory cells. **Basal cells** are small, dark cells that lie on the basement membrane and probably are regenerative in function. Axons of the olfactory cells are collected into small nerve bundles that pass through the cribriform plate of the ethmoid bone as the first cranial nerve, the olfactory nerve. Thus, it should be noted that the cell bodies of the olfactory nerve (cranial nerve I) are located in a rather vulnerable place, in the surface epithelium lining the nasal cavity.

The conducting portion of the respiratory system is supported by a skeleton composed of bone and/or cartilage that assists in the maintenance of a patent lumen, whose diameters are controlled by smooth muscle cells located in their walls. The larynx, a region of the conducting portion, is designed for phonation and to prevent food, liquids, and other foreign objects from gaining access to its lumen. It is composed of three paired and three unpaired cartilages, numerous extrinsic and intrinsic muscles, and several ligaments. The actions of these muscles on the cartilages and ligaments modulate the tension and positioning of the vocal folds, thus permitting variations in the pitch of the sound being produced. The lumen of the **larynx** is subdivided into three compartments: **vestibule**, **ventricle**, and **infraglottic cavity**. The last named region is continuous with the lumen of the trachea, a structure supported by 15 to 20 **C-rings**, horseshoe-shaped segments of **hyaline cartilage**. The tracheal lumen is lined by a respiratory epithelium composed of various cell types, namely, goblet cells, basal cells, ciliated cells, brush cells, and, probably, hormone-producing DNES cells. The trachea subdivides into the two primary bronchi that lead to the right and the left lungs.

Intrapulmonary Region

The intrapulmonary region is composed of **intrapulmonary bronchi** (secondary bronchi), whose walls are supported by irregular plates of hyaline cartilage. Each intrapulmonary bronchus gives rise to several **bronchioles**, tubes of decreasing diameter

TABLE 12-1 • Summary Table of Respiratory System

Division	Region	Skeleton	Glands	Epithelium	Cilia	Goblet Cells	Special Features
Nasal cavity	Vestibule	Hyaline cartilage	Sebaceous and sweat glands	Stratified squamous keratinized	No	No	Vibrissae
	Respiratory	Bone and hyaline cartilage	Seromucous	Pseudostratified ciliated columnar	Yes	Yes	Large venous plexus
	Olfactory	Nasal conchae (bone)	Bowman's glands	Pseudostratified ciliated columnar	Yes	No	Basal cells; sustentacular cells; olfactory cells; nerve fibers
Pharynx	Nasal	Muscle	Seromucous glands	Pseudostratified ciliated columnar	Yes	Yes	Pharyngeal tonsil; eustachian tube
	Oral	Muscle	Seromucous glands	Stratified squamous nonkeratinized	No	No	Palatine tonsils
Larynx		Hyaline and elastic cartilage	Mucous and seromucous glands	Stratified squamous nonkeratinized and pseudostratified ciliated columnar	Yes	Yes	Vocal cords; epiglottis; some taste buds
Trachea and extrapulmonary (primary bronchi)		C-rings of hyaline cartilage	Mucous and seromucous glands	Pseudostratified ciliated columnar	Yes	Yes	Trachealis muscle; elastic lamina
Intrapulmonary conducting	Secondary bronchi	Plates of hyaline cartilage	Seromucous glands	Pseudostratified ciliated columnar	Yes	Yes	Two helical oriented ribbons of smooth muscle
	Bronchioles	Smooth muscle	None	Simple columnar to simple cuboidal	Yes	Only in larger bronchioles	Clara cells
	Terminal bronchiole	Smooth muscle	None	Simple cuboidal	Some	None	Less that 0.5 mm in diameter; Clara cells
Respiratory	Respiratory bronchiole	Some smooth muscle	None	Simple cuboidal and simple squamous	Some	None	Outpocketings of alveoli
	Alveolar duct	None	None	Simple squamous	None	None	Outpocketings of alveoli; type I pneumocytes; type II pneumocytes; dust cells
	Alveolus	None	None	Simple squamous	None	None	Type I pneumocytes; type II pneumocytes; dust cells

that do not possess a cartilaginous supporting skeleton. The epithelial lining of the larger bronchioles is ciliated with a few goblet cells, but those of smaller bronchioles are simple columnar, with goblet cells being replaced by **Clara cells**. Moreover, the thickness of their walls also decreases, as does the luminal diameter. The last region of the conduction portion is composed of **terminal bronchioles,** whose mucosa is further decreased in thickness and complexity. The patency of those airways whose walls do not possess a cartilaginous support is maintained by elastic fibers that radiate from their periphery and intermingle with elastic fibers emanating from nearby structures.

● RESPIRATORY PORTION OF THE RESPIRATORY SYSTEM

The respiratory portion of the respiratory system begins with branches of the terminal bronchiole known as **respiratory bronchioles** (see Graphic 12-2). These are very similar to terminal bronchioles except that they possess outpocketings known as **alveoli**, structures whose thin walls permit gaseous exchange. Respiratory bronchioles lead to alveolar ducts, each of which ends in an expanded region known as an **alveolar sac**, with each sac being composed of a number of alveoli. The epithelium of alveolar sacs and alveoli is composed of two types of cells: highly attenuated **type I pneumocytes**, which form much of the lining of the alveolus and alveolar sac, and **type II pneumocytes**, cells that manufacture **surfactant**, a phospholipid that reduces surface tension. Associated with the respiratory portion of the lungs is an extremely rich capillary network, supplied by the pulmonary arteries and drained by the pulmonary veins. The capillaries invest each alveolus, and their highly attenuated nonfenestrated, continuous endothelial cells closely approximate the type I pneumocytes. In fact, in many areas the basal laminae of the type I pneumocytes and endothelial cells fuse into a single basal lamina, providing for a minimal blood-air barrier, thus facilitating the exchange of gases. Therefore, the **blood-air barrier** is composed of the attenuated endothelial cell of the capillary, the two combined basal laminae, the attenuated type I pneumocyte, and the surfactant and fluid coating of the alveolus.

Since the lung contains about 300 million alveoli with a total surface area of approximately 75 m^2, these small spaces that crowd against each other are separated from one another by walls of various thicknesses known as **interalveolar septa**. The thinnest of these portions often presents communicating **alveolar pores**, whereby air may pass between alveoli. A somewhat thicker septum may possess intervening connective tissue elements that may be as slender as a capillary with its attendant basal lamina, or it may have collagen and elastic fibers as well as smooth muscle fibers and connective tissue cells. Macrophages known as **dust cells** are often noted in interalveolar septa. These dust cells are derived from monocytes and enter the lungs via the bloodstream. Here they mature and become extremely efficient scavengers. It is believed that dust cells are the most numerous of all cell types present in the lungs, even though they are eliminated from the lungs at a rate of 50 million per day. Although it is not known whether they actively migrate to the bronchioles or reach it via fluid flow, it is known that they are transported from there within the mucus layer, via ciliary action of the respiratory epithelium, into the pharynx. Once they reach the pharynx, they are either expectorated or swallowed.

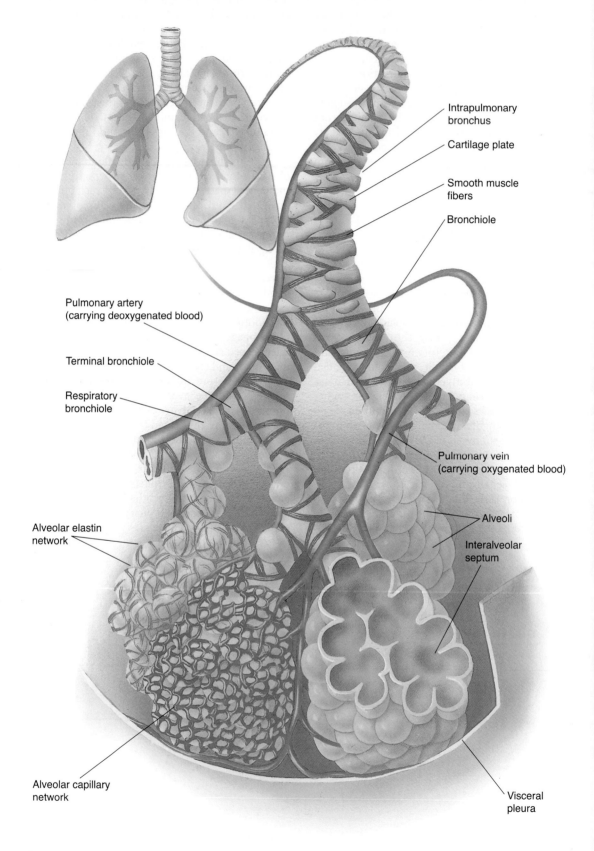

Intrapulmonary bronchus

Cartilage plate

Smooth muscle fibers

Bronchiole

Pulmonary artery (carrying deoxygenated blood)

Terminal bronchiole

Respiratory bronchiole

Pulmonary vein (carrying oxygenated blood)

Alveoli

Interalveolar septum

Alveolar elastin network

Alveolar capillary network

Visceral pleura

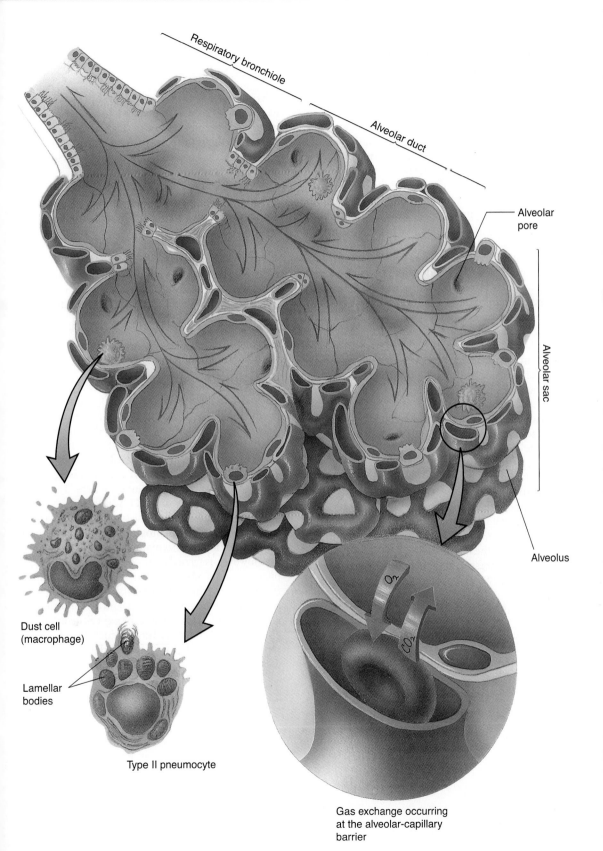

Respiratory bronchiole

Alveolar duct

Alveolar pore

Alveolar sac

Alveolus

Dust cell (macrophage)

Lamellar bodies

Type II pneumocyte

O_2

CO_2

Gas exchange occurring at the alveolar-capillary barrier

Histophysiology

I. MECHANISM OF OLFACTION

The sensory cells of the olfactory epithelium are bipolar neurons whose receptor ends are modified **cilia** that extend into the overlying mucus and whose axons go through the cribriform plate at the roof of the nasal cavity to enter the floor of the cranial cavity to synapse with mitral cells of the olfactory bulb. **Odorant-binding proteins** (integral membrane proteins that are odorant receptors) lying within the plasma membrane of the cilia are sensitive to molecules of specific odor groups, where each of these molecules is known as an **odorant**. When an odorant binds to its corresponding odorant receptor, one of two possibilities occurs. The receptor itself may be a **gated ion channel**, and, upon binding the odorant, the ion channel opens or the bound receptor activates **adenylate cyclase**, causing the formation of cAMP, which, in turn, facilitates the opening of ion channels. In either case, opening of the ion channel results in ion flow into the cell with subsequent **depolarization** of the plasmalemma, and the olfactory cell becomes **excited**. The action potentials generated by the depolarizations of the olfactory cells are transmitted, via synaptic contacts, to the mitral cells of the olfactory bulbs. The axons of the mitral cells form the olfactory tract, which transmits signals to the amygdala of the brainstem.

The odorant must satisfy at least three requirements: it must be **volatile**, **water soluble**, and **lipid soluble,** so that it can enter the nasal cavity (volatility), penetrate the mucus (water solubility), and be able to have access to the phospholipid membrane (lipid solubility).

II. MECHANISM OF RESPIRATION

The process of inspiration requires energy, in that it depends on the contraction of the **diaphragm** and elevation of the **ribs**, increasing the size of the thoracic cavity. Since the **visceral pleura** adheres to the lungs and is separated from the **parietal pleura** by the pleural cavity, that cavity is also enlarged, reducing the pressure within it. Since the pressure in the enlarged pleural cavities is less then the atmospheric pressure in the lungs, air enters the lungs and they become stretched, and the volume of the pleural cavity is reduced.

The process of expiration does not require energy, since it is dependent on **relaxation** of the muscles responsible for inspiration as well as on the stretched **elastic fibers** of the expanded lungs, which return to their **resting length**. As the muscles relax, the volume of the thoracic cage decreases, increasing the pressure inside the lung, which exceeds atmospheric pressure. The additional force of the elastic fibers returning to their resting length drives air out of the lungs.

III. MECHANISM OF GASEOUS EXCHANGE

The partial pressures of O_2 and CO_2 are responsible for the uptake or release of these gases by red blood cells. Since cells convert O_2 to CO_2 during their metabolism, the partial pressure of CO_2 is high in tissues, and this gas is preferentially taken up by red blood cells. Simultaneously, they release oxygen. The converse is true in the lungs, where O_2 is taken up by red blood cells and CO_2 is released.

Oxygen uptake and release is accomplished by the **heme** moiety of the **hemoglobin** molecule without the requirement of enzymatic catalysis. Carbon dioxide, however, is ferried in three different ways: as a gas dissolved in its molecular form (7%); as **carbamino-hemoglobin**, which as molecular CO_2 forms a weak bond with hemoglobin (23%); and as the bicarbonate ion, HCO_3^- (70%). Red blood cells contain the enzyme **carbonic anhydrase**, which facilitates the rapid formation of H_2CO_3, which then immediately dissociates to form bicarbonate and hydrogen ions.

CLINICAL CONSIDERATIONS

Hyaline Membrane Disease

Hyaline membrane disease is frequently observed in premature infants who lack adequate amounts of pulmonary surfactant. This disease is characterized by **labored breathing**, since a high alveolar surface tension, caused by inadequate levels of surfactant, makes it difficult to expand the alveoli. The administration of glucocorticoids prior to birth can induce synthesis of surfactant, thus circumventing the appearance of the disease.

Cystic Fibrosis

Although cystic fibrosis is viewed as a disease of the lungs, it is really a hereditary condition that alters the secretions of a number of glands, such as the liver, pancreas, salivary glands, sweat glands, and glands of the reproductive system. In the case of the lungs, liver, pancreas, and the intestines the mucous secretions become abnormally thickened and block the lumina of these organs. In the respiratory system the walls of the bronchioles thicken with the progression of the disease, areas of the lung become constricted, the thick secretions in the airways become infected, the lungs cease to function, and death ensues. Individuals with cystic fibrosis possess two copies of the defective gene that code for altered ion channels of epithelial cells that interfere with the Cl^- ions leaving the cell, enhances the ability of Na^+ ions to enter the cell, and interferes with

the normal secretion of HCO_3^-. Consequently, the mucus that is produced by these cells is much thicker than normal.

Emphysema

Emphysema is a disease that results from **destruction of alveolar walls** with the consequent formation of large cyst-like sacs, reducing the surface available for gas exchange. Emphysema is marked by **decreased elasticity** of the lungs, which are unable to recoil adequately during expiration. It is associated with exposure to **cigarette smoke** and other substances that inhibit α_1-antitrypsin, a protein that normally protects the lungs from the action of elastase produced by alveolar macrophages.

Bronchial Asthma

Bronchial asthma is a condition in which the bronchi become partially and reversibly obstructed by airway spasm (**bronchioconstriction**), mast cell–induced inflammatory response to allergens and/or other stimuli that would not affect a normal lung, and the formation of excess mucus. Asthma attacks vary with the individual; in some it is hardly noticed, whereas in others shortness of breath is very evident and wheezing accompanies breathing out. Most individuals who suffer from asthmatic conditions use nebulizers containing bronchodilators, such as albuterol, to relieve the attack.

FIGURE 1 • Olfactory area. Human. Paraffin section. ×270.

The olfactory mucosa of the nasal cavity is composed of a thick **olfactory epithelium** (OE) and a **lamina propria** (LP) richly endowed with **blood vessels** (BV), **lymph vessels** (LV), and **nerve fibers** (NF) frequently collected into bundles. The lamina propria also contains **Bowman's glands** (BG), which produce a watery mucus that is delivered onto the ciliated surface by short ducts. The *boxed area* is presented at a higher magnification in Figure 2.

FIGURE 3 • Intraepithelial gland. Human. Paraffin section. ×540.

The epithelium of the nasal cavity occasionally displays small, **intraepithelial glands** (IG). Note that these structures are clearly demarcated from the surrounding epithelium. The secretory product is released into the space (*asterisk*) that is continuous with the **nasal cavity** (NC). The subepithelial **connective tissue** (CT) is richly supplied with **blood vessels** (BV) and **lymph vessels** (LV). Observe the **plasma cells** (PC), characteristic of the subepithelial connective tissue of the respiratory system, which also displays the presence of **glands** (Gl).

FIGURE 2 • Olfactory epithelium. Human. Paraffin section. ×540.

This is a higher magnification of the *boxed area* of the previous figure. The **epithelium** (OE) is pseudostratified ciliated columnar, whose **cilia** (C) are particularly evident. Although hematoxylin and eosin–stained tissue does not permit clear identification of the various cell types, the positions of the nuclei permit tentative identification. **Basal cells** (BC) are short, and their nuclei are near the basement membrane. **Olfactory cell** (OC) nuclei are centrally located, whereas nuclei of **sustentacular cells** (SC) are positioned near the apex of the cell.

FIGURE 4 • Larynx. l.s. Human. Paraffin section. ×14.

The right half of the larynx, at the level of the **ventricle** (V), is presented in this survey photomicrograph. The ventricle is bounded superiorly by the **ventricular folds** (false vocal cords) (VF) and inferiorly by the **vocal folds** (VoF). The space above the ventricular fold is the beginning of the **vestibule** (Ve) and that below the vocal fold is the beginning of the **infraglottic cavity** (IC). The **vocalis muscle** (VM) regulates the vocal ligament present in the vocal fold. Acini of mucous and seromucous **glands** (GI) are scattered throughout the subepithelial connective tissue. The **laryngeal cartilages** (LC) are also shown to advantage.

KEY							
BC	basal cells	LC	laryngeal cartilages	PC	plasma cells
BG	Bowman's glands	LP	lamina propria	SC	sustentacular cells
BV	blood vessels	LV	lymph vessels	V	ventricle
C	cilia	NC	nasal cavity	Ve	vestibule
CT	connective tissue	NF	nerve fibers	VF	ventricular folds
GI	glands	OC	olfactory cells	VM	vocalis muscle
IC	infraglottic cavity	OE	olfactory epithelium	VoF	vocal folds
IG	intraepithelial glands				

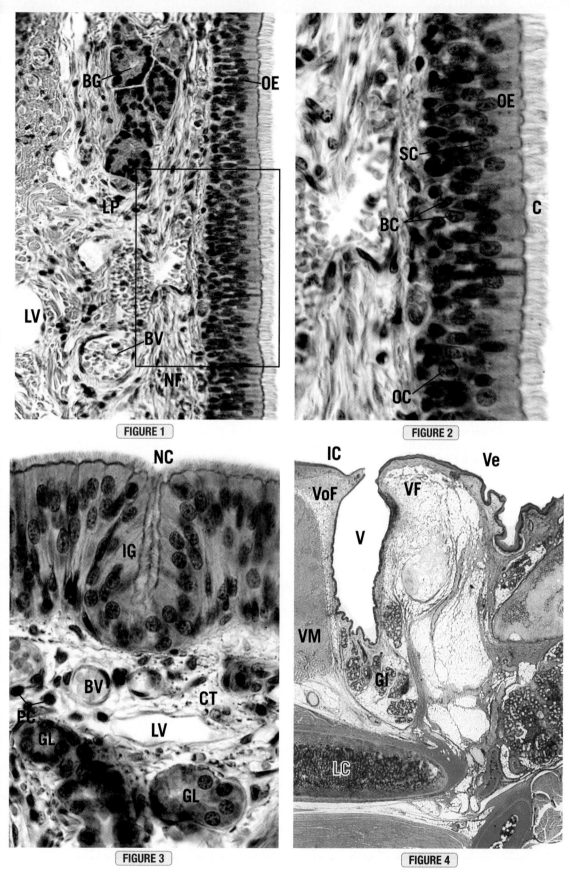

FIGURE 1

FIGURE 2

FIGURE 3

FIGURE 4

FIGURE 1 • Trachea. l.s. Monkey. Paraffin section. ×20.

This survey photomicrograph presents a longitudinal section of the **trachea** (Tr) and **esophagus** (Es). Observe that the **lumen** (LT) of the trachea is patent, due to the presence of discontinuous cartilaginous **C-rings** (CR) in its wall. The C-rings of the trachea are thicker anteriorly than posteriorly and are separated from each other by thick, fibrous connective tissue (*arrows*) that is continuous with the perichondrium of the C-rings. The adventitia of the trachea is adhered to the esophagus via a loose type of **connective tissue** (CT), which frequently contains adipose tissue. Note that the **lumen** (LE) of the esophagus is normally collapsed. A region similar to the *boxed area* is presented at a higher magnification in Figure 3.

FIGURE 2 • Trachea. l.s. Monkey. Plastic section. ×270.

The trachea is lined by a pseudostratified ciliated columnar **epithelium** (E), which houses numerous **goblet cells** (GC) that actively secrete a mucous substance. The **lamina propria** (LP) is relatively thin, whereas the **submucosa** (SM) is thick and contains **mucous** and **seromucous glands** (GI), whose secretory product is delivered to the epithelial surface via ducts that pierce the lamina propria. The **perichondrium** (Pc) of the hyaline cartilage **C-rings** (CR) merges with the submucosal connective tissue. Note a longitudinal section of a **blood vessel** (BV), indicative of the presence of a rich vascular supply.

FIGURE 3 • Trachea. l.s. Monkey. Paraffin section. ×200.

This photomicrograph is a higher magnification of a region similar to the *boxed area* of Figure 1. The pseudostratified, ciliated columnar **epithelium** (E) lies on a basement membrane that separates it from the underlying lamina propria. The outer extent of the lamina propria is demarcated by an elastic lamina (*arrows*), deep to which is the **submucosa** (SM), containing a rich **vascular supply** (BV). The **C-ring** (CR), with its attendant **perichondrium** (Pc), constitutes the most substantive layer of the tracheal wall. The adventitia of the trachea, which some consider to include the C-ring, is composed of a loose type of connective tissue, housing some **adipose cells** (AC), **nerves** (N), and **blood vessels** (BV). Collagen fiber bundles of the adventitia secure the trachea to the surrounding structures.

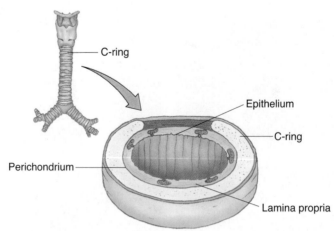

Trachea

KEY					
AC	adipose cells	GC	goblet cells	LT	lumen—trachea
BV	blood vessels	GI	mucous/seromucous	N	nerves
CR	C-rings		glands	Pc	perichondrium
CT	connective tissue	LE	lumen—esophagus	SM	submucosa
E	epithelium	LP	lamina propria	Tr	trachea
Es	esophagus				

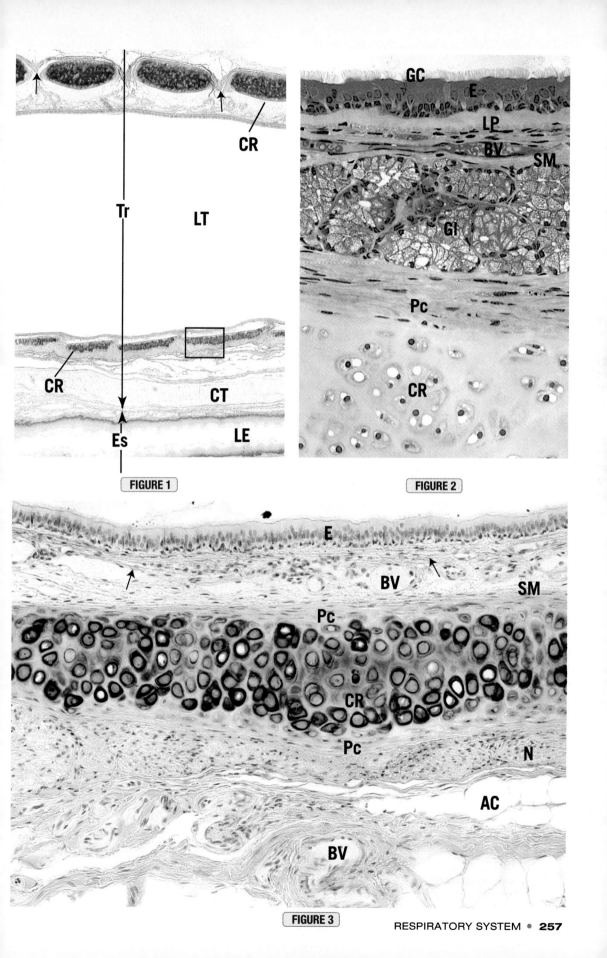

CR

Tr

LT

CR

CT

Es

LE

FIGURE 1

GC

E

LP

BV

SM

Gl

Pc

CR

FIGURE 2

E

BV

SM

Pc

CR

Pc

N

AC

BV

FIGURE 3

PLATE 12-3 Respiratory Epithelium and Cilia, Electron Microscopy

FIGURE 1 • Tracheal epithelium. Hamster. Electron microscopy. ×7,782.

The tracheal epithelium of the hamster presents mucus-producing **goblet cells** (GC) as well as **ciliated columnar cells** (CC), whose cilia (*arrows*) project into the lumen. Note that both cell types are well endowed with

Golgi apparatus (GA), whereas goblet cells are particularly rich in **rough endoplasmic reticulum** (rER). (Courtesy of Dr. E. McDowell.) *Inset.* **Bronchus. Human. Electron microscopy.** × 7,782. The apical region of a ciliated epithelial cell presents both **cilia** (C) and microvilli (*arrow*). (Courtesy of Dr. E. McDowell.)

KEY					
C	cilia	GA	Golgi apparatus	rER	rough endoplasmic
CC	ciliated columnar cell	GC	goblet cell		reticulum

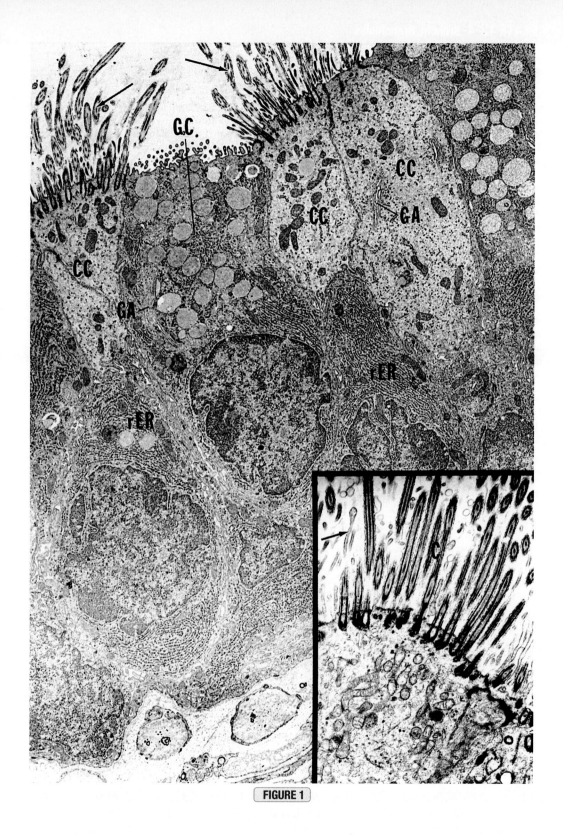

FIGURE 1

FIGURE 1 ● Lung. Paraffin section. ×14.

This survey photomicrograph presents a section of a lung that permits the observation of the various conduits that conduct air and blood to and from the lung. The **intrapulmonary bronchus** (IB) is recognizable by its thick wall, containing plates of **hyaline cartilage** (HC) and **smooth muscle** (Sm). Longitudinal sections of a **bronchiole** (B), **terminal bronchiole** (TB), and **respiratory bronchiole** (RB) are also evident. Smaller bronchioles (*asterisks*) may also be recognized, but their identification cannot be ascertained. *Arrows* point to structures that are probably alveolar ducts leading into alveolar sacs. Several **blood vessels** (BV), branches of the pulmonary circulatory system, may be noted. Observe that **lymphatic nodules** (LN) are also present along the bronchial tree.

FIGURE 3 ● Bronchiole. x.s. Paraffin section. ×270.

Bronchioles maintain their patent **lumen** (L) without the requirement of a cartilaginous support, since they are attached to surrounding lung tissue by elastic fibers radiating from their circumference. The lumina of bronchioles are lined by simple columnar to simple cuboidal **epithelium** (E), interspersed with **Clara cells** (CC), depending on the diameter of the bronchiole. The **lamina propria** (LP) is thin and is surrounded by **smooth muscle** (Sm), which encircles the lumen. Bronchioles have no glands in their walls and are surrounded by **lung tissue** (LT).

FIGURE 2 ● Intrapulmonary bronchus. x.s. Paraffin section. ×132.

Intrapulmonary bronchi are relatively large conduits for air, whose **lumina** (L) are lined by a typical respiratory **epithelium** (E). The **smooth muscle** (Sm) is found beneath the mucous membrane, and it encircles the entire lumen. Note that gaps (*arrows*) appear in the muscle layer, indicating that two ribbons of smooth muscle wind around the lumen in a helical arrangement. Plates of **hyaline cartilage** (HC) act as the skeletal support, maintaining the patency of the bronchus. The entire structure is surrounded by **lung tissue** (LT).

FIGURE 4 ● Terminal bronchioles. x.s. Paraffin section. ×132.

The smallest conducting bronchioles are referred to as **terminal bronchioles** (TB). These have very small diameters, and their lumina are lined with a simple cuboidal **epithelium** (E) interspersed with **Clara cells** (CC). The connective tissue is much reduced, and the smooth muscle layers are incomplete and difficult to recognize at this magnification. Terminal bronchioles give rise to **respiratory bronchioles** (RB), whose walls resemble those of the terminal bronchioles except that the presence of alveoli permit the exchange of gases to occur.

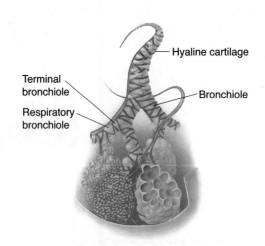

Bronchial system and lung

KEY							
B	bronchiole	IB	intrapulmonary bronchus	LT	lung tissue		
BV	blood vessels	L	lumen	RB	respiratory bronchiole		
CC	Clara cells	LN	lymphatic nodule	Sm	smooth muscle		
E	epithelium	LP	lamina propria	TB	terminal bronchiole		
HC	hyaline cartilage						

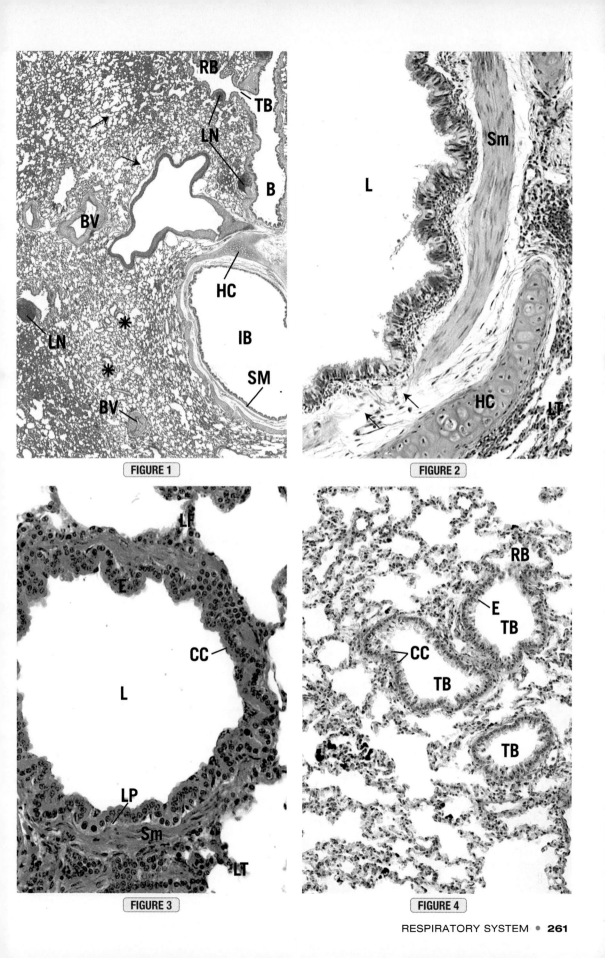

FIGURE 1

FIGURE 2

FIGURE 3

FIGURE 4

FIGURE 1 • Respiratory bronchiole. Paraffin section. ×270.

The respiratory bronchiole whose **lumen** (L) occupies the lower half of this photomicrograph presents an apparently thick wall with small outpocketings of **alveoli** (A). It is in these alveoli that gaseous exchanges first occur. The wall of the respiratory bronchiole is composed of a simple cuboidal epithelium consisting of some ciliated cells and **Clara cells** (CC). The remainder of the wall presents an incomplete layer of smooth muscle cells surrounded by fibroelastic connective tissue. Careful examination of this photomicrograph reveals that the wall of the respiratory bronchiole is folded upon itself, thus giving a misleading appearance of thick walls.

FIGURE 3 • Interalveolar septum. Monkey. Plastic section. ×540.

This photomicrograph is a higher magnification of a region similar to the *boxed area* of Figure 2. Two **alveoli** (A) are presented, recognizable as empty spaces separated from each other by an **interalveolar septum** (IS). The septum is composed of a **capillary** (Ca), the nucleus (*asterisk*) of whose endothelial lining bulges into the lumen containing **red blood cells** (RBC). The interalveolar septum as well as the entire alveolus is lined by **type I pneumocytes** (P1), which are highly attenuated squamous epithelial cells, interspersed with **type II pneumocytes** (P2). Thicker interalveolar septa house **blood vessels** (BV) and connective tissue elements including macrophages known as **dust cells** (DC). Note the presence of **smooth muscle cells** (Sm) and connective tissue elements that appear as knobs at the entrance into the alveolus.

FIGURE 2 • Alveolar duct. l.s. Human. Paraffin section. ×132.

Alveolar ducts (AD), unlike respiratory bronchioles, do not possess a wall of their own. These structures are lined by a simple squamous **epithelium** (E), composed of highly attenuated cells. Alveolar ducts present numerous outpocketings of **alveoli** (A), and they end in **alveolar sacs** (AS), consisting of groups of alveoli clustered around a common air space. Individual alveoli possess small smooth muscle cells that, acting like a purse string, control the opening into the alveolus. These appear as small knobs (*arrow*). A region similar to the *boxed area* is presented at a higher magnification in Figure 3.

FIGURE 4 • Lung. Dust cells. Paraffin section. ×270.

The highly vascular nature of the lung is evident in this photomicrograph, since the **blood vessels** (BV) and the **capillaries** (Ca) of the interalveolar septa are filled with red blood cells. The dark blotches that appear to be scattered throughout the lung tissue represent **dust cells** (DC), macrophages that have phagocytosed particulate matter. *Inset.* **Lung. Dust cell. Monkey. Plastic section.** × 540. The **nucleus** (N) of a **dust cell** (DC) is surrounded by phagosomes containing particulate matter that was probably phagocytosed from an alveolus of the lung.

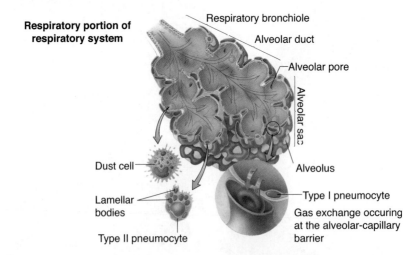

Respiratory portion of respiratory system

Respiratory bronchiole

Alveolar duct

Alveolar pore

Alveolar sac

Dust cell

Lamellar bodies

Type II pneumocyte

Alveolus

Type I pneumocyte

Gas exchange occuring at the alveolar-capillary barrier

KEY							
A	alveolus	CC	Clara cell	N	nucleus
AD	alveolar duct	DC	dust cell	P1	type I pneumocytes
AS	alveolar sac	E	epithelium	P2	type II pneumocytes
BV	blood vessel	IS	interalveolar septum	RBC	red blood cells
Ca	capillary	L	lumen	Sm	smooth muscle

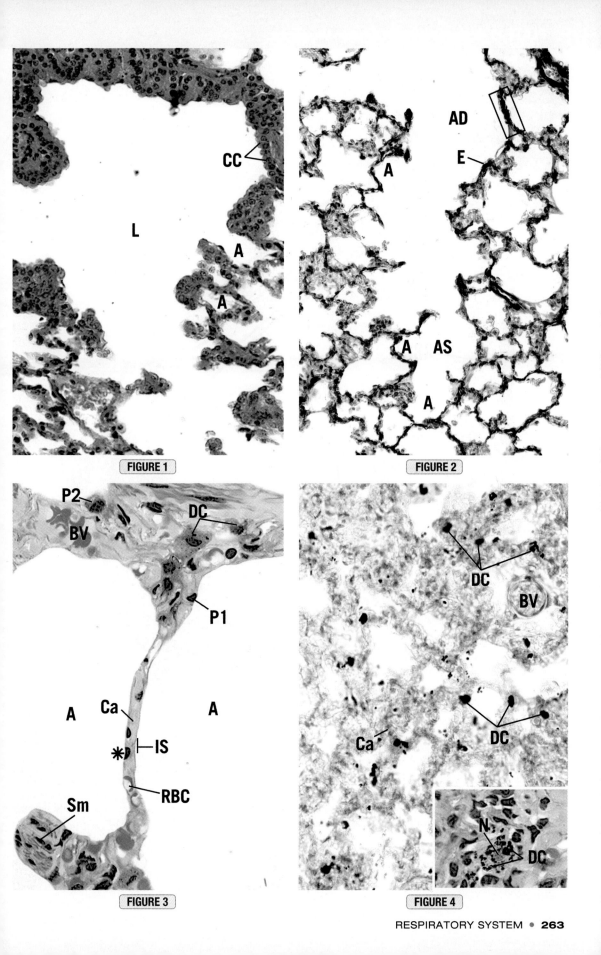

FIGURE 1

FIGURE 2

FIGURE 3

FIGURE 4

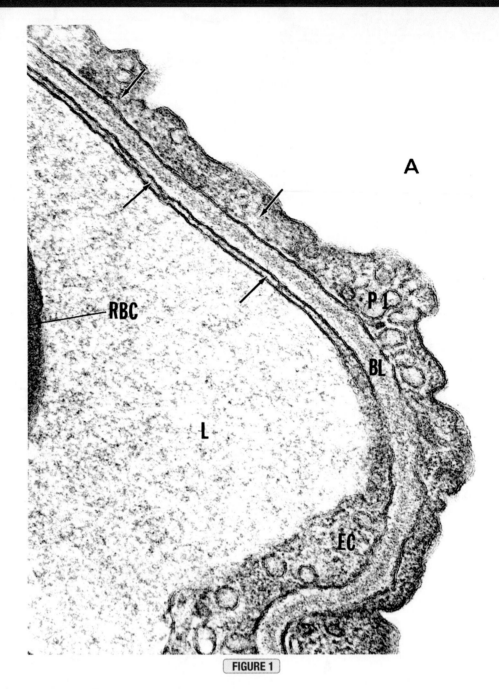

FIGURE 1

FIGURE 1 • Blood-air barrier. Dog. Electron microscopy. ×85,500.

The blood-air barrier is composed of highly attenuated **endothelial cells** (EC), **type I pneumocytes** (P1), and an intervening **basal lamina** (BL). Note that the cytoplasm (*arrows*) of both cell types is greatly reduced, as evidenced by the close proximity of the plasmalemma on either side of the cytoplasm. The air space of the **alveolus** (A) is empty, whereas the capillary **lumen** (L) presents a part of a **red blood cell** (RBC). (From DeFouw D. Vesicle numerical densities and cellular attenuation: comparisons between endothelium and epithelium of the alveolar septa in normal dog lungs. Anat Rec 1984;209:77–84.)

Summary of Histological Organization

I. CONDUCTING PORTION

A. Nasal Cavity

1. Respiratory Region
The **respiratory region** is lined by **respiratory (pseudostratified ciliated columnar) epithelium.** The subepithelial connective tissue is richly vascularized and possesses seromucous glands.

2. Olfactory Region
The epithelium of the **olfactory region** is thick, **pseudostratified ciliated columnar epithelium** composed of three cell types: **basal cell, sustentacular cells,** and **olfactory cells.** The lamina propria is richly vascularized and possesses **Bowman's glands,** which produce a watery mucus.

B. Larynx

The **larynx** is lined by a **respiratory epithelium** except for certain regions that are lined by **stratified squamous nonkeratinized epithelium.** From superior to inferior, the **lumen** of the larynx presents three regions: the **vestibule, the ventricle,** and the **infraglottic cavity.** The **ventricular** and **vocal folds** are the superior and inferior boundaries of the ventricle, respectively. Cartilages, extrinsic and intrinsic muscles, as well as mucous and seromucous glands are present in the larynx.

C. Trachea

1. Mucosa
The **mucosa** of the trachea is composed of a **respiratory epithelium** with numerous **goblet cells,** a **lamina propria,** and a well-defined **elastic lamina.**

2. Submucosa
The **submucosa** houses **mucous** and **seromucous glands.**

3. Adventitia
The **adventitia** is the thickest portion of the tracheal wall. It houses the **C-rings** of **hyaline cartilage** (or thick connective tissue between the rings). Posteriorly, the **trachealis muscle** (smooth muscle) fills in the gap between the free ends of the cartilage.

D. Extrapulmonary Bronchi

Extrapulmonary bronchi resemble the trachea in histologic structure.

E. Intrapulmonary Bronchi

These and subsequent passageways are completely surrounded by lung tissue.

1. Mucosa
Intrapulmonary bronchi are lined by **respiratory epithelium** with **goblet cells.** The subepithelial connective tissue is no longer bordered by an elastic lamina.

2. Muscle
Two ribbons of **smooth muscle** are wound helically around the mucosa.

3. Cartilage
The C-rings are replaced by irregularly shaped **hyaline cartilage plates** that encircle the smooth muscle layer. **Dense collagenous connective tissue** connects the perichondria of the cartilage plates.

4. Glands
Seromucous glands occupy the connective tissue between the cartilage plates and smooth muscle. **Lymphatic nodules** and branches of the pulmonary arteries are also present.

F. Bronchioles

Bronchioles are lined by **ciliated simple columnar** to **simple cuboidal epithelium** interspersed with nonciliated **Clara cells. Goblet cells** are found only in larger bronchioles. The **lamina propria** possesses no glands and is surrounded by **smooth muscle.** The walls of bronchioles are not supported by cartilage. The largest bronchioles are about 1 mm in diameter.

G. Terminal Bronchioles

Terminal bronchioles are usually less than 0.5 mm in diameter. The lumen is lined by **simple cuboidal epithelium** (some ciliated) interspersed with **Clara cells.** The connective tissue and smooth muscle of the wall of the terminal bronchioles are greatly reduced.

II. RESPIRATORY PORTION

A. Respiratory Bronchiole

Respiratory bronchioles resemble terminal bronchioles, but they possess outpocketings of **alveoli** in their walls. This is the first region where exchange of gases occurs.

B. Alveolar Ducts

Alveolar ducts possess no walls of their own. They are long, straight tubes lined by **simple squamous epithelium** and display numerous outpocketings of **alveoli**. Alveolar ducts end in alveolar sacs.

C. Alveolar Sacs

Alveolar sacs are composed of groups of **alveoli** clustered around a common air space.

D. Alveolus

An **alveolus** is a small air space partially surrounded by highly attenuated epithelium. Two types of cells are present in the lining: **type I pneumocytes** (lining cells) and **type II pneumocytes** (produce surfactant). The opening of the alveolus is controlled by **elastic fibers**. Alveoli are separated from each other by richly vascularized walls known as **interalveolar septa**, some of which present **alveolar pores** (communicating spaces between alveoli). **Dust cells** (macrophages), **fibroblasts**, and other **connective tissue elements** may be noted in interalveolar septa. The **blood-air barrier** is a part of the interalveolar septum, the thinnest of which is composed of surfactant, **continuous endothelial cells**, **type I pneumocyte**, and their intervening **fused basal laminae**.

Digestive System I

13

The digestive system functions in the ingestion, digestion, and absorption of food as well as in the elimination of its unusable portions. To accomplish these functions, the digestive system is organized into three major components: (i) the oral cavity, where food is reduced in size, is moistened, begins to be digested, and is introduced as small spherical portions, each known as a **bolus**, into the alimentary canal; (ii) a muscular alimentary canal, along whose lumen the ingested foods are converted, both physically and chemically, into absorbable substances; and (iii) a glandular portion, which provides fluids, enzymes, and emulsifying agents necessary so that the alimentary canal can perform its various functions.

● ORAL REGION: ORAL CAVITY

The **oral cavity** may be subdivided into two smaller cavities: the externally positioned vestibule and the internally placed oral cavity proper. The **vestibule** is the space bounded by the lips and cheeks anteriorly and laterally, whereas its internal boundary is formed by the dental arches. The ducts of the parotid glands deliver their secretory products into the vestibule (see Graphics 13-1 and 13-2).

The **oral cavity proper** is bounded by the teeth externally, the floor of the mouth inferiorly, and the hard and soft palates superiorly. At its posterior extent, the oral cavity proper is separated from the oral pharynx by an imaginary plane drawn between the palatoglossal folds just anterior to the palatine tonsils. Both the oral cavity proper and the vestibule are lined by **stratified squamous epithelium**, which, in regions that are subject to abrasive forces, is modified into **stratified squamous keratinized** (or **parakeratinized**) **epithelium**.

Oral Mucosa

The epithelium and underlining connective tissue constitute the **oral mucosa**. If the epithelium is keratinized (or parakeratinized), the mucosa is said to be **masticatory mucosa**, and if the epithelium is not keratinized, the mucosa is referred to as **lining mucosa**. It should be noted that most of the oral cavity possesses lining mucosa, with the exception of the gingiva, hard palate, and the dorsal surface of the tongue, which are covered by masticatory mucosa. Additionally, the oral cavity has areas of specialized epithelia where intraepithelial structures known as **taste buds** function in taste perception. Most taste buds are located on the dorsal surface of the tongue, although the palate and pharynx also possess a few of these structures. Mucosa whose epithelium contains taste buds is known as **specialized mucosa**. Each taste bud recognizes one or more of the five taste sensations: sour, sweet, salty, umami (savory), or bitter.

The contents of the oral cavity are the teeth, utilized in biting and mastication, and the tongue, a muscular structure that functions in the preparation of the bolus, tasting of the food, and beginning of deglutition (swallowing), among others.

Salivary Glands, Palate, and Tonsils

The three pairs of major salivary glands—parotid, sublingual, and submandibular—deliver their secretions into the oral cavity. The hard palate assists the tongue in the preparation of the bolus, and the soft palate, a moveable structure, seals the communication between the oral and nasal pharynges, thus preventing passage of food and fluids from the former into the latter.

The connective tissue underlying the epithelium of the oral cavity is richly endowed with **minor salivary glands** that, secreting **saliva** in a continuous fashion, contribute to the maintenance of a moist environment. Saliva functions also in assisting in the process of deglutition by acting as a lubricant for dry foods and for holding the bolus together in a semisolid mass. Moreover, enzymes present in saliva initiate digestion of carbohydrates, whereas secretory antibodies protect the body against antigenic substances.

The entrance to the pharynx is guarded against bacterial invasion by the **tonsillar ring**, composed of the **lingual**, **pharyngeal**, and **palatine tonsils**.

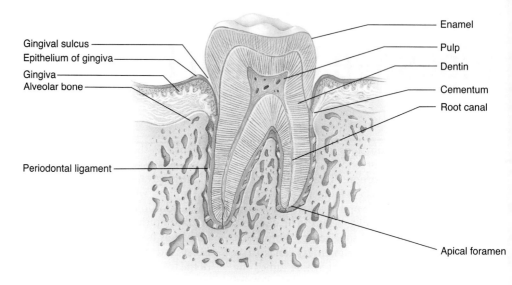

Enamel

Pulp

Dentin

Gingival sulcus

Epithelium of gingiva

Gingiva

Alveolar bone

Cementum

Root canal

Periodontal ligament

Apical foramen

Tooth

The tooth, composed of a crown and root, is suspended in its bony socket, the alveolus, by a dense, collagenous connective tissue, the **periodontal ligament**. The crown of the tooth consists of two calcified tissues, **dentin** and **enamel**, whereas the root is composed of dentin and **cementum**. The pulp chamber of the crown and the root canal of the root are continuous with one another. They are occupied by a gelatinous connective tissue, the **pulp**, which houses blood and lymph vessels, nerve fibers, connective tissue elements, as well as **odontoblasts**, the cells responsible for the maintenance and repair of dentin. Vessels and nerves serving the pulp enter the root canal via the **apical foramen**, a small opening at the apex of the root.

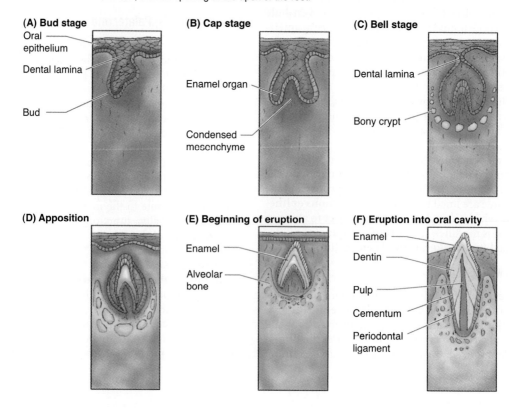

(A) Bud stage

Oral epithelium

Dental lamina

Bud

(B) Cap stage

Enamel organ

Condensed mesenchyme

(C) Bell stage

Dental lamina

Bony crypt

(D) Apposition

(E) Beginning of eruption

Enamel

Alveolar bone

(F) Eruption into oral cavity

Enamel

Dentin

Pulp

Cementum

Periodontal ligament

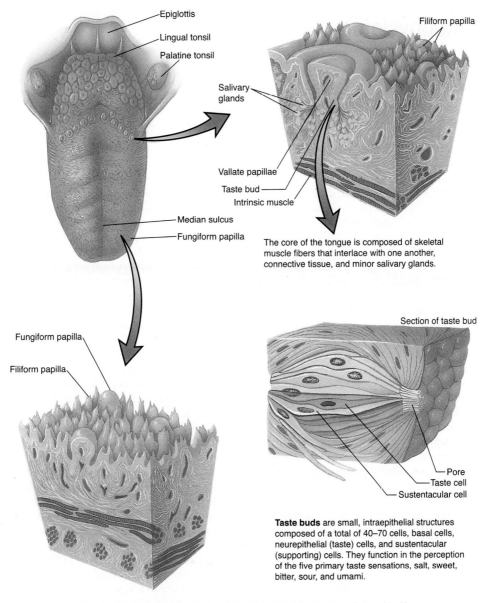

Epiglottis

Lingual tonsil

Palatine tonsil

Filiform papilla

Salivary glands

Vallate papillae

Taste bud

Intrinsic muscle

Median sulcus

Fungiform papilla

The core of the tongue is composed of skeletal muscle fibers that interlace with one another, connective tissue, and minor salivary glands.

Fungiform papilla

Filiform papilla

Section of taste bud

Pore

Taste cell

Sustentacular cell

Taste buds are small, intraepithelial structures composed of a total of 40–70 cells, basal cells, neurepithelial (taste) cells, and sustentacular (supporting) cells. They function in the perception of the five primary taste sensations, salt, sweet, bitter, sour, and umami.

The dorsal surface of the tongue is subdivided into an anterior two-thirds, populated by the four types of lingual papillae, and a posterior one-third housing the lingual tonsils. The two regions are separated from one another by a "V-shaped" depression, the sulcus terminalis. **Filiform papillae** are short, conical, and highly keratinized. **Fungiform papillae** are mushroom-shaped, and the dorsal aspect of their epithelia houses three to five taste buds. **Circumvallate papillae**, the largest of the lingual papillae, are six to twelve in number. Each circumvallate papilla is depressed into the surface of the tongue and is surrounded by a moat-like trough. The lateral aspect of the papilla as well as the lining of the trough houses numerous taste buds. **Foliate papillae** are located on the lateral aspect of the tongue.

Histophysiology

I. TISSUE INTERACTION IN ODONTOGENESIS

Odontogenesis is induced by the ectodermally derived cells of the dental lamina that express **lymphoid enhancer factor-1** (Lef-1), a transcription factor. Lef-1 induces the epithelial cells to synthesize and release **bone morphogenic protein-4** (BMP-4), **sonic hedgehog** (Shh), and **fibroblast growth factor-8** (FGF-8). These signaling molecules act on the underlying ectomesenchymal cells to differentiate into odontogenic tissues. These neural crest–derived cells begin to express **activin βA**, **BMP-4**, the adhesive glycoprotein **tenascin**, and the membrane-bounded proteoglycan **syndecan**. Moreover, they also express several transcription factors, namely, **Egr-1** (early growth response-1), **Msx-1** (homeobox-containing genes), and **Msx-2**. This activation of the ectomesenchyme elicits their role in the induction of the tooth morphology, so that it is the ectomesenchyme that will determine, for instance, whether the developing tooth will become a molar or an incisor. Signaling molecules from the ectomesenchyme induce the formation of the **enamel knot**, an epithelial structure that appears in the vicinity of the stratum intermedium of the enamel organ. The enamel knot synthesizes and releases its own signaling molecules, namely, FGF-4, BMP-2, BMP-4, BMP-7, and Shh. These signaling molecules promote the differentiation of the inner enamel epithelial cells into **ameloblasts** and those of the peripheralmost layer of the dental papilla into **odontoblasts**. Continued maintenance of the enamel knot is responsible for the buckling of the inner enamel epithelium, resulting in the morphodifferentiation of the enamel organ into a template that is the prototype of a molar tooth, whereas if the enamel knot undergoes apoptosis, morphodifferentiation is constrained and an incisor is formed.

II. TASTE RECEPTION

Taste reception is performed by small, barrel-shaped, intraepithelial structures known as **taste buds**, located mostly on the dorsal surface of the tongue, though present also on the soft palate and pharynx. They are composed of 40 to 70 spindle-shaped neuroepithelial cells that are of four types: **basal cells** (**type IV**), which act as regenerative cells; **dark cells** (**type I cells**), which probably arise directly from basal cells and mature into **light cells** (**type II**); and **intermediate cells** (**type III cells**), which will undergo apoptosis and die. The complete life cycle of these cells is about 10 days to 2 weeks, and they are continuously replaced by basal cell derivatives. The cells are compacted together and form an opening known as a **taste pore** at the epithelial surface. Basally, cell types I, II, and III form **synaptic contacts** with nerve fibers; apically, they possess long microvilli known as **taste hairs**, which pass through the taste pore and are exposed to the moist environment of the oral cavity. The taste hairs have two types of **taste receptors** (**TR1** and **TR2**) that bind dissolved chemicals from the food, known as **tastants**, resulting in the activation of G-proteins and/or direct opening of ion channels. The end result is that the neuroepithelial cells become activated and release neurotransmitter substances at their synaptic junctions with the nerve fibers. The central nervous system then registers the signal and interprets the taste that was sensed by the taste bud.

Herpetic Stomatitis

Herpetic stomatitis, a relatively common disease caused by the herpes simplex virus (HSV) type I, is distinguished by painful **fever blisters** appearing on or in the vicinity of the lips. This is a recurring disease since the virus, in its dormant phase, inhabits the trigeminal ganglion. It travels along the axon to cause the appearance of the blisters. During the active stage the patient is highly contagious, since the virus is shed via the seeping clear exudate.

Caries

Caries, or cavities, are formed by the action of acid-secreting bacteria that adhere to very small defects or irregularities of the enamel surface. The acids formed by the bacteria decalcify the enamel, providing larger defects that can house a much larger number of the proliferating bacteria with the formation of more acid and decalcification of more of the enamel. The carious lesion is pain-free until it reaches the underlying dentin. Since the most sensitive region of dentin is at the dentino-enamel junction, the tooth is sensitive to heat, cold, mechanical contact, and sweets. Continued bacterial activity, without the intervention of a dental health professional, could cause eventual loss of the tooth and perhaps even more serious sequalae.

Hemorrhage of the Pulp

Darkening of a tooth may be due to hemorrhage of the pulp. Although frequently the pulp is damaged severly enough that it can no longer be saved, a dental professional should be consulted because tooth discoloration does not necessarily require root canal therapy.

Teeth

Humans have two sets of teeth, a **deciduous** and a **permanent dentition**. The deciduous teeth are smaller and weaker and fewer in number than the permanent dentition because the adult mouth is larger than that of a child. There are 20 deciduous teeth, 10 in each jaw, whereas there are 32 permanent teeth in the adult. At approximately 6 to 13 years of age, the dentition is mixed in that both deciduous and permanent teeth are present in the mouth at the same time. All 20 deciduous teeth are replaced by **successional permanent teeth**, whereas the 12 permanent molars do not replace deciduous teeth and are therefore known as **accessional permanent teeth**.

Necrotizing Ulcerative Gingivitis

Necrotizing ulcerative gingivitis is an acute ulcerative condition of the gingiva with accompanying necrosis, halitosis, erythematous appearance, and moderate to severe pain. Fever and regional lymphadenopathy may also be evident. This is usually a disease of the young adult who is experiencing stress and is not particularly attentive to dental hygiene. Frequently *Treponema vincentii* and fusiform bacillus are present in large numbers, and they are also believed to be causative agents of the condition. Treatment usually consists of rinsing with dilute hydrogen peroxide several times daily and meticulous cleaning by a dental professional. An antibiotic regiment may also be recommended.

FIGURE 1 • Lip. Human. Paraffin section. ×14.

The human lip presents three surfaces and a core (C). The external surface is covered by skin, composed of **epidermis** (E) and **dermis** (D). Associated hair follicles (*arrow*) and glands are evident. The **vermillion** (**red**) **zone** (VZ) is only found in humans. The high dermal papillae (*arrowheads*) carry blood vessels close to the surface, accounting for the pinkish coloration of this region. The internal aspect is lined by a wet, stratified, squamous, nonkeratinized **epithelium** (Ep), and the underlying connective tissue houses minor salivary glands. The core of the lip is composed of skeletal muscle interspersed with fibroelastic connective tissue.

FIGURE 3 • Lip. Human. External aspect. Paraffin section. ×132.

The external aspect of the lip is covered by thin skin. Neither the **epidermis** (E) nor the **dermis** (D) present any unusual features. Numerous **hair follicles** (HF) populate this aspect of the lip, and **sebaceous glands** (Sg) as well as sweat glands are noted in abundance.

FIGURE 2 • Lip. Human. Internal aspect. Paraffin section. ×270.

The internal aspect of the lip is lined by a mucous membrane that is continuously kept moist by saliva secreted by the three major and numerous minor salivary glands. The thick **epithelium** (Ep) is a stratified squamous nonkeratinized type, which presents deep **rete ridges** (RR) that interdigitate with the **connective tissue papillae** (CP). The connective tissue is fibroelastic in nature, displaying a rich **vascular supply** (BV).

FIGURE 4 • Lip. Human. Vermilion zone. Paraffin section. ×132.

The vermilion zone of the lip is covered by a modified skin composed of stratified squamous keratinized **epithelium** (Ep) that forms extensive interdigitations with the underlying **dermis** (D). Neither hair follicles nor sweat glands populate this area (though occasional sebaceous glands may be present). Note the cross-sectional profiles of **skeletal muscle fibers** (SM) and the rich **vascular supply** (BV) of the lip.

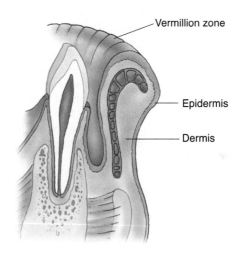

Vermillion zone

Epidermis

Dermis

Lip

KEY					
BV	vascular supply	E	epidermis	Sg	sebaceous glands
C	core	Ep	epithelium	SM	skeletal muscle
CP	connective tissue papillae	HF	hair follicles	VZ	vermillion (red) zone
D	dermis	RR	rete ridges		

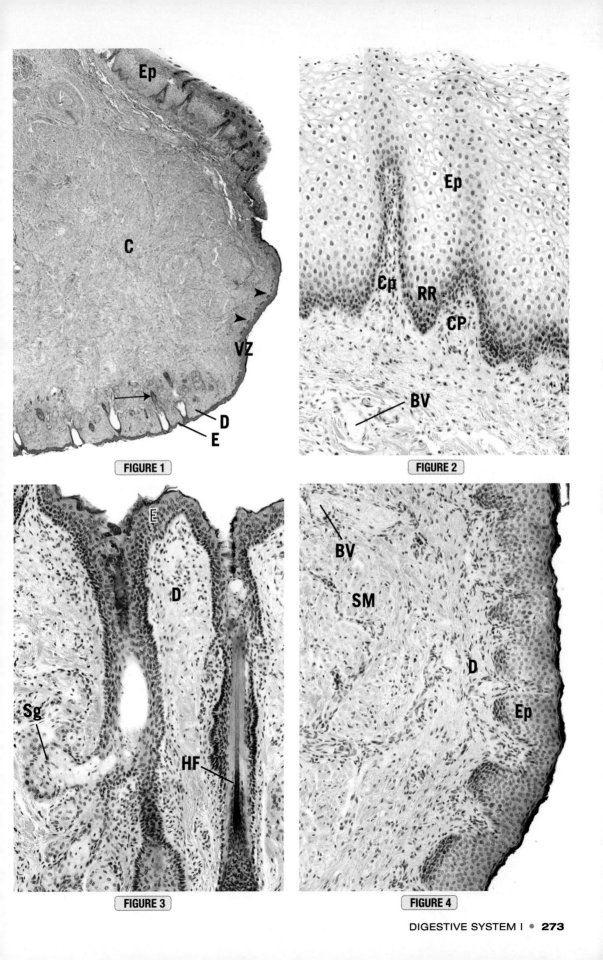

FIGURE 1

FIGURE 2

FIGURE 3

FIGURE 4

FIGURE 1 • Tooth. Human. Ground section. ×14.

The tooth consists of a crown, neck, and root, composed of calcified tissue surrounding a chamber housing a soft, gelatinous pulp. In ground section, only the hard tissues remain. The crown is composed of **enamel** (e) and **dentin** (d), whose interface is known as the **dentinoenamel junction** (DEJ). At the neck of the tooth, enamel meets **cementum** (c), forming the **cementoenamel junction** (CEJ). The **pulp chamber** (PC) is reduced in size as the individual ages. The gap in the enamel (*arrows*) is due to the presence of a carious lesion (cavity). A region similar to the *boxed area* is presented at a higher magnification in Figure 2.

FIGURE 2 • Tooth. Human. Ground section. ×132.

This photomicrograph is a higher magnification of a region similar to the *boxed area* of the previous figure. The **enamel** (e) is composed of enamel rods (*arrows*), each surrounded by a rod sheath. Hypomineralized regions of enamel present the appearance of tufts of grass, **enamel tufts** (ET), which extend from the **dentinoenamel junction** (DEJ) partway into the enamel. **Dentin** (d), not as highly calcified as enamel, presents long, narrow canals, **dentinal tubules** (DT), which in the living tooth house processes of odontoblasts, cells responsible for the formation of dentin.

FIGURE 3 • Pulp. Human. Paraffin section. ×132.

The pulp is surrounded by **dentin** (d) from which it is separated by a noncalcified **dentin matrix** (DM). The pulp is said to possess four regions: the **odontoblastic layer** (OL), the **cell-free zone** (CZ), the **cell-rich zone** (CR), and the **core** (C). The core of the pulp is composed of **fibroblasts** (F), delicate collagen fibers, numerous **nerve bundles** (NB), and **blood vessels** (BV). Branches of these neurovascular structures reach the periphery of the pulp, where they supply the cell-rich zone and the odontoblasts with capillaries and fine nerve fibers.

FIGURE 4 • Pulp. Human. Paraffin section. ×270.

This is a higher magnification of the lower right corner of the previous figure. Note the presence of **blood vessels** (BV) and **nerve fibers** (NF), as well as the numerous **fibroblasts** (F) of this gelatinous connective tissue.

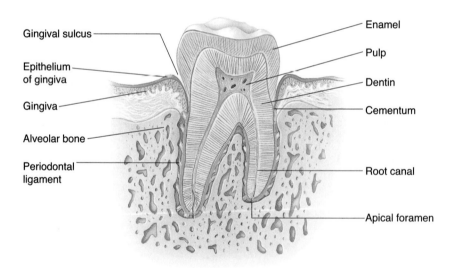

Gingival sulcus

Epithelium of gingiva

Gingiva

Alveolar bone

Periodontal ligament

Enamel

Pulp

Dentin

Cementum

Root canal

Apical foramen

Tooth

KEY					
BV	blood vessel	d	dentin	ET	enamel tufts
C	core	DEJ	dentinoenamel junction	F	fibroblasts
c	cementum	DM	dentin matrix	NB	nerve bundles
CEJ	cementoenamel junction	DT	dentinal tubule	OL	odontoblastic layer
CR	cell-rich zone	e	enamel	PC	pulp chamber
CZ	cell-free zone				

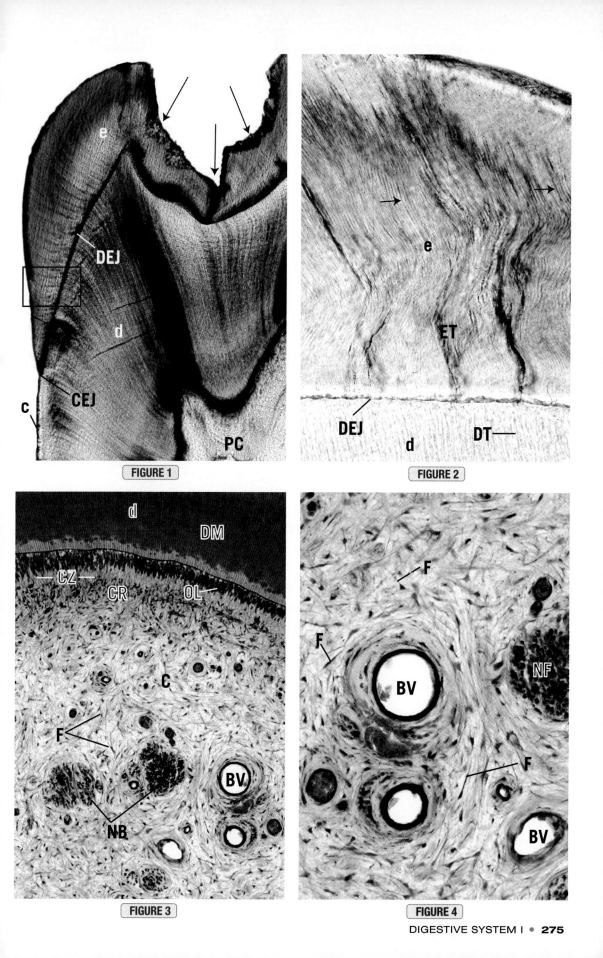

FIGURE 1

FIGURE 2

FIGURE 3

FIGURE 4

FIGURE 1 • Periodontal ligament. Human. Paraffin section. ×132.

The root of the tooth, composed of **dentin** (d) and **cementum** (c), is suspended in its **alveolus** (A) by a collagenous tissue, the **periodontal ligament** (PL). The strong bands of **collagen fibers** (CF) are embedded in the bone via **Sharpey's fibers** (SF). **Blood vessels** (BV) from the bone enter and supply the periodontal ligament. The dentinocemental junction (*arrows*) is clearly evident. Near the apex of the root, the cementum becomes thicker and houses cementocytes.

FIGURE 2 • Periodontal ligament. Human. Paraffin section. ×270.

The root of the tooth, composed of **dentin** (d) and **cementum** (c), is suspended in its bony **alveolus** (A) by fibers of the **periodontal ligament** (PL). Note that this photomicrograph is taken in the region of the **crest** (cr) of the alveolus, above which the periodontal ligament is continuous with the connective tissue of the **gingiva** (G). Note that both the gingiva and the periodontal ligament are highly vascular, as evident from the abundance of **blood vessels** (BV).

FIGURE 3 • Gingiva. Human. Paraffin section. ×14.

This is a decalcified longitudinal section of an incisor tooth; thus, all of the calcium hydroxyapatite crystals have been extracted from the tooth and from its bony **alveolus** (A). Since enamel is composed almost completely of calcium hydroxyapatite crystals, only the space where enamel used to be, the **enamel space** (ES), is represented in this photomicrograph. The **crest** (cr) of the alveolus is evident, as are the **periodontal ligament** (PL) and the **gingiva** (G). The **gingival margin** (GM), **free gingiva** (FG), **attached gingiva** (AG), **sulcular epithelium** (SE), **junctional epithelium** (JE), and **alveolar mucosa** (AM) are also identified.

FIGURE 4 • Gingiva. Human. Paraffin section. ×132.

This photomicrograph is a higher magnification of the gingival margin region of the previous figure. Note that the **enamel space** (ES) is located between the **dentin** (d) of the incisor tooth's crown and the **junctional epithelium** (JE). The **sulcular epithelium** (SE) of the **free gingiva** (FG) borders a space known as the **gingival sulcus** (GS), which would be clearly evident if the enamel were still present in this photomicrograph. Observe the well-developed interdigitations of the epithelium and connective tissue, known as the rete apparatus (*arrows*) of the **free gingiva** (FG) and **attached gingiva**, indicative of the presence of abrasive forces that act on these regions of the oral cavity.

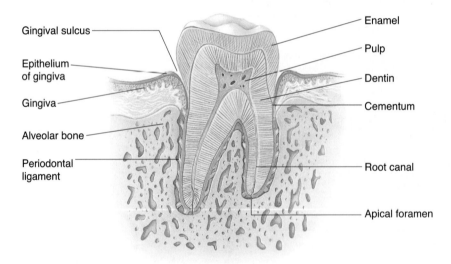

Gingival sulcus
Epithelium of gingiva
Gingiva
Alveolar bone
Periodontal ligament

Enamel
Pulp
Dentin
Cementum
Root canal
Apical foramen

Tooth

KEY					
A	alveolus	d	dentin	GM	gingival margin
AM	alveolar mucosa	DEJ	dentinoenamel junction	GS	gingival sulcus
AT	attached gingiva	DT	dentinal tubule	JE	junctional epithelium
BV	blood vessel	ES	enamel space	PC	pulp chamber
c	cementum	ET	enamel tufts	PL	periodontal ligament
cr	crest of alveolus	FG	free gingiva	SE	sulcular epithelium
CEJ	cementoenamel junction	G	gingiva		
CF	collagen fibers				

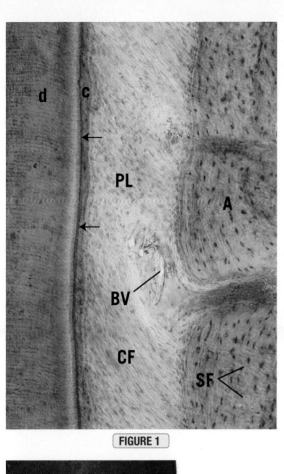

FIGURE 1

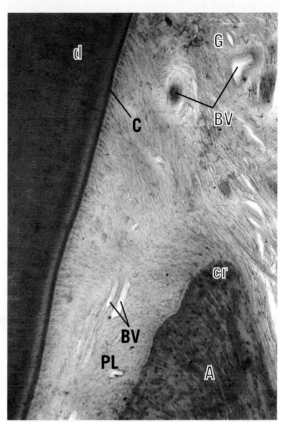

FIGURE 2

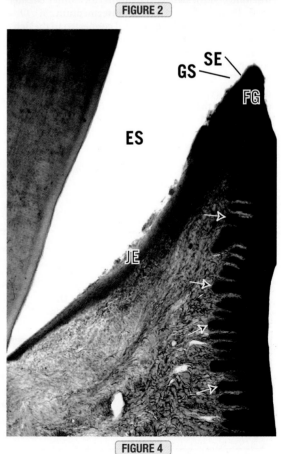

FIGURE 3

FIGURE 4

FIGURE 1a • Tooth development. Dental lamina. Frontal section. Pig. Paraffin section. ×132.

The **dental lamina** (DL) is a horseshoe-shaped band of epithelial tissue that arises from the **oral epithelium** (OE) and is surrounded by **mesenchymal cells** (MC). A frontal section of the dental lamina is characterized by the club-shaped appearance in this photomicrograph. The mesenchymal cells in discrete regions at the distal aspect of the dental lamina become rounded and congregate to form the precursor of the dental papilla responsible for the formation of the pulp and dentin of the tooth.

FIGURE 1b • Tooth development. Bud stage. Frontal section. Pig. Paraffin section. ×132.

At various discrete locations along the **dental lamina** (DL), an epithelial thickening, the **bud** (B), makes its appearance. Each bud will provide the cells necessary for enamel formation for a single tooth. The **dental papilla** (DP) forms a crescent-shaped area at the distal aspect of the bud.

FIGURE 3 • Tooth development. Bell stage. Frontal section. Pig. Paraffin section. ×132.

As the enamel organ expands in size, it resembles a bell, hence the bell stage of tooth development. This stage is characterized by four cellular layers: **outer enamel epithelium** (OEE), **stellate reticulum** (SR), **inner enamel epithelium** (IEE), and **stratum intermedium** (SI). Observe that the enamel organ is still connected to the **dental lamina** (DL). The **dental papilla** (DP) is composed of rounded mesenchymal cells, whose peripheral-most layer (*arrows*) will differentiate to form odontoblasts. Note the wide basement membrane (*arrowheads*) between the future odontoblasts and inner enamel epithelium (the future ameloblasts). Observe also the spindle-shaped cells of the **dental sac** (DS).

FIGURE 2 • Tooth development. Cap stage. Frontal section. Pig. Paraffin section. ×132.

Increased mitotic activity transforms the bud into a cap-shaped structure. Observe that three epithelial layers of the enamel organ may be recognized: the **outer enamel epithelium** (OEE), the **inner enamel epithelium** (IEE), and the intervening **stellate reticulum** (SR). The inner enamel epithelium has begun to enclose the **dental papilla** (DP). Note that mesenchymal cells become elongated, forming the **dental sac** (DS), which will envelop the enamel organ and dental papilla. Moreover, a **bony crypt** (BC) will enclose the dental sac.

FIGURE 4 • Tooth development. Apposition. Frontal section. Pig. Paraffin section. ×132.

The elaboration of **dentin** (d) and **enamel** (e) is indicative of apposition. Dentin is manufactured by **odontoblasts** (O), the peripheral-most cell layer of the **dental papilla** (DP). The odontoblastic processes (*arrows*) are visible in this photomicrograph as they traverse the **dentin matrix** (DM). **Ameloblasts** (A) are highly elongated, columnar cells that manufacture enamel. The long, epithelial structure located to the left is the **succedaneous lamina** (SL), which is responsible for the development of the permanent tooth.

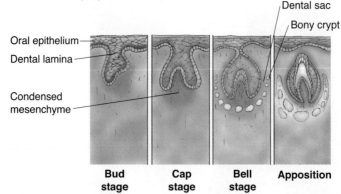

Dental sac

Bony crypt

Oral epithelium

Dental lamina

Condensed mesenchyme

Bud stage

Cap stage

Bell stage

Apposition

KEY					
A	ameloblast	DP	dental papilla	OE	oral epithelium
B	bud	DS	dental sac	OEE	outer enamel epithelium
BC	bony crypt	e	enamel	SI	stratum intermedium
d	dentin	IEE	inner enamel epithelium	SL	succedaneous lamina
DL	dental lamina	MC	mesenchymal cell	SR	stellate reticulum
DM	dentin matrix	O	odontoblast		

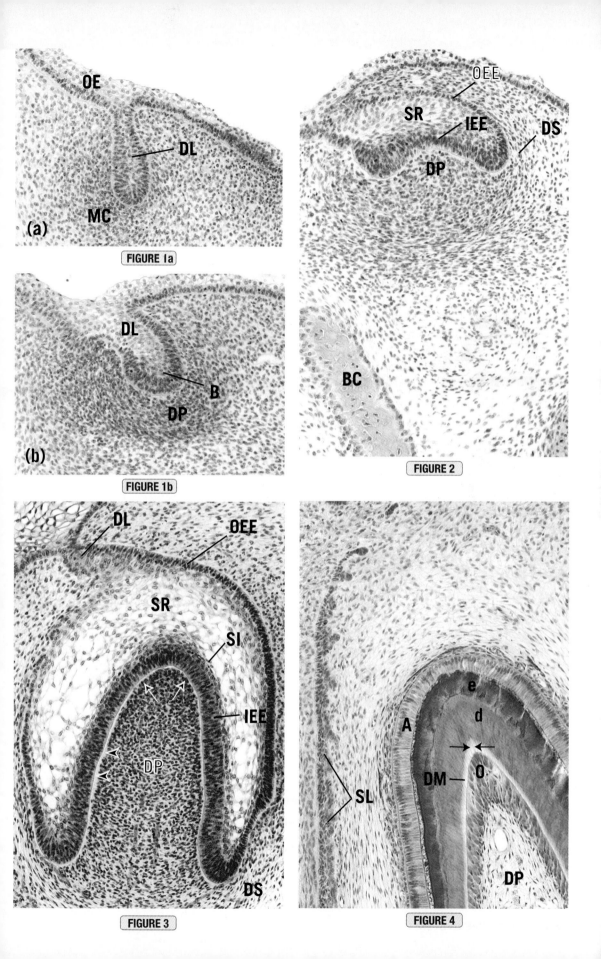

FIGURE 1a

FIGURE 1b

FIGURE 2

FIGURE 3

FIGURE 4

FIGURE 1 • Tongue. Human. l.s. Paraffin section. ×20.

Part of the anterior two-thirds of the tongue is presented in this photomicrograph. This muscular organ bears numerous **filiform papillae** (FP) on its dorsal surface, whose stratified squamous epithelium is keratinized (*arrow*). The ventral surface of the tongue is lined by stratified squamous nonkeratinized **epithelium** (Ep). The intrinsic muscles of the tongue are arranged in four layers: **superior longitudinal** (SL), **vertical** (V), **inferior longitudinal** (IL), and horizontal (not shown here). The mucosa of the tongue tightly adheres to the perimysium of the intrinsic tongue muscles by the subepithelial **connective tissue** (CT).

FIGURE 2 • Tongue. Human. l.s. Paraffin section. ×14.

The posterior aspect of the anterior two-thirds of the tongue presents **circumvallate papillae** (Cp). These papillae are surrounded by a deep groove (*arrow*), the base of which accepts a serous secretion via the **ducts** (Du) of the **glands of von Ebner** (GE). The **epithelium** (Ep) of the papilla houses taste buds along its lateral aspects but not on its superior surface. The core of the tongue contains **skeletal muscle** (SM) fibers of the extrinsic and intrinsic lingual muscles as well as glands and **adipose tissue** (AT). A region similar to the *boxed area* is presented at a higher magnification in Figure 3.

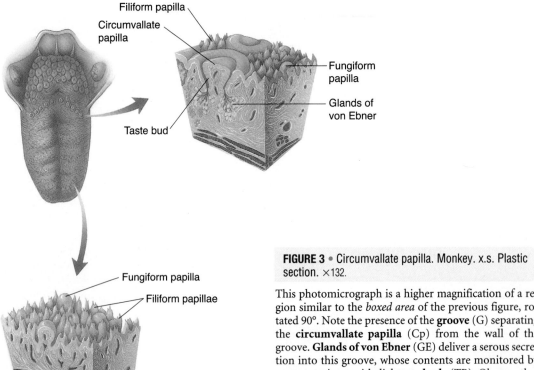

Filiform papilla
Circumvallate papilla
Taste bud
Fungiform papilla
Glands of von Ebner
Fungiform papilla
Filiform papillae

Tongue

FIGURE 3 • Circumvallate papilla. Monkey. x.s. Plastic section. ×132.

This photomicrograph is a higher magnification of a region similar to the *boxed area* of the previous figure, rotated 90°. Note the presence of the **groove** (G) separating the **circumvallate papilla** (Cp) from the wall of the groove. **Glands of von Ebner** (GE) deliver a serous secretion into this groove, whose contents are monitored by numerous intraepithelial **taste buds** (TB). Observe that taste buds are not found on the superior surface of the circumvallate papilla, only on its lateral aspect. The connective tissue core of the papilla is richly endowed by **blood vessels** (BV) and **nerves** (N).

KEY

AT	adipose tissue	FP	filiform papillae	SL	superior longitudinal
BV	blood vessels	G	groove		muscle
Cp	circumvallate papillae	GE	glands of von Ebner	SM	skeletal muscle
CT	connective tissue	IL	inferior longitudinal muscle	TB	taste buds
Du	ducts	N	nerves	V	vertical muscle
Ep	epithelium				

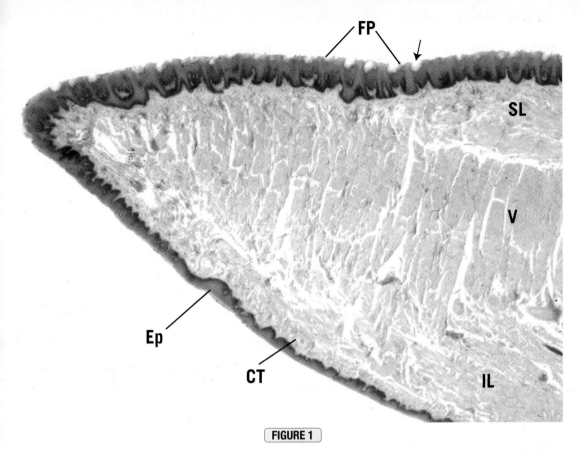

FP

↓

SL

V

Ep

CT

IL

FIGURE 1

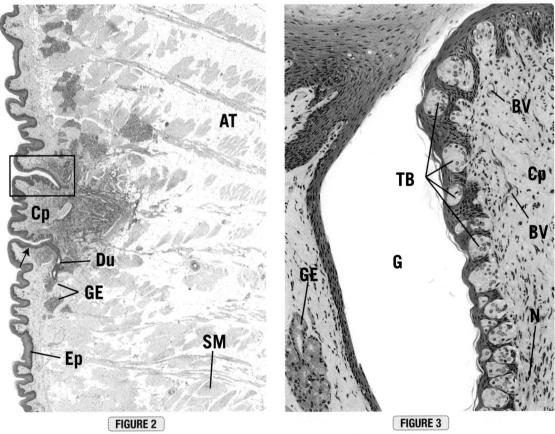

AT

Cp

Du

GE

Ep

SM

FIGURE 2

BV

Cp

TB

BV

G

GE

N

FIGURE 3

FIGURE 1 • Circumvallate papilla. Monkey. Paraffin section. ×132.

The base of the **circumvallate papilla** (Cp), the surrounding **groove** (G), and the wall of the groove are evident in this photomicrograph. The **glands of von Ebner** (GE) deliver their serous secretions via short **ducts** (Du) into the base of the groove. Observe the rich **vascular** (BV) and **nerve** (N) supply to this region. Numerous **taste buds** (TB) populate the epithelium of the lateral aspect of the circumvallate papilla. Each taste bud possesses a taste pore (*arrows*) through which taste hairs (microvilli) protrude into the groove. A region similar to the *boxed area* is presented at a higher magnification in Figure 2.

FIGURE 3 • Hard palate. Human. Paraffin section. ×132.

The hard palate possesses a nasal and an oral surface. The stratified squamous parakeratinized **epithelium** (Ep) of the oral surface forms deep invaginations, **rete ridges** (RR), which interdigitate with the subepithelial **connective tissue** (CT). The thick **collagen fiber bundles** (CF) firmly bind the palatal mucosa to the periosteum of the underlying bone. The hard palate also houses large deposits of adipose tissue and mucous glands.

FIGURE 2 • Taste bud. Monkey. Paraffin section. ×540.

This is a higher magnification of a region similar to the *boxed area* of Figure 1. Note that the stratified squamous parakeratinized **epithelium** (Ep) displays squames in the process of desquamation (*arrowheads*). The **taste buds** (TB) are composed of four cell types. **Basal** (lateral) **cells** (BC) are believed to be regenerative in nature, whereas **light cells** (LC), intermediate cells, and **dark cells** (DC) are gustatory. Observe the presence of **blood vessels** (BV) in the subepithelial **connective tissue** (CT).

FIGURE 4 • Soft palate. Human. Paraffin section. ×132.

The oral surface of the soft palate is lined by a stratified squamous nonkeratinized **epithelium** (Ep), which interdigitates with the **lamina propria** (LP) by the formation of shallow **rete ridges** (RR). The soft palate is a moveable structure, as attested by the presence of **skeletal muscle fibers** (SM). The core of the soft palate also houses numerous **mucous glands** (MG) that deliver their secretory products into the oral cavity via short, straight ducts.

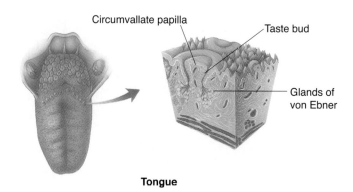

Circumvallate papilla

Taste bud

Glands of von Ebner

Tongue

KEY						
BC	basal cells	Du	ducts	MG	mucous glands
BV	blood vessels	Ep	epithelium	N	nerve
CF	collagen fiber bundles	G	groove	RR	rete ridges
Cp	circumvallate papilla	GE	glands of von Ebner	SM	skeletal muscle
CT	connective tissue	LC	light cells	TB	taste buds
DC	dark cells	LP	lamina propria		

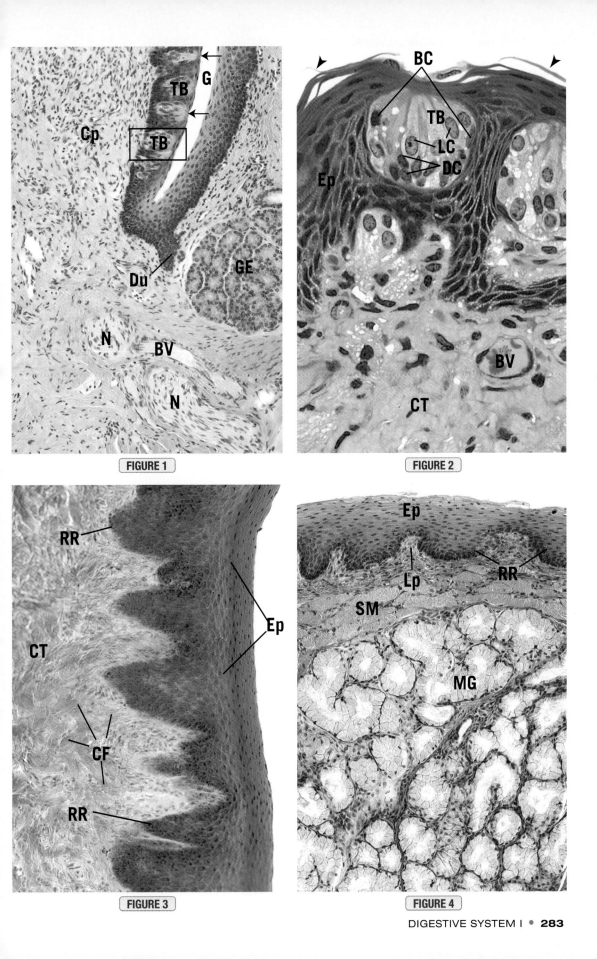

FIGURE 1

FIGURE 2

FIGURE 3

FIGURE 4

FIGURE 1 ● Human central incisor roots. Paraffin section. ×132.

The roots of two human central incisors and their supporting tissues are noted in this composite photomicrograph. Note that the root of one incisor, **Root 1**, is at the top of the figure and progressing down the page the **hyaline layer of Hopewell-Smith** (HL) separates the **dentin** (d) of the root from the **cementum** (c). The **periodontal ligament** (PL1), with its attendant **blood vessels** (BV), of this tooth suspends tooth 1 in its alveolus. The **interdental septum** (IS), positioned between the two incisors and composed of woven bone, is formed by the fusion of the **alveolar bones proper** (ABP 1 and 2) of each root. Note the presence of **osteons** (Os) in the woven bone; the center of these osteons approximates the line of fusion between the two alveolar bones proper. The **periodontal ligament** of the other incisor (PL 2) is located between the alveolar bone proper (ABP 2) and the **cementum** of this tooth. Its **dentin** (d) and **hyaline layer of Hopewell-Smith** (HL) of root 2 are evident.

FIGURE 2 ● Hard palate. Human. Paraffin section. ×132.

The hard palate possesses a nasal and an oral surface. Note that the pseudostratified ciliated columnar **epithelium** (Ep) displays cilia and an **intraepithelial gland** (IeGL). Observe the presence of **glands** (Gl) and **blood vessels** (BV) in the subepithelial **connective tissue** (CT).The epithelium and the subepithelial connective tissue are collectively referred to as the **mucoperiosteum** (MP), which is firmly attached to the **bony shelf** (B) of the palate. A higher magnification of the *boxed area* is presented in Figure 3.

FIGURE 3 ● Hard palate. Human. Paraffin section. ×132.

This is a higher magnification of a region similar to the *boxed area* of Figure 2. Note the presence of **glands** (Gl), **blood vessels** (BV), and **lymph vessels** (LV) within the subepithelial **connective tissue** (CT). The thick **collagen fiber bundles** (CF) firmly bind the palatal mucosa to the periosteum of the underlying bone. Observe the clearly visible **cilia** (c) of the pseudostratified ciliated columnar **epithelium** (Ep) covering the nasal surface of the hard palate.

KEY						
ABP	alveolar bone proper	d	dentin	IeGL	intraepithelial gland
B	bony shelf	Ep	epithelium	IS	interdental septum
BV	blood vessel	Gl	gland	MP	palatal mucosa
C	cementum	HL	hyaline layer of	Os	osteon
CT	connective tissue		Hopewell-Smith	PL	periodontal ligament

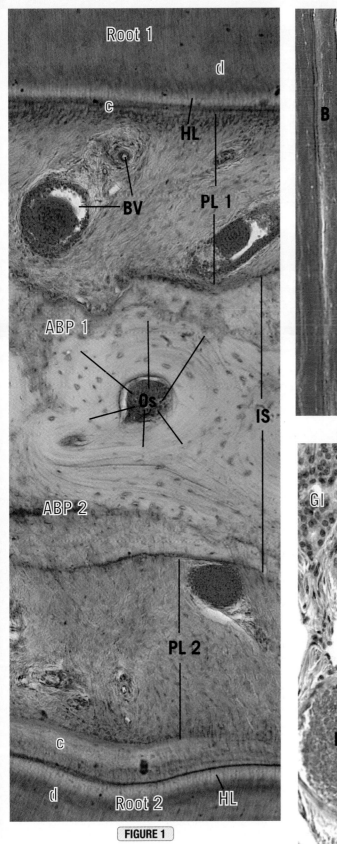

FIGURE 1

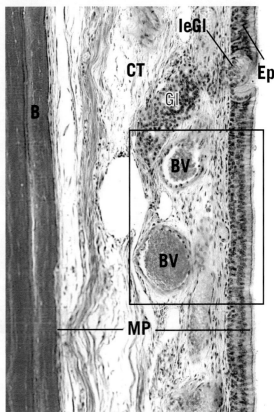

FIGURE 2

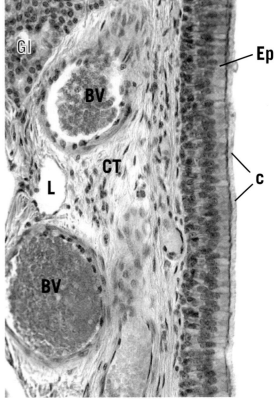

FIGURE 3

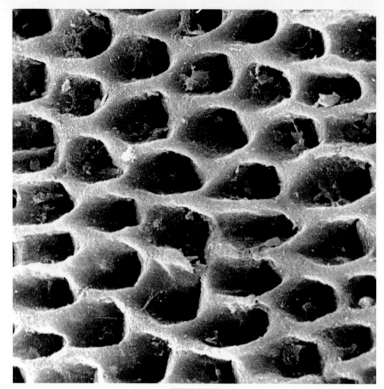

FIGURE 1

FIGURE 1 • Human enamel. Scanning electron microscopy. ×3,150.

This three-dimensional view of the forming mineralized human enamel displays rod spaces (the recesses) surrounded by the inter-rod enamel. The rod spaces were occupied by Tomes' processes of the ameloblasts, and, as the ameloblasts recede, rod spaces are filled in by the secretory mechanism and the spaces are filled by enamel known as rod segments. The arched aspects of the rod spaces are directed occlusally. As rod segments are positioned on top of each other, they form an enamel rod whose shape resembles a keyhole. (From Fejerskov O. Human dentition and experimental animals. J Dent Res 1979;58(Special Issue B):725–734.)

FIGURE 1

FIGURE 1 • Human dentin. Scanning electron microscopy. ×3,800.

This three-dimensional view of mineralized human dentin displays a longitudinal section of dentinal tubules. In a healthy, living dentin, the tubules house the processes of odontoblasts that extend at least 1 mm into the denti-nal tubule. Additionally, some of the tubules also house nerve fibers, and all of the tubules are filled completely with an extracellular fluid that originates in the pulp of the tooth. (From Thomas H. The dentin-predentin complex and its permeability: anatomical overview. J Dent Res 1985;64(Special Issue B):607–612.)

Summary of Histological Organization

I. LIPS

The **lips** control access to the **oral cavity** from the outside environment.

A. External Surface

The external surface is covered with thin **skin** and therefore possesses **hair follicles, sebaceous glands,** and **sweat glands.**

B. Transitional Zone

The **transitional zone** (**vermilion zone**) is the pink area of the lip. Here the connective tissue papillae extend deep into the epidermis. Hair follicles and sweat glands are absent, whereas sebaceous glands are occasionally present.

C. Mucous Membrane

The vestibular aspect of the lip is lined by a **wet epithelium** (stratified squamous nonkeratinized) with numerous **minor mixed salivary glands** in the subepithelial connective tissue.

D. Core of the Lip

The core of the lip contains **skeletal muscle.**

II. TEETH

Teeth are composed of three calcified tissues and a loose connective tissue core, the pulp.

A. Enamel

Enamel is the hardest substance in the body. It is made by **ameloblasts,** cells no longer present in the erupted tooth. Enamel is present only in the crown.

B. Dentin

Dentin is a calcified, collagen-based material that constitutes the bulk of the **crown** and **root**; it surrounds the pulp. Dentin is made by **odontoblasts,** whose long processes remain in channels, the **dentinal tubules,** traversing dentin. The odontoblast cell body forms the peripheral extent of the pulp.

C. Cementum

Cementum is located on the **root** of the tooth, surrounding **dentin.** Cementum is a collagen-based, calcified material manufactured by **cementoblasts,** which may become entrapped and then are referred to as **cementocytes.** Fibers of the **periodontal ligament** are embedded in cementum and bone, thus suspending the tooth in its **bony socket,** the **alveolus.**

D. Pulp

The **pulp** is a gelatinous type of mesenchymal-appearing connective tissue that occupies the **pulp chamber.** It is richly supplied by **nerves** and **blood vessels.**

III. GINGIVA

The **gingiva** (gum) is that region of the oral mucosa that is closely applied to the **neck of the tooth** and is attached to the **alveolar bone.** It is covered by a **stratified squamous partially keratinized (parakeratotic) epithelium.** The underlying connective tissue is densely populated with thick bundles of collagen fibers.

IV. TONGUE

The **tongue** is a **muscular organ** whose oral region is freely moving; its root is attached to the floor of the pharynx. **Skeletal muscle** forms the core of the tongue, among which groups of serous and seromucous glands are interspersed.

A. Oral Region (Anterior Two-Thirds)

The mucosa of the dorsal surface of the anterior two-thirds of the tongue is modified to form four types of lingual papillae.

1. Filiform Papillae

Filiform papillae are long and slender and are the most numerous. They form a roughened surface (especially in animals such as cats) and are distributed in parallel rows along the entire surface. They are covered by a **parakeratinized stratified squamous epithelium** (but bear no taste buds) over a **connective tissue core.**

2. Fungiform Papillae

Fungiform papillae are mushroom shaped, are scattered among the filiform papillae, and may be recognized by their appearance as red dots. They contain **taste buds** along their dorsal aspect.

3. Foliate Papillae

Foliate papillae appear as longitudinal furrows along the side of the tongue near the posterior aspect of the anterior two-thirds. Their **taste buds**

degenerate at an early age in humans. Serous **glands of von Ebner** are associated with these papillae.

4. Circumvallate Papillae

Circumvallate papillae are very large and form a V-shaped row at the border of the oral and pharyngeal portions of the tongue. Circumvallate papillae are each surrounded by a moat or groove, the walls of which contain **taste buds** in their **stratified squamous nonkeratinized epithelium**. Serous **glands of von Ebner** open into the base of the furrow. The connective tissue core of the circumvallate papilla possesses a rich nerve and vascular supply.

B. Pharyngeal Region (Posterior One-Third)

The **mucosa** of the posterior one-third of the tongue presents numerous **lymphatic nodules** that constitute the **lingual tonsils**.

V. PALATE

The **palate,** composed of hard and soft regions, separates the **oral** and **nasal cavities** from each other. Therefore, the palate possesses a **nasal** and an **oral aspect**. The **oral** aspect is covered by **stratified squamous epithelium (partially keratinized** on the hard palate), whereas the **nasal** aspect is covered by a **respiratory epithelium**. The **subepithelial connective tissue** presents dense collagen fibers interspersed with **adipose tissue** and **mucous glands**. The **core** of the hard palate houses a **bony shelf**, whereas that of the soft palate is composed of **skeletal muscle**.

VI. TOOTH DEVELOPMENT

Tooth development (odontogenesis) may be divided into several stages (see Graphic 13-1). These are named according to the morphology and/or the functional state of the developing tooth. **Dental lamina**, the first sign of odontogenesis, is followed by **bud, cap,** and **bell stages**. Dentin formation initiates the **apposition stage**, followed by **root formation** and **eruption**. These stages occur in both **primary** (deciduous teeth) and **secondary** (permanent teeth) **dentition**.

Digestive System II

14

The **alimentary canal** is an approximately 9-meter-long, hollow, tubular structure that extends from the oral cavity to the anus whose wall is modified along its length to perform the various facets of digestion. The oral cavity receives food and, via mastication and bolus formation, delivers it into the oral pharynx, from where it enters the esophagus and eventually the stomach. The gastric contents are reduced to an **acidic chyme**, which is transferred in small aliquots into the small intestine, where most digestion and absorption occur. The liquefied food residue passes into the large intestine, where the digestion is completed and water is resorbed. The solidified feces are then passed to the rectum for elimination through the anus.

A common architectural plan is evident for the alimentary tract from the esophagus to the anus, in that four distinct concentric layers may be recognized to constitute the wall of this long, tubular structure. These layers are described from the lumen outward.

● LAYERS OF THE WALL OF THE ALIMENTARY CANAL

Mucosa

The innermost layer directly surrounding the lumen is known as the **mucosa**, which is composed of three concentric layers: a **wet epithelial lining** with secretory and absorptive functions; a connective tissue **lamina propria** containing glands and components of the circulatory system; and a **muscularis mucosae**, usually consisting of two thin, smooth muscle layers, responsible for the mobility of the mucosa.

Submucosa

The **submucosa** is a coarser connective tissue component that physically supports the mucosa and provides neural, vascular, and lymphatic supply to the mucosa. Moreover, in some regions of the alimentary canal the submucosa houses glands.

Muscularis Externa

The **muscularis externa** usually consists of an **inner circular** and an **outer longitudinal smooth muscle layer**, which is modified in certain regions of the alimentary canal. Although these layers are described as circularly or longitudinally arranged, they are actually wrapped around the alimentary canal in tight and loose helices, respectively. Vascular and neural plexuses reside between the muscle layers. The muscularis externa functions in churning and propelling the luminal contents along the digestive tract via peristaltic action. Thus, as the circular muscles reduce the diameter of the lumen, preventing the movement of the luminal contents in a proximal direction (toward the mouth), the longitudal muscles contract in such a fashion as to push the luminal contents in a distal direction (toward the anus).

Serosa or Adventitia

The outermost layer of the alimentary canal is either a serosa or an adventitia. The intraperitoneal regions of the alimentary canal, i.e., those that are suspended by peritoneum, possess a **serosa**. This structure consists of connective tissue covered by a **mesothclium** (simple squamous epithelium), which reduces frictional forces during digestive movements. Other regions of the alimentary tract are firmly attached to surrounding structures by connective tissue fibers. These regions possess an **adventitia**.

● REGIONS OF THE ALIMENTARY CANAL

Esophagus

The **esophagus** is a short, muscular tube whose mucosa is composed of a **stratified squamous nonkeratinized epithelium**, a loose type of connective tissue housing mucus-producing esophageal **cardiac glands** in the lamina propria, and only longitudinally oriented smooth muscle fibers of the muscularis mucosae. The submucosa of this organ is composed of dense, irregular collagenous connective tissue interspersed with elastic fibers. This is one of the two regions of the alimentary canal (the other is the duodenum) that houses glands in its submucosa. These glands are the mucus-producing **esophageal glands proper**. The **muscularis externa** of the esophagus is composed of **inner circular** and **outer longitudinal layers**. Those in the proximal (upper) one-third are **skeletal**, those in the middle one-third are **skeletal** and **smooth**, whereas those in the distal (lower) one-third are **smooth muscle**. The esophagus functions in conveying boluses of food from the pharynx into the stomach.

Stomach

Based on the types of glands in its lamina propria, histologically, the stomach is subdivided into three regions: **cardia, fundus,** and **pylorus** (see Graphic 14-1). The mucosa of the empty stomach is thrown into longitudinal folds, known as **rugae**. The luminal surface, lined by a simple columnar epithelium (**surface lining cells**), displays **foveolae** (**gastric pits**), whose base is perforated by several gastric glands of the lamina propria. All **gastric glands** are composed of **parietal** (**oxyntic**) **cells, mucous neck cells, surface lining cells, diffuse neuroendocrine system** (**DNES**, also known as **APUD**) **cells,** and **regenerative cells. Fundic glands**, in addition, also house **chief** (**zymogenic**) **cells**.

Oxyntic cells produce HCl and **gastric intrinsic factor**, a factor that assists the ileum in absorbing vitamin B_{12}. These cells possess intracellular canaliculi and a complex tubulovesicular system. **Mucous neck cells** manufacture *soluble mucus* that becomes part of and lubricates chyme, whereas **surface lining cells** manufacture visible mucus that adheres to the lining of the stomach, protecting it from autodigestion. The various types of **DNES** cells produce hormones such as **gastrin, somatostatin, secretin,** and **cholecystokinin** (see Table 14-1 for hormones produced by the alimentary canal). **Regenerative cells**, located mainly in the neck and isthmus, replace the epithelial lining of the stomach and the cells of the glands. **Chief cells**, located in the base of the fundic glands, produce precursors of enzymes (**pepsin, rennin,** and **lipase**).

Small Intestine

The **small intestine** is composed of the **duodenum, jejunum,** and **ileum**. The mucosa of all three regions displays **villi**, extensions of the lamina propria, covered by a simple columnar type of epithelium. The epithelium is composed of goblet, surface absorptive, and DNES cells. **Goblet cells** produce **mucinogen** that becomes hydrated to form **mucin**, which, when mixed with the luminal contents of the stomach, becomes known as **mucus**. **DNES cells** release various hormones (e.g., **secretin, motilin, neurotensin, cholecystokinin, gastric inhibitory peptide,** and **gastrin**) (see Table 14-1 for hormones produced by the alimentary canal). The tall, columnar **surface absorptive cells** possess numerous **microvilli** covered by a thick glycocalyx composed of several enzymes. These cells function in absorption of lipids, amino acids, and carbohydrates. Long-chained lipids, in the form of **chylomicrons**, are delivered to the **lacteals**, blindly ending lymphatic channels of the villus.

Simple tubular glands of the mucosa, **the crypts of Lieberkühn**, open into the intervillar spaces. These crypts are composed of simple columnar cells (similar to surface absorptive cells), goblet (and oligomucous) cells, DNES, and regenerative cells, as well as **Paneth cells**. The last are located in the base of the crypts and house large secretory granules believed to contain the antibacterial enzyme **lysozyme**. The lamina propria of the ileum houses large accumulations of lymphatic nodules, **Peyer's patches**. The surface epithelium interposed between Peyer's patches and the lumen of the ileum instead of being composed of simple columnar cells is formed by **M cells** (see below).

The submucosa of the duodenum contains numerous glands, **duodenal** (**Brunner's**) **glands**, that produce an alkaline, mucin-containing fluid that protects the intestinal lining. They also manufacture **urogastrone**, a polypeptide that inhibits HCl production and enhances epithelial cell division.

Large Intestine

The **large intestine** is subdivided into the **cecum**, the **colon** (**ascending, transverse, descending,** and **sigmoid**), the **rectum**, the **anal canal**, and the **appendix** (see Graphic 14-2). The large intestine possesses no villi but does house **crypts of Lieberkühn** in its lamina propria. The epithelial lining of the lumen and of the crypts is composed of **goblet** (and **oligomucous**) **cells, surface absorptive cells, regenerative cells,** and occasional **DNES cells**. There are no Paneth cells in the large intestine, with the possible exception of the appendix. The large intestine functions in the absorption of the remaining amino acids, lipids, and carbohydrates, as well as fluids, electrolytes, and certain vitamins, and it also is responsible for the compaction of feces.

TABLE 14-1 • Hormones Produced by Cells of the Alimentary Canal

Hormone	Location	Action
Cholecystokinin (CCK)	Small intestine	Contraction of gallbladder; release of pancreatic enzymes
Gastric inhibitory peptide	Small intestine	Inhibits secretion of HCl
Gastrin	Stomach and duodenum	Stimulates secretion of HCl and gastric enzymes
Glycentin	Stomach, small and large intestines	Stimulates glycogenolysis by hepatocytes
Glucagon	Stomach and duodenum	Stimulates glycogenolysis by hepatocytes
Motilin	Small intestine	Increases intestinal peristalsis
Neurotensin	Small intestine	Decreases peristalsis in intestines; stimulates blood supply to ileum
Secretin	Small intestine	Stimulates bicarbonate secretion by pancreas
Serotonin	Stomach, small and large intestines	Increases intestinal peristalsis
Somatostatin	Stomach and duodenum	Inhibits DNES cells in its vicinity of release
Substance P	Stomach, small and large intestines	Increases intestinal peristalsis
Urogastrone	Duodenal glands (Brunner's)	Inhibits secretion of HCl; increases epithelial cell mitosis
Vasoactive intestinal peptide	Stomach, small and large intestines	Increases intestinal peristalsis; stimulates secretion of ions and water by the alimentary canal

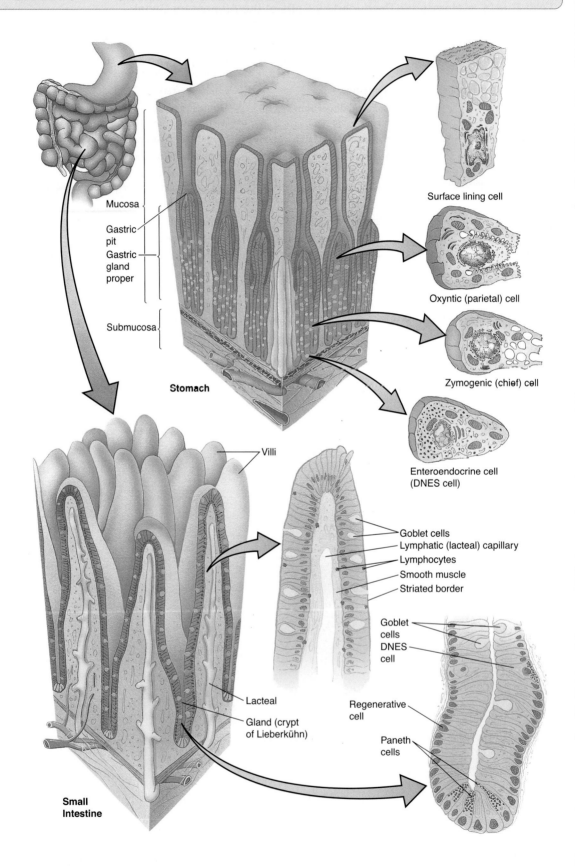

Mucosa

Gastric pit

Gastric gland proper

Submucosa

Stomach

Surface lining cell

Oxyntic (parietal) cell

Zymogenic (chief) cell

Enteroendocrine cell (DNES cell)

Villi

Goblet cells
Lymphatic (lacteal) capillary
Lymphocytes
Smooth muscle
Striated border

Goblet cells
DNES cell

Regenerative cell

Paneth cells

Lacteal

Gland (crypt of Lieberkühn)

Small Intestine

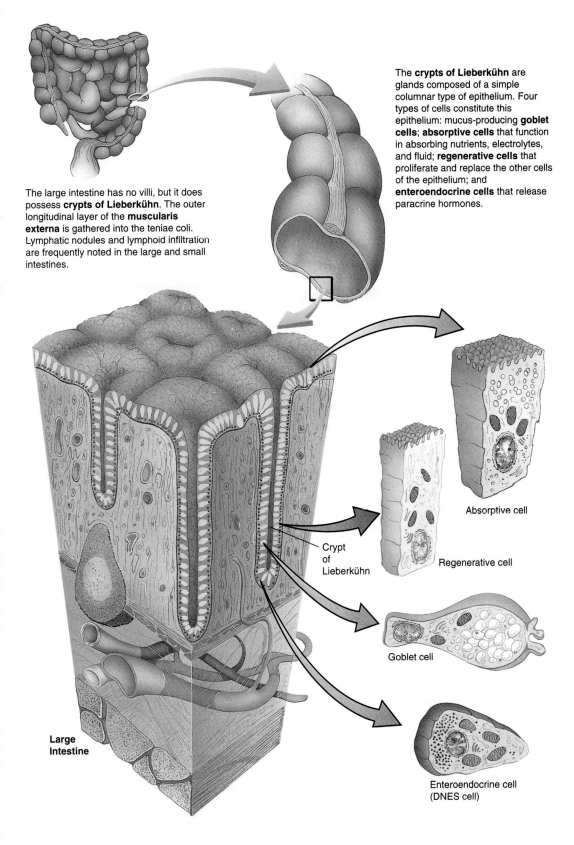

The large intestine has no villi, but it does possess **crypts of Lieberkühn**. The outer longitudinal layer of the **muscularis externa** is gathered into the teniae coli. Lymphatic nodules and lymphoid infiltration are frequently noted in the large and small intestines.

The **crypts of Lieberkühn** are glands composed of a simple columnar type of epithelium. Four types of cells constitute this epithelium: mucus-producing **goblet cells**; **absorptive cells** that function in absorbing nutrients, electrolytes, and fluid; **regenerative cells** that proliferate and replace the other cells of the epithelium; and **enteroendocrine cells** that release paracrine hormones.

Crypt
of
Lieberkühn

Absorptive cell

Regenerative cell

Goblet cell

Enteroendocrine cell
(DNES cell)

Large
Intestine

Histophysiology

I. STOMACH

The **stomach** functions in acidifying and converting the semisolid **bolus** into the viscous fluid, **chyme**, which undergoes initial digestion and is delivered into the **duodenum** in small quantities.

The gastric mucosa is lined by a simple columnar epithelium whose **surface lining cells** (not goblet cells) produce a mucous substance that coats and protects the stomach lining from the low pH environment and from autodigestion.

The lamina propria of the stomach houses **gastric glands**; depending on the region of the stomach, these are cardiac, fundic, or pyloric. **Fundic glands** are composed of five cell types: parietal (oxyntic), mucous neck, chief (zymogenic), DNES, and regenerative cells. Neither **cardiac** nor **pyloric glands** possess chief cells.

Parietal cells secrete hydrochloric acid (HCl) into **intracellular canaliculi**. These cells alter their morphology during HCl secretion, in that they increase their number of **microvilli** that project into the intracellular canaliculi. It is believed that these microvilli are stored as the **tubulovesicular system**, flanking the intracellular canaliculi when the cell is not secreting HCl. Additionally, parietal cells also secrete **gastric intrinsic factor**, a glycoprotein that binds to and forms a complex with vitamin B_{12} in the gastric lumen. When this complex reaches the ileum, it binds to specific receptors on the surface absorptive cells and the vitamin becomes absorbed. **Mucous neck cells** are located in the neck of the gastric glands. As described above, they secrete a **mucus** that is distinct from that secreted by surface lining cells.

Chief cells are located in the deep aspect of fundic glands. They secrete precursors of the enzymes **pepsin**, **rennin**, and **lipase**, which initiate digestion in the stomach.

Enteroendocrine cells (**DNES cells**) belong to cells of the diffuse neuroendocrine system and are known by several synonyms. Although as a group these cells produce a number of different hormones, it is believed that each cell is capable of producing only a single hormone. The hormones that these cells produce may enter vascular or lymphatic channels, but the target cells for most of these hormones are in the vicinity of their release; therefore, these hormones are referred to as **paracrine hormones**. (See Table 14-1 for hormones produced by the alimentary canal.)

II. SMALL INTESTINE

The luminal aspect of the small intestine is modified to increase its surface area. These modifications range from the macroscopic, **plicae circulares** (increase 3×), through the microscopic, **villi** (increase 10×), to the submicroscopic, **microvilli** (increase 20×).

A. Villi

Villi are lined by a simple columnar epithelium composed of surface absorptive cells, goblet cells, and DNES cells.

Surface absorptive cells possess dense accumulations of microvilli, forming the **striated border**. Their tips have a thick coat of **glycocalyx**, rich in **disaccharidases** and **dipeptidases**. These cells function in absorption of sugars, amino acids, fatty acids, monoglycerides, electrolytes, water, and many other substances. These epithelial cells also participate in the immune defense of the body by manufacturing **secretory protein**, which binds to the J protein component of the antibody and protects **immunoglobulin A** (**IgA**) as it traverses the epithelial cell and enters the intestinal lumen.

Goblet cells produce **mucinogen**, which, when released into the intestinal lumen, becomes hydrated, forming **mucin**, a slippery substance that, when mixed with material in its vicinity, becomes the substance known as **mucus**. The mucus protects the intestinal lining.

B. Crypts of Lieberkühn

The simple tubular glands of the lamina propria are known as the **crypts of Lieberkühn**. They open into the intervillar spaces and are lined by a simple columnar epithelium composed of columnar cells (surface absorptive cells), goblet cells, DNES cells, regenerative cells, and Paneth cells.

Regenerative cells are located in the basal half of the crypts of Lieberkühn and function as a population of stem cells that replace the entire intestinal epithelium every 4 to 6 days.

Paneth cells are located in the base of the crypts of Lieberkühn and are easily recognized by their large apical granules. These cells manufacture the enzyme **lysozyme**, an antibacterial agent.

C. Brunner's Glands (Duodenal Glands)

Brunner's glands are located in the **submucosa** of the duodenum. These glands produce an alkaline-rich, mucin-containing fluid that buffers the acidic chyme entering the duodenum from the stomach. Additionally, Brunner's glands manufacture and release **urogastrone**.

III. GUT-ASSOCIATED LYMPHOID TISSUE

Since the lumen of the digestive tract is rich in antigenic substances, bacteria, and toxins and since only a thin, simple columnar epithelium separates the richly vascularized connective tissue from this threatening milieu, the lamina propria of the intestines is well endowed with lymphoid elements. These include scattered cells (B cells, T cells, plasma cells, mast cells, macrophages, etc.), individual lymphatic nodules, and, in the ileum, **Peyer's patches**, clusters of lymphatic nodules. Regions where lymphatic nodules come in contact with the epithelial lining of the intestines display flattened cells that form the interface between the lumen and the lymphatic nodule. These are **M cells** (**microfold cells**), which phagocytose antigens and transport them, via clathrin-coated vesicles, to the basal aspect of the cell. The antigens are released into the lamina propria for uptake by antigen-presenting cells and dendritic cells.

IV. DIGESTION AND ABSORPTION

A. Carbohydrates

Amylases, present in the saliva and in the pancreatic secretion, hydrolyze carbohydrates to disaccharides. **Oligo-** and **disaccharidases**, present in the glycocalyx of surface absorptive cells, break down oligo- and disaccharides into monosaccharides (glucose and galactose) that enter the surface absorptive cell, requiring active transport using sugar-glucose transporter 1. The cells then release the glucose and galactose into the lamina propria, where these sugars enter the circulatory system for transport to the liver.

B. Proteins

Proteins, denatured by HCl in the lumen of the stomach, are hydrolyzed (by the enzyme **pepsin**) into **polypeptides**. These are further broken down into **tri-** and **dipeptides** by proteases of the pancreatic secretions. **Tri-** and **dipeptidases** of the glycocalyx hydrolyze dipeptides into individual amino acids, which enter the surface absorptive cells, involving active transport, and are transferred into the lamina propria, where they enter the capillary network to be transported to the liver.

C. Lipids

Pancreatic lipase breaks lipids down into **fatty acids**, **monoglycerides**, and **glycerol** within the lumen of the duodenum and proximal jejunum. Bile salts, delivered from the gallbladder, emulsify the fatty acids and monoglycerides, forming **micelles**, which, along with glycerol, diffuse into the surface absorptive cells. Within these cells they enter the **smooth endoplasmic reticulum**, are reesterified to **triglycerides**, and are covered by a coat of protein within the Golgi apparatus, forming lipoprotein droplets known as **chylomicrons**. Chylomicrons exit these cells at their basolateral membranes and enter the **lacteals** of the villi, contributing to the formation of **chyle**. Chyle enters the lymph vascular system, makes it way to the thoracic duct, and then into the venous system at the junction of the left internal jugular vein and left brachiocephalic vein. Fatty acids that are shorter than 12 carbon chains in length pass through the surface absorptive cells without being reesterified and gain entrance to the blood capillaries of the villi.

D. Water and Ions

Water and ions are absorbed through the surface absorptive cells of the small and the large intestine.

CLINICAL CONSIDERATIONS

Crohn's Disease

Crohn's disease is a subcategory of **inflammatory bowel disease**, a condition of unknown etiology. It usually involves the small intestine or the colon but may affect any region of the alimentary canal, from the esophagus to the anus, as well as extra-alimentary canal structures such as the skin, the kidney, and the larynx. It is characterized by patchy ulcers and deep fistulas in the intestinal wall. Clinical manifestations include abdominal pain, diarrhea, and fever, and these recur after various periods of ever shortening remission.

Mallory-Weiss Syndrome

Approximately 4% to 6% of the bleeding from the upper GI tract is attributable to **Mallory-Weiss syndrome**. This is a laceration of the lower esophagus or the cardiac/fundic region of the stomach as a result of powerful vomiting or sometimes strenuous hiccuping. Frequently the bleeding is self-limiting, but occasionally it requires surgical intervention to ligate the damaged blood vessels.

Peptic Ulcers

Peptic ulcers are areas of the stomach, but mostly of the duodenum, that are denuded of the epithelial lining due to the action of the acid chyme. Most commonly, the underlying reasons are *Helicobacter pylori* infections and the use of aspirin, corticosteroids, and nonsteroidal antiinflammatory drugs (NSAIDS). Interestingly, people who smoke and/or drink alcoholic beverages develop peptic ulcers more frequently than do nonsmokers and nondrinkers. The symptoms involve mild to sharp pain in the midline of the lower thoracic and upper abdominal regions. The pain may be alleviated by eating and drinking fluids (especially milk), but it usually returns in 2 to 3 hours. The use of antibiotics and the use of antacids are common treatment modalities, as are dietary changes and the use of alternatives to NSAIDS and aspirin.

Zollinger-Ellison Syndrome

Zollinger-Ellison syndrome is a cancerous lesion of gastrin-producing cells in the stomach, duodenum, or the pancreas, resulting in the overproduction of HCl by parietal cells of the stomach and the formation of numeorus recurrent peptic ulcers. A high blood level of gastrin, especially after intravenous administration of secretin, usually is a strong indicator of this syndrome. Surgical resection of the tumor and the administration of proton pump inhibitors alleviates but does not cure the problem.

Antibiotic-Associated Colitis

Antibiotics such as ampicillin, cephalosporin, and clindamycin often cause an imbalance in the intestinal bacterial flora, permitting the vigorous proliferation of *Clostridium difficile*, resulting in infection by this organism. The two major toxins (Toxin A and Toxin B) produced by *C. difficile* frequently cause inflammation of the sigmoid colon. Depending on the severity of the infection, the patient will suffer from abdominal cramps, loose stool, bloody diarrhea, fever, and, in extreme cases, dehydration and perforation of the bowel. In rare, severe cases, powerful antibiotics such as metronidazole and vincomycin may have to be administered, and, even more infrequently, surgical resection of the affected region of the large intestine may be necessary.

Hiatal Hernia

Hiatal hernia is a condition in which a region of the stomach herniates through the **esophageal hiatus** of the diaphragm. It may be of two types, sliding and paraesophageal hiatal hernia. In the former condition, the cardioesophageal junction and the cardiac region of the stomach slides in and out of the thorax, whereas in the latter case the cardioesophageal junction remains in its normal place, below the diaphragm, but a part (or occasionally all) of the stomach pushes into the thorax and is positioned next to the esophagus. Usually, hiatal hernia is asymptomatic, although acid reflux disease is common in patients afflicted with this condition. Patients are advised to eat smaller meals more frequently, and the acid reflux disease is treated. Infrequently, paraesophageal hiatal hernias may result in strangulation of the protruded region with a possible loss of blood supply. In these cases, surgical intervention may be indicated.

FIGURE 1 • Esophagus. x.s. Paraffin section. ×14.

This photomicrograph of a cross-section of the lower one-third of the esophagus displays the general structure of the digestive tract. The **lumen** (L) is lined by a stratified squamous nonkeratinized **epithelium** (Ep) lying on a thin **lamina propria** (LP) that is surrounded by the **muscularis mucosae** (MM). The **submucosa** (Sm) contains glands and is surrounded by the **muscularis externa** (ME), composed of an **inner circular** (IC) and an **outer longitudinal** (OL) layer. The outermost tunic of the esophagus is the fibroelastic **adventitia** (Ad). A region similar to the *boxed area* is presented at a higher magnification in Figure 2.

FIGURE 3 • Esophagus. Human. x.s. Paraffin section. ×132.

The **lamina propria** (LP) and **submucosa** (Sm) of the esophagus are separated from each other by the longitudinally oriented smooth muscle bundles, the **muscularis mucosae** (MM). Observe that the lamina propria is a very vascular connective tissue, housing numerous **blood vessels** (BV) and **lymph vessels** (LV), whose valves (*arrow*) indicate the direction of lymph flow. The submucosa also displays numerous **blood vessels** (BV) as well as the presence of the **esophageal glands proper** (EG), which produce a mucous secretion to lubricate the lining of the esophagus.

FIGURE 2 • Esophagus. Human. x.s. Paraffin section. ×132.

This photomicrograph is a higher magnification of a region similar to the *boxed area* of the previous figure. The **mucosa** (M) of the esophagus consists of a stratified squamous nonkeratinized **epithelium** (Ep), a loose collagenous connective tissue layer, the **lamina propria** (LP), and a longitudinally oriented smooth muscle layer, the **muscularis mucosae** (MM). The **submucosa** (Sm) is composed of a coarser collagenous **connective tissue** (CT), housing **blood vessels** (BV) and various connective tissue cells whose **nuclei** (N) are evident.

FIGURE 4 • Esophagogastric junction. l.s. Dog. Paraffin section. ×14.

The junction of the **esophagus** (Es) and **cardiac stomach** (CS) is very abrupt, as evidenced by the sudden change of the **stratified squamous epithelium** (SE) to the **simple columnar epithelium** (CE) of the stomach. Note that the **esophageal glands proper** (EG) continue for a short distance into the **submucosa** (Sm) of the stomach. Observe also the presence of gastric pits (*arrows*) and the increased thickness of the **muscularis externa** (ME) of the stomach compared with that of the esophagus. The outermost tunic of the esophagus inferior to the diaphragm is a **serosa** (Se) rather than an adventitia. The *boxed area* is presented at a higher magnification in Figure 1 of the next plate.

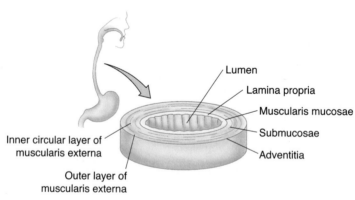

Lumen
Lamina propria
Muscularis mucosae
Submucosae
Adventitia
Inner circular layer of muscularis externa
Outer layer of muscularis externa

Esophagus

KEY

Ad	adventitia	EP	epithelium	MM	muscularis mucosae
BV	blood vessels	Es	esophagus	N	nucleus
CE	simple columnar epithelium	IC	inner circular muscle	OL	outer longitudinal muscle
		L	lumen	SE	stratified squamous epithelium
CS	cardiac stomach	LP	lamina propria		
CT	connective tissue	LV	lymph vessels	Se	serosa
EG	esophageal glands proper	M	mucosa	Sm	submucosa
		ME	muscularis externa		

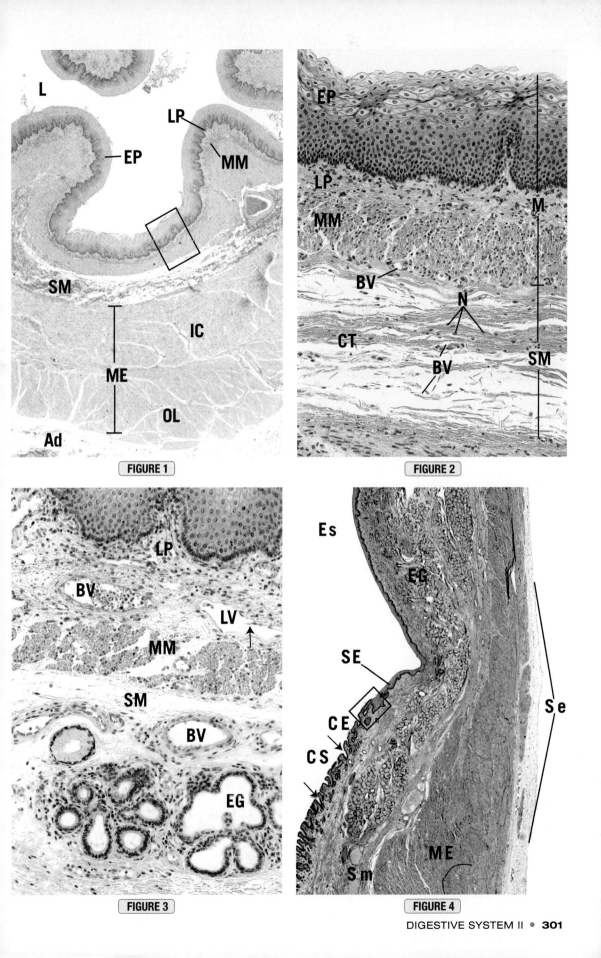

FIGURE 1

FIGURE 2

FIGURE 3

FIGURE 4

FIGURE 1 • Esophagogastric junction. l.s. Dog. Paraffin section. ×132.

This photomicrograph is a higher magnification of the *boxed region* of Figure 4, Plate 14-1. The **stratified squamous epithelium** (SE) of the esophagus is replaced by the **simple columnar epithelium** (CE) of the stomach in a very abrupt fashion (*arrow*). The **lamina propria** (LP) displays **gastric pits** (GP), lined by the typical mucus-secreting **surface lining cells** (SC), characteristic of the stomach. The structure labeled with an *asterisk* is not a lymphatic nodule but is a more or less tangential section through the esophageal epithelium. Note the presence of the **muscularis mucosae** (MM).

FIGURE 3 • Fundic stomach. x.s. Dog. Paraffin section. ×132.

This photomicrograph presents a higher magnification of a region similar to the *boxed area* of Figure 2. The mucosa of the fundic stomach displays numerous **gastric pits** (GP) that are lined by a simple columnar epithelium, consisting mostly of mucus-producing **surface lining (surface mucous) cells** (SC). The base of each pit accepts the isthmus of two to four **fundic glands** (FG). Although fundic glands are composed of several cell types, only two, **parietal cells** (PC) and **chief cells** (CC), are readily distinguishable in this preparation. The **lamina propria** (LP) is richly **vascularized** (BV). Note the **muscularis mucosae** (MM) beneath the lamina propria. A region similar to the *boxed area* is presented at a higher magnification (positioned at a 90° angle) in Figure 4.

FIGURE 2 • Fundic stomach. l.s. Paraffin section. ×14.

The fundic region presents all of the characteristics of the stomach, as demonstrated by this low-power photomicrograph. The **lumen** (L) is lined by a simple columnar epithelium, deep to which is the **lamina propria** (LP), housing numerous **gastric glands** (GG). Each gland opens into the base of a **gastric pit** (GP). The **muscularis mucosae** (MM) separates the lamina propria from the **submucosa** (Sm), a richly **vascularized** (BV) connective tissue, thrown into folds (rugae) in the empty stomach. The **muscularis externa** (ME) is composed of three poorly defined layers of smooth muscle: **innermost oblique** (IO), **middle circular** (MC), and **outer longitudinal** (OL). Serosa (*arrow*) forms the outermost tunic of the stomach. A region similar to the *boxed area* is presented at a higher magnification in Figure 3.

FIGURE 4 • Fundic glands. x.s. Paraffin section. ×540.

This photomicrograph presents a higher magnification (positioned at a 90° angle) of a region similar to the *boxed area* of Figure 3. The **lumina** (L) of several glands can be recognized. Note that **chief cells** (CC) are granular in appearance and are much smaller than the round, plate-like **parietal cells** (PC). Parietal cells, as their name implies, are located at the periphery of the gland. Slender **connective tissue elements** (CT), housing blood vessels, occupy the narrow spaces between the closely packed glands.

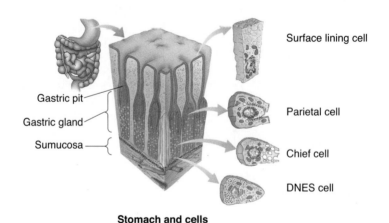

Surface lining cell

Gastric pit

Gastric gland

Sumucosa

Parietal cell

Chief cell

DNES cell

Stomach and cells

KEY					
BV	blood vessels	GP	gastric pits	MM	muscularis mucosae
CC	chief cells	IO	innermost oblique muscle	OL	outer longitudinal muscle
CE	columnar epithelium	L	lumen	PC	parietal cells
CT	connective tissue	LP	lamina propria	SC	surface lining cells
FG	fundic glands	ME	muscularis externa	SE	squamous epithelium
GG	gastric glands	MC	middle circular muscle	Sm	submucosa

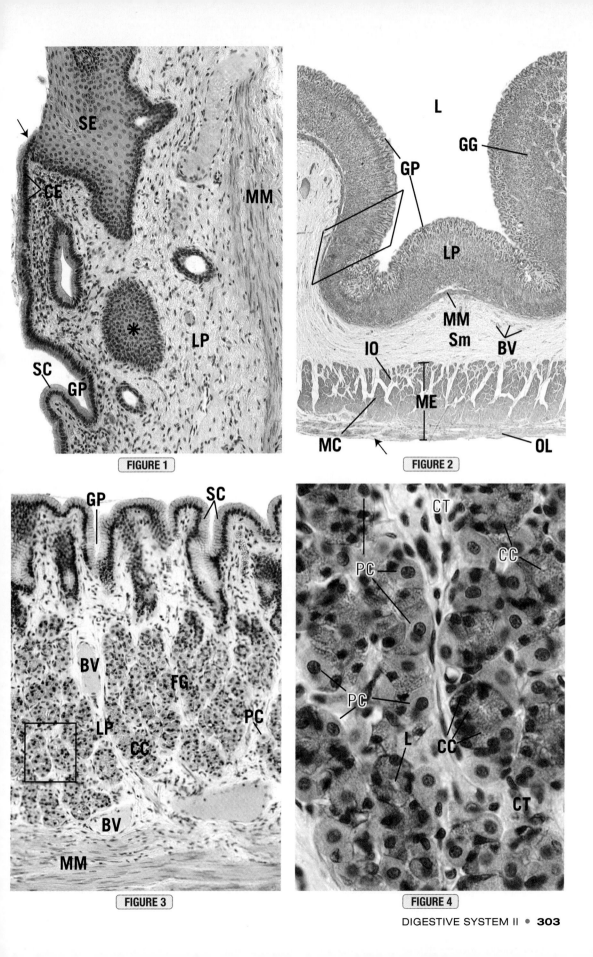

FIGURE 1

FIGURE 2

FIGURE 3

FIGURE 4

FIGURE 1 • Fundic stomach. x.s. Monkey. Plastic section. ×270.

The **gastric pits** (GP) of the fundic stomach are lined mostly by mucus-producing **surface lining cells** (SC). Each gastric pit receives two to four fundic glands, simple tubular structures that are subdivided into three regions: isthmus, neck, and base. The isthmus opens directly into the gastric pit and is composed of **immature cells** (Ic), which are responsible for the renewal of the lining of the gastric mucosa, **surface lining cells** (SC), and **parietal cells** (PC). The neck and base of these glands are presented in Figure 2.

FIGURE 3 • Pyloric gland. Stomach. x.s. Monkey. Plastic section. ×132.

The mucosa of the pyloric region of the stomach presents **gastric pits** (GP) that are deeper than those of the cardiac or fundic regions. The deep aspects of these pits are coiled (*arrows*). As in the other regions of the stomach, the **epithelium** (Ep) is simple columnar, consisting mainly of **surface lining cells** (SC). Note that the **lamina propria** (LP) is loosely packed with **pyloric glands** (PG) and that considerable **connective tissue** (CT) is present. The pyloric glands are composed mainly of **mucous cells** (mc). Observe the two muscle layers of the **muscularis mucosae** (MM). A region similar to the *boxed area* is presented in Figure 4.

FIGURE 2 • Fundic gland. Stomach. x.s. Monkey. Plastic section. ×270.

The **neck** (n) and **base** (b) of the fundic gland both contain the large, plate-shaped **parietal cells** (PC). The neck also possesses a few immature cells as well as **mucous neck cells** (Mn), which manufacture a mucous substance. The base of the fundic glands contains numerous acid-manufacturing **parietal cells** (PC) and **chief cells** (CC), which produce digestive enzymes. Note that the lamina propria is tightly packed with glands and that the intervening **connective tissue** (CT) is flimsy. The bases of these glands extend to the **muscularis mucosae** (MM).

FIGURE 4 • Pyloric gland. Stomach. x.s. Human. Paraffin section. ×270.

This is a photomicrograph of a region similar to the *boxed area* of Figure 3. The simple columnar **epithelium** (Ep) of the **gastric pit** is composed mostly of surface lining cells. These pits are not only much deeper than those of the fundic or cardiac regions but are also somewhat coiled (*arrow*), as are the **pyloric glands** (PG), which empty into the base of the pits. These glands are populated by **mucus-secreting cells** (mc) similar to mucous neck cells, whose **nuclei** (N) are flattened against the basal cell membrane. Note that the glands are not closely packed and that the **lamina propria** (LP) is very cellular and possesses a rich **vascular supply** (BV).

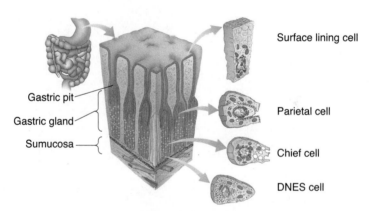

Gastric pit
Gastric gland
Sumucosa

Surface lining cell
Parietal cell
Chief cell
DNES cell

Stomach and cells

KEY					
b	base	Ic	immature cells	n	neck
BV	blood vessels	LP	lamina propria	PC	parietal cells
CC	chief cells	mc	mucous cells	PG	pyloric glands
CT	connective tissue	MM	muscularis mucosae	SC	surface lining cells
EP	epithelium	Mn	mucous neck cell		
GP	gastric pits	N	nucleus		

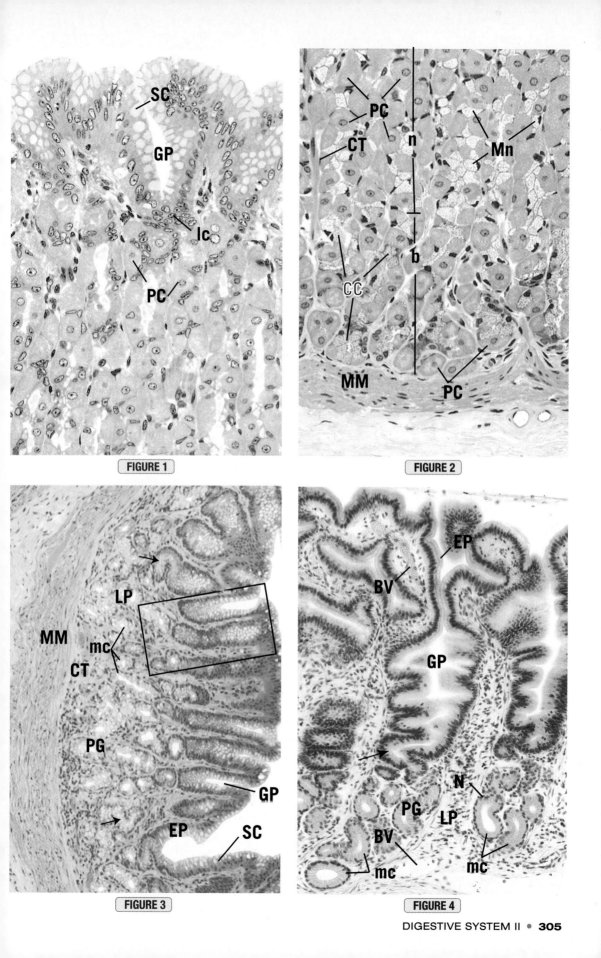

FIGURE 1

FIGURE 2

FIGURE 3

FIGURE 4

DIGESTIVE SYSTEM II • **305**

FIGURE 1a ● Duodenum. l.s. Monkey. Plastic section. Montage. ×132.

The lamina propria of the duodenum possesses finger-like evaginations known as **villi** (V), which project into the **lumen** (L). The villi are covered by **surface absorptive cells** (SA), a simple columnar type of epithelium with a brush border. Interspersed among these surface absorptive cells are **goblet cells** (GC) as well as occasional APUD cells. The **connective tissue** (CT) core (lamina propria) of the villus is composed of lymphoid and other cellular elements whose nuclei stain very intensely. Blood vessels also abound in the lamina propria, as do large, blindly ending lymphatic channels known as **lacteals** (l), recognizable by their large size and lack of red blood cells. Frequently, these lacteals are collapsed. The deeper aspect of the lamina propria houses glands, the **crypts of Lieberkühn** (CL). These simple tubular glands deliver their secretions into the intervillar spaces. The bases of these crypts reach the **muscularis mucosae** (MM), composed of inner circular and outer longitudinal layers of smooth muscle. Deep to this muscle layer is the submucosa, which, in the duodenum, is occupied by compound tubular **glands of Brunner** (GB). These glands deliver their mucous secretion via **ducts** (D), which pierce the muscularis mucosae, into the crypts of Lieberkühn. A region similar to the *boxed area* is presented at a higher magnification in Figure 1b.

FIGURE 1b ● Epithelium and core of villus. Monkey. Plastic section. ×540.

This higher magnification of a region similar to the *boxed area* presents the epithelium and part of the connective tissue core of a villus. Note that the **surface absorptive cells** (SA) display a **brush border** (BB), terminal bars (*arrow*), and **goblet cells** (GC). Although APUD cells are also present, they constitute only a small percentage of the cell population. The **lamina propria** (LP) core of the villus is highly cellular, housing **lymphoid cells** (LC), **smooth muscle cells** (SM), mast cells, **macrophages** (Ma), and fibroblasts, among others.

FIGURE 2 ● Duodenum. l.s. Monkey. Plastic section. ×132.

This photomicrograph is a continuation of the montage presented in Figure 1a (compare *asterisks*). Note that the **submucosa** (Sm), occupied by **glands of Brunner** (GB), is a **vascular** structure (BV) and also houses Meissner's submucosal plexus. The submucosa extends to the **muscularis externa** (ME), composed of an **inner circular** (IC) and **outer longitudinal** (OL) smooth muscle layer. Note the presence of **Auerbach's myenteric plexus** (AP) between these two muscle layers. The duodenum, in part, is covered by a **serosa** (Se), whose mesothelium provides this organ with a smooth, moist surface.

FIGURE 3a ● Duodenum. x.s. Monkey. Plastic section. ×540.

The base of the crypt of Lieberkühn displays the several types of cells that compose this gland. **Paneth cells** (Pc) are readily recognizable due to the large granules in their apical cytoplasm. **DNES cells** (APD) are clear cells with fine granules usually located basally. **Goblet cells** (GC), **columnar cells** (Cc), and **stem cells** (Sc) constitute the remaining cell population.

FIGURE 3b ● Duodenum. x.s. Monkey. Plastic section. ×540.

The submucosa of the intestinal tract displays small parasympathetic ganglia, Meissner's submucosal plexus. Note the large **postganglionic cell bodies** (PB) surrounded by elements of **connective tissue** (CT).

KEY					
AP	Auerbach's plexus	GC	goblet cell	OL	outer longitudinal muscle
APD	DNES cell	IC	inner circular muscle	PB	postganglionic cell body
BB	brush border	I	lacteal	Pc	Paneth cell
BV	blood vessels	L	lumen	SA	surface absorptive cell
Cc	columnar cell	LC	lymphoid cell	Sc	stem cell
CL	crypts of Lieberkühn	LP	lamina propria	Se	serosa
CT	connective tissue	Ma	macrophage	Sm	submucosa
D	duct	ME	muscularis externa	SM	smooth muscle cell
GB	glands of Brunner	MM	muscularis mucosae	V	villi

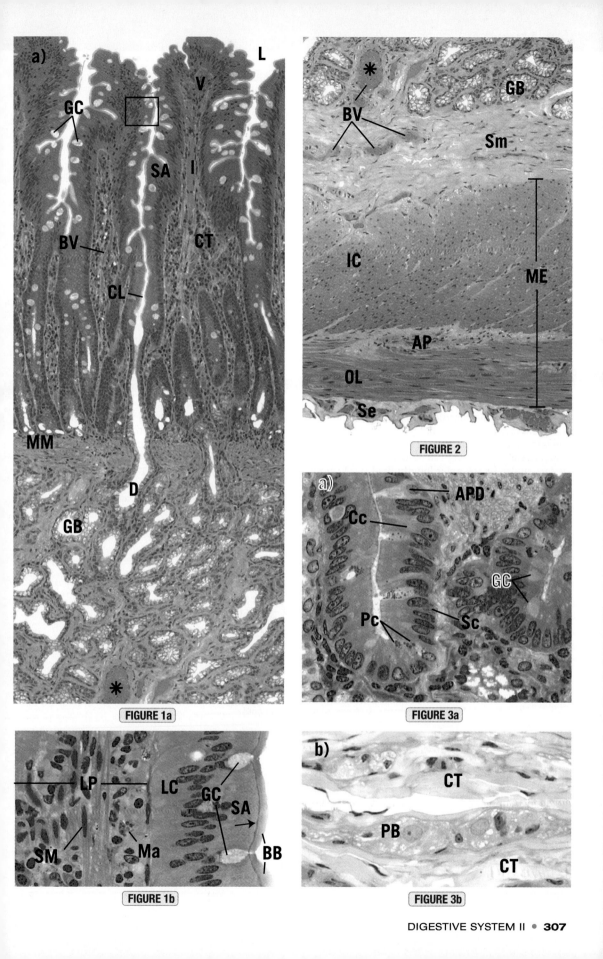

a)

L

V

GC

SA

I

BV

CT

CL

MM

D

GB

✱

FIGURE 1a

✱

BV

GB

Sm

ME

IC

AP

OL

Se

FIGURE 2

a)

APD

Cc

GC

Pc

Sc

FIGURE 3a

LP

LC

GC

SA

SM

Ma

BB

FIGURE 1b

b)

CT

PB

CT

FIGURE 3b

FIGURE 1 ● Jejunum. x.s. Monkey. Plastic section. ×132.

The **mucosa** (M) and **submucosa** (Sm) of the jejunum are presented in this photomicrograph. The **villi** (V) of this region possess more **goblet cells** (GC) than those of the duodenum. Observe that the **crypts of Lieberkühn** (CL) open into the intervillar spaces (*arrow*) and that the lamina propria displays numerous dense nuclei, evidence of lymphatic infiltration. The flimsy **muscularis mucosae** (MM) separates the lamina propria from the submucosa. Large **blood vessels** (BV) occupy the submucosa, which is composed of a loose type of collagenous connective tissue. The **inner circular** (IC) layer of the muscularis externa is evident at the bottom of the photomicrograph. The *boxed region* is presented at a higher magnification in Figure 2.

FIGURE 3 ● Ileum. l.s. Human. Paraffin section. ×14.

The entire wall of the ileum is presented, displaying spiral folds of the submucosa that partially encircle the lumen. These folds, known as **plicae circulares** (Pci), increase the surface area of the small intestines. Note that the lamina propria is clearly delineated from the **submucosa** (Sm) by the muscularis mucosae. The lamina propria forms numerous **villi** (V) that protrude into the **lumen** (L); glands known as **crypts of Lieberkühn** (CL) deliver their secretions into the intervillar spaces. The submucosa abuts the **inner circular** (IC) layer of smooth muscle that, in turn, is surrounded by the **outer longitudinal** (OL) smooth muscle layer of the muscularis externa. Observe the **serosa** (Se) investing the ileum. A region similar to the *boxed area* is presented at a higher magnification in Figure 4.

FIGURE 2 ● Jejunum. x.s. Monkey. Plastic section. ×540.

This photomicrograph is a higher magnification of the *boxed area* of Figure 1. The crypts of Lieberkühn are composed of several cell types, some of which are evident in this figure. **Goblet cells** (GC) that manufacture mucus may be noted in various degrees of mucus production. Narrow **stem cells** (Sc) undergo mitotic activity (*arrowhead*), and newly formed cells reconstitute the cell population of the crypt and villus. **Paneth cells** (PC) are located at the base of crypts and may be recognized by their large granules. **DNES cells** (APD) appear as clear cells, with fine granules usually basally located. The lamina propria displays numerous **plasma cells** (PlC).

FIGURE 4 ● Ileum. x.s. Monkey. Plastic section. ×132.

This is a higher magnification of a region similar to the *boxed area* of Figure 3. Note that the **villi** (V) are covered by a simple columnar epithelium, whose cellular constituents include numerous **goblet cells** (GC). The core of the villus displays **blood vessels** (BV) as well as a large lymphatic vessel known as a **lacteal** (l). The **crypts of Lieberkühn** (CL) open into the intervillar spaces (*arrow*). The group of lymphatic nodules of the ileum are known as **Peyer's patches** (PP). *Inset a.* **Crypt of Lieberkühn. l.s. Monkey. Plastic section.** × 540. The crypts of Lieberkühn also possess **DNES cells** (APD), recognizable by their clear appearance and usually basally oriented fine granules. *Inset b.* **Crypt of Lieberkühn. l.s. Monkey. Plastic section.** × 540. The base of the crypt of Lieberkühn displays cells with large granules. These are **Paneth cells** (PC), which produce the bacteriocidal agent lysozyme.

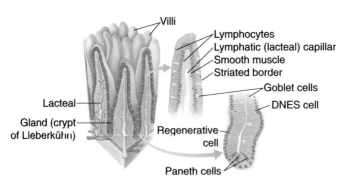

Small intestine

KEY					
APD	DNES cell	L	lumen	PP	Peyer's patch
BV	blood vessels	M	mucosa	OL	outer longitudinal muscle
CL	crypts of Lieberkühn	MM	muscularis mucosae	Sc	stem cell
GC	goblet cell	PC	Paneth cell	Se	serosa
IC	inner circular muscle	Pci	plicae circulares	Sm	submucosa
l	lacteal	PlC	plasma cell	V	villi

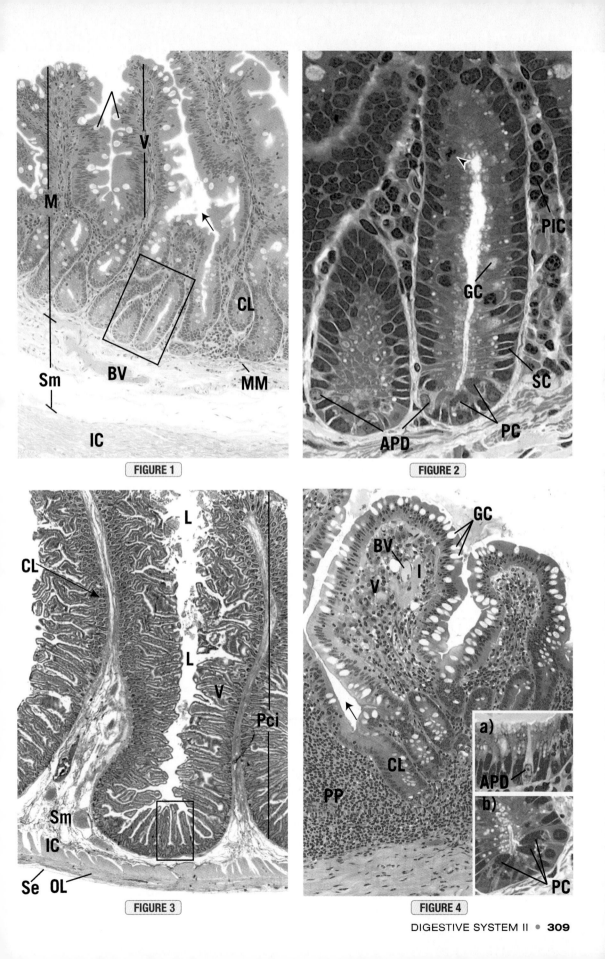

FIGURE 1

FIGURE 2

FIGURE 3

FIGURE 4

a)

b)

FIGURE 1 ● Colon. l.s. Monkey. Plastic section. ×132.

This photomicrograph depicts the mucosa and part of the submucosa of the colon. Note the absence of surface modifications such as pits and villi, which indicate that this section is not of the stomach or small intestines. The **epithelium** (Ep) lining the **lumen** (L) is simple columnar with numerous **goblet cells** (GC). The straight tubular glands are **crypts of Lieberkühn** (CL), which extend down to the **muscularis mucosae** (MM). The **inner circular** (IC) and **outer longitudinal** (OL) layers of smooth muscle comprising this region of the mucosa are evident. The **submucosa** (Sm) is very **vascular** (BV) and houses numerous **fat cells** (FC). The *boxed area* is presented at a higher magnification in Figure 2.

FIGURE 2 ● Colon. l.s. Monkey. Plastic section. ×540.

This photomicrograph is a higher magnification of the *boxed area* of Figure 1. The cell population of the **crypts of Lieberkühn** (CL) is composed of numerous **goblet cells** (GC), which deliver their mucus into the **lumen** (L) of the crypt. **Surface epithelial cells** (SEC) as well as undifferentiated stem cells are also present. The latter undergo mitosis (*arrow*) to repopulate the epithelial lining. **DNES cells** (APD) constitute a small percentage of the cell population. Note that Paneth cells are not present in the colon. The **lamina propria** (LP) is very cellular, housing many **lymphoid cells** (LC). The **inner circular** (IC) and **outer longitudinal** (OL) smooth muscle layers of the **muscularis mucosae** (MM) are evident.

FIGURE 3 ● Appendix. x.s. Paraffin section. ×132.

The cross-section of the appendix displays a **lumen** (L) that frequently contains debris (*arrow*). The lumen is lined by a simple columnar **epithelium** (Ep), consisting of many **goblet cells** (GC). **Crypts of Lieberkühn** (CL) are relatively shallow in comparison with those of the colon. The **lamina propria** (LP) is highly infiltrated with **lymphoid cells** (LC), derived from **lymphatic nodules** (LN) of the **submucosa** (Sm) and lamina propria. The **muscularis mucosae** (MM) delineates the border between the lamina propria and the submucosa.

FIGURE 4 ● Anorectal junction. l.s. Human. Paraffin section. ×132.

The anorectal junction presents a superficial similarity to the esophagogastric junction because of the abrupt epithelial transition. The **simple columnar epithelium** (CE) of the rectum is replaced by the **stratified squamous epithelium** of the **anal canal** (AC). The **crypts of Lieberkühn** (CL) of the anal canal are shorter than those of the colon. The **lamina propria** (LP) is infiltrated by **lymphoid cells** (LC).

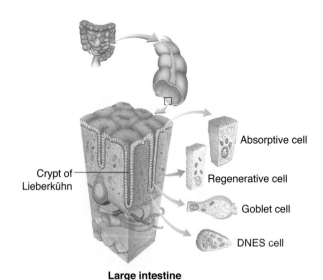

Absorptive cell

Crypt of Lieberkühn

Regenerative cell

Goblet cell

DNES cell

Large intestine

KEY					
AC	anal canal	FC	fat cell	MM	muscularis mucosae
APD	DNES cell	GC	goblet cell	OL	outer longitudinal muscle
BV	blood vessels	IC	inner circular muscle	SE	stratified squamous
CE	simple columnar	L	lumen		epithelium
	epithelium	LC	lymphoid cell	SEC	surface epithelial cell
CL	crypts of Lieberkühn	LN	lymphatic nodule	Sm	submucosa
EP	epithelium	LP	lamina propria		

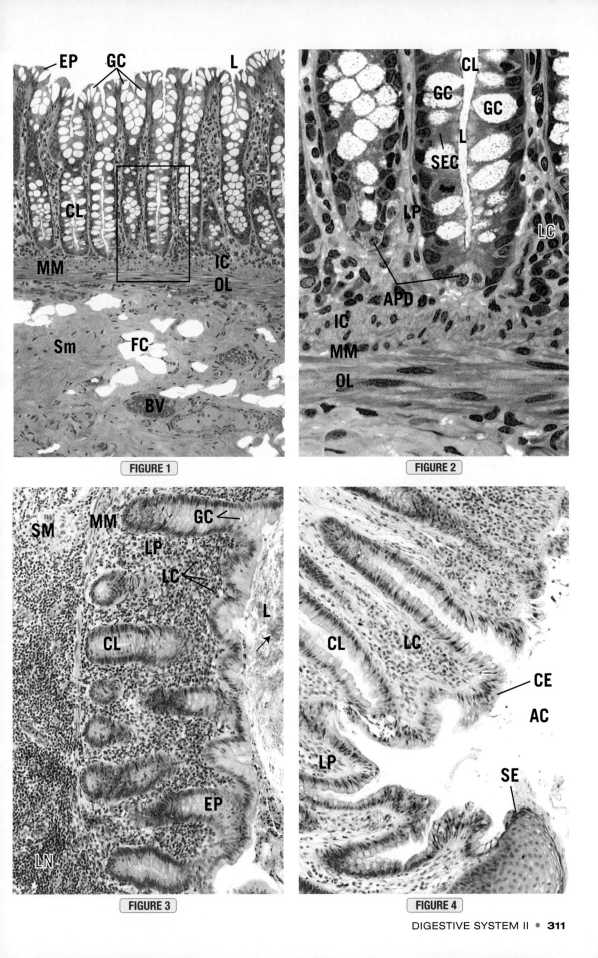

FIGURE 1

FIGURE 2

FIGURE 3

FIGURE 4

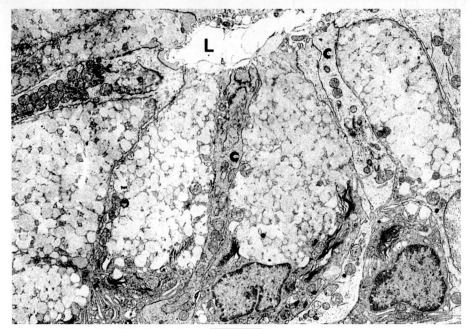

FIGURE 1

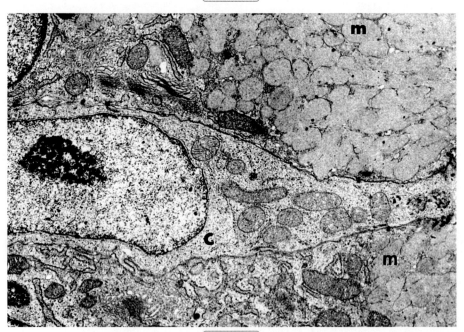

FIGURE 2

FIGURE 1 • Colon. Rat. Electron microscopy. ×3,780.

The deep aspect of the crypt of Lieberkühn presents **columnar cells** (c) and deep crypt cells that produce a mucous type of secretion that is delivered into the **lumen** (L) of the crypt. (From Altmann GG. Morphological observations on mucus-secreting nongoblet cells in the deep crypts of the rat ascending colon. Am J Anat 1983;167:95–117.)

FIGURE 2 • Colon. Rat. Electron microscopy. ×12,600.

At a higher magnification of the deep aspect of the crypt of Lieberkühn, the deep crypt cells present somewhat electron-dense **vacuoles** (m). Note that many of these vacuoles coalesce, forming amorphous vacuolar profiles. The slender **columnar cell** (C) displays no vacuoles but does possess numerous mitochondria and occasional profiles of rough endoplasmic reticulum. Observe the large, oval nucleus and clearly evident nucleolus. (From Altmann GG. Morphological observations on mucus-secreting nongoblet cells in the deep crypts of the rat ascending colon. Am J Anat 1983;167:95–117.)

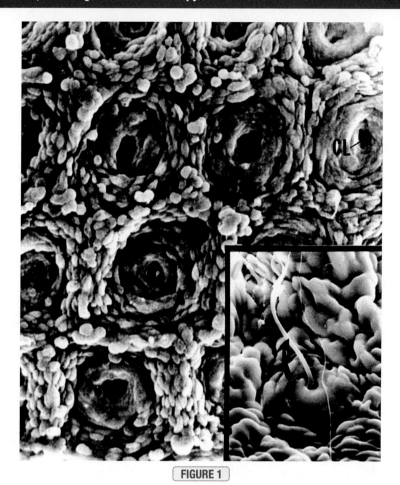

FIGURE 1

FIGURE 1 • Colon. Monkey. Scanning electron microscopy. ×614.

This scanning electron micrograph displays the openings of the **crypts of Lieberkühn** (CL) as well as the cells lining the mucosal surface. (From Specian RD, Neutra MR. The surface topography of the colonic crypt in rabbit and mon- key. Am J Anat 1981;160:461–472.) *Inset.* **Colon. Rabbit. Scanning electron microscopy.** × 778. The openings of the crypts of Lieberkühn are not as regularly arranged in the rabbit as in the monkey. Observe the mucus arising from the crypt opening (*arrow*). (From Specian RD, Neutra MR. The surface topography of the colonic crypt in rabbit and monkey. Am J Anat 1981;160:461–472.)

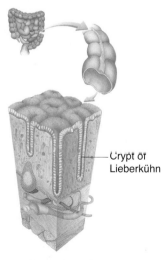

Crypt of Lieberkühn

Large intestine

Summary of Histological Organization

I. ESOPHAGUS

The **esophagus** is a long, muscular tube that delivers the **bolus** of food from the **pharynx** to the **stomach**. The esophagus, as well as the remainder of the alimentary tract, is composed of four concentric layers: **mucosa, submucosa, muscularis externa**, and **adventitia**. The **lumen** of the esophagus is normally collapsed.

A. Mucosa

The **mucosa** has three regions: **epithelium, lamina propria**, and **muscularis mucosae**. It is thrown into longitudinal folds.

1. Epithelium
The **epithelium** is **stratified squamous nonkeratinized**.

2. Lamina Propria
The **lamina propria** is a loose connective tissue that contains mucus-producing **esophageal cardiac glands** in some regions of the esophagus.

3. Muscularis Mucosae
The **muscularis mucosae** is composed of a single layer of **longitudinally** oriented **smooth muscle**.

B. Submucosa

The **submucosa**, composed of fibroelastic connective tissue, is thrown into longitudinal folds. The **esophageal glands proper** of this layer produce a mucous secretion. **Meissner's submucosal plexus** houses postganglionic parasympathetic nerve cells.

C. Muscularis Externa

The **muscularis externa** is composed of **inner circular** (tight helix) and **outer longitudinal** (loose helix) **muscle layers**. In the upper one-third of the esophagus these consist of **skeletal muscle**, in the middle one-third they consist of **skeletal** and **smooth muscle**, and in the lower one-third they consist of **smooth muscle**. **Auerbach's myenteric plexus** is located between the two layers of muscle.

D. Adventitia

The **adventitia** of the esophagus is composed of fibrous connective tissue. Inferior to the diaphragm, the esophagus is covered by a **serosa**.

II. STOMACH

The **stomach** is a sac-like structure that receives food from the **esophagus** and delivers its contents, known as chyme, into the **duodenum**. The stomach has three histologically recognizable regions: **cardiac, fundic**, and **pyloric**. The **mucosa** and **submucosa** of the empty stomach are thrown into folds, known as **rugae**, that disappear in the distended stomach.

A. Mucosa

The **mucosa** presents **gastric pits**, the bases of which accept the openings of **gastric glands**.

1. Epithelium
The **simple columnar epithelium** has no goblet cells. The cells composing this epithelium are known as **surface lining cells** and extend into the gastric pits.

2. Lamina Propria
The **lamina propria** houses numerous **gastric glands**, slender blood vessels, and various connective tissue and **lymphoid cells**.

  a. Cells of Gastric Glands
  Gastric glands are composed of the following cell types: **parietal (oxyntic) cells, chief (zymogenic) cells, mucous neck cells, DNES (enteroendocrine) cells**, and **stem cells**. Glands of the **cardiac region** have no **chief** and only a few **parietal cells**. Glands of the **pyloric region** are short and possess no chief cells and only a few parietal cells. Most of the cells are mucus-secreting cells resembling **mucous neck cells**. Glands of the **fundic region** possess all five cell types.

3. Muscularis Mucosae
The **muscularis mucosae** is composed of an **inner circular** and an **outer longitudinal smooth muscle** layer. A third layer may be present in certain regions.

B. Submucosa

The **submucosa** contains no glands. It houses a vascular plexus as well as **Meissner's submucosal plexus**.

C. Muscularis Externa

The **muscularis externa** is composed of three smooth muscle layers: the **inner oblique**, the **middle** circular, and the **outer longitudinal**. The middle circular forms the **pyloric sphincter. Auerbach's myenteric plexus** is located between the circular and longitudinal layers.

D. Serosa

The stomach is covered by a connective tissue coat enveloped in visceral peritoneum, the **serosa**.

III. SMALL INTESTINE

The **small intestine** is composed of three regions: **duodenum**, **jejunum**, and **ileum**. The **mucosa** of the small intestine presents folds, known as **villi**, that change their morphology and decrease in height from the duodenum to the ileum. The submucosa displays spiral folds, **plicae circulares** (valves of Kerckring).

A. Mucosa

The **mucosa** presents **villi**, evaginations of the epithelially covered **lamina propria**.

1. Epithelium
The **simple columnar epithelium** consists of **goblet**, **surface absorptive**, and **DNES cells**. The number of goblet cells increases from the duodenum to the ileum.

2. Lamina Propria
The **lamina propria**, composed of **loose connective tissue**, houses glands, known as the **crypts of Lieberkühn**, that extend to the muscularis mucosae. The cells composing these glands are **goblet cells**, **columnar cells**, and, especially at the base, **Paneth cells**, **DNES cells**, and **stem cells**. An occasional **caveolated cell** may also be noted. A central **lacteal**, a blindly ending lymphatic vessel, **smooth muscle cells**, **blood vessels**, solitary **lymphatic nodules**, and **lymphoid cells** are also present. **Lymphatic nodules**, with **M cell** epithelial caps, are especially abundant as **Peyer's patches** in the ileum.

3. Muscularis Mucosae
The **muscularis mucosae** consists of an **inner circular** and an **outer longitudinal** layer of **smooth muscle**.

B. Submucosa

The **submucosa** is not unusual except in the **duodenum**, where it contains **Brunner's glands**.

C. Muscularis Externa

The **muscularis externa** is composed of the usual **inner circular** and **outer longitudinal** layers of **smooth muscle**, with **Auerbach's myenteric plexus** intervening.

D. Serosa

The duodenum is covered by **serosa** and **adventitia**, whereas the jejunum and ileum are covered by a serosa.

IV. LARGE INTESTINE

The **large intestine** is composed of the **appendix**, the **cecum**, the **colon** (**ascending**, **transverse**, and **descending**), the **rectum**, and the **anal canal**. The appendix and anal canal are described separately, although the remainder of the large intestine presents identical histologic features.

A. Colon

1. Mucosa
The **mucosa** presents no specialized folds. It is thicker than that of the small intestine.

> #### a. Epithelium
> The **simple columnar epithelium** has goblet cells and columnar cells.
>
> #### b. Lamina Propria
> The **crypts of Lieberkühn** of the **lamina propria** are longer than those of the small intestine. They are composed of numerous **goblet cells**, a few **DNES cells**, and **stem cells**. **Lymphatic nodules** are frequently present.
>
> #### c. Muscularis Mucosae
> The **muscularis mucosae** consists of **inner circular** and **outer longitudinal smooth muscle** layers.

2. Submucosa
The **submucosa** resembles that of the jejunum or ileum.

3. Muscularis Externa
The **muscularis externa** is composed of **inner circular** and **outer longitudinal smooth muscle** layers. The outer longitudinal muscle is modified into **teniae coli**, three flat ribbons of longitudinally arranged smooth muscles. These are responsible for the formation of **haustra coli** (sacculations). **Auerbach's plexus** occupies its position between the two layers.

4. Serosa
The colon possesses both **serosa** and **adventitia**. The serosa presents small, fat-filled pouches, the **appendices epiploicae**.

B. Appendix

The **lumen of the appendix** is usually stellate shaped, and it may be obliterated. The **simple columnar epithelium** covers a **lamina propria** rich in **lymphatic nodules** and some **crypts of Lieberkühn**. The **muscularis mucosae, submucosa,** and **muscularis externa** conform to the general plan of the digestive tract. It is covered by a **serosa**.

C. Anal Canal

The **anal canal** presents longitudinal folds, **anal columns**, which become joined at the orifice of the anus to form **anal valves**, and intervening **anal sinuses**. The epithelium changes from the **simple columnar** of the rectum, to **simple cuboidal** at the **anal valves**, to **stratified squamous** distal to the anal valves, to **epidermis** at the orifice of the anus. **Circumanal glands**, **hair follicles**, and **sebaceous glands** are present here. The **submucosa** is rich in vascular supply. The **muscularis externa** forms the internal anal sphincter muscle. An **adventitia** connects the anus to the surrounding structures.

Digestive System III

15

The major **glands of the digestive system** are located outside the wall of the alimentary canal but are connected to its lumen via ducts. These glands include the major salivary glands, pancreas, and liver.

● MAJOR SALIVARY GLANDS

The three **major salivary glands**, **parotid**, **submandibular**, and **sublingual**, deliver their secretory product, saliva, into the oral cavity. **Saliva** is composed of a thin, watery suspension of enzymes, mucus, inorganic ions, and antibodies. The parotid gland produces **serous secretions**, whereas the submandibular and sublingual glands manufacture **mixed secretions** (a combination of serous and mucous saliva).

● PANCREAS

The **pancreas** is a mixed gland, in that it has exocrine and endocrine functions (see Graphic 15-1). The **exocrine pancreas** produces an alkaline fluid rich in digestive enzymes and proenzymes, which is delivered to the duodenum via the pancreatic duct. Enzymes are manufactured by the acinar cells, whereas the alkaline fluid is released by centroacinar cells and cells of the intercalated ducts. It should be noted that the pancreas, unlike the salivary glands, does not possess striated ducts. The release of the enzymes and alkaline fluid is intermittent and is controlled by the hormones **cholecystokinin** and **secretin**, respectively, and the two types of secretions may be delivered independent of each other. These hormones are produced by the **DNES cells** of the epithelial lining of the alimentary tract mucosa. The **endocrine** pancreas is composed of scattered spherical aggregates of richly vascularized cords of endocrine cells, known as **islets of Langerhans**. Five cell types are present in these structures: **A cells**, producing **glucagon**; **B cells**, manufacturing **insulin**; **G cells**, producing **gastrin**; **D cells**, manufacturing **somatostatin**, and **PP cells**, secreting **pancreatic polypeptide**.

● LIVER

The **liver** is the largest gland of the body. It performs a myriad of functions, many of which are *not* glandular in nature (see Graphic 15-2). The parenchymal cells of the liver, known as **hepatocytes**, perform each of the tasks of the liver. The exocrine by-product, **bile**, is delivered into a system of bile ducts, which then directs the bile into the **gallbladder**, a storage organ associated with the liver. The release of concentrated bile into the duodenum via the cystic and common bile ducts is regulated by hormones of the DNES cells in the alimentary tract. Since each hepatocyte is bordered by a vascular sinusoid, liver cells can absorb toxic materials and by-products of digestion, which they detoxify and store for future use. Additionally, hepatocytes can release various biosynthetic molecules into the bloodstream to be utilized throughout the body. Moreover, foreign particulate matter is phagocytosed in the liver by **Kupffer cells**, macrophages derived from monocytes.

● GALLBLADDER

The **gallbladder** is a small, pear-shaped organ that receives bile from the liver. It not only stores but also concentrates bile and, in response to the **cholecystokinin** released by the DNES cells of the alimentary tract, forces the bile into the lumen of the duodenum via the cystic and common bile ducts. The **bile** emulsifies fats, facilitating the action of the enzyme **pancreatic lipase**. The lamina propria, lined by a simple columnar epithelium, is thrown into highly convoluted folds in the empty gallbladder. These folds disappear on distention. Occasionally, tubuloalveolar mucous glands are present.

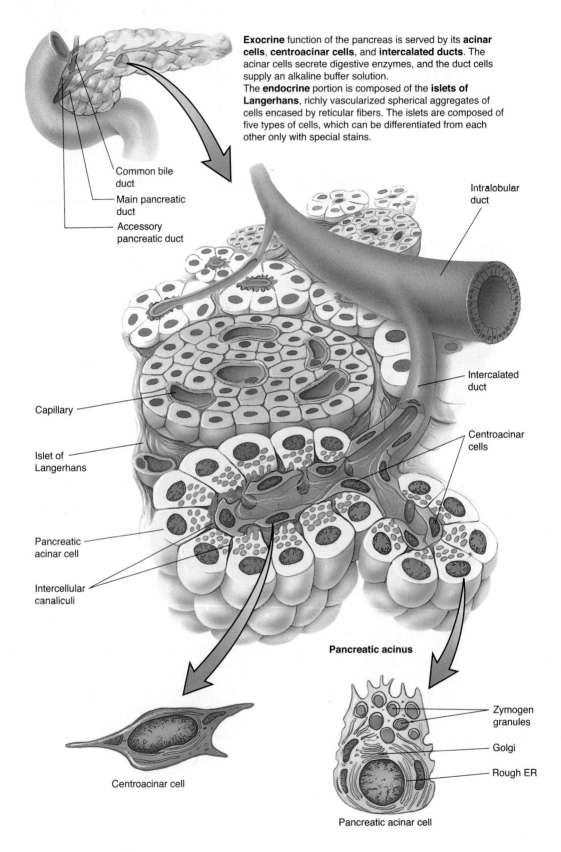

Exocrine function of the pancreas is served by its **acinar cells**, **centroacinar cells**, and **intercalated ducts**. The acinar cells secrete digestive enzymes, and the duct cells supply an alkaline buffer solution.

The **endocrine** portion is composed of the **islets of Langerhans**, richly vascularized spherical aggregates of cells encased by reticular fibers. The islets are composed of five types of cells, which can be differentiated from each other only with special stains.

Common bile duct

Main pancreatic duct

Accessory pancreatic duct

Intralobular duct

Capillary

Islet of Langerhans

Pancreatic acinar cell

Intercellular canaliculi

Intercalated duct

Centroacinar cells

Pancreatic acinus

Centroacinar cell

Zymogen granules

Golgi

Rough ER

Pancreatic acinar cell

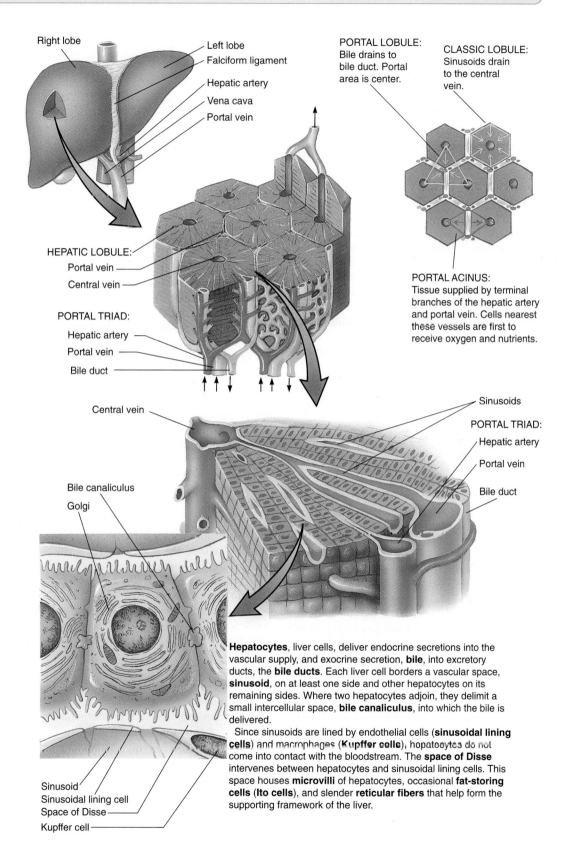

Right lobe

Left lobe
Falciform ligament
Hepatic artery
Vena cava
Portal vein

PORTAL LOBULE:
Bile drains to
bile duct. Portal
area is center.

CLASSIC LOBULE:
Sinusoids drain
to the central
vein.

HEPATIC LOBULE:
Portal vein
Central vein

PORTAL TRIAD:
Hepatic artery
Portal vein
Bile duct

PORTAL ACINUS:
Tissue supplied by terminal
branches of the hepatic artery
and portal vein. Cells nearest
these vessels are first to
receive oxygen and nutrients.

Central vein

Sinusoids

PORTAL TRIAD:
Hepatic artery

Portal vein

Bile duct

Bile canaliculus
Golgi

Hepatocytes, liver cells, deliver endocrine secretions into the
vascular supply, and exocrine secretion, **bile**, into excretory
ducts, the **bile ducts**. Each liver cell borders a vascular space,
sinusoid, on at least one side and other hepatocytes on its
remaining sides. Where two hepatocytes adjoin, they delimit a
small intercellular space, **bile canaliculus**, into which the bile is
delivered.

Since sinusoids are lined by endothelial cells (**sinusoidal lining
cells**) and macrophages (**Kupffer cells**), hepatocytes do not
come into contact with the bloodstream. The **space of Disse**
intervenes between hepatocytes and sinusoidal lining cells. This
space houses **microvilli** of hepatocytes, occasional **fat-storing
cells** (**Ito cells**), and slender **reticular fibers** that help form the
supporting framework of the liver.

Sinusoid
Sinusoidal lining cell
Space of Disse
Kupffer cell

Histophysiology

I. MAJOR SALIVARY GLANDS

The major salivary glands are the **parotid, submandibular**, and **sublingual glands**. These produce about 1 L of saliva per day, approximately 95% of the daily salivary secretion. These glands possess a secretory component that is responsible for the formation of **primary saliva** (**isotonic saliva**), which is modified by the initial portion of the **duct** system (**striated ducts**) to form the **secondary saliva** (**hypotonic saliva**). Saliva, therefore, is a **hypotonic** solution whose functions include lubrication and cleansing of the oral cavity (and reducing bacterial flora by the **lysozyme, lactoferrin, peroxidases**, histidine-rich proteins, and **immunoglobulin A [IgA]** that it contains), initial digestion of carbohydrates by **salivary amylase**, and assisting in the process of **taste** (by dissolving food substances). Saliva also acts as a buffer due to its contents of bicarbonates produced by cells of the striated duct.

II. PANCREAS

Acinar cells of the **exocrine pancreas** secrete digestive enzymes in response to the hormone **cholecystokinin**, released by the **enteroendocrine cells** of the small intestine and by the **acetylcholine released** by nerve cells of the enteric nervous system. Some of these enzymes are released as proenzymes (chymotrypsin, trypsin, elastase, and carboxypeptidase), and others are released as active enzymes (DNase, RNase, pancreatic lipase, and pancreatic amylase). In response to **secretin** (released by **enteroendocrine cells** of the small intestine) and by the **acetylcholine released** by nerve cells of the enteric nervous system, **centroacinar cells** and cells of **intercalated ducts** release a copious amount of an alkaline fluid that is believed to help neutralize and buffer the acidic chyme entering the duodenum from the stomach.

Islets of Langerhans are composed of five different types of cells, each of which is responsible for the secretion of a hormone, the most notable of which are **insulin** and **glucagon**.

III. LIVER AND GALLBLADDER

A. Hepatocytes

It is believed that every **hepatocyte** is capable of performing each of the approximately 100 different functions of the liver.

Bile formation and secretion are the **exocrine** functions of the liver. Bile is a green, somewhat viscous fluid composed of water, ions, cholesterol, phospholipids, bilirubin glucuronide, and bile acids. One of these components, **bilirubin glucuronide**, is a water-soluble conjugate of nonsoluble **bilirubin**, a toxic breakdown product of **hemoglobin**. It is in the **smooth endoplasmic reticulum** (**sER**) of the hepatocytes that detoxification of bilirubin occurs.

Detoxification of various drugs, toxins, metabolic by-products, and chemicals occurs either by the **microsomal mixed-function oxidase** system of the sER or by **peroxidases** of peroxisomes.

Endocrine functions of the liver include the synthesis and release of numerous plasma proteins and components, such as fibrinogen, urea, albumin, prothrombin, and lipoproteins; **storage** of glycogen and lipids for release during intervals between eating; synthesis of glucose; **gluconeogenesis** from noncarbohydrate sources (amino acids and lipids); and **transport** of IgA into the bile and, subsequently, into the lumen of the small intestine.

B. Kupffer Cells and Ito Cells

Kupffer cells of the liver participate in removing defunct red blood cells and other undesirable particulate matter from the bloodstream. **Fat-storing** (**Ito**) **cells** are believed to function in the accumulation and storage of **vitamin A**, but in the case of alcoholic cirrhosis, these cells also manufacture type I collagen, responsible for fibrosis of the liver.

C. Gallbladder

The **gallbladder** stores and concentrates bile. It releases bile in response to the enteroendocrine cell hormone **cholecystokinin**.

CLINICAL CONSIDERATIONS

Gastrinoma

Gastrinoma is a disease in which the **G cells** of the pancreas undergo **excess proliferation** (frequently cancerous), resulting in an **overproduction of the hormone gastrin**. This hormone is responsible for binding to parietal cells of the stomach, causing them to over-secrete hydrochloric acid with a resultant formation of peptic ulcers in the stomach and the duodenum. Antiulcer drugs may alleviate the hyper-acidity and resolve the ulcerations; otherwise surgical intervention may be indicated.

Type I Diabetes

Type I (**insulin-dependent**) diabetes is characterized by **polyphagia** (insatiable hunger), **polydipsia** (un-quenchable thirst), and **polyuria** (excessive urina-tion). It usually has a sudden onset before 20 years of age, is distinguished by damage to and destruction of beta cells, results from a **low level of plasma insulin**, and is treated with a combination of insulin therapy and diet.

Type II Diabetes Mellitus

Type II (**non–insulin-dependent**) diabetes mellitus commonly occurs in overweight individuals over 40 years of age. It does not result from low levels of plasma insulin and is **insulin resistant**, which is a major factor in its pathogenesis. The resistance to insulin is due to decreased binding of insulin to its plasmalemma receptors and to defects in postre-ceptor insulin action. Type II diabetes is usually con-trolled by diet.

Hepatitis

Hepatitis is inflammation of the liver and, although it could have various causes such as abuse of alcohol and certain drugs, its most common cause is one of the five types of hepatitis viruses, denoted by the first five letters of the alphabet, A through E. **Hepatitis A** is usually spread by poor hygiene (fecal-oral route and contaminated water) as well as by sexual con-tact. Usually there are no symptoms, the patient re-covers, and does not become a carrier. **Hepatitis B**, a more serious condition than Hepatitis A, is usually transmitted by body fluids and, in case of drug ad-dicts, by the sharing of needles. Patients can become carriers of the virus and in 10% of the patients the condition may become chronic, leading to cirrhosis and cancer of the liver. In the past, **Hepatitis C** was transmitted by blood transfusions, but screening has almost completely eradicated that route and now it is transmitted mostly by shared needles among drug addicts. About three-quarters of people who have the Hepatitis C virus will reach the chronic stage, and of these, 20% to 25% will develop cirrhosis and then liver cancer. **Hepatitis D** is also transmitted by the sharing of needles and is always accompanied by Hepatitis B. The double infection is a more severe condition. **Hepatitis E** is spread by the fecal-oral route and is responsible for epidemics, but mostly in un-derdeveloped countries. Neither chronic nor carrier states are present with this form of the Hepatitis virus. Universal vaccination is recommended to pro-tect the population from Hepatitis B, and this has the added benefit of protection against Hepatitis D; it is recommended that travelers to underdeveloped coun-tries where Hepatitis A is prevalent be vaccinated against Hepatitis A. There are no vaccines currently available against Hepatitis C or E.

Jaundice (Icterus)

Jaundice (icterus) is characterized by excess biliru-bin in the blood and deposition of **bile pigment** in the skin and sclera of the eyes, resulting in a yellow-ish appearance. It may be hereditary or due to patho-logic conditions such as excess destruction of red blood cells (**hemolytic jaundice**), liver dysfunction, and obstruction of the biliary passages (**obstructive jaundice**).

Gallstones (Biliary Calculi)

Gallstones (biliary calculi) are concretions, usually of fused crystals of **cholesterol** that form in gallbladder or bile duct. They may accumulate to such an extent that the cystic duct is blocked, thus preventing emp-tying of the gallbladder, and they may require surgi-cal removal if less invasive methods fail to dissolve or pulverize them.

FIGURE 1 • Parotid gland. Monkey. Plastic section. ×132.

The parotid gland is purely serous, with a connective tissue capsule sending **trabeculae** (T) into the substance of the gland, subdividing it into **lobules** (Lo). Slender connective tissue sheets penetrate the lobules, surrounding small **blood vessels** (BV) and **intralobular ducts** (iD). **Interlobular ducts** (ID) are surrounded by increased amounts of **connective tissue** (CT) and large blood vessels. Observe that the **acini** (Ac) are closely packed within each lobule. *Inset.* **Parotid gland. Monkey. Plastic section.** × 540. Note that the round **nuclei** (N) of these serous acini are basally located. The lateral cell membranes (*arrows*) are not clearly visible, nor are the lumina of the acini. Observe the slender sheets of connective tissue (*arrowheads*) investing each acinus.

FIGURE 3 • Sublingual gland. Monkey. Plastic section. ×540.

This photomicrograph is a higher magnification of the *boxed area* of Figure 2. The flattened, dark **nuclei** (N) of the mucous acini are clearly evident as they appear to be pressed against the basal cell membrane. Observe that much of the cytoplasm is occupied by small, mucin-containing vesicles (*arrows*), that the lateral cell membrane (*arrowheads*) is evident, and that the **lumen** (L) is usually identifiable. **Serous demilunes** (SD) are composed of serous-producing cells whose **nuclei** (N) are round to oval in morphology. Note also that the lateral cell membranes are not distinguishable in serous cells.

FIGURE 2 • Sublingual gland. Monkey. Plastic section. ×270.

The sublingual gland is a mixed gland in that it produces both serous and mucous secretory products. The **mucous acini** (MA) possess dark **nuclei** (N) that are flattened against the basal cell membrane. Moreover, the cytoplasm is filled with a frothy-appearing material, representing the viscous secretory product. Many of the mucous acini are capped by serous cells, forming a crescent-shaped cap, the **serous demilune** (SD). The sublingual gland is subdivided into lobes and lobules by **connective tissue septa** (CT) that act as the supporting network for the nerves, vessels, and ducts of the gland. The *boxed area* is presented at a higher magnification in Figure 3.

FIGURE 4 • Submandibular gland. Monkey. Plastic section. ×132.

The submandibular gland also produces a mixed type of secretion; however, unlike in the sublingual gland, serous acini predominate. **Serous** (SA) and **mucous acini** (MA) are easily distinguishable from each other, but most mucous units display a cap of serous demilunes. Moreover, the submandibular gland is characterized by an extensive system of **ducts** (D), recognizable by their pale cytoplasm, comparatively large **lumina** (L), and round nuclei. This gland is also subdivided into lobes and lobules by **connective tissue septa** (CT). *Inset.* **Submandibular gland. Monkey. Plastic section.** × 540. Note the granular appearance of the cells comprising the **serous demilune** (SD) in contrast with the "frothy" appearing cytoplasm of the **mucous acinus** (MA).

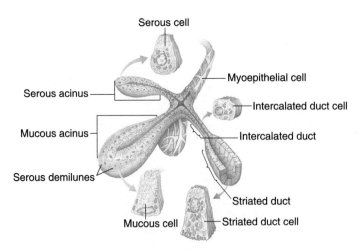

Serous cell

Myoepithelial cell

Serous acinus

Intercalated duct cell

Mucous acinus

Intercalated duct

Serous demilunes

Striated duct

Mucous cell

Striated duct cell

Salivary glands

KEY						
Ac	acinus	ID	interlobular duct	SA	serous acini
BV	blood vessel	L	lumen	SD	serous demilune
CT	connective tissue	Lo	lobule	T	trabeculae
D	duct	MA	mucous acini		
iD	intralobular duct	N	nucleus		

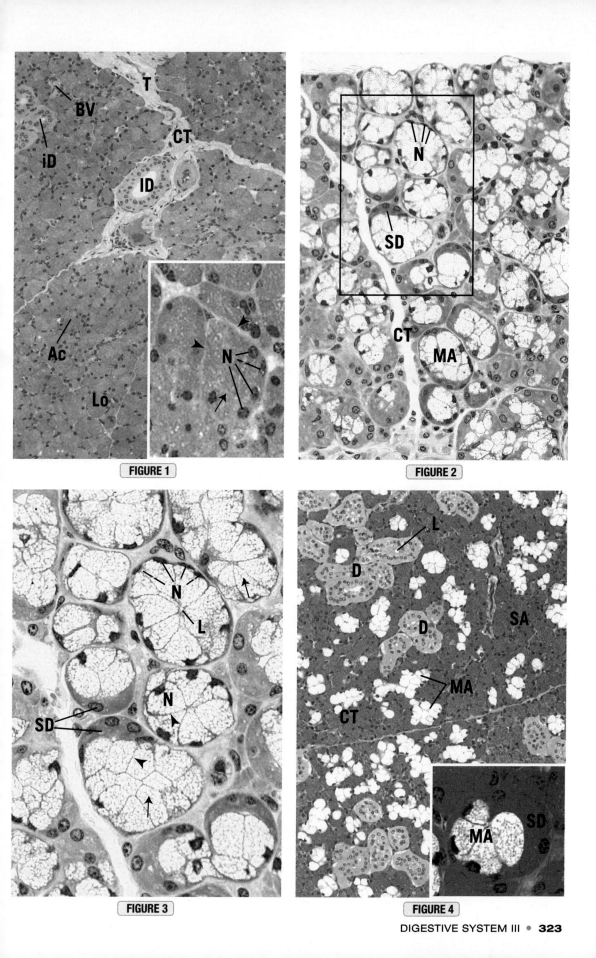

FIGURE 1

FIGURE 2

FIGURE 3

FIGURE 4

FIGURE 1 • Pancreas. Human. Paraffin section. ×132.

The pancreas is a complex gland since it has both exocrine and endocrine components. The exocrine portion comprises the bulk of the organ as a compound tubuloaveolar gland, secreting a serous fluid. The gland is subdivided into lobules by **connective tissue septa** (CT). Each **acinus** (Ac) is composed of several pyramid-shaped cells, possessing round nuclei. Cells located in the center of the acinus, **centroacinar cells** (CA), form the smallest ducts of the gland. The endocrine portion of the pancreas is composed of small, spherical clumps of cells, **islets of Langerhans** (IL), which are richly endowed by capillaries. These islets of Langerhans are haphazardly scattered among the serous acini of the pancreas. The *boxed area* is presented at a higher magnification in Figure 2.

FIGURE 3 • Pancreas. Monkey. Plastic section. ×540.

With the use of plastic sections, the morphology of the pancreatic acinus is well defined. Observe that in fortuitous sections the acinus resembles a pie, with the individual cells clearly delineated (*arrows*). The **nucleus** (N) of each trapezoid-shaped cell is round and the basal cytoplasm (*arrowhead*) is relatively homogeneous, whereas the apical cytoplasm is packed with **zymogen granules** (ZG). **Centroacinar cells** (CA) may be recognized both by their locations as well as by the pale appearance of their nuclei. *Inset.* **Pancreas. Monkey. Plastic section.** × 540. Observe the **centroacinar cell** (CA), whose pale nucleus is readily differentiated from the surrounding acinar cell nuclei.

FIGURE 2 • Pancreas. Human. Paraffin section. ×270.

This photomicrograph is a higher magnification of the *boxed area* of Figure 1. Note that the **connective tissue septa** (CT), while fairly extensive in certain regions, are quite slender in the interlobular areas. The trapezoidal morphologies of individual cells of the serous acini are clearly evident in fortuitous sections (*arrow*). Observe also the **centroacinar cells** (CA), located in the center of acini, which represent the smallest units of the pancreatic duct system.

FIGURE 4 • Islets of Langerhans. Monkey. Plastic section. ×270.

The **islets of Langerhans** (IL), the endocrine portion of the pancreas, is a more or less spherical configuration of cells randomly scattered throughout the exocrine portion of the gland. As such, each islet is surrounded by serous **acini** (Ac). The islets receive their rich **blood supply** (BV) from the **connective tissue elements** (CT) of the exocrine pancreas. *Inset.* **Islets of Langerhans. Monkey. Plastic section.** × 540. Observe the rich vascularity of the islets of Langerhans, as evidenced by the presence of **erythrocyte** (RBC)-engorged blood vessels. Although each islet is composed of A, B, C, and D cells, they can only be distinguished from each other by the use of special stains. However, it should be noted that in the human, B cells are the most populous and are usually located in the center of the islet, whereas A cells are generally found at the periphery. This situation is reversed in the monkey.

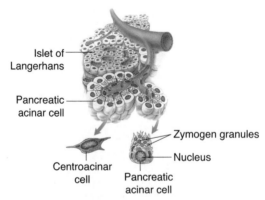

Islet of Langerhans

Pancreatic acinar cell

Zymogen granules

Nucleus

Centroacinar cell

Pancreatic acinar cell

Pancreatic cells

KEY

Ac	acinus	CT	connective tissue septa	RBC	erythrocyte
BV	blood vessel	IL	islets of Langerhans	ZG	zymogen granule
CA	centroacinar cell	N	nucleus		

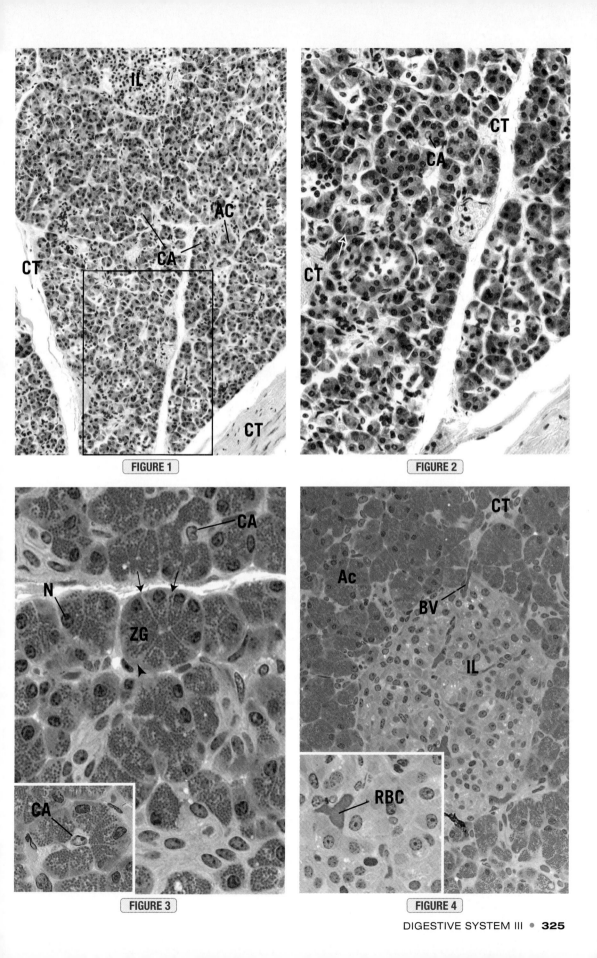

FIGURE 1

FIGURE 2

FIGURE 3

FIGURE 4

FIGURE 1 • Liver. Pig. Paraffin section. ×14.

Note that the liver is invested by a connective tissue capsule, **Glisson's capsule** (GC), from which, in the pig, **septa** (S) extend to subdivide the gland into more or less hexagon-shaped classical **lobules** (Lo). Blood vessels, lymph vessels, and bile ducts travel within the connective tissue septa to reach the apices of the classic lobules, which are known as the **portal areas** (PA). Bile reaches the portal areas from within the lobules, whereas blood enters the substance of the lobules from the portal areas. Within each lobule, the blood flows through tortuous channels, the liver sinusoids, to enter the **central vein** (CV) in the middle of the classical lobule.

FIGURE 2 • Liver. Dog. Paraffin section. ×132.

The portal area of the liver houses terminal branches of the **hepatic artery** (HA) and **portal vein** (PV). Note that the vein is much larger than the artery and its wall is very thin in comparison to the size of its lumen. Branches of **lymph vessels** (LV) and **bile ducts** (BD) are also present in the portal area. Bile ducts may be recognized by their cuboidal-to-columnar epithelium. Observe that unlike in the pig, connective tissue septa do not demarcate the boundaries of classic liver lobules, although the various structures of the portal area are invested by connective tissue elements. **Plates of liver cells** (PL) and **sinusoids** (Si) extend from the portal areas.

FIGURE 3 • Liver. Monkey. Plastic section. ×132.

The **central vein** (CV) of the liver lobule (a terminal radix of the hepatic vein) collects blood from the **sinusoids** (Si) and delivers it to sublobular veins. The **plates of liver cells** (PL) and hepatic sinusoids appear to radiate, as spokes of a wheel, from the central vein. The *boxed area* is presented at a higher magnification in Figure 4.

FIGURE 4 • Liver. Monkey. Plastic section. ×270.

This photomicrograph is a higher magnification of the *boxed area* of the previous figure. Note that the lumen of the **central vein** (CV) is lined by a simple squamous **epithelium** (Ep), which is continuous with the endothelial lining of the hepatic **sinusoids** (Si), tortuous vascular channels that freely communicate with each other. Observe also that the **liver plates** (LP) are composed of **hepatocytes** (H), one to two cell layers thick, and that each plate is bordered by sinusoids.

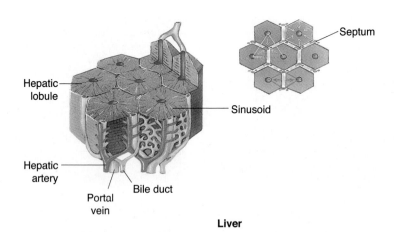

Liver

KEY					
BD	bile duct	HA	hepatic artery	PL	plates of liver cells
CV	central vein	Lo	lobule	PV	portal vein
Ep	epithelium	LP	liver plates	S	septa
GC	Glisson's capsule	LV	lymph vessel	Si	sinusoid
H	hepatocyte	PA	portal area		

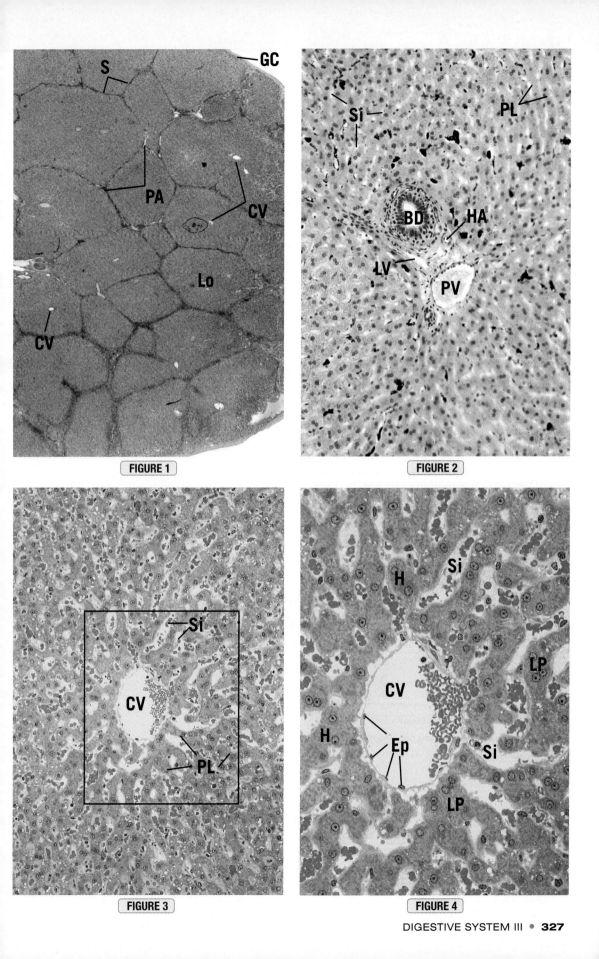

FIGURE 1

FIGURE 2

FIGURE 3

FIGURE 4

FIGURE 1 • Liver. Monkey. Plastic section. ×540.

This photomicrograph is a high magnification of **liver plates** (LP). Observe that individual **hepatocytes** (H) are polygonal in shape. Each hepatocyte possesses one or two nuclei, although occasionally some have three nuclei. Plates of hepatocytes enclose hepatic **sinusoids** (Si) that are lined by **sinusoidal lining cells** (SC); therefore, hepatocytes do not come into direct contact with the bloodstream. The space between the sinusoidal lining cells and the hepatocytes, the space of Disse, is at the limit of resolution of the light microscope. *Inset.* **Liver. Human. Paraffin section.** × 540. The hepatocyte cell membranes are clearly evident in this photomicrograph. Note that in fortuitous sections, small intercellular spaces (*arrows*) are recognizable. These are bile canaliculi through which bile flows to the periphery of the lobule.

FIGURE 3 • Gallbladder. Human. Paraffin section. ×132.

The gallbladder is a pear-shaped, hollow organ that functions in storing and concentrating bile. Its histologic structure is relatively simple, but its appearance may be deceiving. The mucosa of an empty gallbladder, as in this photomicrograph, is thrown into numerous folds (*arrows*), providing it with a glandular morphology. However, close observation of the **epithelium** (Ep) demonstrates that all of the simple columnar cells of the mucous membrane are identical. A loose **connective tissue** (CT), sometimes referred to as a lamina propria, lies deep to the epithelium. Observe that a muscularis mucosae is lacking, and the **smooth muscle** (SM) surrounding the connective tissue is the muscularis externa. The outermost coat of the gallbladder is a serosa or adventitia. A region similar to the *boxed area* is presented in Figure 4.

FIGURE 2 • Liver. Paraffin section. ×540.

A system of macrophages known as **Kupffer cells** (KC) are found interspersed among the endothelial lining cells of liver **sinusoids** (Si). These macrophages are larger than the epithelial cells and may be recognized by the presence of phagocytosed material within them. Kupffer cells may be demonstrated by injecting an animal intravenously with india ink, as is the case in this specimen. Observe that some cells appear as large, black smudges since they are filled with phagocytosed ink (*asterisk*), whereas other cells possess only small quantities of the phagocytosed material (*arrowheads*). Note also that much of the sinusoidal lining is devoid of ink, indicating that the endothelial cells are probably not phagocytic.

FIGURE 4 • Gallbladder. Human. Paraffin section. ×540.

This photomicrograph is a higher magnification of a region similar to the *boxed area* of Figure 3. Note that the **epithelium** (Ep) is composed of identical-appearing tall columnar cells, whose **nuclei** (N) are basally oriented. The lateral cell membranes are evident in certain regions (*arrows*), whereas the apical brush border is usually not visible in hematoxylin and eosin–stained specimens. Observe that a relatively thick **basal membrane** (BM) separates the epithelium from the underlying loose **connective tissue** (CT).

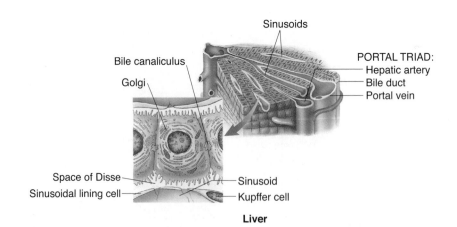

Liver

KEY					
BM	basal membrane	KC	Kupffer cell	Si	sinusoid
CT	connective tissue	LP	liver plate	SM	smooth muscle
Ep	epithelium	N	nucleus		
H	hepatocyte	SC	sinusoidal lining cell		

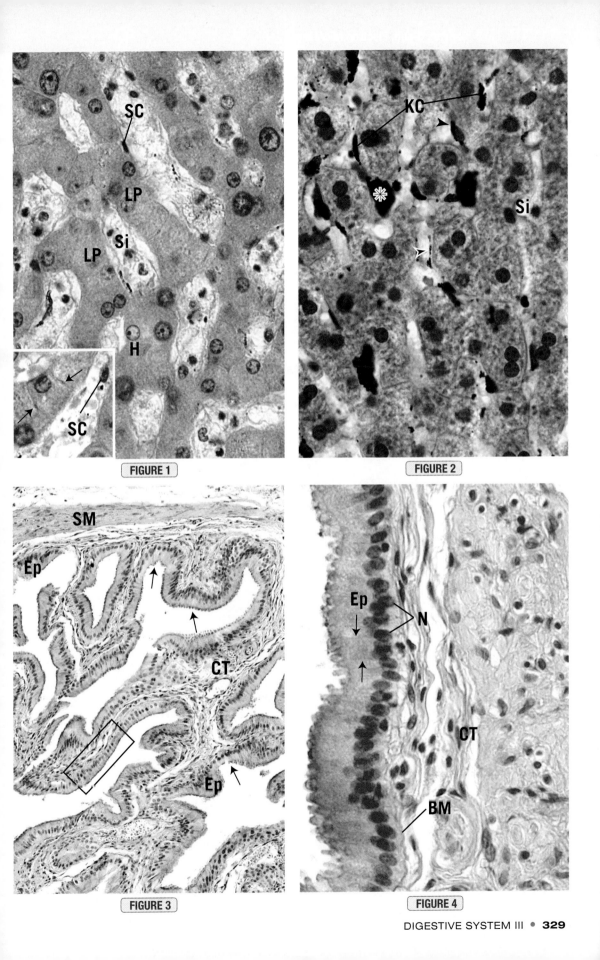

FIGURE 1

FIGURE 2

FIGURE 3

FIGURE 4

FIGURE 1 • Sublingual gland. Human. Electron microscopy. ×4,050.

The human sublingual gland is composed mostly of mucous acini capped by serous demilunes. The **mucous cells** (mc) display numerous **filamentous bodies** (f) and secre-tory granules, which appear to be empty (*asterisks*). The **serous cells** (dc) may be recognized by their paler cyto-plasm and the presence of secretory granules (*arrows*) housing electron-dense materials. Note also the presence of **myoepithelial cells** (myo), whose processes (*arrow-heads*) encircle the acinus. (Courtesy of Dr. A. Riva.)

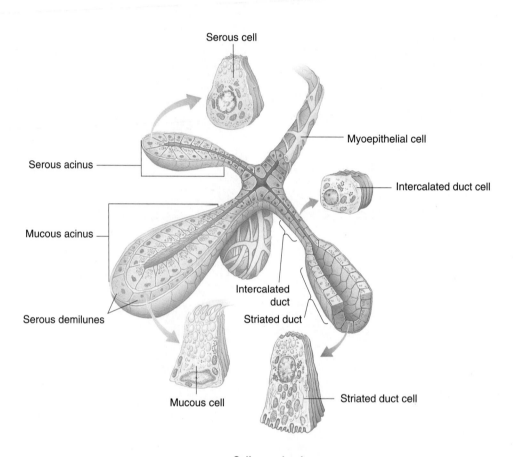

Serous cell

Myoepithelial cell

Serous acinus

Intercalated duct cell

Mucous acinus

Intercalated duct

Serous demilunes

Striated duct

Mucous cell

Striated duct cell

Salivary glands

KEY			
dc	serous cells	mc	mucous cells
f	filamentous bodies	myo	myoepithelial cells

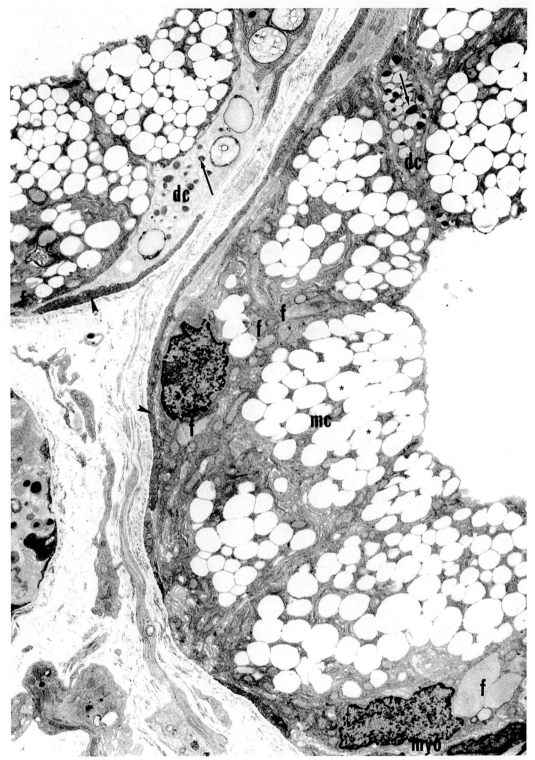

FIGURE 1

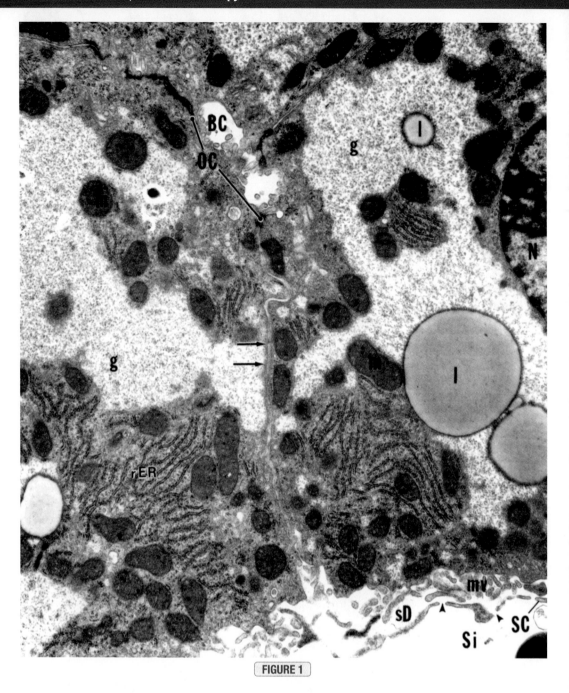

FIGURE 1

FIGURE 1 • Liver. Mouse. Electron microscopy.
×11,255.

The hepatocytes of this electron micrograph display two of their surfaces, one bordering a **sinusoid** (Si) and the other where two parenchymal cells contact each other (*arrows*). The sinusoidal surface displays **microvilli** (mv) that extend into the **space of Disse** (sD). They almost contact **sinusoidal lining cells** (SC) that present numerous fenestrae (*arrowheads*). The parenchymal contacts are characterized by the presence of **bile canaliculi** (BC), intercellular spaces that are isolated by the formation of **occluding junctions** (OC). The cytoplasm of hepatocytes houses the normal cellular complements, such as numerous **mitochondria** (m), elements of **rough endoplasmic reticulum** (rER), Golgi apparatus, smooth endoplasmic reticulum, lysosomes, and inclusions such as **glycogen** (g) and **lipid droplets** (l). The **nucleus** (N) of one of the hepatocytes is evident.

PLATE 15-7 Islet of Langerhans, Electron Microscopy

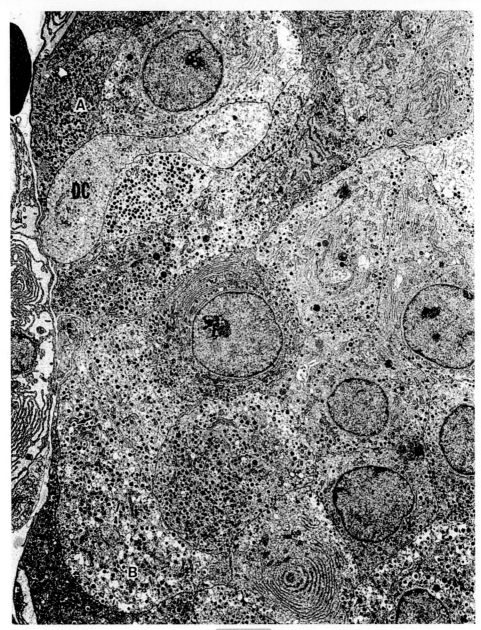

FIGURE 1

FIGURE 1 • Islet of Langerhans. Rabbit. Electron microscopy. ×3,578.

The islets of Langerhans house four types of parenchymal cells, namely, A, B, C, and D cells. **B cells** (B) are the most numerous and may be recognized by the presence of secretory granules whose electron-dense core is surrounded by a clear zone (*arrows*). **A cells** (A), the second most numerous secretory cell, also house many secretory granules; however, these lack an electron-lucent periphery. **D cells** (DC) are the least numerous and are characterized by secretory granules that are much less electron-dense than those of the other two cell types. (From Sato T, Herman L. Stereological analysis of normal rabbit pancreatic islets. Am J Anat 1981,161.71–84.)

Summary of Histological Organization

I. MAJOR SALIVARY GLANDS

Three **major salivary glands** are associated with the oral cavity. These are the **parotid, submandibular,** and **sublingual glands.**

A. Parotid Gland

The **parotid gland** is a purely serous **compound tubuloalveolar gland** whose **capsule** sends **septa** (frequently containing adipose cells) into the substance of the gland, dividing it into **lobes** and **lobules**. **Serous acini,** surrounded by **myoepithelial cells,** deliver their secretions into **intercalated ducts.**

B. Submandibular Gland

This compound **tubuloalveolar gland** is mostly **serous,** although it contains enough **mucous units,** capped by **serous demilunes,** to manufacture a mixed secretion. **Acini** are surrounded by **myoepithelial (basket) cells.** The **capsule** sends **septa** into the substance of the gland, subdividing it into **lobes** and **lobules**. The **duct** system is extensive.

C. Sublingual Gland

The **sublingual gland** is a **compound tubuloalveolar gland** whose capsule is not very definite. The gland produces a **mixed** secretion, possessing mostly **mucous acini** capped by **serous demilunes** and surrounded by **myoepithelial (basket) cells.** The **intralobular duct** system is not very extensive.

II. PANCREAS

The **exocrine pancreas** is a **compound tubuloalveolar serous gland** whose connective tissue **capsule** sends **septa** to divide the parenchyma into lobules. **Acini** present **centroacinar cells,** the beginning of the ducts that empty into **intercalated ducts,** which lead to **intralobular,** then **interlobular ducts.** The **main duct** receives secretory products from the interlobular ducts. The **endocrine pancreas** with its **islets of Langerhans** (composed of **A, B, G,** and **D cells**) are scattered among the serous acini.

III. LIVER

A. Capsule

Glisson's capsule invests the liver and sends **septa** into the substance of the liver at the **porta hepatis** to subdivide the parenchyma into lobules.

B. Lobules

1. Classical Lobule
Classical lobules are hexagonal with **portal areas** (**triads**) at the periphery and a **central vein** in the center. **Trabeculae (plates)** of liver cells anastomose. **Sinusoids** are lined by **sinusoidal lining cells** and **Kupffer cells** (macrophages). Within the **space of Disse, fat-accumulating cells** may be noted. **Portal areas** housing **bile ducts, lymph vessels,** and branches of the **hepatic artery** and the **portal vein** are surrounded by **terminal plates** composed of **hepatocytes.** Bile passes peripherally within **bile canaliculi,** intercellular spaces between liver cells, to enter **bile ductules,** then **canals of Hering** (and **cholangioles**), to be delivered to **bile ducts** at the portal areas.

2. Portal Lobule
The apices of triangular cross-sections of **portal lobules** are **central veins.** Thus, **portal areas** form the centers of these lobules. The portal lobule is based on bile flow.

3. Acinus of Rappaport (Liver Acinus)
The **acinus of Rappaport** in section is a diamond-shaped area of the liver whose long axis is the straight line between neighboring **central veins** and whose short axis is the intersecting line between neighboring portal areas. The liver acinus is based on **blood flow.**

IV. GALLBLADDER

The **gallbladder** is connected to the liver via its **cystic duct,** which joins the **common hepatic duct.**

A. Epithelium

The gallbladder is lined by a **simple columnar epithelium.**

B. Lamina Propria

The **lamina propria** is thrown into intricate folds that disappear in the distended gallbladder. **Rokitansky-Aschoff sinuses** (epithelial diverticula) may be present.

C. Muscularis Externa

The **muscularis externa** is composed of an obliquely oriented **smooth muscle** layer.

D. Serosa

Adventitia attaches the gallbladder to the capsule of the liver, whereas **serosa** covers the remaining surface.

16

Urinary System

The urinary system, composed of the kidneys, ureters, urinary bladder, and urethra, functions in the formation of urine, regulation of blood pressure and fluid volume of the body, acid-base balance, and formation and release of certain hormones.

The functional unit of the kidney is the **uriniferous tubule** (see Graphic 16-1), consisting of the **nephron** and the **collecting tubule**, each of which is derived from a different embryologic primordium.

KIDNEY

The **kidneys** possess a convex and a concave border, the latter of which is known as the **hilum**. It is here that arteries enter and the ureter and veins leave the kidney. Each kidney is divided into a **cortex** and a **medulla**.

The cortical region is subdivided into the **cortical labyrinth** and the **medullary rays**, whereas the medulla is composed of 10 to 18 **renal pyramids**, each of which is said to constitute a **lobe** of the kidney. The apex of each pyramid is perforated by 15 to 20 **papillary ducts** (of Bellini) at the **area cribrosa**. The region of the medulla between neighboring renal pyramids is occupied by cortical-like material known as **renal columns** (of Bertin). Each medullary ray is an extension of the renal medulla into the cortex, where it forms the core of a kidney **lobule**.

The vascular supply of the kidney must be appreciated to understand the histophysiology of the kidney. Each kidney is supplied by a renal artery, a direct branch of the abdominal aorta. This vessel subdivides into several major branches as it enters the hilum of the kidney, each of which subsequently divides to give rise to two or more interlobar arteries.

Interlobar arteries pass between neighboring pyramids toward the cortex and, at the corticomedullary junction, give rise to **arcuate arteries** that follow the base of the pyramid. Small, **interlobular arteries** derived from arcuate arteries enter the cortical labyrinth, equidistant from neighboring medullary rays, to reach the **renal capsule**. Along the extent of the interlobular arteries, smaller vessels, known as **afferent glomerular arterioles**, arise, become enveloped by **Bowman's capsule**, and form a capillary plexus known as the **glomerulus**. Collec-

tively, Bowman's capsule and the glomerulus are referred to as the **renal corpuscle** (see Graphic 16-2). **Efferent glomerular arterioles** drain the glomerulus, passing into the cortex, where they form the **peritubular capillary network** or into the medulla as **arteriolae rectae spuriae**, a part of the vasa recta.

The interstitium of the cortical labyrinth and the capsule of the kidney are drained by **interlobular veins**, most of which enter the **arcuate veins**, tributaries of the **interlobar veins**. Blood from the interlobar veins enters the **renal vein**, which delivers its blood to the inferior vena cava.

Uriniferous Tubule

The functional unit of the kidney is the **uriniferous tubule**, consisting of the **nephron** and the **collecting tubule**, each of which is derived from a different embryologic primordium.

Nephron

There are two types of nephrons, classified by the location of their renal corpuscles in the kidney cortex: **juxtamedullary nephrons**, possessing long, thin limbs of Henle's loop, and **cortical nephrons**. It is the long, thin limbs of Henle's loop that assist in the establishment of a concentration gradient in the renal medulla, permitting the formation of hypertonic urine.

The nephron begins at **Bowman's capsule**, a distended, blindly ending, invaginated region of the tubule. The modified cells of the inner, **visceral layer** are known as **podocytes**. Some of their **primary (major)** processes but mainly their secondary processes and terminal **pedicels** wrap around the glomerular capillaries. These capillaries are fenestrated with large pores (60 to 90 nm in diameter) lacking diaphragms.

A thick **basal lamina** manufactured by both and interposed between the podocytes and the endothelial cells of the capillary. The spaces between adjoining pedicels, known as **filtration slits**, are bridged by thin slit diaphragms that extend from one pedicel to the next. Interstitial tissue composed of **intraglomerular mesangial cells** and the extracellular matrix they manufacture is also associated with the glomerulus.

The ultrafiltrate from the capillaries enters **Bowman's (urinary) space** and is drained from there by

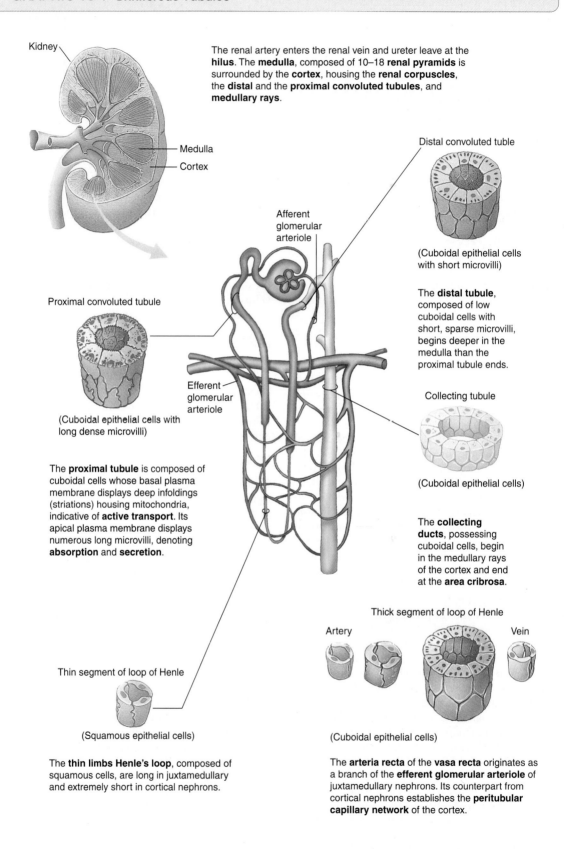

Kidney

The renal artery enters the renal vein and ureter leave at the **hilus**. The **medulla**, composed of 10–18 **renal pyramids** is surrounded by the **cortex**, housing the **renal corpuscles**, the **distal** and the **proximal convoluted tubules**, and **medullary rays**.

Medulla

Cortex

Distal convoluted tuble

(Cuboidal epithelial cells with short microvilli)

The **distal tubule**, composed of low cuboidal cells with short, sparse microvilli, begins deeper in the medulla than the proximal tubule ends.

Afferent glomerular arteriole

Proximal convoluted tubule

Efferent glomerular arteriole

(Cuboidal epithelial cells with long dense microvilli)

The **proximal tubule** is composed of cuboidal cells whose basal plasma membrane displays deep infoldings (striations) housing mitochondria, indicative of **active transport**. Its apical plasma membrane displays numerous long microvilli, denoting **absorption** and **secretion**.

Collecting tubule

(Cuboidal epithelial cells)

The **collecting ducts**, possessing cuboidal cells, begin in the medullary rays of the cortex and end at the **area cribrosa**.

Thick segment of loop of Henle

Artery   Vein

Thin segment of loop of Henle

(Squamous epithelial cells)

(Cuboidal epithelial cells)

The **thin limbs Henle's loop**, composed of squamous cells, are long in juxtamedullary and extremely short in cortical nephrons.

The **arteria recta** of the **vasa recta** originates as a branch of the **efferent glomerular arteriole** of juxtamedullary nephrons. Its counterpart from cortical nephrons establishes the **peritubular capillary network** of the cortex.

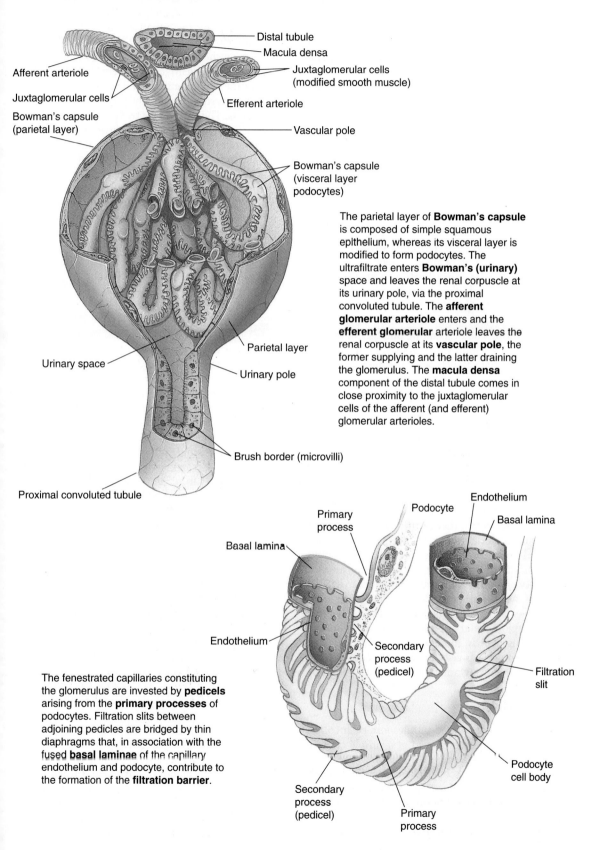

Distal tubule

Macula densa

Juxtaglomerular cells
(modified smooth muscle)

Afferent arteriole

Juxtaglomerular cells

Efferent arteriole

Bowman's capsule
(parietal layer)

Vascular pole

Bowman's capsule
(visceral layer
podocytes)

The parietal layer of **Bowman's capsule**
is composed of simple squamous
eplthelium, whereas its visceral layer is
modified to form podocytes. The
ultrafiltrate enters **Bowman's (urinary)**
space and leaves the renal corpuscle at
its urinary pole, via the proximal
convoluted tubule. The **afferent
glomerular arteriole** enters and the
efferent glomerular arteriole leaves the
renal corpuscle at its **vascular pole**, the
former supplying and the latter draining
the glomerulus. The **macula densa**
component of the distal tubule comes in
close proximity to the juxtaglomerular
cells of the afferent (and efferent)
glomerular arterioles.

Parietal layer

Urinary space

Urinary pole

Brush border (microvilli)

Proximal convoluted tubule

Endothelium

Podocyte

Basal lamina

Primary
process

Basal lamina

Endothelium

Secondary
process
(pedicel)

Filtration
slit

The fenestrated capillaries constituting
the glomerulus are invested by **pedicels**
arising from the **primary processes** of
podocytes. Filtration slits between
adjoining pedicels are bridged by thin
diaphragms that, in association with the
fused **basal laminae** of the capillary
endothelium and podocyte, contribute to
the formation of the **filtration barrier**.

Podocyte
cell body

Secondary
process
(pedicel)

Primary
process

the **neck** of the **proximal tubule**. The simple cuboidal epithelium of the proximal tubule adjoins the simple squamous epithelium of the parietal layer of Bowman's capsule.

The cells of the next portion, the **proximal convoluted tubule**, possess an extensive **brush border** (microvilli) on their luminal surface. Their lateral and basal plasma membranes are considerably convoluted, and the lateral membranes form numerous interdigitations with membranes of adjoining cells. The exaggerated folding of the basal plasmalemma presents a region rich in mitochondria and provides a striated appearance when viewed with the light microscope.

The straight portion, or **pars recta**, of the proximal tubules is also referred to as the **descending thick limb of Henle's loop**. It is histologically similar to the convoluted portion; however, its brush border becomes shorter at its distal terminus, where it joins the descending thin limb of Henle's loop.

The **descending thin limb** of juxtaglomerular nephrons extends to the apex of the medullary pyramid, where it forms a hairpin loop and continues toward the cortex as the **ascending thin limb of Henle's loop**. The descending and ascending thin limbs of Henle's loop are composed of simple squamous epithelial cells (types I through IV) whose structure varies according to their permeability to water, organelle content, and complexity of tight junctions. Type I cells are present only in cortical nephrons, whereas types II, III, and IV cells are present in juxtaglomerular nephrons.

The **ascending thick limb of Henle's loop**, also known as the **pars recta of the distal tubule**, is composed of simple cuboidal cells that resemble the cells of the **distal tubule**. Cells of the distal tubule that contact the afferent (and efferent) glomerular arteriole are modified, in that they are thin, tall cuboidal cells whose nuclei are close to one another. This region is referred to as the **macula densa** of the distal tubule.

Cells of the macula densa communicate with modified smooth muscle cells, **juxtaglomerular (JG) cells**, of the afferent (and efferent) glomerular arterioles. The macula densa and the JG cells together form the **juxtaglomerular apparatus**. The **extraglomerular mesangial cells**, modified interstitial tissue cells, also known as lacis cells, are likewise considered to belong to the juxtaglomerular apparatus.

Collecting Duct

Several distal convoluted tubules join each **collecting duct**, which is composed of a simple cuboidal epithelium whose lateral cell membranes are evident with the light microscope. The collecting ducts descend from the medullary rays of the cortex through the renal pyramids. As they descend, several collecting ducts merge to form the ducts of Bellini, which terminate at the area cribrosa. The cuboidal cells of the collecting tubule are of two types, the lightly staining **principal cells** and the **intercalated cells** that stain darker. Principal cells possess a single, nonmotile, apically situated cilium that probably functions as a mechanosensor that monitors fluid flow along the lumen of the tubule. Principal cells possess ADH-sensitive aquaporin-2 channels that permit the cell to be permeable to water. They also have polycystin-1 and polycystin-2 in their plasmalemma. The latter of the two proteins is a calcium channel. Intercalated cells are of two types, A and B; the former transports H^+ into the tubular lumen and the latter resorbs H^+ and secretes HCO_3^-.

The **ducts of Bellini** then deliver the urine formed by the uriniferous tubule to the intrarenal passage, namely, the **minor calyx**, to be drained into a **major calyx** and then into the **pelvis** of the **ureter**. These excretory passages, lined by **transitional epithelium**, possess a fibroelastic subepithelial connective tissue, a smooth muscle tunic composed of **inner longitudinal** and **outer circular** layers, as well as a fibroelastic adventitia.

● EXTRARENAL EXCRETORY PASSAGES

The **extrarenal excretory passages** consist of the ureters, urinary bladder, and urethra. The ureters and bladder are also lined by transitional epithelia. The **ureters** possess a fibroelastic lamina propria and two to three layers of smooth muscle, arranged as above. The third muscle layer, the **outermost longitudinal layer**, appears in the lower one-third of the ureter.

The **transitional epithelial lining** of the **bladder** and of the other urinary passages offers an impermeable barrier to urine. To be able to perform its function, the plasma membrane of the surface-most cells is thicker than the average plasma membrane and is composed of a lattice structure consisting of hexagonally arrayed elements. Furthermore, since cells of the transitional epithelium must line an ever larger surface as the urinary bladder distends, the plasma membrane is folded in a mosaic-like fashion. Folding occurs at the **interplaque regions**, whereas the thickened **plaque regions** present **vesicular profiles**, which probably become unfolded as urine accumulates in the bladder.

The subepithelial connective tissue of the bladder is composed, according to most, of a lamina propria and a submucosa. The three smooth muscle layers are extensively interlaced, making them indistinguishable in some areas.

The **urethra** of the male differs from that of the female not only in its length but also in its function and epithelial lining. The lamina propria of both sexes contain mucous **glands of Littré** and **intraepithelial glands**, which lubricate the lining of the urethra, facilitating the passage of urine to the outside. The urethra is described in Chapter 17, "Female Reproductive System," and Chapter 18, "Male Reproductive System."

Histophysiology

I. FORMATION OF THE ULTRAFILTRATE

Since the renal artery is a direct branch of the abdominal aorta, the two kidneys receive 20% of the total blood volume per minute. Most of this blood enters the glomeruli, where the high arterial pressure expresses approximately 10% of its fluid volume, 125 mL/min, into Bowman's spaces. Vascular pressure is opposed by two forces, the **colloid osmotic pressure** of the blood and the pressure exerted by the ultrafiltrate present in Bowman's space. However, the average net **filtration force**, expressing ultrafiltrate from the blood into Bowman's space, is relatively high, about 25 mm Hg.

The renal **filtration barrier**, composed of the fenestrated endothelial cell, the fused **basal laminae** of the podocyte and capillary, and the diaphragm-bridged filtration slits between pedicels, permits only the passage of water, ions, and small molecules into Bowman's space. The presence of the polyanionic **heparan sulfate** in the **lamina rara** of the basal lamina impedes the passage of large and negatively charged proteins through the barrier. Moreover, type IV collagen of the **lamina densa** acts as a molecular sieve and traps proteins larger than 69,000 MW.

To maintain the efficiency of the filtering system, **intraglomerular mesangial cells** phagocytose the lamina densa, which then is renewed by the combined actions of the podocytes and endothelial cells. Additionally, the intraglomerular mesangial cells also form the mesangial matrix around themselves and release prostaglandins, interleukin-1, and other cytokines. These cells also have contractile properties that, by constricting the glomerulus, modulate blood pressure within the glomerular network. Finally, intraglomerular mesangial cells form a structural support for the glomerulus. The modified plasma that enters Bowman's space is known as the **ultrafiltrate**.

II. FUNCTION OF THE PROXIMAL TUBULE

In a healthy individual, the **proximal tubule** resorbs approximately 80% of the water, sodium, and chloride, as well as 100% of the proteins, amino acids, and glucose from the ultrafiltrate. The resorbed materials are eventually returned into the **peritubular capillary network** of the cortical labyrinth for distribution to the remainder of the body. The movement of sodium is via an active transport mechanism utilizing a **sodium-potassium-ATPase pump** in the basal plasmalemma, with chloride and water following passively. Since salt and water are resorbed in equimolar concentrations, the **osmolarity** of the ultrafiltrate is **not** altered in the proximal tubule but remains the same as that of blood. The endocytosed proteins are degraded into amino acids that are also released into the renal interstitium for distribution by the vascular system. The proximal tubule also secretes organic acids, bases, and other substances into the ultrafiltrate.

III. FUNCTIONS OF THE THIN LIMBS OF HENLE'S LOOP

The **descending thin limb of Henle's loop** is completely permeable to water and only somewhat permeable to salts, hence the ultrafiltrate in the lumen will attempt to equilibrate its osmolarity with the renal interstitium in its vicinity.

The **ascending thin limb** is mostly impermeable to water but is relatively permeable to salts; thus the movement of water is impeded, but that of sodium and chloride is not. The ultrafiltrate will maintain the same osmolarity as the renal interstitium in its immediate surroundings as the concentration gradient decreases, approaching the cortex.

IV. FUNCTIONS OF THE DISTAL TUBULE

The **pars recta** of the distal tubule (ascending thick limb of Henle's loop) is impermeable to water but possesses a $Na^+/K^+/2Cl^-$ cotransporter on the luminal surface of the its cells that actively pumps sodium and chloride from the lumen into the cell. The basally located Na^+/K^+ ATPase pump transfers sodium and chloride out of the cell into the renal interstitium. However, since water cannot enter or leave the lumen, the ultrafiltrate is **hypoosmotic** by the time it reaches the macula densa region.

The distal convoluted tubule, whose cells possess **aldosterone receptors**, resorbs sodium ions from and secretes hydrogen, potassium, and ammonium ions into the ultrafiltrate, which it then delivers to the collecting duct.

V. FUNCTION OF THE JUXTAGLOMERULAR APPARATUS

It is believed that the **macula densa cells** monitor the osmolarity and volume of the ultrafiltrate. If either of these is elevated, the macula densa cells, via gap junctions, instruct the **juxtaglomerular cells** to release their stored proteolytic enzyme, **renin**, into the bloodstream. Renin cleaves two amino acids from the circulating decapeptide **angiotensinogen**, changing it to **angiotensin I**, which, in turn, is cleaved by **converting enzyme** located on the luminal surfaces of capillaries (especially in the lungs), forming **angiotensin II**. This powerful vasoconstrictor also prompts the release of the mineralocorticoid aldosterone from the suprarenal cortex.

Aldosterone binds to receptors on cells of the distal convoluted tubules, prompting them to resorb sodium (and chloride) from the ultrafiltrate. The addition of sodium to the extracellular compartment causes the retention of fluid with the subsequent elevation in blood pressure.

VI. CONCENTRATION OF URINE

A. Nephron (Countercurrent Multiplier System)

The concentration of urine occurs only in juxtamedullary nephrons, whose long, thin limbs of Henle's loop function in the establishment of an **osmotic concentration gradient**. This gradient gradually increases from about 300 mOsm/L in the interstitium of the outer medulla to as much as 1,200 mOsm/L at the renal papilla.

The $Na^+/K^+/2Cl^-$ cotransporter of the ascending thick limb of Henle's loop transfers chloride and sodium ions from the lumen into the renal interstitium. Water is not permitted to leave, hence the salt concentration of the interstitium increases. Since the supply of sodium and chloride inside the ascending thick limb decreases as the ultrafiltrate proceeds toward the cortex (because it is constantly being removed from the lumen), less and less sodium and chloride is available for transport; consequently, the interstitial salt concentration decreases closer to the cortex.

The osmotic concentration gradient of the inner medulla, deep to the junction of the thin and thick ascending limbs of Henle's loop, is controlled by **urea** rather than sodium and chloride.

As the ultrafiltrate passes down the descending thin limb of Henle's loop, it reacts to the increasing gradient of osmotic concentration in the interstitium. Water leaves, and a limited amount of salts enter the lumen, **reducing the volume** and **increasing the salt concentration** of the ultrafiltrate (which becomes **hypertonic**).

In the ascending thin limb of Henle's loop, water is conserved but salts are permitted to leave the ultrafiltrate, decreasing its osmolarity and contributing to the maintenance of the osmotic concentration gradient.

B. Collecting Duct

The ultrafiltrate that enters the collecting duct is **hypoosmotic**. As it passes down the collecting duct it is subject to the increasing osmotic gradient of the renal interstitium.

If **antidiuretic hormone** (**ADH**) is released from the pars nervosa of the pituitary, the cells of the collecting ducts become permeable to water, which leaves the lumen of the collecting duct, increasing the concentration of the urine. In the absence of ADH, the cells of the collecting duct are impermeable to water, and the urine remains **hypotonic**.

The collecting duct is also responsible for permitting **urea** to diffuse into the interstitium of the **inner medulla**. The high interstitial osmolarity of this region is attributed to the urea concentration.

C. Vasa Recta (Countercurrent Exchange System)

The **vasa recta** assists in the maintenance of the osmotic concentration gradient of the renal medulla, since these capillary loops are completely permeable to salts and water. Thus, as the blood descends in the arteria recta, it becomes hyperosmotic, but as it ascends in the vena recta, its osmolarity returns to normal.

It is also important to realize that the arteria recta carries a smaller volume than the vena recta, permitting the removal of the fluid and salts transported into the renal interstitium by the uriniferous tubules.

CLINICAL CONSIDERATIONS

Odor and Color of Urine
The odor and color of urine may provide clues to the individual's disease state. Normal urine is either colorless or has a yellow color if the urine is concentrated. Similarly, dilute urine has very little odor, whereas concentrated urine has a pungent smell. If the color of urine is reddish, the individual may have porphyria or fresh blood in the urine; if the color is brown, the possibility is that breakdown by-products of damaged muscle or breakdown by-products of

hemoglobin are in the urine. Black discoloration could be due to the presence of melanin pigment in the urine, whereas cloudy urine could be an indication of the presence of acidic crystals or the presence of pus derived from urinary tract infection. Additionally, certain medications can discolor the urine, and the patient should be warned in advance about the color change. Changes in the odor of urine can be due to diabetes that is not being controlled (a sweet odor); fetid odor could indicate the presence of a urinary tract infection; and a musty odor of urine in a young patient may suggest phenylketonuria.

Tubular Necrosis

Tubular necrosis may result in **acute renal failure**. Cells of the renal tubules die either by being poisoned due to exposure to toxic chemicals, such as mercury or carbon tetrachloride, or die because of severe cardiovascular shock that reduces blood flow to the kidneys. The dead cells become sloughed off and occlude the lumina of their tubules. If the basal laminae remain intact, epithelial cell division may be able to repair the damage in less than 3 weeks.

Acute Glomerulonephritis

Acute glomerulonephritis is usually the result of a localized beta Streptococcal infection in a region of the body other than the kidney (e.g., strep throat). Plasma cells secrete antibodies that complex with streptococcal antigens, forming an insoluble antigen-antibody complex that is filtered by the basal lamina between the podocytes and the endothelial cells of the glomerulus. As the immune complex builds up in the glomerular basal lamina, the epithelial cells and mesangial cells proliferate. Additionally, leukocytes accumulate in the glomerulus, congesting and blocking it. Moreover, pharmacologic agents released at the site of damage cause the glomerulus to become leaky, and proteins, platelets, and erythrocytes may enter the glomerular filtrate. Usually after the acute inflammation abates, the glomeruli repair themselves and the normal kidney function returns. Occasionally, however, the damage is extensive and kidney function becomes permanently impaired.

Diabetes Insipidus

Diabetes insipidus occurs because of damage to the cells of the hypothalamus that manufacture ADH (antidiuretic hormone). The low levels of ADH interfere with the ability of the collecting tubules of the kidney to concentrate urine. The excess fluid loss in the formation of copious quantities of dilute urine results in **polydipsia** (excessive thirst) and dehydration.

Kidney Stones

Kidney stones usually form due to the condition known as **hyperparathyroidism**, in which the formation of excess parathyroid hormone (PTH) by the parathyroid glands results in an increased level of osteoclastic activity. The resorption of bone, as well as the increased absorption of calcium and phosphates from the gastrointestinal tract, eventuate higher than normal blood calcium levels. As the kidneys excrete higher than normal concentrations of calcium and phosphates, their presence in the urine, especially under alkaline conditions, causes their precipitation in the kidney tubules. Continued accretion of these ions onto the crystal surface causes an increase in the size of the crystals, and they become known as **kidney stones**.

Cancers of the Kidney

Cancers of the kidney are usually solid tumors, whereas cysts of the kidney are usually benign. The most common symptom of kidney cancer is **blood in the urine**, although the amount of blood may be undetectable without a microscopic examination of the urine. Usually, kidney cancers are accompanied by pain and fever, but frequently they are discovered by abdominal palpation during routine physicals when the physician detects a lump in the region of the kidney. If the cancer has not metastasized, the treatment of choice is removal of the affected kidney and regional lymph nodes. Since kidney cancers spread early and usually to the lung, the prognosis is poor, but interleukine-2 therapy has been shown to be promising.

Bladder Cancer

Annually there are more than 50,000 new cases of transitional cell carcinomas of the bladder in the United States. Interestingly, almost 65% of the affected individuals are male, and about half of these patients smoke cigarettes. The most prominent symptom of bladder cancer is blood in the urine, followed by burning sensation and pain on urination, as well as an increased frequency of the urge to urinate. Although these symptoms are frequently confused with cystitis, the condition becomes suspicious once the antibiotics fail to alleviate the problem and cytology of the urine demonstrates the presence of cancerous transitional cells. If caught early, before the carcinoma invades the deeper tissues, the survival rate is as great as 95%; however, if the tumor is a rapidly dividing one that invades the muscular layers of the bladder and reaches the lymph nodes, the 5-year survival rate drops to less than 45%.

FIGURE 1 • Kidney cortex and medulla. Human. Paraffin section. ×14.

The kidney cortex and part of the medulla are presented at a low magnification to provide an insight into the cortical architecture. The **capsule** (Ca) appears as a thin, light line at the top of the photomicrograph. The darker area below it, occupying the top half of the photomicrograph, is the **cortex** (C); the lower lighter region is the **medulla** (M). Note that longitudinal rays of the medulla appear to invade the cortex; these are known as **medullary rays** (MR). The tissue between medullary rays appears convoluted and is referred to as the **cortical labyrinth** (CL). It is occupied by dense, round structures, the **renal corpuscles** (RC). These are the first part of the nephrons, and their location in the cortex is indicative of their time of development as well as of their function. They are referred to as **superficial** (1), **midcortical** (2), or **juxta-medullary nephrons** (3). Each medullary ray and one-half of the cortical labyrinth on either side of it constitutes a lobule of the kidney. The lobule extends into the medulla, but its borders are undefinable histologically (approximated by vertical lines). The large vessels at the corticomedullary junction are **arcuate vessels** (AV); those in the cortical labyrinth are **interlobular vessels** (IV).

FIGURE 3 • Kidney cortex. Human. Paraffin section. ×132.

The various components of the cortical labyrinth and portions of two medullary rays are evident. The orientation of this photomicrograph is perpendicular to that of Figure 1. Note that two **renal corpuscles** (RC) in the center of the photomicrograph display a slight shrinkage artifact and thus clearly demonstrate **Bowman's space** (BS). The renal corpuscles are surrounded by cross-sections of **proximal convoluted tubules** (PT), **distal convoluted tubules** (DT), and **macula densa** (MD). Since the proximal convoluted tubule is much longer than the convoluted portion of the distal tubule, the number of proximal convoluted tubule profiles around a renal corpuscle outnumber the distal convoluted tubule profiles by approximately 7 to 1. The medullary rays contain the **pars recta** (PR) of the **proximal tubule**, the **ascending thick limbs of Henle's loop** (AT), and **collecting tubules** (CT).

FIGURE 2 • Kidney capsule. Monkey. Plastic section. ×540.

The kidney is invested by a **capsule** (Ca) composed of dense collagenous connective tissue containing occasional **fibroblasts** (Fb). Although this structure is not highly vascular, it does possess some **capsular vessels** (CV). Observe the numerous red blood cells in the lumina of these vessels. The deeper aspect of the capsule possesses a rich **capillary network** (CN) that is supplied by the terminal branches of the interlobular arteries and is drained by the stellate veins, tributaries of the interlobular veins. Note the cross-sections of the **proximal convoluted tubules** (PT).

FIGURE 4 • Colored colloidin-injected kidney. Paraffin section. ×132.

This specimen was prepared by injecting the renal artery with colored colloidin, and a thick section was taken to demonstrate the vascular supply of the renal corpuscle. Each renal corpuscle contains tufts of capillaries, the **glomerulus** (G), which is supplied by the **afferent glomerular arteriole** (AA) and drained by the **efferent glomerular arteriole** (EA). Note that the outer diameter of the afferent glomerular arteriole is greater than that of the efferent glomerular arteriole; however, the diameters of the two lumina are about equal. It is important to realize that the glomerulus is an arterial capillary network; therefore, the pressure within these vessels is greater than that of normal capillary beds. This results in more effective filtration pressure. The large vessel on the lower right is an **interlobular artery** (IA), and it is the parent vessel of the afferent glomerular arterioles.

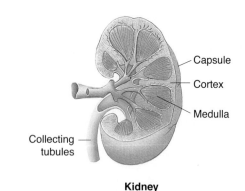

Capsule

Cortex

Medulla

Collecting tubules

Kidney

KEY						
AA	afferent arteriole	CN	capillary network	IV	interlobular vessel
AT	ascending thick limb of	CT	collecting tubule	M	medulla
	Henle's loop	CV	capsular vessel	MD	macula densa
AV	arcuate vessel	DT	distal convoluted tubule	MR	medullary ray
BS	Bowman's space	EA	efferent arteriole	PR	pars recta
C	cortex	Fb	fibroblast	PT	proximal convoluted
Ca	capsule	G	glomerulus		tubule
CL	cortical labyrinth	IA	interlobular artery	RC	renal corpuscle

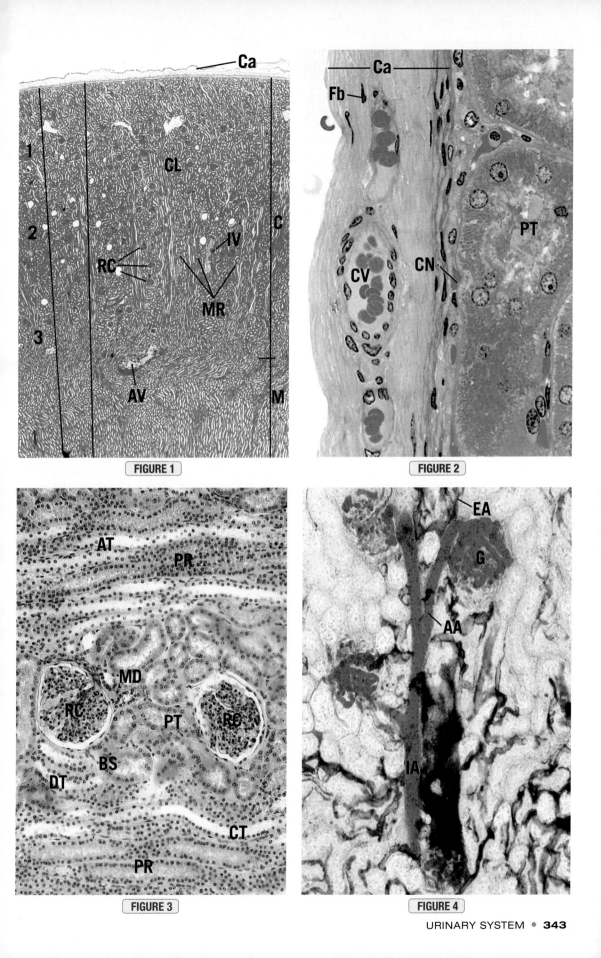

FIGURE 1

FIGURE 2

FIGURE 3

FIGURE 4

FIGURE 1 • Kidney cortical labyrinth. Monkey. Plastic section. ×270.

The center of this photomicrograph is occupied by a renal corpuscle. The urinary pole is evident as the short neck empties into the convoluted portion of the **proximal tubule** (PT). The renal corpuscle is composed of the **glomerulus** (G), tufts of capillaries, the visceral layer of Bowman's capsule (podocytes) that is intimately associated with the glomerulus, **Bowman's space** (BS), into which the ultrafiltrate is expressed from the capillaries, and the **parietal layer** (PL) of Bowman's capsule, consisting of a simple squamous epithelium. Additionally, mesangial cells are also present in the renal corpuscle. Most of the tubular profiles surrounding the renal corpuscle are transverse sections of the darker-staining **proximal tubules** (PT), which outnumber the cross-sections of the lighter-staining **distal tubules** (DT).

FIGURE 3 • Kidney cortical labyrinth. Monkey. Plastic section. ×270.

The vascular pole of this renal corpuscle is very clearly represented. It is in this region that the **afferent glomerular arteriole (AA)** enters the renal corpuscle and the **efferent glomerular arteriole** (EA) leaves, draining the glomerulus. Observe that these two vessels and their capillaries are supported by **mesangial cells** (Mg). Note that although the outer diameter of the afferent glomerular arteriole is greater than that of the efferent glomerular arteriole, their luminal diameters are approximately the same. The renal corpuscle is surrounded by cross-sectional profiles of **distal** (DT) and **proximal** (PT) **tubules**. The *boxed area* is presented at a higher magnification in Figure 4. *Inset.* **Glomerulus. Kidney. Monkey. Plastic section.** × 720. The glomerulus is composed of capillaries whose **endothelial cell** (En) nuclei bulge into the lumen. The endothelial cells are separated from **podocytes** (P), modified visceral cell layer of Bowman's capsule, by a thick basal lamina (*arrows*). **Mesangial cells** (Mg) form both supporting and phagocytic elements of the renal corpuscle. Note that major processes (*asterisks*) of the podocytes are also distinguishable in this photomicrograph.

FIGURE 2 • Kidney cortical labyrinth. Monkey. Plastic section. ×270.

The renal corpuscle in the center of the photomicrograph displays all of the characteristics identified in Figure 1, except that instead of the urinary pole, the **vascular pole** (VP) is presented. That is the region where the afferent and efferent glomerular arterioles enter and leave the renal corpuscle, respectively. Some of the smooth muscle cells of the afferent (and sometimes efferent) glomerular arterioles are modified in that they contain renin granules. These modified cells are known as **juxtaglomerular cells** (JC). They are closely associated with the **macula densa** (MD) region of the distal tubule. Again, note that most of the cross-sectional profiles of tubules surrounding the renal corpuscle belong to the convoluted portion of the **proximal tubules** (PT), whereas only one or two are distal tubules. Observe the rich **vascularity** (BV) of the renal cortex as well as the scant amount of connective tissue elements (*arrows*) associated with these vessels.

FIGURE 4 • Juxtaglomerular apparatus. Kidney. Monkey. Plastic section. ×1,325.

The *boxed area* of Figure 3 is magnified to present the juxtaglomerular apparatus. This is composed of the **macula densa** (MD) region of the distal tubule and apparent **juxtaglomerular cells** (JC), modified smooth muscle cells of the **afferent glomerular arteriole** (AA). Observe the granules (*arrowheads*) in the juxtaglomerular cells, which are believed to be the enzyme renin. Note the nuclei (*asterisks*) of the endothelial cells lining the afferent glomerular arteriole.

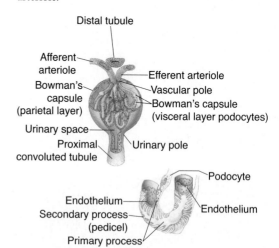

Renal corpuscle

KEY						
AA	afferent arteriole	En	endothelial cell	P	podocyte
BS	Bowman's space	G	glomerulus	PL	parietal layer
BV	blood vessel	JC	juxtaglomerular cell	PT	proximal tubule
DT	distal tubule	MD	macula densa	VP	vascular pole
EA	efferent arteriole	Mg	mesangial cell		

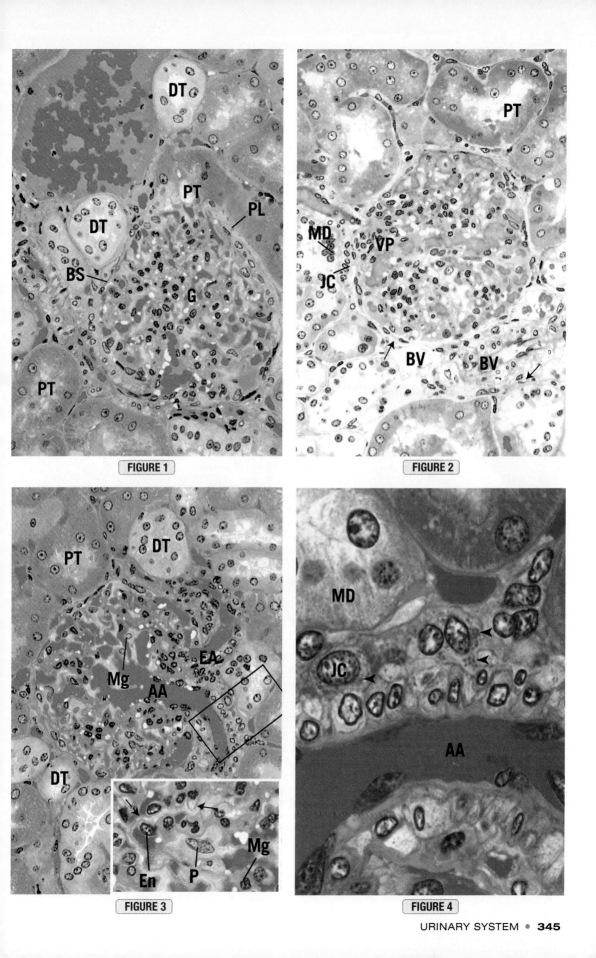

FIGURE 1

FIGURE 2

FIGURE 3

FIGURE 4

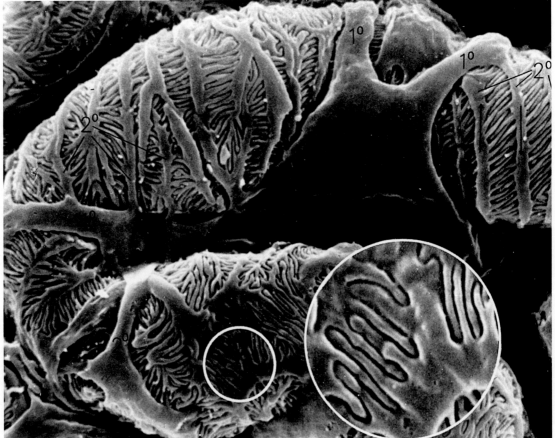

FIGURE 1

FIGURE 1 • Scanning electron micrograph of a glomerulus, displaying the primary and secondary processes and pedicels of podocytes. Top, ×700; bottom, ×4,000; and inset, ×6,000. (From Ross MH, Reith EJ, Romrell LJ. Histology: A Text and Atlas. 2nd Ed. Baltimore: Williams & Wilkins, 1989:536.)

PLATE 16-4 Renal Corpuscle, Electron Microscopy

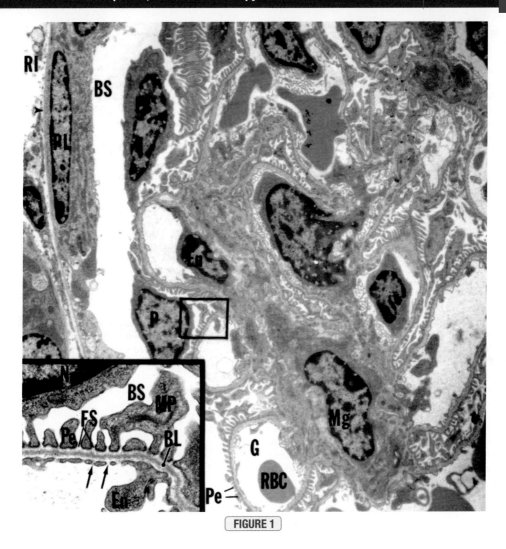

FIGURE 1

FIGURE 1 • Kidney cortex. Renal corpuscle. Mouse. Electron microscopy. ×3,780.

Various components of the renal corpuscle are displayed in this electron micrograph. Note the basal lamina (*arrowhead*) separating the simple squamous cells of the **parietal layer** (PL) of Bowman's capsule from the **renal interstitium** (RI). **Bowman's space** (BS) and the **podocytes** (P) are shown to advantage, as are the **glomeruli** (G) and surrounding **pedicels** (Pe). **Mesangial cells** (Mg) occupy the space between capillary loops, and several **red blood cells** (RBC) and **endothelial cells** (En) are also evident. *Inset*. **Podocyte and glomerulus. Mouse. Electron microscopy.** ×6,300. This is a higher magnification of the *boxed area*, presenting a portion of a podocyte. Observe its **nucleus** (N), **major process** (MP), and **pedicels** (Pe). Note that the pedicels lie on a **basal lamina** (BL) that is composed of a lamina rara externa, lamina densa, and lamina rara interna. Observe the fenestrations (*arrows*) in the **endothelial lining** (En) of the glomerulus. The spaces between the pedicels, known as **filtration slits** (FS), lead into **Bowman's space** (BS).

FIGURE 1 • Renal medulla. Monkey. Plastic section. ×270.

This photomicrograph of the renal medulla demonstrates the arrangement of the various tubular and vascular structures. The formed connective tissue elements among the tubules and vessels are very sparse and constitute mainly fibroblasts, macrophages, and fibers (*asterisks*). The major tubular elements in evidence are the **collecting tubules** (CT), recognizable by the conspicuous lateral plasma membranes of their tall cuboidal (or low columnar) cells, **thick limbs of Henle's loop** (TH), and occasional **thin limbs of Henle's loop** (TL). Many vascular elements are noted; these are the vasa recta spuria, whose thicker-walled descending limbs are the **arteriolae rectae spuriae** (AR) and thinner-walled ascending limbs are the **venulae rectae spuriae** (VR).

FIGURE 3 • Renal papilla. x.s. Monkey. Plastic section. ×540.

In the deeper aspect of the medulla, collecting tubules merge with each other, forming larger and larger structures. The largest of these ducts are known as **papillary ducts** (PD), or ducts of Bellini, which may be recognized by their tall, pale columnar cells and their easily discernible lateral plasma membranes (*arrows*). These ducts open at the apex of the renal papilla, in the region known as the area cribrosa. The **thin limbs of Henle's loop** (TL) are evident. These structures form the hairpin-like loops of Henle in this region, where the ascending thin limbs recur to ascend in the medulla, eventually to become thicker, forming the straight portion of the distal tubule. Note that the **arteriolae rectae spuriae** (AR) and the **venulae rectae spuriae** (VR) follow the thin limbs of Henle's loop deep into the renal papilla. Some of the connective tissue elements are marked by *asterisks*.

FIGURE 2 • Renal papilla. x.s. Human. Paraffin section. ×270.

The most conspicuous tubular elements of the renal papilla are the **collecting tubules** (CT), with their cuboidal cells, whose lateral plasma membranes are evident. The numerous thin-walled structures are the **thin limbs of Henle's loop** (TL), as well as the **arteriolae rectae spuriae** (AR) and **venulae rectae spuriae** (VR) that may be identified by the presence of blood in their lumina. The formed connective tissue elements (*asterisks*) may be discerned in the interstitium among the various tubules of the kidney. An occasional thick limb of Henle's loop (TH) may also be observed.

FIGURE 4 • Renal medulla. l.s. Monkey. Plastic section. ×270.

This photomicrograph is similar to Figure 1, except that it is a longitudinal rather than a transverse section of the renal medulla. The center is occupied by a **collecting tubule** (CT), as is distinguished by the tall cuboidal cells whose lateral plasma membranes are evident. The collecting tubule is flanked by **thick limbs of Henle's loop** (TH). The vasa recta are filled with blood, and the thickness of their walls identifies whether they are **arteriolae rectae spuriae** (AR) or **venulae rectae spuriae** (VR). A **thin limb of Henle's loop** (TL) is also identifiable.

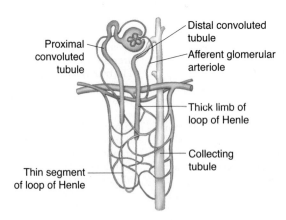

Proximal convoluted tubule

Distal convoluted tubule

Afferent glomerular arteriole

Thick limb of loop of Henle

Collecting tubule

Thin segment of loop of Henle

Uriniferous tubule

KEY					
AR	arteriolae rectae spuriae	PD	papillary duct	TL	thin limb of Henle's loop
CT	collecting tubule	TH	thick limb of Henle's loop	VR	venulae rectae spuriae

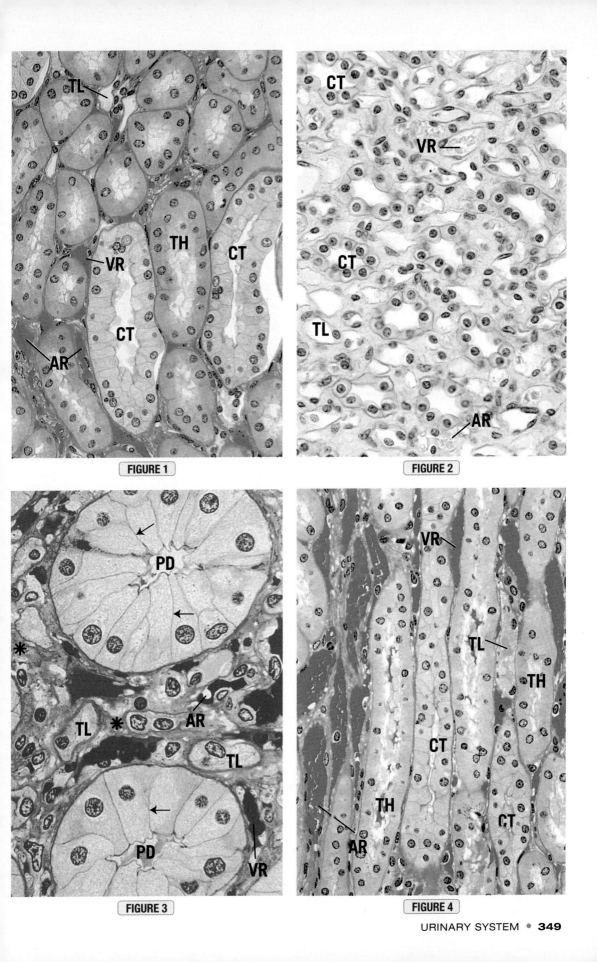

FIGURE 1

FIGURE 2

FIGURE 3

FIGURE 4

FIGURE 1 • Ureter. x.s. Human. Paraffin section. ×14.

This low-power photomicrograph of the ureter displays its stellate-shaped **lumen** (L) and thick lining **epithelium** (E). The interface between the **subepithelial connective tissue** (SCT) and the **smooth muscle coat** (SM) is indicated by *arrows*. The muscle coat is surrounded by a fibrous **adventitia** (Ad), which houses the numerous vascular channels and nerve fibers that travel with the ureter. Thus, the wall of the ureter consists of the mucosa (epithelium and underlying connective tissue), muscularis, and adventitia.

FIGURE 3 • Urinary bladder. Monkey. Plastic section. ×14.

The urinary bladder stores urine until it is ready to be voided. Since the volume of the bladder changes with the amount of urine it contains, its mucosa may or may not display folds. This particular specimen is not distended, hence the numerous folds (*arrows*). Moreover, the **transitional epithelium** (TE) of this preparation is also thick, whereas in the distended phase, the epithelium would be much thinner. Note also that the thick **muscularis** is composed of three layers of smooth muscle: **inner longitudinal** (IL), **middle circular** (MC), and **outer longitudinal** (OL). The muscle layers are surrounded either by an adventitia composed of loose connective tissue—as is the case in this photomicrograph—or by a serosa, depending on the region of the bladder being examined.

FIGURE 2 • Ureter. x.s. Monkey. Plastic section. ×132.

The mucosa is highly convoluted and consists of a thick, transitional epithelium whose free surface possesses characteristic **dome-shaped cells** (D). The basal cell layer sits on a basal lamina (*arrows*), which separates the epithelium from the underlying fibrous connective tissue. The **muscularis** consists of three layers of smooth muscle: **inner longitudinal** (IL), **middle circular** (MC), and **outer longitudinal** (OL). These three layers are not always present, for the outer longitudinal layer is found only in the inferior one-third of the ureter, that is, the portion nearest the urinary bladder. The **adventitia** (Ad) is composed of fibrous connective tissue that anchors the ureter to the posterior body wall and adjacent structures.

FIGURE 4 • Urinary bladder. Monkey. Plastic section. ×132.

The bladder is lined by **transitional epithelium** (TE), whose typical surface dome-shaped cells are shown to advantage. Some of these cells are binucleated. The epithelium is separated from the underlying connective tissue by a basal lamina (*arrows*). This subepithelial connective tissue is frequently said to be divided into a **lamina propria** (LP) and a **submucosa** (Sm). The vascularity of this region is demonstrated by the numerous **venules** (V) and **arterioles** (A). These vessels possess smaller tributaries and branches that supply the regions closer to the epithelium. *Inset.* **Transitional epithelium. Monkey. Plastic section.** × 540. The *boxed region* of the transitional epithelium is presented at a higher magnification to demonstrate the large, dome-shaped cells (*arrow*) at the free surface. These cells are characteristic of the empty bladder. When that structure is distended with urine, the dome-shaped cells assume a flattened morphology and the entire epithelium becomes thinner (being reduced from 5 to 7 to only 3 cell layers thick). Note that occasional cells may be binucleated.

KEY						
A	arteriole	L	lumen	SCT	subepithelial connective
Ad	adventitia	LP	lamina propria		tissue
D	dome-shaped cell	MC	middle circular	SM	smooth muscle coat
E	epithelium		muscularis	Sm	submucosa
IL	inner longitudinal	OL	outer longitudinal	TE	transitional epithelium
	muscularis		muscularis	V	venule

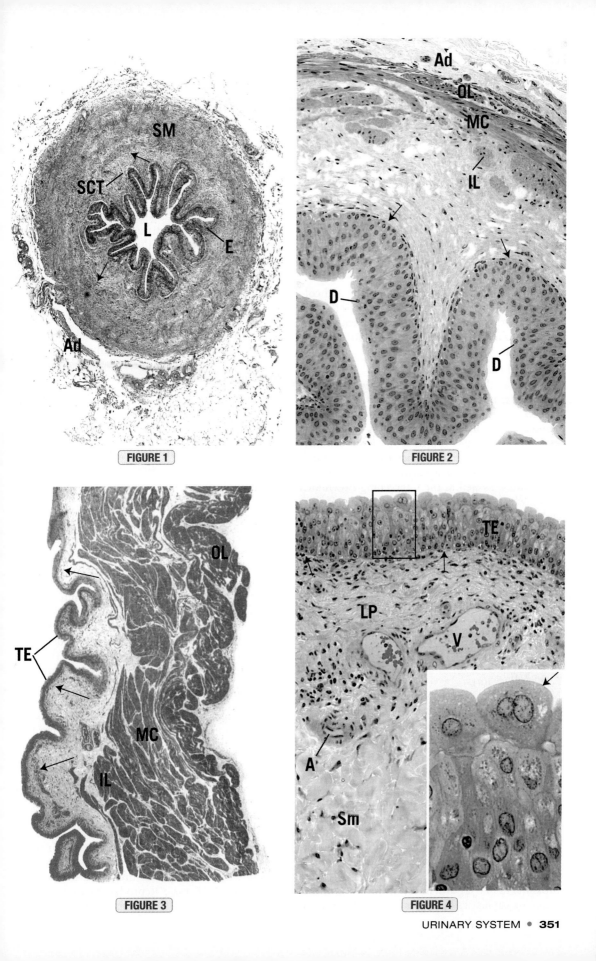

FIGURE 1

FIGURE 2

FIGURE 3

FIGURE 4

Summary of Histological Organization

I. KIDNEY

A. Capsule

The **capsule** is composed of dense, irregular collagenous connective tissue. Occasional **fibroblasts** and blood vessels may be seen.

B. Cortex

The **cortex** consists of parts of **nephrons** and **collecting tubules** arranged in **cortical labyrinths** and **medullary rays**. Additionally, blood vessels and associated connective tissue (**renal interstitium**) are also present.

1. Cortical Labyrinth
The **cortical labyrinth** is composed of **renal corpuscles** and cross-sections of **proximal convoluted tubules**, **distal convoluted tubules**, and the **macula densa** region of **distal tubules**. Renal corpuscles consist of **mesangial cells, parietal** (simple squamous) and **visceral** (modified to **podocytes**) **layers** of Bowman's capsule, and an associated capillary bed, the **glomerulus**, as well as the intervening **Bowman's space**, which receives the ultrafiltrate. The **afferent** and **efferent glomerular arterioles** supply and drain the glomerulus, respectively, at its vascular pole. **Bowman's space** is drained at the **urinary pole** into the **proximal convoluted tubule**, composed of eosinophilic simple cuboidal epithelium with a brush border. The **distal convoluted tubule** profiles are fewer in number and may be recognized by the pale cuboidal epithelial cells. The **macula densa** region of the distal tubule is associated with the **juxtaglomerular** (modified smooth muscle) **cells** of the afferent (and sometimes efferent) glomerular arterioles.

2. Medullary Rays
Medullary rays are continuations of medullary tissue extending into the cortex. They are composed mostly of **collecting tubules, pars recta of proximal tubules, ascending thick limbs of Henle's loop**, and blood vessels.

C. Medulla

The **medulla** is composed of **renal pyramids** that are bordered by **cortical columns**. The renal pyramids consist of **collecting tubules** whose simple cuboidal epithelium displays 1) clearly defined lateral cell membranes; 2) **thick descending limbs of Henle's loop**, whose cells resemble those of the proximal tubule; 3) **thin limbs of Henle's loop**, resembling capillaries but containing no blood; and

4) **ascending thick limbs of Henle's loop**, whose cells are similar to those of the distal tubule. Additionally, numerous blood vessels, the **vasa recta**, are also present, as well as slight connective tissue elements, the **renal interstitium**. The apex of the renal pyramid is the **renal papilla**, whose perforated tip is the **area cribrosa**, where the large **collecting ducts** (**of Bellini**) open to deliver the urine into the **minor calyx**.

D. Pelvis

The **renal pelvis**, subdivided into the **minor** and **major calyces**, constitutes the beginning of the main excretory duct of the kidney. The **transitional epithelium** of the minor calyx is reflected onto the renal papilla. The calyces are lined by transitional epithelium. The subepithelial connective tissue of both is loosely arranged and abuts the **muscularis**, composed of **inner longitudinal** and **outer circular** layers of **smooth muscle**. An **adventitia** of loose connective tissue surrounds the muscularis.

II. EXTRARENAL PASSAGES

A. Ureter

The **ureter** possesses a stellate-shaped lumen that is lined by **transitional epithelium**. The subepithelial connective tissue (sometimes said to be subdivided into **lamina propria** and **submucosa**) is composed of a fibroelastic connective tissue. The **muscularis** is again composed of **inner longitudinal** and **outer circular** layers of **smooth muscle**, although in its lower portion near the bladder a third, **outermost longitudinal** layer of **smooth muscle** is present. The muscularis is surrounded by a fibroelastic **adventitia**.

B. Bladder

The **urinary bladder** resembles the ureter except that it is a much larger structure and does not possess a stellate lumen, although the mucosa of the empty bladder is thrown into folds. The **lamina propria** is fibroelastic in character and may contain occasional **mucous glands** at the internal orifice of the urethra. The **muscularis** is composed of three indefinite layers of smooth muscle: **inner longitudinal, middle circular,** and **outer longitudinal**. The circular muscle coat forms the **internal sphincter** at the neck of the bladder. An **adventitia** or **serosa** surrounds the bladder. The urethra is described in Chapter 17, "Female Reproductive System," and Chapter 18, "Male Reproductive System."

Female Reproductive System

17

The female reproductive system (see Graphic 17-1) is composed of the ovaries, genital ducts, external genitalia, and the mammary glands, although, in a strict sense, the mammary glands are not considered to be genital organs. The reproductive system functions in the propagation of the species and is under the control of a complex interplay of hormonal, neural, and, at least in the human, psychologic factors.

OVARY

Each **ovary** is a small, almond-shaped structure whose thick connective tissue capsule, the **tunica albuginea**, is covered by a **simple squamous** to **cuboidal mesothelium** known as the **germinal epithelium**. The ovary is divisible into the **cortex**, rich in ovarian follicles and the medulla, a highly vascular connective tissue stroma.

The **cortex**, located just deep to the tunica albuginea, houses the female germ cells, **oogonia**, which have undergone a series of cell divisions to form numerous oocytes. Each **oocyte** is surrounded by a layer of epithelial cells known as **follicular cells** (whose origin is controversial), and these two structures together constitute an **ovarian follicle**. Under the influence initially of local factors and later of **follicle stimulating hormone**, follicles enlarge, are modified, become encapsulated by the ovarian **stroma** (connective tissue), and mature.

Ovarian Follicles

The follicle passes through various maturational stages, from the primordial follicle, through the primary, secondary, and, finally, the Graafian (mature) follicle. The **primordial follicle** is composed of a **primary oocyte** surrounded by a single layer of flattened follicular cells. As maturation progresses, the follicular cells become cuboidal in shape, and the follicle is referred to as a **unilaminar primary follicle**. Multilaminar primary follicles display an oocyte surrounded by several layers of follicular cells and an intervening **zona pellucida**, as well as an externally positioned **theca interna**.

With further growth of the follicle, accumulations of follicular fluid in the intercellular spaces of the follicular cells form. At this point, the entire structure is known as a **secondary follicle**, and it presents a well-developed zona pellucida, a clearly distinguishable basal membrane that is surrounded by both a theca interna and a **theca externa**.

As maturation progresses, the **Graafian follicle** (also referred to as the **mature follicle**) stage is reached. This large structure is characterized by a follicular fluid containing the central antrum, whose wall is composed of the **membrana granulosa**. Jutting into the antrum is the **cumulus oophorus**, housing the primary oocyte and its attendant zona pellucida and **corona radiata**. The membrana granulosa is separated from the theca interna by the basal membrane. The theca externa merges imperceptibly with the surrounding ovarian stroma. The Graafian follicle, mostly because of the activity of **luteinizing hormone**, ruptures, thus releasing the oocyte with its attendant follicular cells.

Corpus Luteum and Corpus Albicans

Once the Graafian follicle loses its oocyte, it becomes transformed into the **corpus hemorrhagicum**. Within a couple of days the corpus hemorrhagicum is transformed into the **corpus luteum**, a yellow structure that produces **estrogens** and **progesterone**. When the corpus luteum degenerates it becomes the fibrotic **corpus albicans**.

GENITAL DUCTS

Oviduct

Each **oviduct** (**fallopian tube**) is a short muscular tube leading from the vicinity of the ovary to the uterine lumen. The oviduct is subdivided into four regions: the **infundibulum** (whose **fimbriae** approximate the ovary), the **ampulla**, the **isthmus**, and the **intramural portion**, which pierces the wall of the uterus. The mucosa of the oviduct is extensively folded in the infundibulum and ampulla, but the folding is reduced in the isthmus and intramural portions.

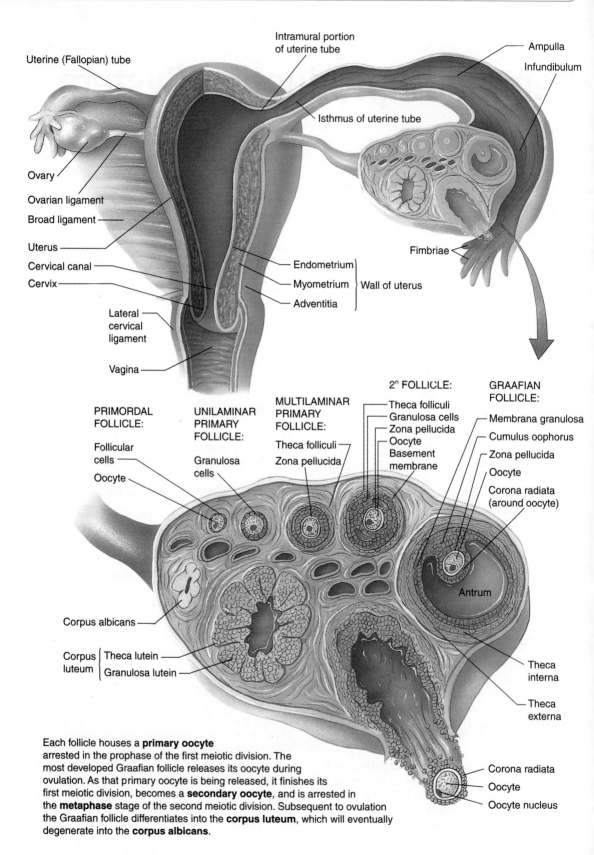

PRIMORDAL FOLLICLE:
- Follicular cells
- Oocyte

UNILAMINAR PRIMARY FOLLICLE:
- Granulosa cells

MULTILAMINAR PRIMARY FOLLICLE:
- Theca folliculi
- Zona pellucida

2ⁿ FOLLICLE:
- Theca folliculi
- Granulosa cells
- Zona pellucida
- Oocyte
- Basement membrane

GRAAFIAN FOLLICLE:
- Membrana granulosa
- Cumulus oophorus
- Zona pellucida
- Oocyte
- Corona radiata (around oocyte)

Uterine (Fallopian) tube
Intramural portion of uterine tube
Ampulla
Infundibulum
Isthmus of uterine tube
Ovary
Ovarian ligament
Broad ligament
Uterus
Cervical canal
Cervix
Endometrium
Myometrium
Adventitia
Wall of uterus
Fimbriae
Lateral cervical ligament
Vagina

Corpus albicans
Corpus luteum { Theca lutein / Granulosa lutein
Antrum
Theca interna
Theca externa
Corona radiata
Oocyte
Oocyte nucleus

Each follicle houses a **primary oocyte** arrested in the prophase of the first meiotic division. The most developed Graafian follicle releases its oocyte during ovulation. As that primary oocyte is being released, it finishes its first meiotic division, becomes a **secondary oocyte**, and is arrested in the **metaphase** stage of the second meiotic division. Subsequent to ovulation the Graafian follicle differentiates into the **corpus luteum**, which will eventually degenerate into the **corpus albicans**.

Placental Structure

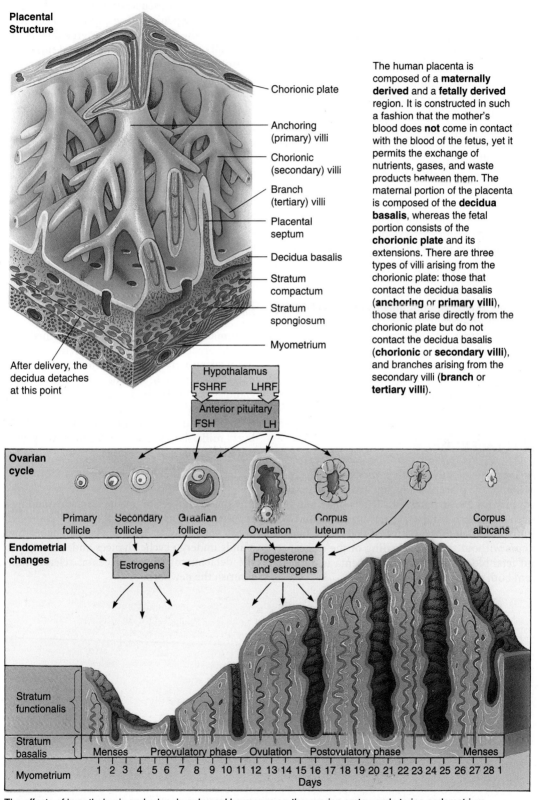

Chorionic plate

Anchoring (primary) villi

Chorionic (secondary) villi

Branch (tertiary) villi

Placental septum

Decidua basalis

Stratum compactum

Stratum spongiosum

Myometrium

After delivery, the decidua detaches at this point

The human placenta is composed of a **maternally derived** and a **fetally derived** region. It is constructed in such a fashion that the mother's blood does **not** come in contact with the blood of the fetus, yet it permits the exchange of nutrients, gases, and waste products between them. The maternal portion of the placenta is composed of the **decidua basalis**, whereas the fetal portion consists of the **chorionic plate** and its extensions. There are three types of villi arising from the chorionic plate: those that contact the decidua basalis (**anchoring** or **primary villi**), those that arise directly from the chorionic plate but do not contact the decidua basalis (**chorionic** or **secondary villi**), and branches arising from the secondary villi (**branch** or **tertiary villi**).

Hypothalamus

FSHRF   LHRF

Anterior pituitary

FSH   LH

Ovarian cycle

Primary follicle

Secondary follicle

Graafian follicle

Ovulation

Corpus luteum

Corpus albicans

Endometrial changes

Estrogens

Progesterone and estrogens

Stratum functionalis

Stratum basalis

Menses   Preovulatory phase   Ovulation   Postovulatory phase   Menses

Myometrium

1 2 3 4 5 6 7 8 9 10 11 12 13 14 15 16 17 18 19 20 21 22 23 24 25 26 27 28 1

Days

The effects of hypothalamic and adenohypophyseal hormones on the ovarian cortex and uterine endometrium.

Uterus

The **uterus**, a pear-shaped viscus, is divisible into a **fundus**, **body**, and **cervix**. During pregnancy, this organ houses and supports the developing embryo and fetus. The uterus is composed of a thick, muscular **myometrium** (covered by serosa and/or adventitia) and a spongy mucosal layer, the **endometrium**. The endometrium, composed of an epithelially lined lamina propria, with its superficial functional and deep basal layers, undergoes hormonally modulated cyclic changes during the menstrual cycle. The three stages of the endometrium are:

a. **Follicular (proliferative) phase**, during which the free surface of the endometrium is reepithelialized, and the glands, connective tissue elements, and vascular supply of the endometrium are reestablished.

b. **Luteal (secretory) phase**, occurring within a few days after ovulation, during which the glands further enlarge and become tortuous and their lumina become filled with secretory products. Additionally, the helical arteries become more coiled, and fibroblasts of the stroma accumulate glycogen and fat.

c. **Menstrual phase**, during which the functional layer of the endometrium is desquamated, resulting in menstrual flow, whereas the basal layer remains more or less undisturbed.

● PLACENTA

During pregnancy the uterus participates in the formation of the **placenta**, a highly vascular structure that permits the exchange of various materials between the maternal and fetal circulatory systems (see Graphic 17-2). It must be stressed that the exchange occurs without the commingling of the maternal and fetal bloods and that the placenta is derived from both maternal and fetal tissues.

● VAGINA

The **vagina** is a muscular sheath adapted for the reception of the penis during copulation and for the passage of the fetus from the uterus during birth. The wall of the vagina is composed of three layers: an **outer fibrous layer**, a **middle muscular layer**, and an **inner mucosal layer**. The lamina propria of the mucosa possesses no glands. A stratified squamous nonkeratinized epithelium lines the vagina.

● EXTERNAL GENITALIA

The **external genitalia**, composed of **labia majora**, **labia minora**, **clitoris**, and **vestibular glands**, are also referred to as the **vulva**. These structures are richly innervated and function during sexual arousal and copulation.

● MAMMARY GLANDS

Mammary Gland

The **mammary glands**, highly modified **sweat glands**, are identical in males and females until the onset of puberty, when, due to hormonal influences, the female breasts develop. The mammary gland is composed of numerous individual compound glands, each of which is considered a lobe. Each lobe is drained by a **lactiferous duct** that delivers **milk**, the secretion of the mammary glands, onto the surface of the nipple.

Areola

The pigmented region of the skin surrounding the nipple, known as the **areola**, is richly endowed by sweat, sebaceous, and areolar glands. The mammary glands undergo cyclic changes and, subsequent to the detachment of the placenta, release milk to nourish the newborn.

Histophysiology

I. REGULATION OF FOLLICLE MATURATION AND OVULATION

Early development of the follicle from the primordial through the secondary follicle stage is dependent on local factors. Later development depends on **gonadotropin-releasing hormones** from the hypothalamus, which activate gonadotrophs of the adenohypophysis to release follicle-stimulating hormone (FSH) and luteinizing hormone (LH).

FSH not only induces secondary follicles to mature into Graafian follicles but also causes cells of the **theca interna** to secrete **androgens**. Additionally, FSH prompts **granulosa cells** to develop **LH receptors**, to convert androgens to **estrogens**, and to secrete **inhibin**, **activin**, and **folliculostatin**. These hormones assist in the feedback regulation of FSH release. Moreover, as estrogen reaches a threshold level, it causes a surge of LH release.

The **LH** surge results not only in resumption of meiosis I in the primary oocyte and initiation of meiosis II in the (now) secondary oocyte but also in **ovulation**. Additionally, LH induces the development of the **corpus luteum** from the theca interna and membrana granulosa, and this can occur only when the granulosa cells respond to FSH to produce LH receptors.

II. FUNCTION AND FATE OF THE CORPUS LUTEUM

The **corpus luteum** secretes **progesterone**, a hormone that suppresses LH release by inhibiting gonadotropin-releasing hormone (GnRH) and facilitates the thickening of the uterine **endometrium**. Additionally, **estrogen** (inhibitor of FSH) and **relaxin** (which causes the fibrocartilage of the pubic symphysis to become more pliable) are also released by the corpus luteum.

In case pregnancy does not occur, the corpus luteum **atrophies,** a process known as **luteolysis,** and the absence of estrogen and progesterone will once again permit the release of FSH and LH from the adenohypophysis. In this case the corpus luteum is known as the **corpus luteum of menstruation** and will degenerate into the **corpus albicans**.

In case pregnancy does occur, the **syncytiotrophoblasts** of the forming placenta release **human chorionic gonadotropin (hCG)**, a hormone that maintains the placenta well into the second trimester. These cells also secrete **human chorionic mammotropin** (facilitates milk production and growth), **thyrotropin**, **corticotropin**, **relaxin**, and **estrogen**. A few months into the pregnancy, when the placenta has been well established, the corpus luteum, known as the **corpus luteum of pregnancy**, is no longer needed, and it also undergoes luteolysis to form the corpus albicans.

III. UTERINE RESPONSE TO HORMONES

A. Endometrium

The **endometrium** is separated into a deeper basal and a more superficial functional layer, each with its own blood supply. The **basal layer**, which remains intact during menstruation, is served by short, **straight arteries** and is occupied by the base of the **uterine glands**. The **functional layer,** served by the **helicine (coiled) arteries**, undergoes hormonally modulated cyclic changes.

FSH facilitates the **proliferative phase**, a thickening of the endometrium and the renewal of the connective tissue, glandular structures, and blood vessels (**helicine arteries**) subsequent to the menstrual phase.

LH facilitates the **secretory phase**, characterized by the further thickening of the endometrium, coiling of the endometrial glands, accumulation of glandular secretions, and further coiling and lengthening of the **helicine arteries**.

Decreased levels of LH and progesterone are responsible for the **menstrual phase**, which begins with long-term, intermittent **vasoconstriction** of the helicine arteries, with subsequent necrosis of the vessel walls as well as of the endometrial tissue of the functional layer. It should be understood that the basal layer is unaffected because it is being supplied by the straight arteries. During relaxation (between events of vasoconstriction), the helicine arteries rupture, and the rapid blood flow dislodges the blood-filled necrotic functional layer, which becomes sloughed as the **hemorrhagic discharge**, so that only the basal layer of the endometrium remains as the lining of the uterus.

B. Myometrium

During pregnancy the smooth muscle cells of the **myometrium** undergo both **hypertrophy** and **hyperplasia**, increasing the thickness of the muscle wall of the uterus. Additionally, these smooth muscle cells also acquire **gap junctions** that facilitate their coordinated contractile actions. At parturition, **oxytocin** and **prostaglandins** cause the uterine muscles to undergo rhythmic contractions that assist in expelling the fetus.

IV. HORMONAL EFFECTS ON THE MAMMARY GLAND

During pregnancy, several hormones interact to promote the development of the secretory units of the mammary gland. Cells of the **terminal interalveolar ducts** proliferate to form secretory **alveoli**. The hormones involved in promoting this process are **progesterone**, **estrogen**, and **human chorionic mammotropin** from the placenta and **lactogenic hormone** (**prolactin**) from the **acidophils** of the adenohypophysis.

Alveoli and terminal interalveolar ducts are surrounded by **myoepithelial cells** that contract as a result of the release of **oxytocin** from the neurohypophysis (in response to suckling), forcing milk out of the breast (**milk ejection reflex**).

V. MILK

Milk is composed of water, proteins, lipids, and lactose. However, milk secreted during the first few days (**colostrum**) is different, in that it is rich in vitamins, minerals, **lymphoid cells**, and proteins, especially **immunoglobulin A**, providing antibodies for the neonate for the first few months of life.

CLINICAL CONSIDERATIONS

Papanicolaou (Pap) Smear

The Papanicolaou (Pap) smear is performed as part of routine gynecological examination to examine stained exfoliative cells of the lining of the cervix and vagina. Evaluation of the smeared cells permits the recognition of precancerous conditions as well as cancer of the cervix. An annual smear test is recommended since cervical cancer is relatively slow growing and the Pap smear is an extremely cost-effective procedure that has been responsible for the early detection of cervical cancer and for saving lives of affected individuals.

Gonorrhea

Gonorrhea is a sexually transmitted bacterial infection caused by the gram-negative diplococcus *Neisseria gonorrhoeae*. In the United States, over a million cases of gonorrhea occur annually. Frequently, this sexually transmitted disease (STD) is responsible for pelvic inflammatory disease and for acute salpingitis.

Pelvic Inflammatory Disease (PID)

Pelvic inflammatory disease (PID) is infection of the cervix, uterus, fallopian tubes, and/or ovary, usually a sequel to microbial infection. Individuals suffering from PID exhibit tenderness and pain in the lower abdominal region, fever, unpleasant-smelling vaginal discharge, and episodes of abnormal bleeding. In severe conditions the pain may be debilitating, requiring bed rest and the administration of powerful analgesics.

Adenomyosis

Adenomyosis is a common condition in which the endometrial glands invade the myometrium and cause the uterus to enlarge, occasionally becoming two or three times its normal dimensions. In most women, adenomyosis has no symptoms, and it is only on gynecological examination that the condition is discovered. When it becomes symptomatic, the woman is usually between 35 and 50 years of age, she may experience pain during intercourse, and she notices an increase in menstrual flow as well as bleeding between periods. Although the condition is benign, if the symptoms are severe and uncontrollable, hysterectomy may be indicated.

Endometriosis

Endometriosis is distinguished by the presence of ectopic endometrial tissue dispersed to various sites along the peritoneal cavity. Occasionally the tissues may migrate to extraperitoneal areas, including the eyes and brain. The etiology of this disease is not known, but possibly during the menstrual cycle some of the endometrial cells may migrate along the oviducts and thus enter the peritoneal cavity. In most cases the lesions of endometriosis involve small cysts attached separately or in small clumps on the visceral or parietal peritoneum.

Endometrial Cancer

Endometrial cancer is a malignancy of the uterine endometrium usually occurring in postmenopausal women. The most common type of endometrial cancer is adenocarcinoma. Since during the early stages the cancer cells do not invade the cervix, Pap smears are not very effective in diagnosing this disease until it has entered its later stages. The major symptom of endometrial cancer is abnormal uterine bleeding.

Hydatidiform Mole

Occasionally an ovum does not develop normally and instead of becoming a fetus forms a mass of tissue that initially mimics pregnancy or, in some patients, after delivery, remnants of placental tissue may proliferate. Known as a hydatidiform mole, these growths increase in size much faster than would a fetus. When the physician does not hear a heartbeat, the patient's abdomen swells more than expected, and the patient complains of vomiting and severe nausea, a hydatidiform mole should be suspected. This is especially true in individuals who complain of a vaginal discharge of grape-like clusters of tissue. In most of the cases the hydatidiform mole resorbs on its own. Only in about 20% of the cases does it become invasive and in very rare cases does it becomes malignant (then it is known as a choriocarcinoma). If cells of the hydatidiform mole do not invade other tissues or organs, the patient's probability of being cured is 100%. The usual treatment is dilatation and curettage, although occasionally, hysterectomy is indicated. Since the favored site of metastasis is the lung, it is advisable to order chest X-rays and to monitor blood chorionic gonadotropin levels to ensure that all of the hydatidiform mole was removed.

Paget's Disease of the Nipple

Paget's disease of the nipple usually occurs in elderly women and is associated with breast cancer of ductal origin. Initially the disease manifests as scaly or crusty nipple frequently accompanied by a fluid discharge from the nipple. Usually the patient has no other symptoms and frequently neglects the condition. The treatment of choice is a mastectomy with removal of regional lymph nodes.

FIGURE 1 • Ovary. Monkey. Plastic section. ×14.

The ovary is subdivided into a **medulla** (Me) and a **cortex** (Co). The medulla houses large **blood vessels** (BV) from which the cortical vascular supply is derived. The cortex of the ovary contains numerous ovarian follicles, most of which are very small (*arrows*); a few maturing follicles have reached the **Graafian follicle** (GF) stage. The thick, fibrous connective tissue capsule, **tunica albuginea** (TA), is shown to advantage; the **germinal epithelium** (GE) is evident occasionally. Observe that the **mesovarium** (Mo) not only suspends the ovary but also conveys the vascular supply to the medulla. A region similar to the *boxed area* is presented at a higher magnification in Figure 2.

FIGURE 3 • Primary follicles. Monkey. Plastic section. ×270.

Primary follicles differ from primordial follicles not only in size but also in morphology and number of follicular cells. The unilaminar primary follicle of the *inset* (× 270) displays a single layer of **cuboidal follicular cells** (FC) that surround the relatively small **primary oocyte** (PO), whose **nucleus** (N) is clearly evident. The multilaminar primary follicle displays a **primary oocyte** (PO) that has increased in size. The **follicular cells** (FC) now form a stratified layer around the oocyte, being separated from it by the intervening **zona pellucida** (ZP). The **stroma** (St) is being reorganized around the follicle to form the **theca interna** (TI). Note the presence of a **basal membrane** (BM) between the follicular cells and the theca interna.

FIGURE 2 • Ovary. Monkey. Plastic section. ×132.

This photomicrograph is a higher magnification of a region similar to the *boxed area* of Figure 1. Observe that the **germinal epithelium** (GE) covers the collagenous capsule, the **tunica albuginea** (TA). This region of the **cortex** (Co) houses numerous **primordial follicles** (PF). Observe that the connective tissue of the ovary is highly cellular and is referred to as the **stroma** (St). *Inset.* **Ovary. Cortex. Monkey. Plastic section.** ×540. The primordial follicle is composed of a **primary oocyte** (PO), whose **nucleus** (N) and **nucleolus** (*arrow*) are evident. Observe the single layer of flat **follicular cells** (FC) surrounding the oocyte. The **tunica albuginea** (TA) and the **germinal epithelium** (GE) are also shown to advantage in this photomicrograph.

FIGURE 4 • Secondary follicle. Rabbit. Paraffin section. ×132.

Secondary follicles are very similar to primary multilaminar follicles, the major difference being their larger size. Moreover, the stratification of the **follicular cells** (FC) has increased, displaying more layers and, more important, a **follicular fluid** (FF) begins to appear in the intercellular spaces, which coalesces into several Call-Exner bodies. Note also that the stroma immediately surrounding the follicular cells is rearranged to form a cellular **theca interna** (TI) and a more fibrous **theca externa** (TE).

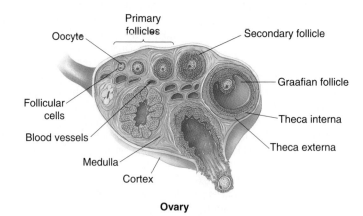

Primary follicles

Oocyte

Secondary follicle

Graafian follicle

Follicular cells

Theca interna

Blood vessels

Theca externa

Medulla

Cortex

Ovary

KEY					
BM	basal membrane	GF	Graafian follicle	St	stroma
BV	blood vessel	Me	medulla	TA	tunica albuginea
Co	cortex	Mo	mesovarium	TE	theca externa
FC	follicular cell	N	nucleus	TI	theca interna
FF	follicular fluid	PF	primordial follicle	ZP	zona pellucida
GE	germinal epithelium	PO	primary oocyte		

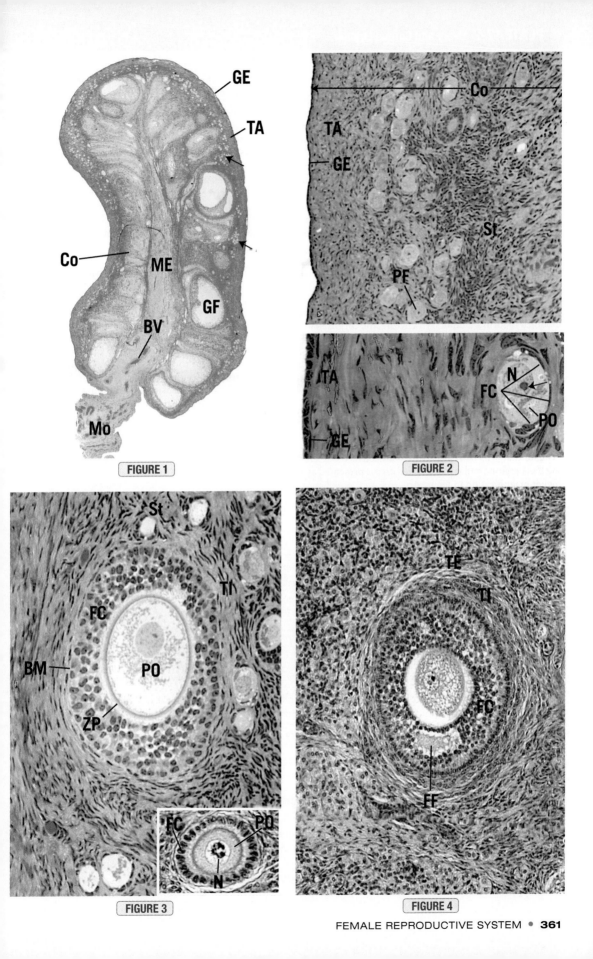

FIGURE 1

FIGURE 2

FIGURE 3

FIGURE 4

FIGURE 1 • Graafian follicle. Paraffin section. ×132.

The Graafian follicle is the most mature of all ovarian follicles and is ready to release its primary oocyte in the process
of ovulation. The **follicular fluid** (FL) fills a single chamber,
the antrum, which is surrounded by a wall of granulosa
(follicular) cells known as the **membrana granulosa** (MG).
Some of the granulosa cells, which surround the **primary
oocyte** (PO), jut into the antrum as the **cumulus oophorus**
(CO). Observe the **basal membrane** (BM), which separates
the granulosa cells from the **theca interna** (TI). The fibrous
theca externa (TE) merges almost imperceptibly with the
surrounding stroma. The *boxed area* is presented at a higher
magnification in Figure 2.

FIGURE 2 • Graafian follicle. Cumulus oophorus.
Paraffin section. ×270.

This photomicrograph is a higher magnification of the
boxed area of Figure 1. Observe that the cumulus oophorus houses the **primary oocyte** (PO), whose **nucleus** (N)
is just visible in this section. The **zona pellucida** (ZP) surrounds the oocyte, and processes (*arrows*) of the surrounding follicular cells extend into this acellular region.
The single layer of follicular cells appears to radiate as a
crown at the periphery of the primary oocyte and is referred to as the **corona radiata** (CR). Note the **basal membrane** (BM), as well as the **theca interna** (TI) and the
theca externa (TE).

FIGURE 3 • Corpus luteum. Human. Paraffin section.
×14.

Subsequent to ovulation, the Graafian follicle becomes
modified to form a temporary structure, the corpus hemorrhagicum, which will become the corpus luteum. The
cells comprising the membrana granulosa enlarge, become vesicular in appearance, and are referred to as **granulosa lutein cells** (GL), which become folded; the spaces
between the folds are occupied by connective tissue elements, blood vessels, and cells of the theca interna (*arrows*). These theca interna cells also enlarge, become
glandular, and are referred to as the theca lutein cells. The
remnants of the antrum are filled with fibrin and serous
exudate that will be replaced by connective tissue elements. A region similar to the *boxed area* is presented at a
higher magnification in Figure 4.

FIGURE 4 • Corpus luteum. Human. Paraffin section.
×132.

This photomicrograph is a higher magnification of a region similar to the *boxed area* of Figure 3. The **granulosa
lutein cells** (GL) of the corpus luteum are easily distinguished from the **connective tissue** (CT) elements, since
the former display round **nuclei** (N), mostly in the center
of large round cells (*arrowheads*). The center of the field is
occupied by a fold, housing **theca lutein cells** (TL) amid
numerous **connective tissue** (CT) and **vascular** (BV) elements. A region similar to the *boxed area* is presented at
a higher magnification in Figure 1 of the next plate.

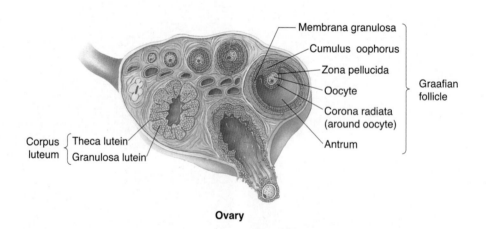

Ovary

KEY					
BM	basal membrane	FL	follicular fluid	TE	theca externa
BV	vascular elements	GL	granulosa lutein cells	TI	theca interna
CO	cumulus oophorus	MG	membrana granulosa	TL	theca lutein cells
CR	corona radiata	N	nucleus	ZP	zona pellucida
CT	connective tissue	PO	primary oocyte		

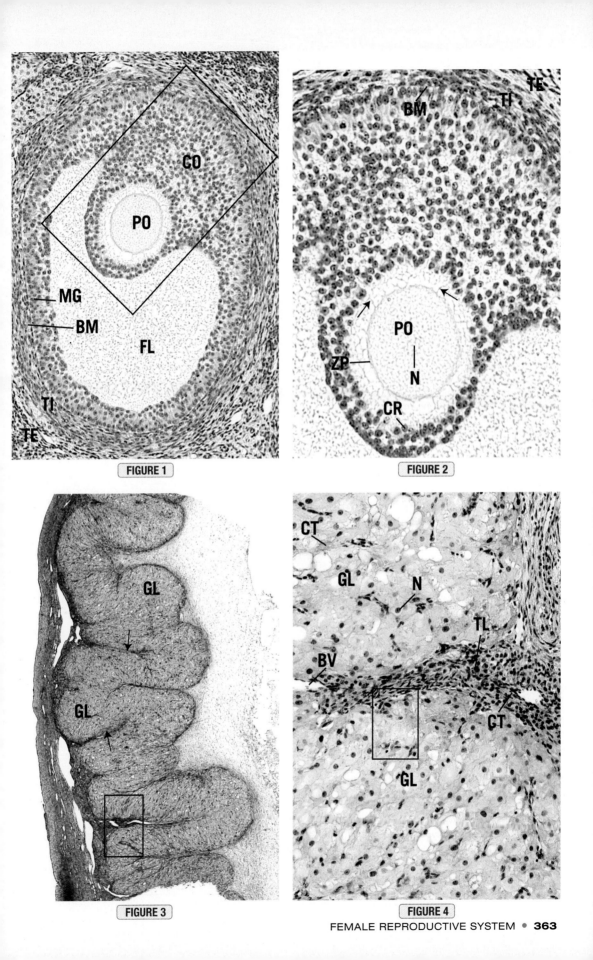

FIGURE 1

FIGURE 2

FIGURE 3

FIGURE 4

FIGURE 1 • Corpus luteum. Human. Paraffin section. ×540.

This photomicrograph is similar to the *boxed area* of Figure 4 of the previous plate. Observe the large **granulosa lutein cells** (GL), whose cytoplasm appears vesicular, representing the spaces occupied by lipids in the living tissue. Note that the **nuclei** (N) of these cells are farther away from each other than the nuclei of the smaller **theca lutein cells** (TL), which also appear to be darker staining (*arrowheads*). The flattened nuclei (*arrows*) belong to various connective tissue cells.

FIGURE 2 • Corpus albicans. Human. Paraffin section. ×132.

As the corpus luteum involutes, its cellular elements degenerate and undergo autolysis. The corpus luteum becomes invaded by macrophages that phagocytose the dead cells, leaving behind relatively acellular **fibrous tissue** (FT). The previously rich **vascular supply** (BV) also regressed, and the entire corpus albicans appears pale in comparison to the relatively dark staining of the surrounding ovarian **stroma** (St). The corpus albican will regress until it becomes a small scar on the surface of the ovary.

FIGURE 3 • Oviduct. x.s. Human. Paraffin section. ×14.

The oviduct, also referred to as the fallopian or uterine tube, extends from the ovary to the uterine cavity. It is suspended from the body wall by the **broad ligament** (BL), which conveys a rich **vascular supply** (BV) to the **serosa** (S) of the oviduct. The thick **muscularis** (M) is composed of ill-defined inner circular and outer longitudinal muscle layers. The **mucosa** (Mu) is thrown into longitudinal folds, which are so highly exaggerated in the infundibulum and ampulla that they subdivide the **lumen** (L) into labyrinthine spaces. A region similar to the *boxed area* is presented at a higher magnification in Figure 4.

FIGURE 4 • Oviduct. x.s. Monkey. Plastic section. ×132.

This photomicrograph is a higher magnification of a region similar to the *boxed area* of Figure 3. The entire thickness of the wall of the oviduct displays its **vascular** (BV) **serosa** (S) that envelops the thick muscularis, whose **outer longitudinal** (OL) and **inner circular** (IC) layers are not very well delineated. The **mucosa** (Mu) is highly folded and is lined by a simple columnar **epithelium** (Ep). The loose connective tissue of the **lamina propria** (LP) is richly vascularized (*arrows*). The *boxed area* is presented in a higher magnification in Figure 1 in the following plate.

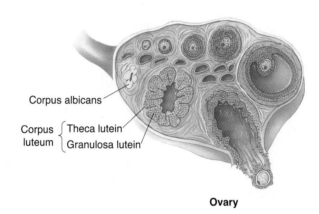

Corpus albicans

Corpus luteum { Theca lutein / Granulosa lutein

Ovary

KEY					
BL	broad ligament	IC	inner circular muscle	N	nucleus
BV	vascular supply	L	lumen	OL	outer longitudinal muscle
Ep	epithelium	LP	lamina propria	S	serosa
FT	fibrous tissue	M	muscularis	St	stroma
GL	granulosa lutein cell	Mu	mucosa	TL	theca lutein cell

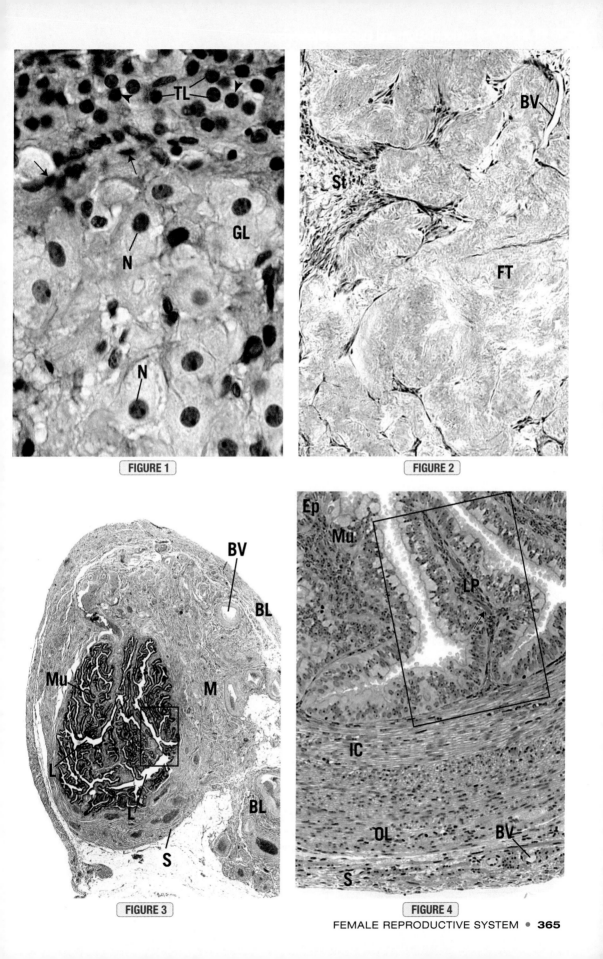

FIGURE 1

FIGURE 2

FIGURE 3

FIGURE 4

PLATE 17-4 Oviduct, Light and Electron Microscopy

FIGURE 1 • Oviduct. x.s. Monkey. Plastic section. ×270.

This photomicrograph is a higher magnification of the *boxed area* of Figure 4 of the previous plate. Observe the **inner circular muscle** (IC) layer of the muscularis. The **lamina propria** (LP) is very narrow in this region (*arrows*) but presents longitudinal epithelially lined folds. The core of these folds is composed of a **vascular** (BV), loose, but highly cellular **connective tissue** (CT). The simple columnar **epithelium** (Ep) lines the labyrinthine **lumen** (L) of the oviduct. A region similar to the *boxed area* is presented at a higher magnification in Figure 2.

FIGURE 3 • Oviduct epithelium. Human. Electron microscopy. ×4,553.

The human oviduct at midcycle (day 14) presents two types of epithelial cells, the **peg cell** (PC) and the **ciliated cell** (CC). The former are secretory cells, as indicated by their extensive **Golgi apparatus** (GA) situated in the region of the cell apical to the **nucleus** (N). Observe the electron-dense secretory products (*arrows*) in the expanded, apical free ends of these cells. Note also that some ciliated cells display large accumulations of **glycogen** (Gl) at either pole of the nucleus. (From Verhage H, Bareither M, Jaffe R, Akbar M. Cyclic changes in ciliation, secretion and cell height of the oviductal epethelium in women. Am J Anat 1979;156:505–522.)

FIGURE 2 • Oviduct. x.s. Monkey. Plastic section. ×540.

This photomicrograph is a higher magnification of a region similar to the *boxed area* of Figure 1. The **lamina propria** (LP) is a highly cellular, loose connective tissue that is richly **vascularized.** The **basal membrane** (BM) separating the connective tissue from the epithelial lining is clearly evident. Note that the epithelium is composed of two different cell types, a thinner **peg cell** (PC), which bears no cilia but whose apical extent bulges above the ciliated cells. These bulges (*arrowheads*) contain nutritive materials that nourish gametes. The second cell type of the oviduct epithelium is a **ciliated cell** (CL), whose cilia move in unison with those of neighboring cells, propelling the nutrient material toward the uterine lumen.

KEY					
BV	vascular elements	Ep	epithelium	L	lumen
BM	basal membrane	GA	Golgi apparatus	LP	lamina propria
CC	ciliated cell	Gl	glycogen	N	nucleus
CT	connective tissue	IC	inner circular muscle	PC	peg cell

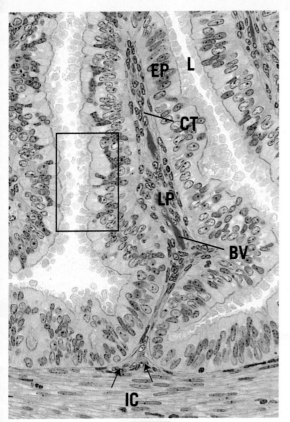

FIGURE 1

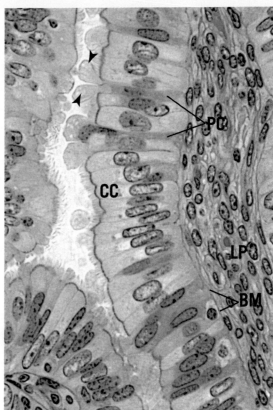

FIGURE 2

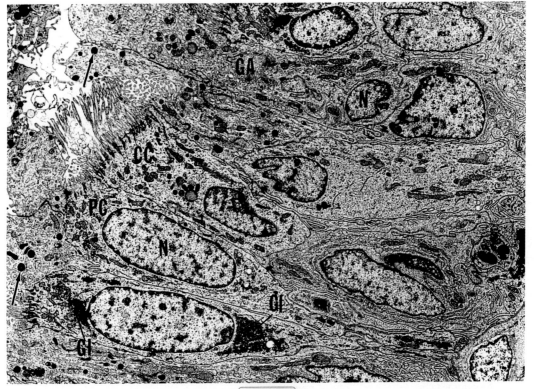

FIGURE 3

FIGURE 1 • Uterus. Follicular phase. Human. Paraffin section. ×14.

The uterus is a thick-walled organ whose wall consists of three layers. The external serosa (or in certain regions, adventitia) is unremarkable and is not presented in this photomicrograph. The thick **myometrium** (My) is composed of smooth muscle, subdivided into three poorly delineated layers: **outer longitudinal** (OL), **middle circular** (MC), and **inner longitudinal** (IL). The **endometrium** (En) is subdivided into a **basal layer** (B) and a **functional layer** (F). The functional layer varies in thickness and constitution and passes through a sequence of phases during the menstrual cycle. Note that the functional layer is in the process of being built up and that the forming **glands** (GL) are straight. The deeper aspects of some of these glands display branching (*arrow*). The *boxed area* is presented at a higher magnification in Figure 2.

FIGURE 3 • Uterus. Luteal phase. Human. Paraffin section. ×14.

The **myometrium** (My) of the uterus remains constant during the various endometrial phases. Observe its three layers, noting especially that the middle circular layer of smooth muscle is richly vascularized and is therefore frequently referred to as the **stratum vasculare** (SV). The **endometrium** (En) is richly endowed with **glands** (GL) that become highly tortuous in anticipation of the blastocyst that will be nourished by secretions of these glands subsequent to implantation. A region similar to the *boxed area* is presented at a higher magnification in Figure 4.

FIGURE 2 • Uterus. Follicular phase. Human. Paraffin section. ×132.

This photomicrograph is a higher magnification of the *boxed area* of Figure 1. Note that the **functional layer** (F) of the endometrium is lined by a simple columnar **epithelium** (Ep) that is displaying mitotic activity (*arrows*). The forming **glands** (GL) also consist of a simple columnar **epithelium** (Ep) whose cells are actively dividing. The **stroma** (St) is highly cellular, as evidenced by the numerous connective tissue cell nuclei visible in this field. Note also the rich **vascular supply** (BV) of the endometrial stroma.

FIGURE 4 • Uterus. Early luteal phase. Human. Paraffin section. ×132.

This photomicrograph is a higher magnification of a region similar to the *boxed area* of Figure 3. The functional layer of the endometrium is covered by a simple columnar **epithelium** (Ep), separating the endometrial **stroma** (St) from the uterine **lumen** (L). Note that the **glands** (GL), also composed of simple columnar epithelium, are more abundant than those in the follicular phase (Figure 2, above). Observe also that these glands appear more tortuous and are dilated and their lumina contain a slight amount of secretory product (*arrow*).

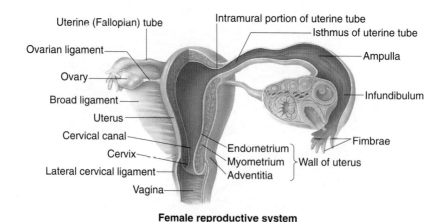

Uterine (Fallopian) tube
Intramural portion of uterine tube
Isthmus of uterine tube
Ovarian ligament
Ampulla
Ovary
Broad ligament
Infundibulum
Uterus
Cervical canal
Cervix
Fimbrae
Endometrium
Myometrium — Wall of uterus
Lateral cervical ligament
Adventitia
Vagina

Female reproductive system

KEY					
B	basal layer	GL	gland	OL	outer longitudinal muscle
BV	vascular supply	IL	inner longitudinal muscle	St	stroma
En	endometrium	L	lumen	SV	stratum vasculare
Ep	epithelium	MC	middle circular muscle		
F	functional layer	My	myometrium		

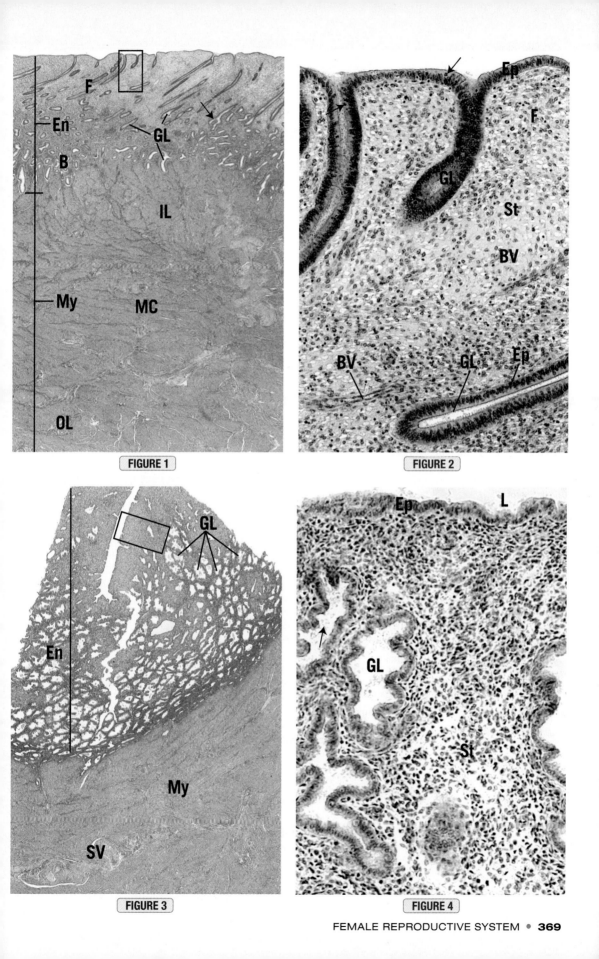

FIGURE 1

FIGURE 2

FIGURE 3

FIGURE 4

FIGURE 1 ● Uterus. Midluteal phase. Human. Paraffin section. ×270.

During the midluteal phase the endometrial **glands** (GL) become quite tortuous and corkscrew-shaped, and the simple **columnar cells** (CC) accumulate glycogen (*arrow*). Observe that during this phase of the endometrium, the glycogen is basally located, displacing the **nucleus** (N) toward the center of the cell. Note also that the **stroma** (St) is undergoing a decidual reaction in that some of the connective tissue cells enlarge as they become engorged with lipid and glycogen. A **helical artery** (HA) is evident as several cross-sections.

FIGURE 2 ● Uterus. Late luteal phase. Human. Paraffin section. ×132.

During the late luteal phase of the endometrium, the glands assume a characteristic ladder (or sawtooth) shape (*arrows*). The simple columnar **epithelial cells** (CC) appear pale and, interestingly, the position of the glycogen is now apical (*arrowheads*) rather than basal. The apical location of the glycogen imparts a ragged, torn appearance to the free surface of these cells. Note that the **lumina** (L) of the glands are filled with a glycogen-rich, viscous fluid. Observe also that the **stroma** (St) is infiltrated by numerous **leukocytes** (Le).

FIGURE 3 ● Uterus. Menstrual phase. Human. Paraffin section. ×132.

The menstrual phase of the endometrium is characterized by periodic constriction and sequential opening of **helical arteries** (HA), resulting in ischemia with subsequent necrosis of the superficial aspect of the functional layer. Due to these spasmodic contractions, sudden spurts of arterial blood detach **necrotic fragments** (NF) of the superficial layers of the endometrium that are then discharged as menstrual flow. The endometrial stroma becomes engorged with blood, increasing the degree of ischemia, and eventually the entire functional layer is desquamated. Observe that the **lumen** (L) no longer possesses a complete epithelial lining (*arrowheads*). The *boxed area* is presented at a higher magnification in Figure 4.

FIGURE 4 ● Uterus. Menstrual phase. Human. Paraffin section. ×270.

This photomicrograph is a higher magnification of the *boxed area* of Figure 3. Observe that some of the endometrial **glands** (GL) are torn and a **necrotic fragment** (NF) has been detached from the **functional layer** (F) of the endometrium. The **stroma** (St) is infiltrated by leukocytes, whose dense **nuclei** (N) mask most of the endometrial cells. Note that some of the endometrial cells are still enlarged, indicative of the decidual reaction.

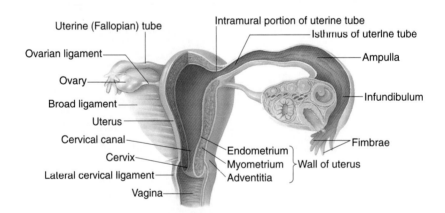

Female reproductive system

KEY							
CC	columnar cell	HA	helical artery	N	nucleus
F	functional layer	L	lumen	NF	necrotic fragment
GL	gland	Le	leukocyte	St	stroma

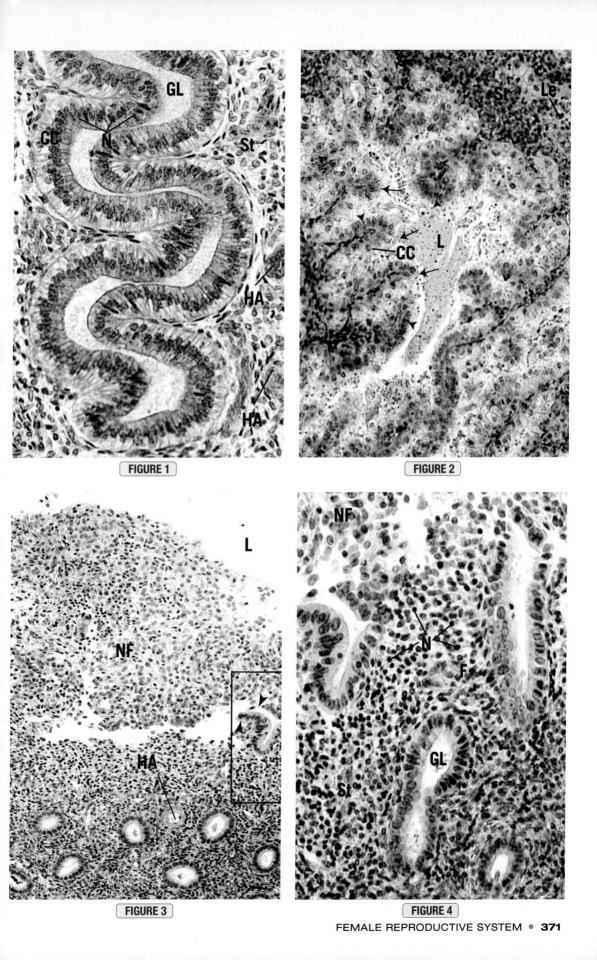

FIGURE 1

FIGURE 2

FIGURE 3

FIGURE 4

FIGURE 1 • Placenta. Human. Paraffin section. ×132.

The human placenta is intimately associated with the uterine endometrium. At this junction, the **decidua basalis** (DB) is rich in clumps of large, round to polygonal **decidual cells** (DC), whose distended cytoplasm is filled with lipid and glycogen. Anchoring **chorionic villi** (AV) are attached to the decidua basalis; other villi are blindly ending in the **intervillous space** (IS). These are the most numerous and are referred to as **terminal villi** (TV), most of which are cut in cross or oblique sections. These villi are freely branching and, in the mature placenta, are smaller in diameter than in the immature placenta. *Inset.* **Placenta. Human. Paraffin section.** ×270. Note that the **decidual cells** (DC) are round to polygonal in shape. Their **nuclei** (N) are more or less centrally located, and their cytoplasm appears vacuolated due to the extraction of glycogen and lipids during histologic preparation.

FIGURE 2 • Placenta. Human. Paraffin section. ×270.

Cross-sections of **terminal villi** (TV) are very simple in the mature placenta. They are surrounded by the **intervillous space** (IS) that, in the functional placenta, is filled with maternal blood. Hence, the cells of the villus act as a placental barrier. This barrier is greatly reduced in the mature placenta, as presented in this photomicrograph. The external layer of the terminal villus is composed of **syncytial trophoblasts** (ST), whose numerous **nuclei** (N) are frequently clustered together as **syncytial knots** (SK). The core of the villus houses numerous fetal **capillaries** (Ca) that are located usually in regions of the villus void of syncytial nuclei (*arrowheads*). Larger fetal **blood vessels** (BV) are also found in the core, surrounded by **mesoderm** (Me). The cytotrophoblasts and phagocytic Hofbauer cells of the immature placenta mostly disappear by the end of the pregnancy.

FIGURE 3 • Vagina. l.s. Monkey. Plastic section. ×14.

The vagina is a fibromuscular tube, whose **vaginal space** (VS) is mostly obliterated since its walls are normally in contact with each other. This wall is composed of four layers: **mucosa** (Mu), **submucosa** (SM), **muscularis** (M), and **adventitia** (A). The mucosa consists of an **epithelium** (Ep) and underlying **lamina propria** (LP). Deep to the mucosa is the submucosa, whose numerous large blood vessels impart to it an erectile tissue appearance. The smooth muscle of the muscularis is arranged in two layers, an **inner circular** (IC) and a thicker **outer longitudinal** (OL). A region similar to the *boxed area* is presented at a higher magnification in Figure 4.

FIGURE 4 • Vagina. l.s. Human. Paraffin section. ×132.

This photomicrograph is a higher magnification of a region similar to the *boxed area* in Figure 3. The stratified squamous nonkeratinized **epithelium** (Ep) of the vagina is characterized by the empty appearance of the cells, comprising most of its thickness. This is due to the extraction lipids and glycogen during histologic preparation. Observe that the cells in the deeper aspect of the epithelium possess fewer inclusions; therefore, their cytoplasm appears normal. Note also that the **lamina propria** (LP) is richly **vascularized** (BV) and always possesses numerous **leukocytes** (Le) (*arrows*). Finally, note the absence of glands and muscularis mucosae.

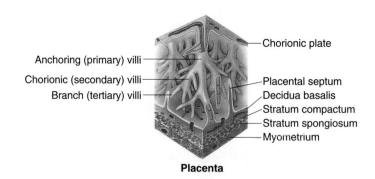

Anchoring (primary) villi
Chorionic (secondary) villi
Branch (tertiary) villi

Chorionic plate
Placental septum
Decidua basalis
Stratum compactum
Stratum spongiosum
Myometrium

Placenta

KEY							
A	adventitia	IC	inner circular muscle	N	nucleus
AV	anchoring chorionic villus	IS	intervillous space	OL	outer longitudinal muscle
		Mu	mucosa	SK	syncytial knot
BV	blood vessel	Le	leukocyte	SM	submucosa
Ca	capillary	LP	lamina propria	ST	syncytial trophoblast
DB	decidua basalis	M	muscularis	TV	terminal villus
DC	decidual cell	Me	mesoderm	VS	vaginal space
Ep	epithelium				

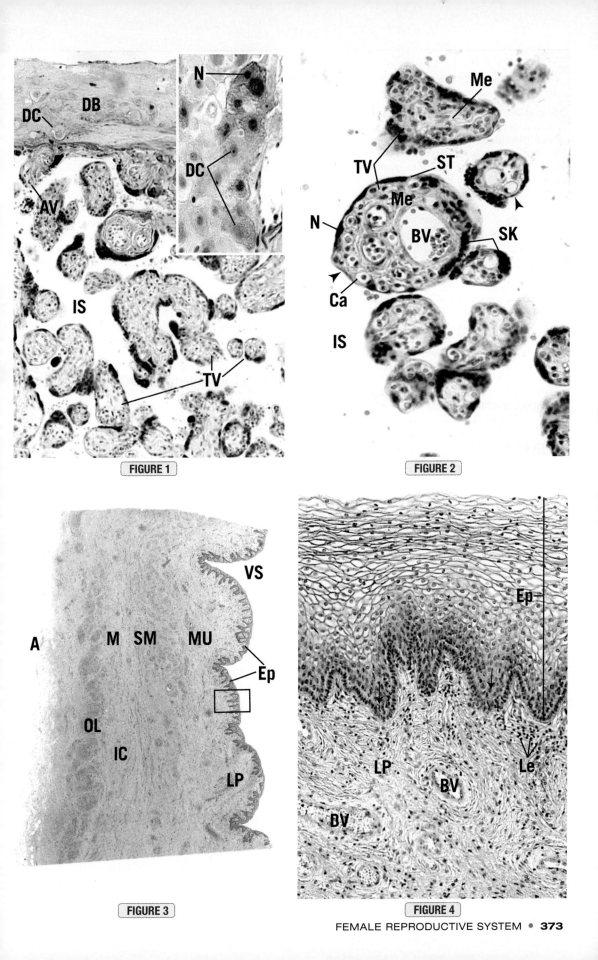

FIGURE 1

FIGURE 2

FIGURE 3

FIGURE 4

FIGURE 1 • Mammary gland. Inactive. Human. Paraffin section. ×132.

The mammary gland is a modified sweat gland that, in the resting stage, presents **ducts** (D) with occasional **buds of alveoli** (BA) branching from the blind ends of the duct. The remainder of the breast is composed of **dense collagenous connective tissue** (dCT) interspersed with lobules of fat. However, in the immediate vicinity of the ducts and buds of alveoli, the **connective tissue** (CT) is more loosely arranged. It is believed that this looser connective tissue is derived from the papillary layer of the dermis. Compare this photomicrograph with Figure 2.

FIGURE 3 • Mammary gland. Lactating. Human. Paraffin section. ×132.

The active mammary gland presents numerous **lobules** (Lo) of **alveoli** (Al) that are tightly packed so that the **connective tissue** (CT) elements are greatly compressed. This photomicrograph clearly illustrates the crowded nature of this tissue. Although this tissue bears a superficial resemblance to the histology of the thyroid gland, the presence of ducts and branching alveoli (*arrows*), as well as the lack of colloid material, should assist in distinguishing this tissue as the active mammary gland. *Inset.* **Mammary gland. Active. Human. Paraffin section.** ×270. Observe the branching (*arrows*) of this alveolus, some of whose simple cuboidal **epithelial cells** (Ep) appear vacuolated (*arrowheads*). Note also that the lumen (L) contains fatty secretory product.

FIGURE 2 • Mammary gland. Lactating. Human. Paraffin section. ×132.

During pregnancy, the **ducts** (D) of the mammary gland undergo major development, in that the buds of alveoli proliferate to form lobules (Lo) composed of numerous alveoli (Al). The interlobular **connective tissue** (CT) becomes reduced to thin sheets in regions; elsewhere it maintains its previous character to support the increased weight of the breast. Observe that the connective tissue in the immediate vicinity of the ducts and lobules (*arrows*) retains its loose consistency. Compare this photomicrograph with Figure 1.

FIGURE 4 • Mammary gland. Nipple. Human. Paraffin section. ×14.

The large, conical nipple of the breast is covered by a thin **epidermis** (Ed), composed of stratified squamous keratinized epithelium. Although the nipple possesses neither hair nor sweat glands, it is richly endowed with **sebaceous glands** (SG). The dense irregular collagenous **connective tissue** (CT) core displays numerous longitudinally positioned lactiferous ducts that pierce the tip of the nipple to convey milk to the outside. The lactiferous ducts are surrounded by an extensive network of **smooth muscle fibers** (SM) that are responsible for the erection of the nipple, elevating it to facilitate the suckling process. The region immediately surrounding the nipple is know as the **arcola** (Ar).

KEY					
Al	alveolus	D	duct	L	lumen
Ar	areola	dCT	dense connective tissue	Lo	lobule
BA	buds of alveoli	Ed	epidermis	SM	smooth muscle
CT	connective tissue	Ep	epithelium	SG	sebaceous gland

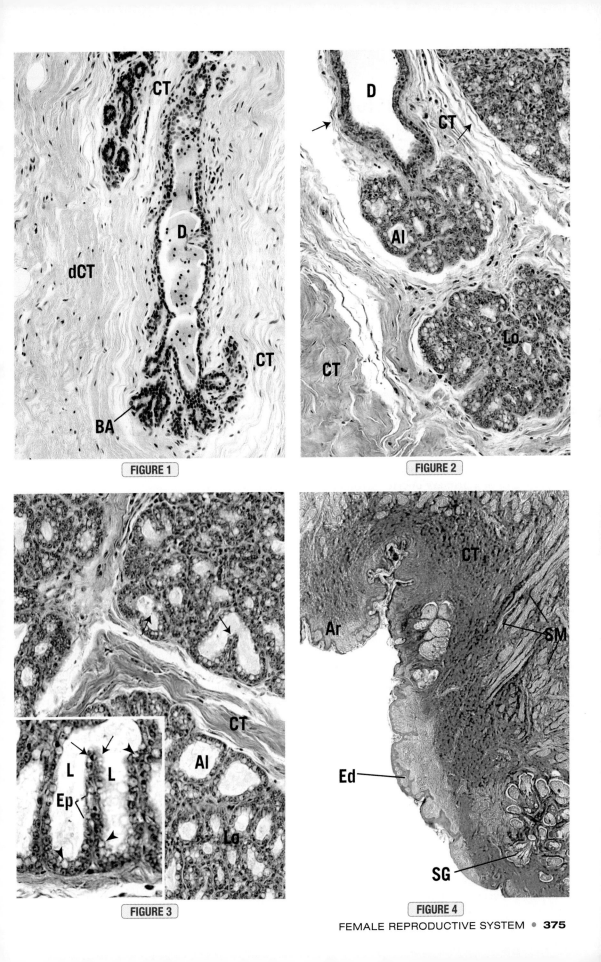

FIGURE 1

FIGURE 2

FIGURE 3

FIGURE 4

Summary of Histological Organization

I. OVARY

A. Cortex

The **cortex** of the **ovary** is covered by a modified mesothelium, the **germinal epithelium**. Deep to this simple cuboidal to simple squamous epithelium is the **tunica albuginea**, the fibrous connective tissue capsule of the ovary. The remainder of the ovarian connective tissue is more cellular and is referred to as the **stroma**. The cortex houses ovarian **follicles** in various stages of development.

1. Primordial Follicles
Primordial follicles consist of a **primary oocyte** surrounded by a single layer of flattened **follicular (granulosa) cells**.

2. Primary Follicles

a. Unilaminar Primary Follicles
Consist of a **primary oocyte** surrounded by a single layer of cuboidal **follicular cells**.

b. Multilaminar Primary Follicles
Consist of a **primary oocyte** surrounded by several layers of **follicular cells**. The **zona pellucida** is visible. The **theca interna** is beginning to be organized.

3. Secondary (Vesicular) Follicle
The **secondary follicle** is distinguished from the primary multilaminar follicle by its larger size, by a well-established **theca interna** and **theca externa**, and especially by the presence of **follicular fluid** in small cavities formed from intercellular spaces of the **follicular cells**. These fluid-filled cavities are known as **Call-Exner bodies**.

4. Graafian (Mature) Follicles
The **Graafian follicle** is very large; the Call-Exner bodies have coalesced into a single space, the **antrum**, filled with **follicular fluid**. The wall of the antrum is referred to as the **membrana granulosa**, and the region of the oocyte and follicular cells jutting into the antrum is the **cumulus oophorus**. The single layer of follicular cells immediately surrounding the oocyte is the **corona radiata**. Long apical processes of these cells extend into the **zona pellucida**. The **theca interna** and **theca externa** are well developed; the former displays numerous cells and capillaries, whereas the latter is less cellular and more fibrous.

5. Atretic Follicles
Atretic follicles are in the state of degeneration. They are characterized in later stages by the presence of **fibroblasts** in the follicle and a degenerated oocyte.

B. Medulla

The **medulla** of the ovary is composed of a relatively loose fibroelastic connective tissue housing an extensive **vascular** supply, including spiral arteries and convoluted veins.

C. Corpus Luteum

Subsequent to the extrusion of the **secondary oocyte** with its attendant **follicular cells**, the remnant of the **Graafian follicle** becomes partly filled with blood and is known as the **corpus hemorrhagicum**. Cells of the **membrana granulosa** are transformed into large **granulosa lutein cells**. Moreover, the cells of the **theca interna** also increase in size to become **theca lutein cells**, although they remain smaller than the **granulosa lutein cells**.

D. Corpus Albicans

The **corpus albicans** is a **corpus luteum** that is in the process of involution and hyalinization. It becomes fibrotic, with few **fibroblasts** among the intercellular materials. Eventually, the corpus albicans will become **scar tissue** on the ovarian surface.

II. GENITAL DUCTS

A. Oviduct

1. Mucosa
The **mucosa** of the oviduct is highly folded in the **infundibulum** and **ampulla**. It is composed of a loose, cellular connective tissue, **lamina propria**, and a **simple columnar epithelial** lining. The epithelium is composed of **peg cells** and **ciliated cells**.

2. Muscularis
The **muscle coat** is composed of an **inner circular** and an **outer longitudinal smooth muscle layer**.

3. Serosa
The oviduct is invested by a **serosa**.

B. Uterus

1. Endometrium
The **endometrium** is subdivided into a **basal** and a **functional layer**. It is lined by a **simple columnar epithelium**. The **lamina propria** varies with the phases of the menstrual cycle.

a. Follicular Phase

The **glands** are straight and display mitotic figures, and the helical arteries grow into the functional layer.

b. Luteal Phase

Glands become tortuous, and the **helical arteries** become coiled. The **lumina** of the glands accumulate **secretory products**. **Fibroblasts** enlarge and accumulate glycogen.

c. Menstrual Phase

The **functional layer** is desquamated, and the lamina propria displays extravasated blood.

2. Myometrium

The **myometrium** is thick and consists of three poorly delineated **smooth muscle** layers: **inner longitudinal**, **middle circular**, and **outer longitudinal**. During pregnancy the myometrium increases in size as a result of hypertrophy of existing muscle cells and the accumulation of new smooth muscle cells.

3. Serosa

Most of the uterus is covered by a **serosa**; the remainder is attached to surrounding tissues by an **adventitia**.

C. Placenta

1. Decidua Basalis

The **decidua basalis**, the maternally derived **endometrial layer**, is characterized by the presence of large, glycogen-rich **decidual cells**. **Coiled arteries** and straight **veins** open into the labyrinth-like **intervillous spaces**.

2. Chorionic Plate and Villi

The **chorionic plate** is a region of the **chorionic sac** of the fetus from which **chorionic villi** extend into the intervillous spaces of the **decidua basalis**. Each villus has a core of **fibromuscular connective tissue** surrounding **capillaries** (derived from the umbilical vessels). The villus is covered by **trophoblast cells**. During the first half of pregnancy, there are two layers of trophoblast cells, an inner cuboidal layer of **cytotrophoblasts**, and an outer layer of **syncytiotrophoblasts**. During the second half of pregnancy, only the **syncytiotrophoblasts** remain. However, at points where chorionic villi are anchored into the decidua basalis, **cytotrophoblasts** are present.

D. Vagina

1. Mucosa

The vagina is lined by a **stratified squamous nonkeratinized epithelium**. The **lamina propria**, composed of a **fibroelastic connective tissue**, possesses no glands. The **mucosa** is thrown into longitudinal folds known as **rugae**.

2. Submucosa

The **submucosa** is also composed of a fibroelastic type of connective tissue housing numerous blood vessels.

3. Muscularis

The **muscularis** is composed of interlacing bundles of **smooth muscle** fibers. Near its external orifice, the vagina is equipped with a **skeletal muscle sphincter**.

4. Adventitia

The vagina is connected to surrounding structures via its **adventitia**.

E. Mammary Glands

1. Inactive Gland

The **inactive gland** is composed mainly of **dense irregular collagenous connective tissue** interspersed with lobules of **adipose tissue** and numerous **ducts**. Frequently, at the blind ends of ducts, **buds of alveoli** and attendant **myoepithelial cells** are present.

2. Lactating Gland

The **mammary gland** becomes active during pregnancy and lactation. The expanded **alveoli** that form numerous **lobules** are composed of **simple cuboidal cells**, resembling the thyroid gland. However, the presence of **ducts** and **myoepithelial cells** provides distinguishing characteristics. **Alveoli** and the **lumen** of the ducts may contain a fatty secretory product.

3. Areola and Nipple

The **areola** is composed of thin, **pigmented epidermis** displaying large **apocrine areolar glands**. Additionally, **sweat** and large **sebaceous glands** are also present. The **dermis** presents numerous **smooth muscle fibers**. The **nipple** possesses several minute pores representing the distal ends of **lactiferous ducts**. These ducts arise from **lactiferous sinuses**, enlarged reservoirs at the base of the nipple. The **epidermis** covering the nipple is thin, and the dermis is richly supplied by **smooth muscle fibers** and **nerve endings**. Although the nipple possesses no hair follicles or sweat glands, it is richly endowed with **sebaceous glands**.

Male Reproductive System

18

The male reproductive system (see Graphic 18-1) consists of the two testes (the male gonads), a system of genital ducts, accessory glands, and the penis. The male reproductive system functions in the formation of spermatozoa, the elaboration of male sex hormones, and the delivery of male gametes into the female reproductive tract.

● TESTES

Each **testis** is an oval structure housed in its separate compartment within the scrotum. The **tunica albuginea**, the fibromuscular connective tissue capsule of the testis, is thickened at the **mediastinum testis**, from which septa are derived to subdivide the testis into approximately 250 small, incomplete compartments, known as the **lobuli testis**. Each lobule houses one to four highly tortuous **seminiferous tubules** that function in the production of **spermatozoa**. The lumen of each seminiferous tubule is lined by a **seminiferous epithelium** several cell layers thick. The **basal cells** of this epithelium are composed of **Sertoli cells** and three types of spermatogonia, **dark type A**, **pale type A**, and **type B spermatogonia**. Type B spermatogonia divide by *mitotic* activity to produce primary **spermatocytes**. These diploid primary spermatocytes enter the **first** *meiotic* **division**, forming **secondary spermatocytes** that, by completing the **second** *meiotic* **division**, give rise to **haploid spermatids**. Subsequent to shedding much of their cytoplasm, reorganizing their organelle population, and acquiring certain specialized organelles, spermatids become **spermatozoa**, the **male gamete**. All of these differentiating cells are supported by Sertoli cells both physically and nutritionally. Moreover, occluding junctions between adjacent Sertoli cells establish a **blood-testis barrier** that protects the developing germ cells from autoimmune phenomena. The seminiferous epithelium sits on a basal membrane that is surrounded by a fibromuscular tunica propria.

The connective tissue surrounding the seminiferous tubules houses, in addition to neural and vascular elements, small clusters of **androgen-producing endocrine cells**, the **interstitial cells of Leydig** that produce the male sex hormone **testosterone**. Prior to puberty, testosterone is not produced, but at the onset of puberty the pituitary gland releases **luteinizing hormone** (**LH**) and **follicle-stimulating hormone** (**FSH**). The former activates the interstitial cells of Leydig that release testosterone, whereas FSH induces the Sertoli cells to produce **adenylate cyclase**, which, via a cAMP intermediary, stimulates the production of **androgen-binding protein** (**ABP**). The androgens testosterone and dihydrotestosterone (a transformation product of testosterone by the enzyme 5α-reductase), bind to ABP, and the complex is released into the lumen of the seminiferous tubule, where the elevated testosterone concentration enhances **spermatogenesis**.

● GENITAL DUCTS

A system of **genital ducts** conveys the spermatozoa and the fluid component of the semen to the outside. The **seminiferous tubules** are connected by short, straight tubules, the **tubuli recti**, to the **rete testis**, which is composed of labyrinthine spaces located in the **mediastinum testis**. From here, spermatozoa enter the first part of the epididymis, the 15 to 20 **ductuli efferentes** that lead into the **ductus epididymis**. During their sojourn in the epididymis, spermatozoa mature. The head of the epididymis is composed of the ductuli efferentes, whereas the body and tail consist of the ductus epididymis, whose continuation is the **ductus deferens** (**vas deferens**) (Graphic 18-1). This thick, muscular structure passes through the inguinal canal, as a part of the spermatic cord, to gain access to the abdominal cavity. Just prior to reaching the prostate gland, the **seminal vesicle** empties its secretions into the ductus deferens, which terminates at this point. The continuation of the ductus deferens, known as the **ejaculatory duct**, enters the **prostate gland**, which delivers its secretory product into the ejaculatory duct. The right and left **ejaculatory ducts** empty into the **urethra**, which conveys both urine and **semen** to the outside. The urethra, which passes through the length of the penis, has three regions: prostatic, membranous, and cavernous (spongy) portions.

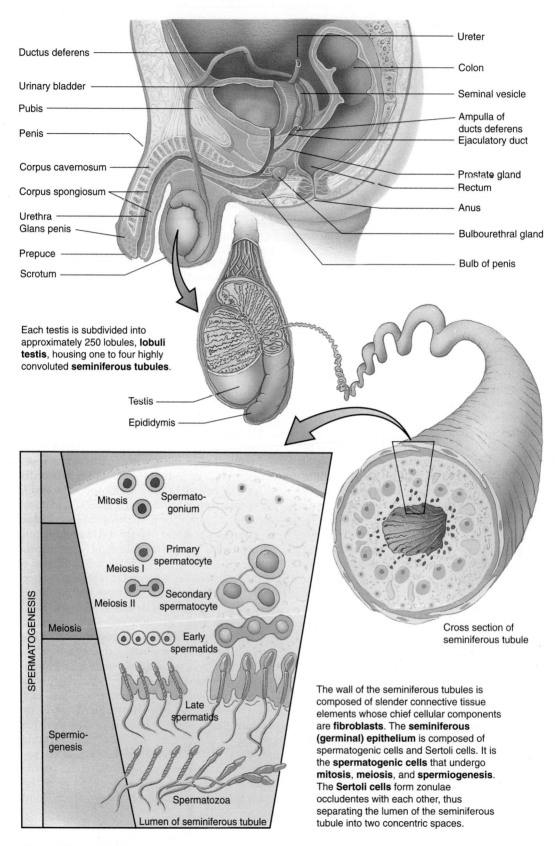

Ductus deferens

Urinary bladder

Pubis

Penis

Corpus cavernosum

Corpus spongiosum

Urethra
Glans penis

Prepuce

Scrotum

Ureter

Colon

Seminal vesicle

Ampulla of
ducts deferens
Ejaculatory duct

Prostate gland
Rectum

Anus

Bulbourethral gland

Bulb of penis

Each testis is subdivided into
approximately 250 lobules, **lobuli
testis**, housing one to four highly
convoluted **seminiferous tubules**.

Testis

Epididymis

Cross section of
seminiferous tubule

SPERMATOGENESIS

Mitosis

Spermato-
gonium

Primary
spermatocyte

Meiosis I

Secondary
spermatocyte

Meiosis II

Meiosis

Early
spermatids

Late
spermatids

Spermio-
genesis

Spermatozoa

Lumen of seminiferous tubule

The wall of the seminiferous tubules is
composed of slender connective tissue
elements whose chief cellular components
are **fibroblasts**. The **seminiferous
(germinal) epithelium** is composed of
spermatogenic cells and Sertoli cells. It is
the **spermatogenic cells** that undergo
mitosis, **meiosis**, and **spermiogenesis**.
The **Sertoli cells** form zonulae
occludentes with each other, thus
separating the lumen of the seminiferous
tubule into two concentric spaces.

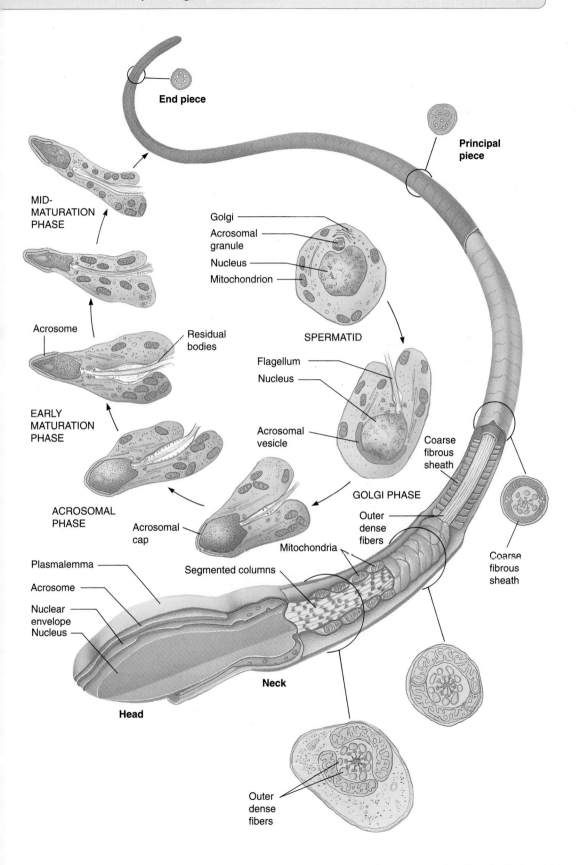

End piece

Principal piece

MID-MATURATION PHASE

Golgi

Acrosomal granule

Nucleus

Mitochondrion

SPERMATID

Acrosome

Residual bodies

Flagellum

Nucleus

EARLY MATURATION PHASE

Acrosomal vesicle

Coarse fibrous sheath

ACROSOMAL PHASE

Acrosomal cap

GOLGI PHASE

Outer dense fibers

Coarse fibrous sheath

Plasmalemma

Acrosome

Nuclear envelope

Nucleus

Segmented columns

Mitochondria

Neck

Head

Outer dense fibers

Outer dense fibers

● ACCESSORY GLANDS

The three **accessory glands** of the male reproductive system, which supply the fluid component of semen, are the two **seminal vesicles** and the **prostate gland**. Additionally, a pair of small **bulbourethral glands** deliver their viscous secretions into the cavernous (spongy) urethra. Each seminal vesicle, a long, narrow gland that is highly folded on itself, produces a rich, nutritive substance with a characteristic yellow color. The prostate gland is composed of numerous individual glands that surround, and whose ducts pierce, the wall of the urethra. These glands are distributed in three regions of the prostate and are therefore categorized as **mucosal**, **submucosal**, and **external** (**main**) **prostatic glands**. The secretion of the prostate gland is a whitish, thin fluid containing proteolytic enzymes and acid phosphatase. **Prostatic concretions** are frequently found in the lumina of the prostate gland.

● PENIS

The **penis**, the male organ of copulation, is normally in the flaccid state. During erotic stimulation, however, its three cylindrical bodies of erectile tissues, the two **corpora cavernosa** and the **corpus spongiosum**, become distended with blood. The fluid turgid pressure within the vascular spaces of the erectile tissues greatly enlarges the penis, causing it to become erect and hard. Subsequent to ejaculation or the termination of erotic stimulation, detumescence follows and the penis returns to its flaccid state.

Histophysiology

I. SERTOLI CELL FUNCTIONS

Sertoli cells sit on the basal lamina of the seminiferous tubule and form **zonulae occludentes** with one another, thus separating the lumen of the seminiferous tubule into an outer **basal compartment** and an inner **adluminal compartment**. By doing so, they isolate the adluminal compartment from connective tissue elements and thus protect the developing sperm cells from the immune system.

Prompted by follicle-stimulating hormone (**FSH**) secreted by the anterior pituitary gland, Sertoli cells secrete androgen-binding protein (**ABP**), which binds **testosterone** and **dihydrotestosterone,** and the complex enters the lumen of the seminiferous tubules, where it is maintained at a sufficiently high threshold level to permit spermatogenesis to occur. These cells also secrete the hormone **inhibin**, which blocks the release of FSH and activin, which enhances the release of FSH, both via a biofeedback mechanism.

Spermatocytes, spermatids, and spermatozoa are physically and metabolically **supported** by Sertoli cells. Moreover, cytoplasm discarded during **spermiogenesis** is **phagocytosed** by Sertoli cells. Sertoli cells also secrete a fructose-rich fluid that supports spermatozoa and provides a fluid medium for their transport through the seminiferous tubules and the genital ducts.

During embryonic development, fetal Sertoli cells produce **anti-müllerian hormone (müllerian-inhibiting factor)**, which prevents the development of the müllerian duct, thus ensuring the development of a male rather than a female embryo. Additionally, the presence of dihydrotestosterone in the fetus encourages the development of male genitalia, whereas in its absence the default female genitalia will develop even if the chromosomal complement calls for a male gender.

II. SPERMATOGENESIS

Spermatogenesis, the process of producing haploid male gametes, is dependent on several hormones, including **luteinizing hormone (LH)**, **prolactin**, and **FSH** from the adenohypophysis (see Graphic 18-2). Prolactin induces the intersititial cells of Leydig to express LH receptors. Once LH binds to its receptors on the Leydig cells, these cells secrete **testosterone**, and FSH causes Sertoli cells to release

ABP. ABP maintains a high enough concentration of testosterone in the seminiferous epithelium for spermatogenesis to occur. Testosterone acts as a **negative feedback** for LH release, and **inhibin**, produced by Sertoli cells, inhibits the release of FSH, whereas activin, also produced by Sertoli cells, enhances FSH release. For spermatogenesis to proceed normally, the testes must be maintained at 35° C, a temperature that is slightly below normal body temperature.

Spermatogenesis occurs in a cyclic but asynchronous fashion along the length of the seminiferous tubule. These **cycles of the seminiferous epithelium** consist of repeated aggregates of cells in varying stages of development. Each aggregate is composed of groups of cells that are connected to one another by **intercellular bridges**, forming a synchronized syncytium that migrates toward the lumen of the seminiferous tubule as a unit. The three phases of spermatogenesis are spermatocytogenesis, meiosis, and spermiogenesis.

Spermatocytogenesis is a process involving *mitosis*, in which **pale type A spermatogonia** divide to form two types of sparmatogonia, more pale type A as well as **type B** spermatogonia, both of which are diploid. **Dark type A spermatogonia** represent a reserve population of cells that normally do not undergo cell division, but when they do, they form pale type A spermatogonia.

Type B spermatogonia divide via mitosis to form diploid **primary spermatocytes**. All spermatogonia are located in the **basal compartment**, whereas primary spermatocytes migrate into the **adluminal compartment**.

Meiosis phase starts when primary spermatocytes (**4CDNA** content) undergo the first meiotic division, forming two short-lived **secondary spermatocytes** (**2CDNA** content). Secondary spermatocytes do not replicate their DNA but immediately start the second meiotic division, and each forms two **haploid (N)** spermatids.

Spermiogenesis (Graphic 18-2) is the process of cytodifferentiation of the spermatids into spermatozoa and involves no cell division. Instead, the spermatid loses much of its cytoplasm (phagocytosed by Sertoli cells), forms an **acrosomal granule**, a long **cilium**, and associated **outer dense fibers** and a **coarse fibrous sheath**. The **spermatozoon** that is formed and released into the lumen of the seminiferous tubule is **nonmotile** and is incapable of fertilizing an ovum. The spermatozoa remain immotile until they leave the epididymis. They become capable of fertilizing once they have been **capacitated** in the female reproductive system.

III. ERECTION AND EJACULATION

The **penis** during **copulation** delivers spermatozoa-containing **semen** to the female reproductive tract. It is also the excretory organ for urine. The penis is covered by skin and is composed of three **erectile bodies**, the two **corpora cavernosa** and the ventrally positioned **corpus spongiosum** (**urethrae**).

Each erectile body, housing large, endothelially lined **cavernous spaces**, is surrounded by a thick connective tissue capsule, the **tunica albuginea**. The erectile bodies are supplied by **helicine arteries** that are usually bypassed via arteriovenous shunts, maintaining the penis in a flaccid state. **Parasympathetic impulses** to these shunts cause vasoconstriction, directing blood into the helicine arteries and thus into the cavernous spaces. The erectile bodies (especially the corpora cavernosa) become engorged with blood, and the penis becomes **erect**.

Subsequent to ejaculation or in the absence of continued stimulation, parasympathetic stimulation ceases; blood flow to the helicine arteries is diminished; blood slowly leaves the cavernous spaces; and the penis returns to its flaccid condition.

Ejaculation is the forceful expulsion of **semen** from the male reproductive tract. The force required for ejaculation is derived from rhythmic contraction of the thick smooth muscle layers of the **ductus (vas) deferens** and the rapid contraction of the **bulbospongiosus muscle**.

Each ejaculate contains spermatozoa suspended in **seminal fluid**. The accessory glands of the male reproductive system, the **prostate** and **bulbourethral glands**, as well as the **seminal vesicles** (and even the glands of Littré) contribute to the formation of the fluid portion of semen. Secretions of the bulbourethral glands lubricate the urethra, whereas secretions of the prostate assist the spermatozoa in achieving motility by neutralizing the acidic secretions of the ductus deferens and of the female reproductive tract. Energy for the spermatozoa is provided by fructose-rich secretions of the seminal vesicles.

Cryptorchidism

Cryptorchidism is a developmental defect in which one or both testes fail to descend into the scrotum. When neither descends, it results in sterility because normal body temperature inhibits spermatogenesis. Usually, the condition can be surgically corrected; however, the patient's sperm may be abnormal.

Vasectomy

Vasectomy is a method of sterilization that is performed by making a small slit in the wall of the scrotum through which the ductus deferens is severed.

A normal **ejaculate** averages about 3 mL of semen that contains 60 to 100 million spermatozoa per mL. It is interesting to note that about 20% of the ejaculated spermatozoa are abnormal and 25% immotile. An individual producing less than 20 million spermatozoa per milliliter of ejaculate is considered **sterile**.

Benign Prostatic Hypertrophy

The prostate gland undergoes hypertrophy with age, resulting in benign prostatic hypertrophy (BPH), a condition that may constrict the urethral lumen resulting in difficulty in urination. At age 50, about 40% of the male population is affected, and at age 80, about 95% of the male population is affected by this condition.

Adenocarcinoma of the Prostate

Adenocarcinoma of the prostate affects about 30% of the male population over 75 years of age. Although this carcinoma is slow growing, it may metastasize to bone. Analysis of elevated levels of **prostate specific antigen** (**PSA**) in the bloodstream is utilized as an early diagnostic test for prostatic cancer. Surgical removal of the gland or radiation therapy are the usual treatments; however, complications may result in impotence and incontinence.

Testicular Cancer

Testicular cancer affects mostly men younger than 40 years of age. It is discovered on palpation as a lump in the scrotum. If the lump is not associated with the testis it is usually benign, whereas if it is associated with the testis it is usually malignant; therefore, a lump noticed on the testis, whether or not it is painful, should be examined by a physician. Frequently, individuals with testicular cancer present with elevated blood **alpha-fetoprotein** and **human chorionic gonadotropin** levels. The common treatment for testicular cancer is surgical removal of the affected testis. If metastasis has occurred, the surgery is supplemented by radiation and chemotherapy.

Balanoposthitis

Accumulation of a thick, yellowish-white exudate underneath the foreskin of uncircumcised men can be a breeding ground for yeast and bacteria that, if not cleaned, may cause inflammation of the foreskin, known as **posthitis**, as well as inflammation of the glans penis, known as **balanitis**. When the two occur together, the condition is known as **balanoposthitis**. The condition may be accompanied by redness, pain, and itching as well as a swelling of the glans with a concommitant stricture of the urethera.

Phimosis

Phimosis, a tight foreskin that cannot easily be pulled over the glans penis, is a normal condition in uncircumcised infants, but in mature men the condition can be very painful and may result in interference with urination and sexual activity. As the penis becomes erect the foreskin cannot expand to accommodate the increase girth and may result in balanoposthistis and urinary tract infections. Circumcision can usually alleviate this condition.

FIGURE 1 • Testis. Monkey. Plastic section. ×14.

This low magnification photomicrograph of the testis displays its thick **tunica albuginea** (TA), as well as the slender **septa** (Se) that attach to it. Observe that sections of **seminiferous tubules** (ST) present various geometric profiles, attesting to their highly convoluted form. Note that each **lobule** (Lo) is densely packed with seminiferous tubules, and the connective tissue stroma (*arrows*) occupies the remaining space. A region similar to the *boxed area* is presented at a higher magnification in Figure 2.

FIGURE 3 • Testis. Seminiferous tubule. Monkey. Plastic section. ×540.

The adjacent walls of two **seminiferous tubules** (ST), in close proximity to each other, are composed of **myoid cells** (MC), **fibroblasts** (F), and fibromuscular **connective tissue** (CT). The stratified **seminiferous epithelium** (SE) is separated from the tubular wall by a basal membrane (*arrowheads*). **Spermatogonia** (Sg) and **Sertoli cells** (SC) lie on the basal membrane and are in the **basal compartment** (BC), whereas **primary spermatocytes** (PS), secondary spermatocytes, **spermatids** (Sp), and **spermatozoa** (Sz) are in the **adluminal compartment** (AC). Observe that the **lumen** (L) of the seminiferous tubule contains spermatozoa as well as cellular debris discarded during the transformation of spermatids into spermatozoa. Compare the cells of the seminiferous epithelium with those of Figure 4.

FIGURE 2 • Testis. Seminiferous tubules. Monkey. Plastic section. ×132.

This photomicrograph is a higher magnification of a region similar to the *boxed area* of Figure 1. Observe that the **tunica vasculosa** (TV) of the **tunica albuginea** (TA) is a highly vascular region (*arrows*) and that **blood vessels** (BV) penetrate the lobuli testis in connective tissue **septa** (Se). The walls of the **seminiferous tubules** (ST) are closely apposed to each other (*arrowheads*), although in certain regions the cellular **stroma** (St) is evident. Observe that the **lumen** (L) of the seminiferous tubule is lined by a stratified **seminiferous epithelium** (SE).

FIGURE 4 • Testis. Seminiferous tubule. Monkey. Plastic section. ×540.

Observe that the fibromuscular walls of the two tubular cross-sections are very close to each other (*arrows*); however, in regions, **arterioles** (A) and **venules** (V) are evident. The **Sertoli cells** (SC) may be recognized by their pale nuclei and dense **nucleoli** (n). In comparing the **seminiferous epithelia** (SE) of the tubules in the right and left halves of this photomicrograph, as well as those of Figure 3, it should be noted that their cellular compositions are different, indicative of the cyclic stages of the seminiferous epithelium. Note also that three types of spermatogonia are recognizable by their nuclear characteristics: **dark spermatogonia A** (Ad) possessing dark, flattened nuclei; **pale spermatogonia A** (Ap) with flattened pale nuclei; and **spermatogonia B** (B) with round nuclei.

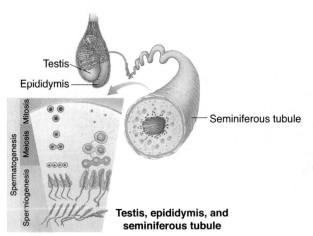

Testis, epididymis, and seminiferous tubule

KEY							
A	arterioles	L	lumen			Sg	spermatogonia
AC	adluminal compartment	Lo	lobule			Sp	spermatid
Ad	dark spermatogonia A	MC	myoid cell			ST	seminiferous tubules
Ap	pale spermatogonia A	n	nucleoli			St	stroma
B	spermatogonia B	PS	primary spermatocyte			Sz	spermatozoa
BC	basal compartment	SC	Sertoli cell			TA	tunica albuginea
BV	blood vessel	SE	seminiferous epithelium			TV	tunica vasculosa
CT	connective tissue	Se	septum			V	venule
F	fibroblast						

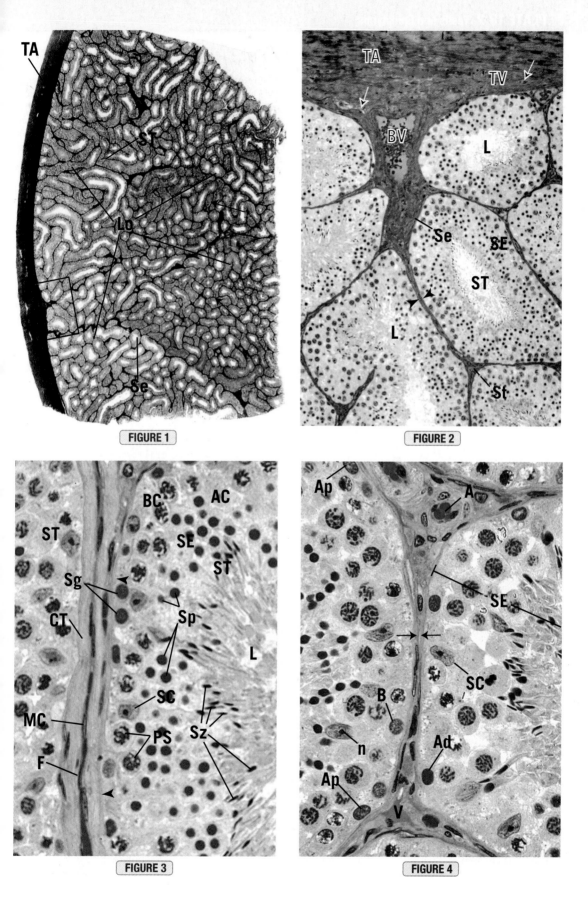

FIGURE 1

FIGURE 2

FIGURE 3

FIGURE 4

FIGURE 1 • Interstitial cells. Testis. Monkey. Plastic section. ×270.

The **stroma** (St) surrounding **seminiferous tubules** (ST) possesses a rich **vascular supply** (BV) as well as extensive **lymphatic drainage** (LV). Much of the vascular elements are associated with the endocrine cells of the testis, the **interstitial cells of Leydig** (IC), which produce testosterone. *Inset.* **Interstitial cells. Testis. Monkey. Plastic section.** ×540. The **interstitial cells** (IC), located in small clumps, are recognizable by their round-to-oval **nuclei** (N) and the presence of lipid (*arrow*) within their cytoplasm.

FIGURE 3 • Ductuli efferentes. Human. Paraffin section. ×132.

The first part of the epididymis, the **ductuli efferentes** (De), receives **spermatozoa** (Sz) from the rete testis. The lumina of the ductuli are lined by a simple columnar **epithelium** (Ep), composed of tall and short cells, which are responsible for the characteristic fluted (uneven) appearance of these tubules. The thick fibroelastic **connective tissue** (CT) wall of the ductuli houses numerous smooth muscle cells (SM).

FIGURE 2 • Rete testis. Human. Paraffin section. ×132.

The **rete testis** (RT), located in the **mediastinum testis** (MT), is composed of labyrinthine, anastomosing spaces lined by a simple cuboidal **epithelium** (Ep). The dense collagenous **connective tissue** (CT) of the mediastinum testis is evident, as are the profiles of **seminiferous tubules** (ST). Spermatozoa gain access to the rete testis via the short, straight **tubuli recti** (TR).

FIGURE 4 • Ductus epididymis. Monkey. Plastic section. ×132.

The **ductus epididymis** (DE) may be distinguished from the ductuli efferentes with relative ease. Note that the **nuclei** (N) of the pseudostratified **epithelial lining** (Ep) are of two types, oval and round, whereas those of the ductuli are round. Observe that the lumen contains numerous **spermatozoa** (Sz) and that the epithelium sits on a basal lamina. The connective tissue wall of the ductus epididymis may be differentiated easily from its circularly arranged **smooth muscle coat** (SM).

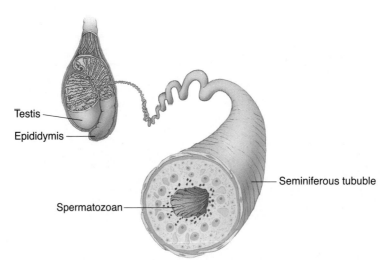

Testis

Epididymis

Seminiferous tububle

Spermatozoan

Testis, epididymis, and seminiferous tubule

KEY					
BV	blood vessel	IC	interstitial cells of Leydig	SM	smooth muscle
CT	connective tissue	LV	lymphatic vessels	ST	seminiferous tubules
DE	ductus epididymis	MT	mediastinum testis	St	stroma
De	ductuli efferentes	N	nuclei	Sz	spermatozoa
Ep	epithelium	RT	rete testis	TR	tubuli recti

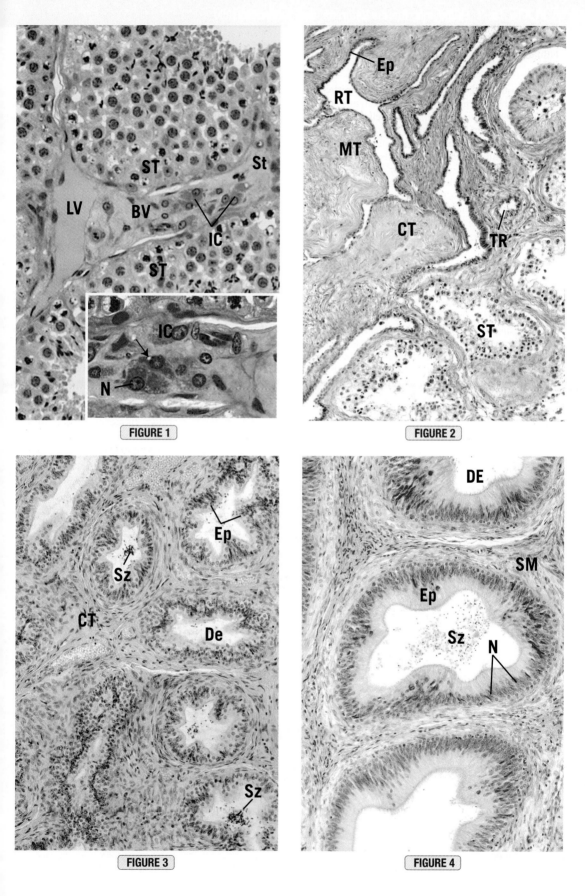

FIGURE 1

FIGURE 2

FIGURE 3

FIGURE 4

PLATE 18-3 Epididymis, Ductus Deferens, and Seminal Vesicle

FIGURE 1 • Ductus epididymis. Monkey. Plastic section. ×270.

The pseudostratified stereociliated columnar **epithelium** (Ep) lining the lumen of the ductus epididymis is composed of two types of cells: short **basal cells** (BC), recognizable by their round nuclei, and tall columnar **principal cells** (PC), whose oval nuclei display one or more **nucleoli** (n). The **smooth muscle** (SM) cells, composing the wall of the epididymis, are circularly oriented and are surrounded by **connective tissue** (CT) elements. *Inset.* **Ductus epididymis. Monkey. Plastic section.** ×540. Observe the round nuclei of the **basal cells** (BC) and oval nuclei of the **principal cells** (PC). Clumped stereocilia (*arrows*) extend into the **spermatozoa** (Sz)-filled lumen.

FIGURE 2 • Ductus deferens. Monkey. Plastic section. ×132.

The ductus deferens is a thick-walled, muscular tube that conveys spermatozoa from the ductus epididymis to the ejaculatory duct. The thick, muscular coat is composed of three layers of smooth muscle: **outer longitudinal** (OL), **middle circular** (MC), and **inner longitudinal** (IL). The fibroelastic **lamina propria** (LP) receives its **vascular supply** (BV) from vessels (*arrow*) that penetrate the three muscle layers. A pseudostratified columnar **epithelium** (Ep) lines the spermatozoa-filled **lumen** (L). *Inset.* **Ductus deferens. Monkey. Plastic section.** ×270. A higher magnification of the pseudostratified columnar **epithelium** (Ep) displays the presence of **stereocilia** (Sc).

FIGURE 3 • Seminal vesicle. Human. Paraffin section. ×132.

The paired seminal vesicles are elongated tubular glands whose ducts join the ductus deferens just prior to the beginning of the ejaculatory ducts. The highly folded **mucous membrane** (MM) of the seminal vesicle is composed of pseudostratified **epithelium** (Ep) with a thin **connective tissue core** (CT). The folded membrane anastomoses with itself, partitioning off small spaces (*asterisks*) that, although continuous with the central lumen, appear to be discrete regions. A region similar to the *boxed area* is presented at a higher magnification in Figure 4.

FIGURE 4 • Seminal vesicle. Monkey. Plastic section. ×540.

This photomicrograph is a higher magnification of a region similar to the *boxed area* of the previous figure. Note that the tall **columnar cells** (CC) have basally located, round **nuclei** (N) and that their cytoplasm displays secretory granules (*arrows*). Short **basal cells** (BC) are occasionally present, which may function as regenerative cells for the epithelium. The secretory product is released into the **lumen** (L) as a thick fluid that coagulates in histological sections. Observe the presence of numerous **capillaries** (C) in the connective tissue core deep to the epithelium. Although **spermatozoa** (Sz) are frequently noted in the lumen of the seminal vesicles, they are not stored in this structure.

KEY

BC	basal cell	L	lumen	OL	outer longitudinal muscle layer
BV	blood vessel	LP	lamina propria	PC	principal cell
C	capillaries	MC	middle circular muscle layer	Sc	stereocilia
CC	columnar cell	MM	mucous membrane	SM	smooth muscle
CT	connective tissue	N	nucleus	Sz	spermatozoa
Ep	epithelium	n	nucleoli		
IL	inner longitudinal muscle layer				

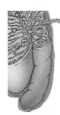

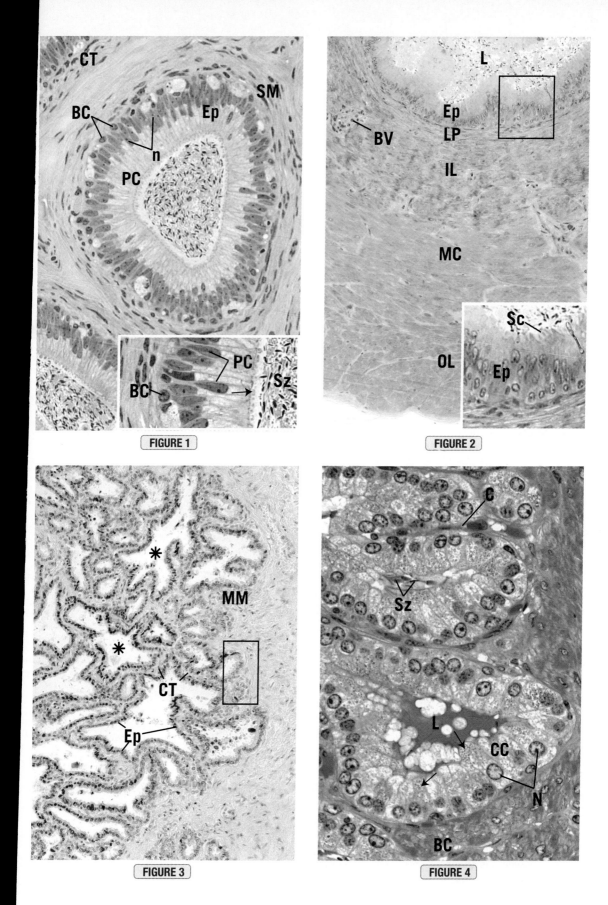

FIGURE 1

CT
SM
BC
Ep
n
PC
PC
BC
Sz

FIGURE 2

L
Ep
BV
LP
IL
MC
OL
Sc
Ep

FIGURE 3

*
MM
*
CT
Ep

FIGURE 4

C
Sz
L
CC
N
BC

FIGURE 1 • Prostate gland. Monkey. Plastic section. ×132.

The prostate gland, the largest of the male reproductive accessory glands, possesses a thick fibroelastic connective tissue capsule with which the connective tissue **stroma** (St) is continuous. Note that the stroma houses **smooth muscle** (SM) and blood vessels. The secretory portion of the prostate gland is composed of individual glands of varied shapes but consisting of a simple cuboidal-to-low columnar type of **epithelium** (Ep), although regions of pseudostratified columnar epithelia are readily apparent. A region similar to the *boxed area* is presented at a higher magnification in Figure 2.

FIGURE 3 • Penis. Human. x.s. Paraffin section. ×14.

The penis is composed of three erectile bodies: the two corpora cavernosa and the corpus spongiosum. The cross-section of the **corpus spongiosum** (CS) displays the **urethra** (U), which is surrounded by **erectile tissue** (ET), whose irregular, endothelially lined **cavernous spaces** (Cs) contain blood. The spongy tissue is surrounded by the thick, fibrous **tunica albuginea** (TA). The three cavernous bodies are surrounded by a looser connective tissue sheath to which the skin (removed here) is attached. The *boxed area* is presented at a higher magnification in Figure 4. *Inset.* **Penis. Human. x.s. Paraffin section.** ×14. The **cavernous spaces** (Cs) of the corpus cavernosum are larger than those of the corpus spongiosum. Moreover, the **fibrous trabeculae** (FT) are thinner, resulting in the corpora cavernosa becoming more turgid during erection than the corpus spongiosum.

FIGURE 2 • Prostate gland. Monkey. Plastic section. ×540.

This photomicrograph is a higher magnification of a region similar to the *boxed area* of the previous figure. Observe that the fibroelastic connective tissue **stroma** (St) presents numerous **blood vessels** (BV) and **smooth muscle cells** (SM). The parenchyma of the gland is composed of **columnar cells** (CC) as well as short **basal cells** (BC). Note that the dome-shaped apices (*arrows*) of some of the columnar cells appear to protrude into the lumen, which contain a **prostatic concretion** (Pc). The number of these concretions, which may calcify, increases with age.

FIGURE 4 • Urethra. Human. Paraffin section. ×132.

This photomicrograph is a higher magnification of the *boxed area* of the previous figure. Note that the spongy **urethra** (U) is lined by a pseudostratified columnar **epithelium** (Ep) surrounded by a loose **connective tissue sheath** (CT), housing a rich **vascular supply** (BV). The entire urethra is enveloped by the **erectile tissue** (ET) of the corpus spongiosum. Additionally, the mucous **glands of Littré** (GL) deliver their secretory product into the lumen of the urethra, lubricating its epithelial lining.

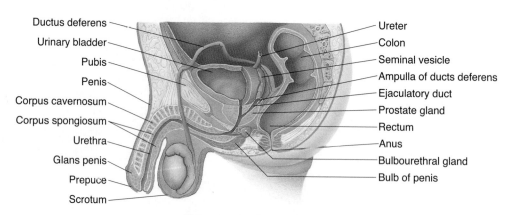

Ductus deferens
Urinary bladder
Pubis
Penis
Corpus cavernosum
Corpus spongiosum
Urethra
Glans penis
Prepuce
Scrotum

Ureter
Colon
Seminal vesicle
Ampulla of ducts deferens
Ejaculatory duct
Prostate gland
Rectum
Anus
Bulbourethral gland
Bulb of penis

Male reproductive system

KEY							
BC	basal cell	CT	connective tissue	Pc	prostatic concretion
BV	blood vessel	Ep	epithelium	SM	smooth muscle
CC	columnar cell	ET	erectile tissue	St	stroma
CS	corpus spongiosum	FT	fibrous trabeculae	TA	tunica albuginea
Cs	cavernous space	GL	glands of Littré	U	urethra

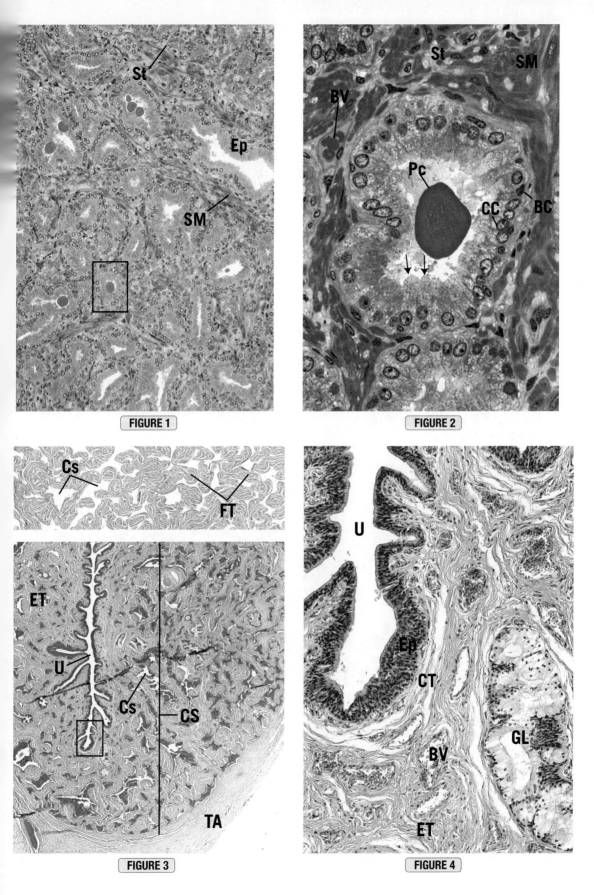

FIGURE 1

FIGURE 2

FIGURE 3

FIGURE 4

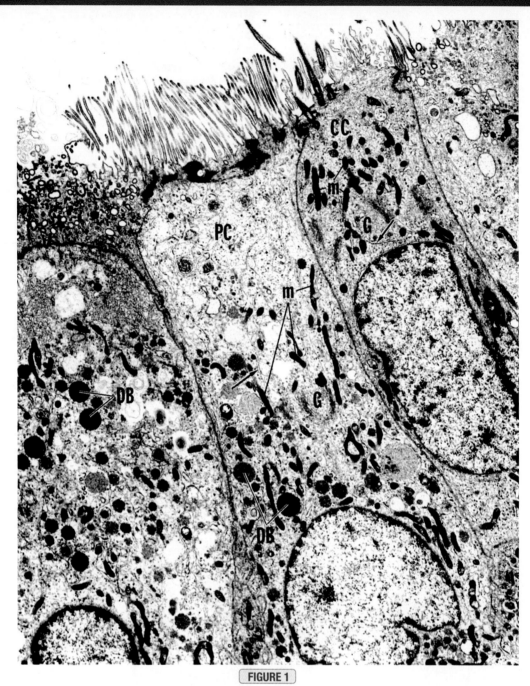

FIGURE 1

FIGURE 1 • Epididymis. Rabbit. Electron microscopy. ×7,200.

The epithelial lining of the rabbit ductuli efferentes is composed of two types of tall columnar cells: **principal cells** (PC) and **ciliated cells** (CC). Note that both cell types possess numerous organelles, such as **Golgi** (G), **mitochondria** (m), and rough endoplasmic reticulum (*arrows*). Additionally, principal cells contain **dense bodies** (DB), probably a secretory material. (Courtesy of Dr. R. Jones.)

KEY					
CC	ciliated cell	G	Golgi apparatus	PC	principal cell
DB	dense bodies	m	mitochondrion		

Summary of Histological Organization

I. TESTES

A. Capsule

The fibromuscular connective tissue **capsule** of the testes is known as the **tunica albuginea**, whose inner vascular layer is the **tunica vasculosa**. The capsule is thickened at the **mediastinum testis** from which **septa** emanate, subdividing the testis into approximately 250 incomplete **lobuli testis**, with each containing one to four **seminiferous tubules** embedded in a connective tissue **stroma**.

B. Seminiferous Tubules

Each highly convoluted **seminiferous tubule** is composed of a fibromuscular **tunica propria**, which is separated from the **seminiferous epithelium** by a **basal membrane**.

1. Seminiferous Epithelium

The **seminiferous epithelium** is composed of sustentacular **Sertoli cells** and a stratified layer of developing **male gametes**. Sertoli cells establish a blood-testis barrier by forming occluding junctions with each other, thus subdividing the seminiferous tubule into **adluminal** and **basal compartments**. The basal compartment houses **spermatogonia A** (both **light** and **dark**), **spermatogonia B**, and the basal aspects of Sertoli cells. The adluminal compartment contains the apical portions of Sertoli cells, **primary spermatocytes**, **secondary spermatocytes**, **spermatids**, and **spermatozoa**.

2. Tunica Propria

The **tunica propria** consists of loose collagenous connective tissue, **fibroblasts**, and **myoid cells**.

C. Stroma

The loose vascular connective tissue **stroma** surrounding seminiferous tubules houses small clusters of large, vacuolated-appearing endocrine cells, the **interstitial cells** (of Leydig).

II. GENITAL DUCTS

A. Tubuli Recti

Short, straight tubes, the **tubuli recti**, lined by **Sertoli-like cells** initially and **simple cuboidal epithelium** later, connect the seminiferous tubules to the **rete testis**.

B. Rete Testis

The **rete testis** is composed of cuboidal cell–lined labyrinthine spaces within the **mediastinum testis**.

C. Epididymis

1. Ductuli Efferentes

The **ductuli efferentes** compose the **head of the epididymis**, whose lumina are lined by **simple columnar** (tall ciliated and low nonciliated) **epithelium**. The walls of the ductules consist of fibroelastic connective tissue and **smooth muscle cells**.

2. Ductus Epididymis

The **ductus epididymis** comprises the **body** and **tail** of the **epididymis**. Its lumen is lined by a **pseudostratified** type of **epithelium** composed of short **basal** and tall **principal cells** bearing **stereocilia** (long microvilli). The epithelium is separated by a **basal membrane** from the connective tissue wall that houses **smooth muscle cells**.

D. Ductus (Vas) Deferens

The enlarged continuation of the ductus epididymis, the **ductus deferens**, is a highly muscular structure. The **mucosal lining** of its small **lumen** is composed of **pseudostratified stereociliated epithelium** lying on a thin fibroelastic **lamina propria**. Its thick, muscular coat is composed of three layers of **smooth muscle**: an **inner** and **outer longitudinal** and a **middle circular** layer. A loose, fibroelastic **adventitia** surrounds the outer longitudinal muscle layer.

III. ACCESSORY GLANDS

A. Seminal Vesicles

As the **seminal vesicles**, two highly convoluted tubular structures, join the ductus deferens, they form the paired **ejaculatory ducts**. The highly folded **mucous membrane** of the seminal vesicle is composed of a **pseudostratified epithelium**, whose columnar cells are interspersed with short **basal cells**, sitting on a fibroelastic **lamina propria**. The muscular coat is composed of **inner circular** and **outer longitudinal** layers of **smooth muscle** and is invested by a fibrous **adventitia**.

B. Prostate Gland

The ejaculatory ducts join the urethra as these three structures traverse the substance of the **prostate gland**, whose **capsule** is composed of fibroelastic connective tissue and **smooth muscle cells**. The dense **stroma** of the gland is continuous with the capsule. The **parenchyma** of the prostate is composed of numerous individual glands disposed in three layers: **mucosal**, **submucosal**, and **external** (**main**). The **lumina** of these three groups drain into three systems of **ducts** that lead into the expanded **urethral sinus**. The folded mucosa of the glands is composed of **simple cuboidal** to **columnar** (with regions of pseudostratified columnar) **epithelia** supported by fibroelastic vascular **stroma** displaying **smooth muscle cells**. Frequently, the lumina of the glands of older men possess round-to-ovoid **prostatic concretions** that are often lamellated and may become calcified.

C. Bulbourethral Glands

Each small **bulbourethral** (**Cowper's**) **gland** possesses a thin connective tissue **capsule** whose septa subdivide the gland into **lobules**. The **cuboidal-to-columnar cells** lining the lumen of the gland possess flattened, basally located **nuclei**. The main **duct** of each gland delivers its mucous secretory product into the **cavernous** (**spongy**) **urethra**.

IV. PENIS

The **penis**, ensheathed in **skin**, possesses a thick, collagenous capsule, the **tunica albuginea**, that encloses the three cylindrical bodies of **erectile tissue**. The two dorsally positioned **corpora cavernosa** are incompletely separated from each other by **septa** derived from the tunica albuginea. The **corpus cavernosum urethrae** (**corpus spongiosum**) contains the spongy portion of the **urethra**. The vascular spaces of the erectile tissues are lined by **endothelium**.

V. URETHRA

The male **urethra** is subdivided into three regions: **prostatic**, **membranous**, and **spongy** (**penile**) urethra.

A. Epithelium

The **prostatic portion** is lined by **transitional epithelium**, whereas the **membranous** and **spongy portions** are lined by **pseudostratified-to-stratified columnar epithelium**. The **spongy urethra** frequently displays regions of **stratified squamous epithelium**. **Goblet cells** and **intraepithelial glands** are also present.

B. Lamina Propria

The **lamina propria** is composed of a type of **loose connective tissue** housing **elastic fibers** and **glands of Littré**. **Smooth muscle**, oriented longitudinally and circularly, is also evident.

19

Special Senses

The organs of special senses include the gustatory, olfactory, visual, auditory, and vestibular systems. The gustatory apparatus, consisting of taste buds, is discussed in Chapter 13, and the olfactory epithelium is treated in Chapter 12. The present chapter details the microscopic morphology of the eye, involved with visual sensations, and the ear, involved with auditory and vestibular sensations.

● EYE

The **eye** is a sensory organ whose **lens** focuses rays of light originating in the external environment onto photosensitive cells of the **retina** (see Graphic 19-1). The intensity, location, and wavelengths of the transmitted light are partially processed by the retina and the information is transmitted for further processing and interpretation by the visual cortex of the brain as three-dimensional color images of the external milieu. Each eyeball, protected by the eyelids, is movable by means of a group of extrinsic skeletal muscles that insert into its fibrous outer tunic, thus assisting in suspending it in its bony orbit. The anterior surface of the eye is bathed in **tears**, a complex mixture of proteins, salts, peptides, and organic molecules in a fluid medium secreted by the **lacrimal gland**. Three coats constitute the wall of the orb: the outer fibrous tunic, the middle vascular tunic (uvea), and the inner retinal tunic.

The **fibrous tunic (corneoscleral layer)** is composed of the opaque, white **sclera** that covers the posterior aspect of the orb and the transparent **cornea** that covers the anterior one-sixth of the orb. The junction between the sclera and the cornea is known as the **limbus.**

The **vascular tunic** consists of several regions: the anteriorly positioned **iris** and **ciliary body** and the posteriorly located, highly vascular and pigmented **choroid**. Intrinsic smooth muscles located in the iris function to adjust the **pupil**, the aperture of the iris, whereas intrinsic muscles located within the ciliary body function to release tension on the lens, thus permitting near focus (accommodation) by altering the thickness of the lens.

The innermost **retinal tunic** is composed of 10 layers responsible for photoreception and impulse gen-

eration. The two photoreceptors are the **rhodopsin-synthesizing rods** and **iodopsin-forming cones**, with the former sensitive to dim and the latter sensitive to bright light. Axons of connecting neurons, located within the retina, leave the eye via the **optic nerve** to synapse in the brain.

The additional components of the orb are the **aqueous humor**, a fluid; the **vitreous body**, a gel; and the **lens**, all of which serve as parts of the refractive media. The aqueous humor, located the posterior and anterior chambers of the eye, and the vitreous body, located behind the lens of the eye, are also important in providing nutrients to the avascular lens and cornea.

● EAR

The **ear** functions in the reception of sound as well as in the perception of the orientation of the head and therefore the body in relation to the directional forces of gravity (see Graphic 19-2). To perform both functions of hearing and equilibrium (balance), the ear is subdivided into the external, middle, and inner ears.

The **external ear** is composed of a cartilaginous, skin-covered **auricle** (pinna) and the **external auditory meatus**, with its cartilaginous outer and bony inner aspects, whose internal extent is separated from the middle ear by the thin **tympanic membrane**.

The **tympanic cavity** of the **middle ear** houses the three **auditory ossicles**: the outermost **malleus** (hammer), the middle **incus** (anvil), and the innermost **stapes** (stirrup). This cavity is connected to the **nasopharynx** via the cartilaginous **auditory (eustachian) tube**, which permits equalization of atmospheric pressures on either side of the tympanic membrane. Sound waves are funneled by the auricle to the tympanic membrane, whose vibrations are amplified and transmitted by the movements of the ossicles to the **oval window** of the inner ear's **cochlea**.

The **inner ear**, concerned with both hearing and balance, is housed within a **labyrinth** in the petrous portion of the temporal bone. The region closest to the middle ear, the **bony cochlea**, houses the apparatus responsible for hearing, whereas its

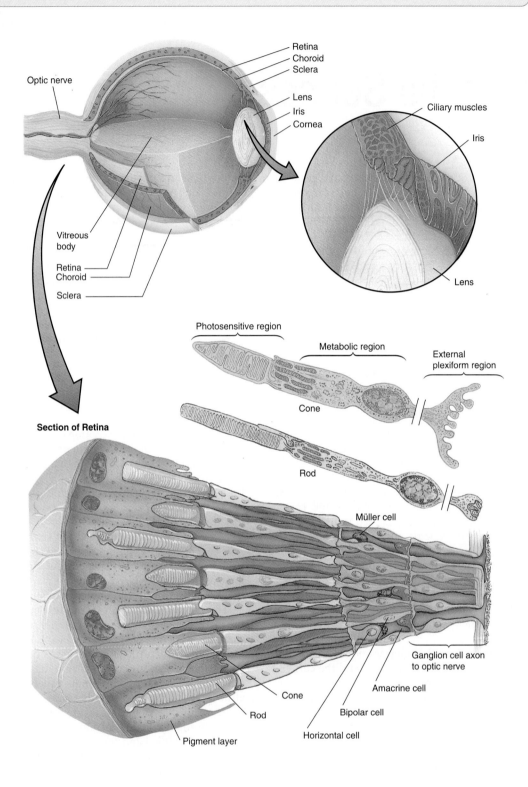

Optic nerve

Retina
Choroid
Sclera

Lens
Iris
Cornea

Ciliary muscles

Iris

Lens

Vitreous body

Retina
Choroid

Sclera

Section of Retina

Photosensitive region

Metabolic region

External plexiform region

Cone

Rod

Müller cell

Ganglion cell axon to optic nerve

Amacrine cell

Cone

Bipolar cell

Rod

Horizontal cell

Pigment layer

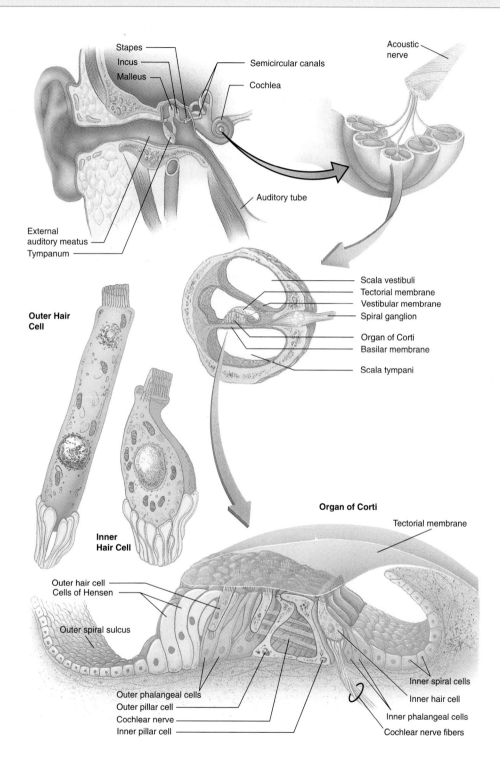

Stapes
Incus
Malleus
Semicircular canals
Cochlea
Acoustic nerve
Auditory tube
External auditory meatus
Tympanum

Outer Hair Cell

Inner Hair Cell

Scala vestibuli
Tectorial membrane
Vestibular membrane
Spiral ganglion
Organ of Corti
Basilar membrane
Scala tympani

Organ of Corti

Tectorial membrane

Outer hair cell
Cells of Hensen

Outer spiral sulcus

Outer phalangeal cells
Outer pillar cell
Cochlear nerve
Inner pillar cell

Inner spiral cells
Inner hair cell
Inner phalangeal cells
Cochlear nerve fibers

deeper aspect contains the structures responsible for vestibular function (balance).

The bony cochlea contains the **endolymph-filled cochlear duct**, which is surrounded by **perilymph**, housed in the **scala vestibuli** (located superiorly) and the **scala tympani** (positioned inferiorly). The two scalae communicate with each other via a small slit-like opening known as the **helicotrema**.

Within the **cochlear duct** is the **spiral organ of Corti**, the apical aspects of whose **inner** and **outer hair cells** are in close association with the **tectorial membrane**. Vibrations of the **basilar membrane**, on which the hair cells stand, induced by disturbances in the perilymph, result in stimulation of the **cochlear nerves** by the hair cells. Dendrites of the cochlear nerves lead to the spiral ganglion located in the modiolus. Oscillations set in motion at the **oval window** are dissipated at the secondary tympanic membrane covering the **round window** of the cochlea. The hair cells, associated with the tectorial membrane, are responsible for transducing sound (reaching them in the form of pressure waves) into electrical signals transmitted to the brain.

The bony labyrinth also contains the endolymph-filled **utricle, saccule,** and the three **semicircular canals**, membranous structures responsible for balance and orientation in three-dimensional space.

The principal functional components of the utricle and saccule, oriented perpendicularly to each other, are known as **maculae**. These structures house **neuroepithelial hair cells** whose **microvilli** and **kinocilia** (nonmotile cilia) project into the otolith-containing proteinaceous **otolithic membrane**. The utricle and saccule respond to linear acceleration.

A similar collection of hair cells is located on the **crista ampullaris** of the ampulla of each semicircular canal. The microvilli and kinocilia of these neuroepithelial cells also project into a proteinaceous material known as the **cupula**, which contains no otoliths. Since each semicircular canal is oriented perpendicular to the other two, angular acceleration along any of the three axes is registered and interpreted as a vector in three dimensions.

● Histophysiology

I. EYE

A. Globe of the Eye

The **eye** functions as the photosensitive organ responsible for vision. It receives light through the **cornea**, which is subsequently focused on the **retina** via the **lens**. It is here that specialized cells (**rods** and **cones**) sense the light and those points of sensations are assembled and relayed for transmission to the brain via the **optic nerve**. **Extrinsic muscles** attached to the globe direct the pupil to the most advantageous position for perceiving the image viewed. Because the eyes are set apart and because their visual fields overlap, three-dimensional imaging becomes possible. **Intrinsic smooth muscles** represented by the **sphincter pupillae** and **dilatator pupillae muscles** adjust the aperture of the **iris**. The **ciliary smooth muscles** alter tension of the suspensory (zonular) fibers anchored in the lens and thus alter the shape of the lens (accommodation) for near and far vision.

Melanocytes located in the epithelium and stroma of the iris block light from passing through the iris, except at the pupil. Additionally, eye color is related to the abundance of melanin produced by these melanocytes: A large amount of melanin imparts dark eyes, whereas less melanin renders the eyes light in color.

The aqueous humor, a plasma filtrate produced by the cells covering the ciliary processes, passes from the posterior chamber of the eye into the anterior chamber via the opening between the lens and the pupil.

The wall of the globe of the eye is composed of three tunics: the **tunica fibrosa**, the **tunica vasculosa**, and the **tunica retina**. The tunica retina is responsible for **photoreception**. The retina displays 10 distinctive layers, whose cells receive images that they partially interpret and relay via the optic nerve to the brain for further interpretation. The two deepest layers, the retinal pigment epithelium and the layer of rods and cones, bear the major responsibility for photoreception.

Retinal pigment epithelium functions in **esterifying vitamin A** and transporting it to the rods and cones, **phagocytosing** the shed tips of rods and cones, and **synthesizing melanin**, which absorbs light after rods and cones have been stimulated.

Rods are sensitive to low light intensity and possess many flattened discs containing **rhodopsin** (an integral membrane protein, **opsin**, bound to **retinal**, the aldehyde form of **vitamin A**) in their outer segment. When light is absorbed by rhodopsin, it dissociates into **retinal** and **opsin** (bleaching), permitting diffusion of bound Ca^{2+} into the outer segment. Excess levels of Ca^{2+} hyperpolarize the cell by closing Na^+ channels, thus preventing the entry of Na^+ into the cell. The electrical potential thus generated is relayed to other rods via gap junctions and then along the pathway to the optic nerve. Dissociated retinal and opsin reassemble, and the Ca^{2+} ions are recaptured, establishing a normal resting potential.

Cones, sensitive to light of high intensity, producing **greater visual acuity**, are much more numerous than rods and produce **iodopsin**, the photopigment sensitive to red, green, or blue light. The mechanism of transducing photoenergy into electrical energy for transmission to the brain via the optic nerve is similar to that described in the rods.

Rods and cones are either stimulated (on) or inhibited (off) by light, that is, they indicate the location of a light pixel and, in the case of cones, its color. Dendrites of 10 different types of **bipolar cells** receive information from the rods and cones and then this information is conveyed by the axons of the bipolar cells into specific strata of the **inner plexiform layer** of the retina. The further transmission of the impulses is monitored and modulated by one or more of the 27 types of **amacrine cells**, whose axons can span several millimeters or just a few micrometers of the retinal expanse. The outer layer of the retina contains 12 types of **ganglion cells** whose interactions with bipolar cells and amacrine cells result in the transmission of 12 different moving images (a continuous moving stream that resembles but is not created frame by frame) of the same scene via the optic nerve to the visual cortex of the brain for further analysis, assembly, and interpretation. These moving images are very different from each other, in that some consist of highlights, others consist of line drawings of outlines, and still others generate shadows. It is the function of the visual cortex to assemble these movies into the world that we recognize. It must be stressed that this is a simplified description of some of the current concepts of vision that will certainly be modified as more information is gained from research in this field.

The **optic disc**, the region where the optic nerve exits the eyeball, contains neither cones nor rods;

consequently, it represents and is called a **blind spot**. Just lateral to the blind spot is the **fovea centralis**, a depression in the wall of the eyeball. The fovea contains mostly cones that are packed so tightly that not all layers of the retina are present. Visual acuity is the greatest in the fovea centralis.

B. Accessory Structures

Accessory structures of the eye include the conjunctiva, eyelids, and lacrimal gland. The **conjunctiva** is a transparent mucous membrane that lines the eyelids and reflects on the eye. The **eyelids** contain modified sebaceous glands, the **meibomian glands**, which are responsible for altering the surface tension of the watery tears, thus slowing evaporation. The **lacrimal glands** secrete tears, which keep the conjunctiva and cornea moist. **Tears** also contain **lysozyme**, an antibacterial enzyme.

II. EAR

The **ear** is composed of three parts: the **external ear** (pinna and external acoustic meatus), which receives the sound waves; the **middle ear** (containing the bony ossicles), which transmits the sound waves; and the **inner ear** (containing the cochlea), where sound waves are transduced into nerve impulses and the sensation of equilibrium/dysequilibrium is perceived by the vestibular apparatus.

The **tympanic membrane** (i.e., the **ear drum**), located at the deepest aspect of the external acoustic meatus, separates the external from the middle ear. The membrane is responsible for the transduction of sound waves into mechanical vibrations that will be transmitted by the bony ossicles. The tympanic cavity of the middle ear contains the **malleus, incus,** and **stapes** (bony ossicles), connected in series to each other and between the tympanic membrane and the **oval window** of the bony wall. The ossicles amplify and translate movements of the tympanic membrane to the oval window.

The **bony labyrinth** of the inner ear, subdivided into the **semicircular canals**, **vestibule**, and **cochlea**, is filled with perilymph. Loosely contained within it and all of its subdivisions is the endolymph-containing **membranous labyrinth**. Movements of the fluid environment within this system are perceived by apical hairs of specialized sensory cells contained within the membranous labyrinth and ultimately transduced to electrical impulses for transmission to the brain.

The **saccule** and **utricle**, specialized structures of the membranous labyrinth in the vestibule, contain **type I** and **type II hair cells** (**neuroepithelial cells** containing many **stereocilia** and a single **kinocilium**), whose free ends are embedded in the **otolithic membrane** containing calcium carbonate crystals known as **otoliths** (**otoconia**). **Static equilibrium** and **linear acceleration** are determined by movements (or the lack of movements) in the stereocilia or kinocilia of these hair cells. Threshold bending of the stereocilia or kinocilia will depolarize the hair cells, which, in turn, relay (via neurotransmission) information to the processes of primary vestibular neurons located in Scarpa's ganglion.

Semicircular ducts, specializations of the membranous labyrinth in the semicircular canals, contain **neuroepithelial hair cells** located in the **cristae ampullares** (sensory regions) of the **ampullae**. Free ends of these hair cells have stereocilia that are embedded in a viscous glycoprotein known as the **cupula**. Movement of the endolymph bathing the cupula depolarize the hair cells, which, in turn, alter the activity in the synaptic endings associated with the base of the hair cells. This process is sensitive to **rotational acceleration** in any of the three directions of orientation of the semicircular canals. Thus, these structures are responsible for the vestibular sensations of balance and orientation.

The **endolymphatic sac** (terminal end of the **endolymphatic duct**) contains phagocytic cells in its lumen and may function in **resorption of endolymph**.

The **cochlear duct** contains the **spiral organ of Corti**, which is bordered by the **scala vestibuli** and the **scala tympani** (both scalae contain perilymph and communicate at the **helicotrema**). The **vestibular membrane** located between the scala vestibuli and the cochlear duct functions to maintain the **high ion gradient** between the perilymph and endolymph.

The **spiral organ of Corti**, sitting on the **basilar membrane**, contains, among other supporting cells, neuroepithelial **inner** and **outer hair cells** whose free ends are embedded in the gel-like **tectorial membrane**. Sound transmission/conduction via the tympanic membrane and ossicle to the oval window sets waves translated to the oval window and sets the perilymph of the scala tympani in motion, which displaces the basilar membrane, thus moving the hair cells but not the tectorial membrane. Bending of the hair cells causes them to release neurotransmitter substance, exciting the **bipolar cells** of the spiral ganglion, resulting in transmission of the impulse to higher centers of the brain. Although the basilar membrane vibrates at many frequencies, certain regions vibrate optimally at specific frequencies. For example, low frequency sound waves are detected farther away from the oval window. It should be noted that loud sounds, such as those at rock concerts, create a great deal of energy within the hearing mechanism, such that it may take 2 or 3 days for the energy to be completely dissipated and the buzzing to stop.

CLINICAL CONSIDERATIONS

Blue Eye Color

Until approximately 6,000 to 10,000 years ago, every human being had brown eyes; then, a small mutation in the switch that turned off OCA2 gene resulted in the inability of that individual to manufacture P protein in the iris. Protein P is involved in melanin formation; thus, the person with this particular mutation was able to synthesize melanin normally except in the iris, and, instead of having brown eyes, that person's eyes were blue. Thus, it is believed that all blue-eyed individuals are descendants of that one person born in the 6th to 8th millenium BCE.

Myopia and Hyperopia

As an individual ages, the longitudinal axis of the orb changes, as may the curvature of the cornea, and the lens, instead of focusing the image on the retina, focuses it either in front of the retina (**myopic vision**) or behind the retina (**hyperopic vision**). The condition may be corrected with lenses (eye glasses or contact lenses) or by refractive surgery, assisting the lens in focusing on the retina.

Glaucoma

Glaucoma is a condition of high intraocular pressure caused by an obstruction that prevents the aqueous humor from exiting the anterior chamber of the eye. If left untreated, the pressure damages the optic nerve to such an extent that blindness may result.

Cataract

Cataract, a common condition of aging, is caused by excessive UV radiation and by pigments and other substances accumulating in the lens, making it opaque and thus impairing vision. This condition may be corrected by excising the lens and replacing it with a plastic lens.

Detached Retina

Detached retina may result from a trauma in which the neural and pigmented layers of the retina become separated, resulting to ischemic damage to the neurons. This condition may cause partial blindness, but it may be corrected by surgical intervention.

Conductive Hearing Loss

Conductive hearing loss may arise from a middle ear infection (otitis media), an obstruction, or osteosclerosis of the middle ear.

Nerve Deafness

Nerve deafness results from a lesion in the cochlear portion of the vestibulocochlear nerve (cranial nerve VIII). This condition may be the result of disease, prolonged exposure to loud sounds, and/or drugs.

Ménière's Disease

Ménière's disease is an inner ear disorder characterized by symptoms such as hearing loss due to excess fluid accumulation in the endolymphatic duct, vertigo, tinnitus, nausea, and vomiting. Many of the symptoms may be relieved by drugs that are prescribed for vertigo and nausea, or, in more severe cases, vestibular neurectomy (cutting the vestibular nerve) may be performed. In very severe cases, labyrinthectomy is the treatment of choice, in which the semicircular canals and the cochlea are surgically removed.

Hearing Without Sound

It has been shown that individuals who are deaf as well as normally hearing individuals can hear things in the absence of sounds. It appears that some of the phalangeal cells and pillar cells of the cochlea release ATP spontaneously; this released ATP activates hair cells in their vicinity to release their neurotransmitter substances that cause the auditory neurons to fire, and the impulses are transmitted to the brain. These sounds can be as nondescript as tinnitus (ringing in the ear) or as complex as a musical melody.

FIGURE 1 • Cornea. Monkey. Paraffin section. ×132.

The cornea is a multilayered, transparent structure. Its anterior surface is covered by a stratified squamous nonkeratinized **epithelium** (Ep) on the right-hand side of the image, deep to which is a thin, acellular Bowman's membrane. The bulk of the cornea, the **stroma** (St), is composed of regularly arranged **collagen fibers** (CF) and intervening fibroblasts, whose **nuclei** (N) are readily evident. The posterior surface of the cornea is lined by a simple squamous-to-cuboidal **epithelium** (Ep) on the left-hand side of the image. A thin, acellular Descement's membrane lies between the simple epithelium and the stroma. *Inset.* **Cornea. Monkey. Paraffin section.** × 270. A higher magnification of the anterior surface displays the stratified squamous **epithelium** (Ep) as well as the acellular **Bowman's membrane** (BM). Note the regularly arranged bundles of **collagen fibers** (CF) and intervening **fibroblasts** (F), whose nucleus is labeled by the lead line.

FIGURE 3 • Iris. Monkey. Paraffin section. ×132.

The **iris** (I) is a pigmented diaphragm that delineates the **pupil** (P) of the eye. It separates the **anterior chamber** (AC) from the **posterior chamber** (PC). The iris is composed of three layers: an outer discontinuous layer of melanocytes and fibroblasts; the intermediate **fibrous layer** (FL), housing **pigment cells** (Pc) and fibroblasts; and the posterior double-layered **pigmented epithelium** (PEp). The **sphincter** (sM) and dilatator muscles are composed of smooth muscle and smooth muscle–like myoepithelial cells, respectively. The pupillary region of the iris contacts the **capsule** (Ca) of the **lens** (L) in living individuals.

FIGURE 2 • Sclera. Monkey. Paraffin section. ×132.

The sclera is similar to and continuous with the cornea, but it is not transparent. Note that the **epithelium** (Ep) of the conjunctiva covers the anterior surface of the sclera. Deep to the epithelium is the loose **episcleral tissue** (ET), whose small **blood vessels** (BV) are evident. The **stroma** (St) is composed of thick **collagen fiber** (CF) bundles, between which numerous **fibroblasts** (F) can be seen. The deepest layer of the sclera is the **suprachoroid lamina** (SL), whose **melanocytes** (M) containing dark melanin pigment characterize this layer.

FIGURE 4 • Ciliary body. Monkey. Paraffin section. ×132.

The ciliary body is composed of **ciliary processes** (CP), projecting into the **posterior chamber** (PC), from which suspensory ligaments (zonular fibers) extend to the lens. The bulk of the ciliary body is composed of **smooth muscle** (SM) disposed more or less in three layers, not evident in this photomicrograph. Numerous **pigment cells** (Pc) are present in this region. Note that the epithelium of the ciliary body is composed of two layers: an **outer pigmented** (OP) and an **inner nonpigmented** (IN) epithelium. The narrow **vascular layer** (VL) intervenes between the epithelium and ciliary muscles. The base, or root, of the iris is anchored to the ciliary body.

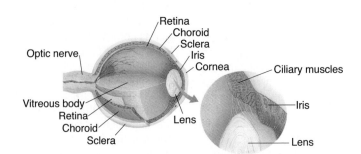

Eye, ciliary muscles, iris, and lens

KEY					
AC	anterior chamber	FL	fibrous layer	PC	posterior chamber
BM	Bowman's membrane	I	iris	Pc	pigment cells
BV	blood vessel	IN	inner nonpigmented	PEp	pigmented epithelium
Ca	capsule		layer	SEp	squamous epithelium
CF	collagen fibers	L	lens	SL	suprachoroid lamina
CP	ciliary process	M	melanocytes	SM	smooth muscle
Ep	epithelium	N	nucleus	sM	sphincter muscle
ET	episcleral tissue	OP	outer pigmented layer	St	stroma
F	fibroblasts	P	pupil	VL	vascular layer

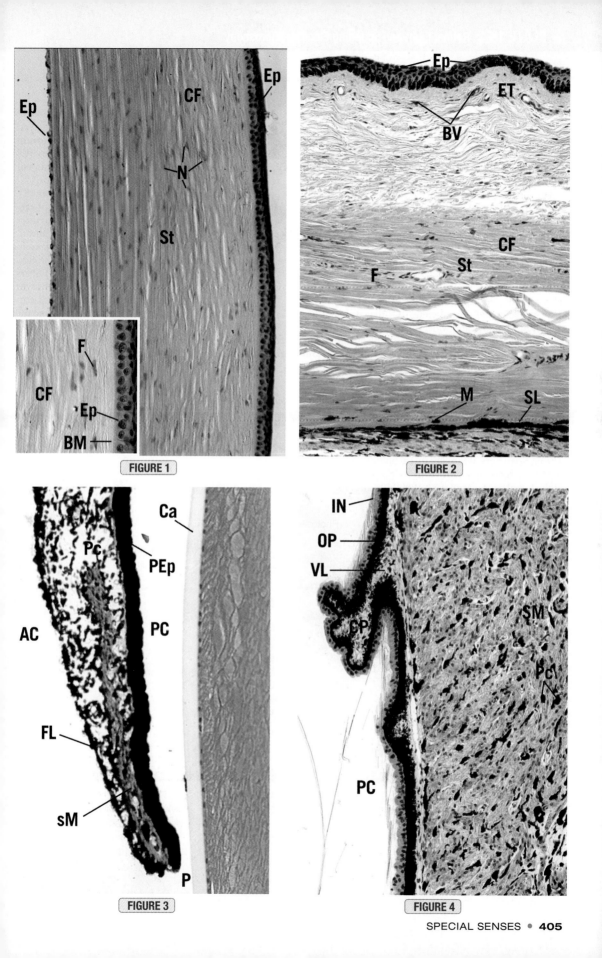

FIGURE 1

FIGURE 2

FIGURE 3

FIGURE 4

FIGURE 1 • Tunics of the eye. Monkey. Paraffin section. ×14.

This survey photomicrograph is of an anterolateral section of the globe of the eye, as evidenced by the presence of the **lacrimal gland** (LG). Note that the three layers of the globe of the eye are extremely thin in relation to its diameter. The **sclera** (S) is the outermost layer. The pigment **choroid** (Ch) and multilayered **retina** (Re) are easily distinguishable even at this low magnification. The **posterior compartment** (PCo) lies behind the lens and houses the vitreous body. A region similar to the *boxed area* is presented at a higher magnification in Figure 2.

FIGURE 3 • Rods and cones. Monkey. Scanning electron microscopy. ×6,300.

This scanning electron micrograph of the monkey retina displays regions of several **cones** (C) that display their thicker morphology and wider nuclear zone and of a few **rods** (R) whose diameter is narrower, with a thinner nuclear zone. The inner segments of the **lamina of rods and cones** (2), **external limiting membrane** (3), and outer nuclear layer (4) are clearly recognizable. The microvilli (Mv) noted in the vicinity of the external limiting membrane belong to the Müller cells, which were removed during specimen preparation. Observe the longitudinal ridges (*arrows*) along the surface of the inner segments. (From Borwein B, Borwein D, Medeiros J, McGowan J. The ultrastructure of monkey foveal photoreceptors, with special reference to the structure, shape, size, and spacing of the foveal cones. Am J Anat 1980;159:125–146.)

FIGURE 2 • Retina. Pars optica. Monkey. Paraffin section. ×270.

The pars optica of the retina is composed of 10 distinct layers. The **pigment epithelium** (1), the outermost layer, is closely apposed to the vascular and pigmented **choroid** (Ch). Various regions of the **rods** (R) and **cones** (C) characterize the next four layers. These are the **lamina of rods and cones** (2), **external limiting membrane** (3), **outer nuclear layer** (4), and **outer plexiform layer** (5). The **inner nuclear layer** (6) houses the cell bodies of various associative glial (Müller) and neural cells. The **inner plexiform layer** (7) is a region of synapse formation, whereas the **ganglion cell layer** (8) houses the cell bodies of multipolar neurons and associated neuroglia. The centrally directed (toward the central nervous system) fibers of these ganglion cells form the **optic nerve fiber layer** (9), whereas the **inner limiting membrane** (10) is composed of the expanded processes of Müller cells along the inner surface of the eye. A region similar to the *boxed area* is presented in Figure 3, a scanning electron micrograph of the rods and cones.

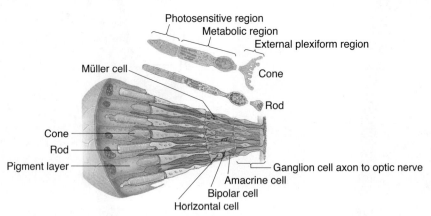

Section of retina

KEY						
1	pigment epithelium	7	inner plexiform layer	LG	lacrimal gland
2	lamina of rods and cones	8	ganglion cell layer	Mv	microvilli
3	external limiting membrane	9	optic nerve fiber layer	PCo	posterior compartment
4	outer nuclear layer	10	inner limiting membrane	R	rods
5	outer plexiform layer	C	cones	Re	retina
6	inner nuclear layer	Ch	choroid	S	sclera

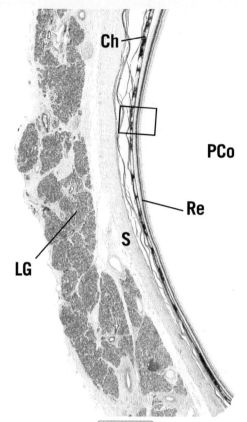

FIGURE 1

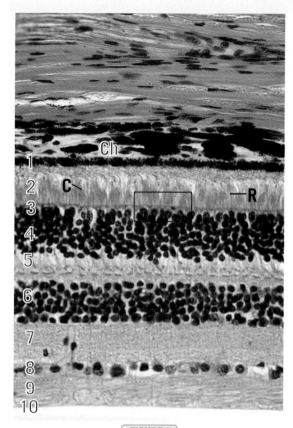

FIGURE 2

FIGURE 3

FIGURE 1 ● Fovea centralis. Monkey. Paraffin section. ×132.

The retina is greatly reduced in thickness at the **fovea centralis** (FC) of the macula lutea. This is the region of greatest visual acuity, and **cones** (C) are the only photoreceptor cells in this area. Note that the retinal layers present are the **pigmented epithelium** (1), **lamina of cones** (2), **external limiting membrane** (3), **outer nuclear layer** (4), **outer plexiform layer** (5), **ganglion cell layers** (8), and **inner limiting membrane** (10). Due to the presence of numerous melanocytes, the vascular **choroid** (Ch) appears dark.

FIGURE 3 ● Eyelid. Paraffin section. ×14.

The external aspect of the eyelid is covered by thin **skin** (Sk). The deep surface of the eyelid is lined by a stratified columnar epithelium, the **palpebral conjunctiva** (pC). The substance of the eyelid is formed by the thick connective tissue **tarsal plate** (TP) and **tarsal glands** (TG). Two skeletal muscles are associated with the upper eyelid, the circularly disposed **orbicularis oculi** (OO) and the longitudinally oriented levator palpebrae superioris. Although the latter muscle is not present in this photomicrograph, its connective tissue aponeurosis is evident (*arrow*). Eyelashes and the sebaceous **ciliary glands** (CG) are present at the free end of the lid.

FIGURE 2a ● Lens. Monkey. Paraffin section. ×132.

The lens is a biconvex, flexible, transparent disc covered by a homogenous **capsule** (Ca), deep to which lies the simple cuboidal lens **epithelium** (Ep). The fibers (*arrows*), constituting the bulk of the lens, are composed of closely packed, hexagon-shaped cells whose longitudinal axes are oriented parallel to the surface. The lens is avascular, hence the absence of blood vessels. *Inset.* **Lens. Monkey. Paraffin section.** ×270. Note the presence of the homogeneous **capsule** (Ca) overlying the simple cuboidal lens **epithelium** (Ep).

FIGURE 2b ● Lens. Monkey. Paraffin section. ×132.

The equator of the lens displays the presence of younger cells that still possess their **nuclei** (N) and organelles but lose them as these cells mature. Note the **suspensory ligaments** (SL), **capsule** (Ca), and the lens **epithelium** (Ep).

FIGURE 4 ● Lacrimal gland. Monkey. Paraffin section. ×132.

Lacrimal glands are compound tubuloalveolar glands, separated into lobes and **lobules** (Lo) by **connective tissue** (CT) elements. Since these glands produce a lysozyme-rich, watery secretion, they are composed of numerous **serous acini** (SA), as evidenced by the round, basally located **nuclei** (N) of the secretory cells.

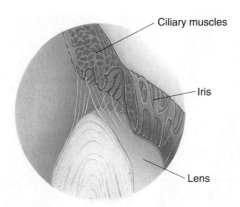

Ciliary muscles

Iris

Lens

Ciliary muscles, iris, and lens

KEY						
1	pigmented epithelium	C	cones	N	nucleus
2	lamina of cones	Ca	capsule	OO	orbicularis oculi
3	external limiting membrane	Ch	choroid	pC	palpebral conjunctiva
		CG	ciliary gland	SA	serous acini
4	outer nuclear layer	CT	connective tissue	Sk	skin
5	outer plexiform layer	Ep	epithelium	SL	suspensory ligaments
8	ganglion cell layer	FC	fovea centralis	TG	tarsal glands
10	inner limiting membrane	Lo	lobule	TP	tarsal plate

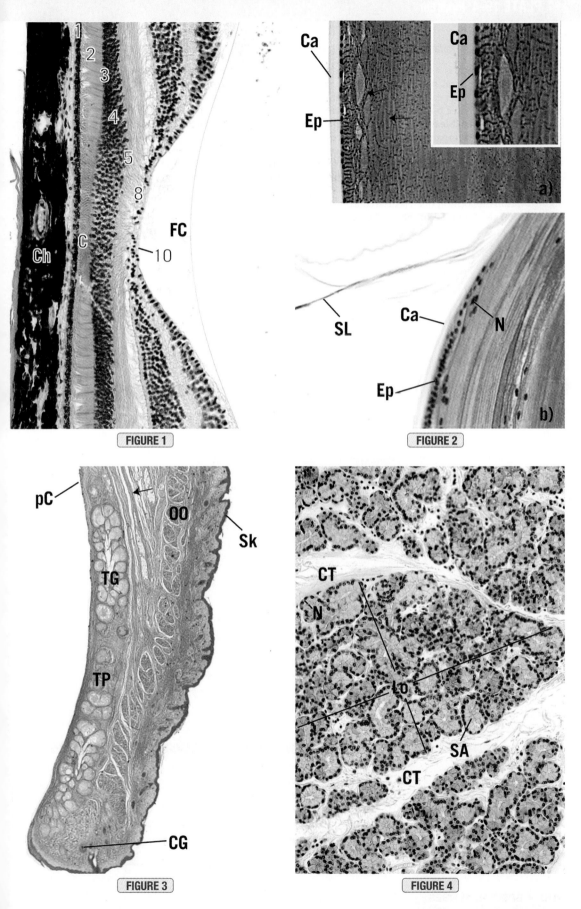

FIGURE 1

a)

FIGURE 2

b)

FIGURE 3

FIGURE 4

FIGURE 1 • Inner ear. Paraffin section. ×21.

This photomicrograph is a survey section of the petrous portion of the temporal bone displaying the various components of the inner ear. At the extreme right, note that the spirally disposed **bony cochlea** (BC) encases the endolymph-filled **cochlear duct** (CD) and the perilymph-filled **scala tympani** (ST) and **scala vestibuli** (SV). The apex of the cochlea displays the **helicotrema** (H), the space through which perilymph may be exchanged between the scala tympani and the scala vestibuli. Innervation to the **spiral organ of Corti** (OC), located within the cochlear duct, is derived from the **spiral ganglion** (SG), housed in the **modiolus** (M). Two cranial nerves, **vestibulocochlear** (VN) and **facial** (FN), are evident in this photomicrograph. The **vestibule** (V), as well as sections of the **ampullae** (A) of the semicircular canals containing the **crista ampullaris** (CA), are clearly recognizable. Finally, note one of the **auditory ossicles** (AO) of the middle ear. *Inset.* **Crista ampullaris. Paraffin section.** ×132. The **crista ampullaris** (CA) is housed within the expanded **ampulla** (A) of each semicircular canal. **Nerve fibers** (NF) enter the connective tissue core of the crista and reach the neuroepithelial **hair cells** (HC) that are supported by **sustentacular cells** (SC). Kinocilia and microvilli of the hair cells extend into the gelatinous **cupula** (Cu) associated with the crista.

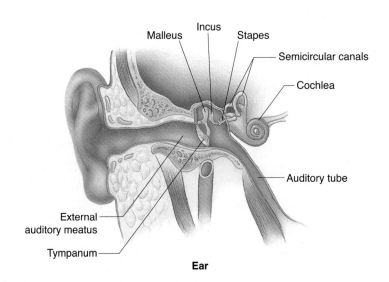

Ear

KEY					
A	ampulla	H	helicotrema	SG	spiral ganglion
AO	auditory ossicle	HC	hair cells	ST	scala tympani
BC	bony cochlea	M	modiolus	SV	scala vestibuli
CA	crista ampullaris	NF	nerve fibers	V	vestibule
CD	cochlear duct	OC	spiral organ of Corti	VN	vestibulocochlear nerve
Cu	cupula	SC	sustentacular cells		
FN	facial nerve				

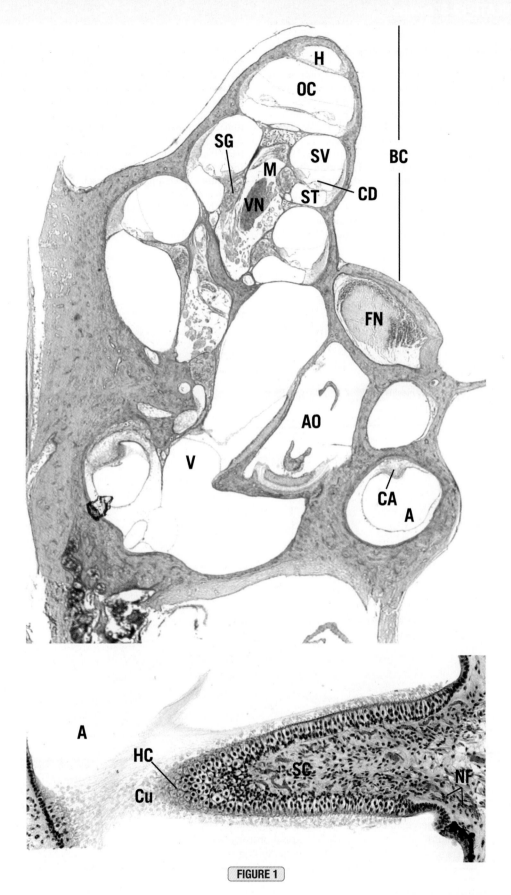

FIGURE 1

This photomicrograph is a higher magnification of one of the turns of the cochlea. Observe that the **scala vestibuli** (SV) and **scala tympani** (ST), enclosed in the **bony cochlea** (BC), are **epithelially** (Ep) lined spaces, filled with perilymph. The **cochlear duct** (CD), filled with endolymph, is separated from the scala vestibuli by the thin **vestibular membrane** (VM) and from the scala tympani by the **basilar membrane** (BM). Within the bony casing lies the **spiral ganglion** (SG), containing the large cell bodies (*arrows*) of primary sensory neurons. **Cochlear nerve fibers** (CNF) from the spiral ganglion traverse bony tunnels of the **osseous spiral lamina** (OL) to reach the hair cells of the **spiral organ of Corti** (OC).

This structure, responsible for the sense of hearing, is an extremely complex entity. It rests on the basilar membrane, a taut, collagenous sheet extending from the **spiral ligament** (SL) to the **limbus spiralis** (LS). Attached to the limbus spiralis is the **tectorial membrane** (TM) (whose elevation in this photomicrograph is an artifact of fixation), which overlies the spiral organ of Corti. Observe the presence of the **stria vascularis** (Sv), which extends from the vestibular membrane to the **spiral prominence** (SP). The stria vascularis possesses a pseudostratified **epithelium** (Ep) composed of basal, dark, and light cells, which are intimately associated with a rich capillary network. It is believed that endolymph is elaborated by some or all of these cells. The morphology of the spiral organ of Corti is presented at a higher magnification in Plate 19-6.

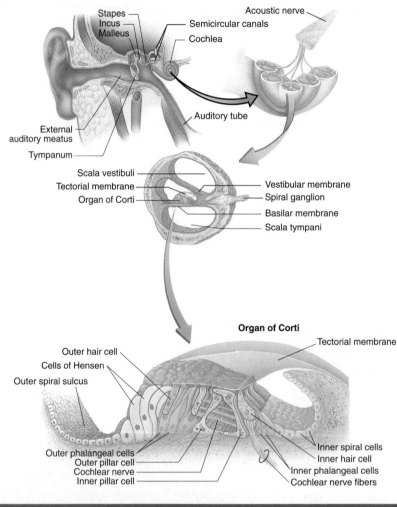

KEY							
BC	bony cochlea	OC	spiral organ of Corti	SV	scala vestibuli		
BM	basilar membrane	OL	osseous spiral lamina	Sv	stria vascularis		
CD	cochlear duct	SG	spiral ganglion	TM	tectorial membrane		
CNF	cochlear nerve fibers	SL	spiral ligament	VM	vestibular membrane		
Ep	epithelium	SP	spiral prominence				
LS	limbus spiralis	ST	scala tympani				

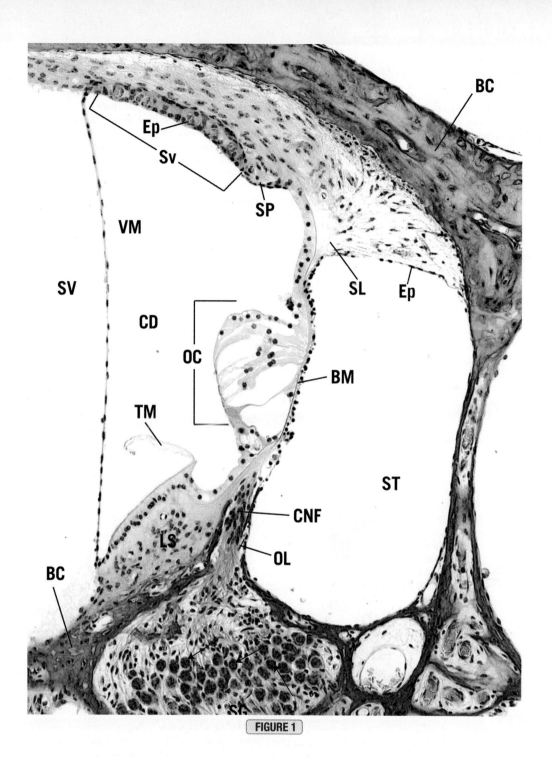

FIGURE 1

FIGURE 1 • Spiral organ of Corti (Montage). Paraffin section. ×540.

The spiral organ of Corti lies on the **basilar membrane** (BM), whose two regions, the **zona pectinata** (ZP) and the **zona arcuata** (ZA), are delineated by the base of the **outer pillar cells** (OPC). The basilar membrane extends from the **spiral ligament** (SL) to the **tympanic lip** (TL) of the limbus spiralis. The **tectorial membrane** (TM) is anchored to the **vestibular lip** (VL) of the limbus spiralis. The tectorial membrane forms a roof over the **internal spiral sulcus** (IS). Observe the **cochlear nerve fibers** (CNF) traversing the tunnels of the **osseous spiral lamina** (OL). The lateral wall of the internal spiral sulcus is formed by the single row of **inner hair cells** (IH), flanked by the **inner phalangeal cells** (IPh) and **border cells** (Bc). The floor of the internal spiral sulcus is formed by **inner**

sulcus cells (IC). Proceeding laterally, the **inner pillar cell** (IPC) and **outer pillar cell** (OPC) form the **inner tunnel of Corti** (ITC). The **spaces of Nuel** (SN) separate the three rows of **outer hair cells** (OH) from each other and from the outer pillar cells. Fine **nerve fibers** (NF) and **phalangeal processes** (PP) traverse these spaces. The outer hair cells are supported by **outer phalangeal cells** (OPh). The space between the **cells of Hensen** (CH) and the outermost row of outer phalangeal cells is the **outer tunnel** (OT). Lateral to the cells of Hensen are the darker staining, deeper positioned **cells of Boettcher** (CB) and the lighter staining, larger **cells of Claudius** (CC), which enclose the **outer spiral sulcus** (OSS). Note that the space above the spiral organ of Corti is the **cochlear duct** (CD), whereas the space below the basilar membrane is the scala tympani.

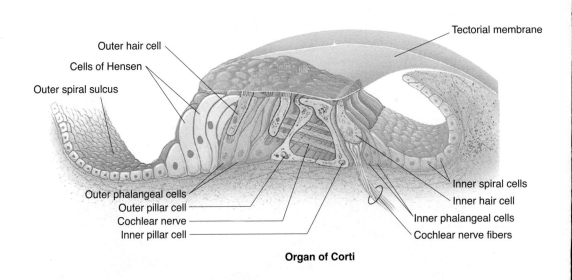

Organ of Corti

KEY					
Bc	border cells	IPh	inner phalangeal cells	OT	outer tunnel
BM	basilar membrane	IS	internal spiral sulcus	PP	phalangeal processes
CB	cells of Boettcher	ITC	inner tunnel of Corti	SL	spiral ligament
CC	cells of Claudius	NF	nerve fibers	SN	spaces of Nuel
CD	cochlear duct	OH	outer hair cells	TL	tympanic lip
CH	cells of Hensen	OL	osseous spiral lamina	TM	tectorial membrane
CNF	cochlear nerve fibers	OPC	outer pillar cells	VL	vestibular lip
IC	inner sulcus cells	OPh	outer phalangeal cells	ZA	zona arcuata
IH	inner hair cells	OSS	outer spiral sulcus	ZP	zona pectinata
IPC	inner pillar cells				

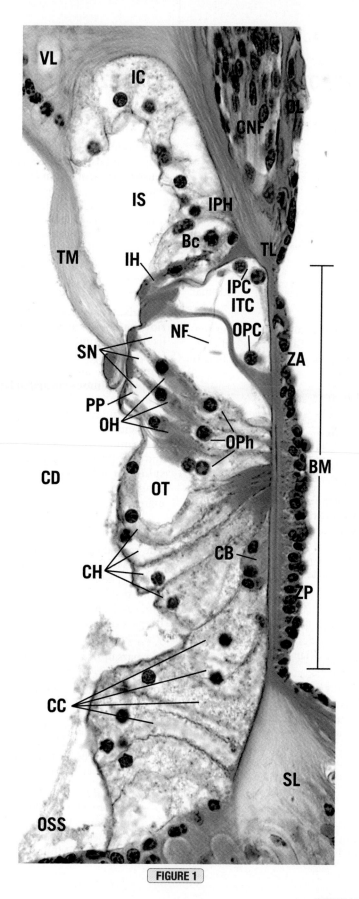

FIGURE 1

Summary of Histological Organization

I. EYE

A. Fibrous Tunic

1. Cornea
The **cornea** is composed of five layers. From superficial to deep, they are

- a. Stratified, Squamous, Nonkeratinized, Epithelium

- b. Bowman's Membrane
  The outer, homogeneous layer of the stroma.

- c. Stroma
  A transparent, dense, regular, collagenous connective tissue housing **fibroblasts** and occasional **lymphoid cells**, comprising the bulk of the cornea.

- d. Descemet's Membrane
  A thick, basal lamina.

- e. Corneal Endothelium
  Not a true endothelium, a simple **squamous-to-cuboidal epithelium**.

2. Sclera
The **sclera**, the white of the eye, is composed of three layers: the outer **episcleral tissue** housing blood vessels; the middle **stroma**, composed of dense, regular, collagenous connective tissue; and the **suprachoroid lamina**, a loose connective tissue housing **fibroblasts** and **melanocytes**.

B. Vascular Tunic

The **vascular tunic** (**uvea**) is a pigmented, vascular layer housing smooth muscles. It is composed of the **choroid membrane**, the **ciliary body**, and the **iris**.

1. Choroid Membrane
The **choroid membrane** is composed of four layers. The **suprachoroid layer** is shared with the sclera and houses **fibroblasts** and **melanocytes**. The **vascular** and **choriocapillary layers** house larger vessels and capillaries, respectively. The **glassy membrane** (of Bruch), interposed between the choroid and the retina, is composed of basal lamina, collagen, and elastic fibers.

2. Ciliary Body
The **ciliary body** is the region of the vascular tunic located between the **ora serrata** and the iris. The ciliary body is composed of the numerous, radially arranged, aqueous humor–forming **ciliary processes** that together compose the **ciliary crown** from which **suspensory ligaments** extend to the lens. Three layers of smooth muscle, oriented more or less meridianally, radially, and circularly, function in visual accommodation. The **vascular layer** and **glassy membrane** of the choroid continue into the ciliary body. The inner aspect of the ciliary body is covered by the inner nonpigmented and outer pigmented layers of the **ciliary epithelium**.

3. Iris
The **iris**, separating the **anterior** from the **posterior chamber**, is attached to the ciliary body along its outer circumference. The free edge of the iris forms the **pupil** of the eye. The iris is composed of three layers: the outer (frequently incomplete) **simple squamous epithelial layer**, a continuation of the corneal epithelium; the intermediate **fibrous layer**, composed of the nonvascular **anterior stromal** and vascular **general stromal layers** that house numerous **melanocytes** and **fibroblasts**; and the posterior **pigmented epithelium**. The **sphincter** and **dilator muscles** of the pupil are composed of myoepithelial cells derived from the pigmented epithelium.

C. Retinal Tunic

The **retinal tunic**, the deepest of the three layers, consists of the **pars iridica**, **pars ciliaris**, and **pars optica**. The last of these is the only region of the retina that is sensitive to light, extending as far anteriorly as the **ora serrata**, where it is continuous with the pars ciliaris.

1. Pars Optica
The **pars optica** is composed of 10 layers.

- a. Pigment Epithelium
  The **pigment epithelium** is attached to the choroid membrane.

- b. Lamina of Rods and Cones
  The **outer** and **inner segments** of the photoreceptor cells form the first layer; the remainder of these cells constitutes the next three layers.

- c. External Limiting Membrane
  The **external limiting membrane** is not a true membrane. It is merely a junctional specialization between the photoreceptor cells and processes of **Müller's** (supportive) **cells**.

d. Outer Nuclear Layer

The **outer nuclear layer** houses the cell bodies (and nuclei) of the photoreceptor cells. At the **fovea centralis**, only cones are present.

e. Outer Plexiform Layer

The **outer plexiform layer** is the region of synapse formation between the **axons** of photoreceptor cells and the processes of **bipolar** and **horizontal cells**.

f. Inner Nuclear Layer

The **inner nuclear layer** houses the **cell bodies of Müller, amacrine** (associative), **bipolar,** and **horizontal cells**.

g. Inner Plexiform Layer

The **inner plexiform layer** is the region of synapses between **dendrites** of **ganglia cells** and **axons** of **bipolar cells**. Moreover, processes of **Müller** and **amacrine cells** are also present in this layer.

h. Ganglion Cell Layer

The **ganglion cell layer** houses the **cell bodies** of **multipolar neurons**, which are the final link in the neuronal chain of the retina, and their **axons** form the optic nerve. Additionally, **neuroglia** are also located in this layer.

i. Optic Nerve Fiber Layer

The **optic nerve fiber layer** is composed of the **unmyelinated axons** of the **ganglion cells**, which are collected as the optic nerve.

j. Inner Limiting Membrane

The **inner limiting membrane** is composed of the expanded terminal processes of **Müller cells.**

2. Pars Ciliaris and Pars Iridica Retinae

At the **pars ciliaris** and **pars iridica retinae**, the retinal layer has been reduced to a thin epithelial layer consisting of a columnar and a pigmented layer lining the ciliary body and iris.

D. Lens

The **lens** is a biconvex, flexible, transparent disc that focuses the incident rays of light on the retina. It is composed of three layers, an elastic **capsule** (basement membrane), an anteriorly placed **simple cuboidal epithelium**, and **lens fibers**, modified epithelial cells derived from the **equator** of the lens.

E. Lacrimal Gland

The **lacrimal gland** is external to the eye, located in the superolateral aspect of the orbit. It is a **compound tubuloalveolar gland**, producing a lysozyme-rich serous fluid with an alkaline pH.

F. Eyelid

The **eyelid** is covered by **thin skin** on its external aspect and by **conjunctiva**, a mucous membrane, on its inner aspect. A thick, dense, fibrous connective tissue **tarsal plate** maintains and reinforces the eyelid. Associated with the tarsal plate are the **tarsal glands,** secreting an oily sebum that is delivered to the margin of the eyelid. Muscles controlling the eyelid are located within its substance. Associated with the eyelashes are **sebaceous glands**. Ciliary glands are located between eyelashes.

II. EAR

A. EXTERNAL EAR

1. Auricle

The **auricle** is covered by thin skin and is supported by highly flexible **elastic cartilage plate**.

2. External Auditory Meatus

The **external auditory meatus** is a **cartilaginous tube** lined by skin, containing **ceruminous glands** and some fine **hair**. The skin of the external meatus is continuous with the external covering of the tympanic membrane. In the medial aspect of the meatus, the cartilage is replaced by **bone**.

3. Tympanic Membrane

The **tympanic membrane** is a thin, taut membrane separating the external from the middle ear. It is lined by **stratified squamous keratinized epithelium** externally and low **cuboidal epithelium** internally and possesses a core of **collagen fibers** disposed in two layers.

B. Middle Ear

The **middle ear** is composed of the **simple cuboidal epithelium**–lined **tympanic cavity** containing the three **ossicles** (**malleus, incus,** and **stapes**). The tympanic cavity communicates with the nasopharynx via the cartilaginous and bony **auditory tube**. The medial wall of the middle ear communicates with the inner ear via the **oval** (**vestibular**) and **round** (**cochlear**) **windows**.

C. Inner Ear

1. Cochlea

The bony **cochlea** houses the endolymph-filled **cochlear duct** that subdivides the perilymph-filled cochlea into the superiorly positioned **scala vestibuli** and the inferiorly located **scala tympani**.

a. Cochlear Duct

The **cochlear duct** houses the **spiral organ of Corti** that lies on the **basilar membrane**. The spiral organ of Corti is composed of **cells of Claudius, cells of Boettcher,** and **cells of**

Hensen, all of which assist in the formation of the **outer tunnel** along with the **outer hair cells** and **outer phalangeal cells**. The **tectorial membrane** lies over the outer hair cells as well as the **inner hair cells**, thus forming the **internal spiral tunnel**. The region between the inner and outer hair cells is occupied by **pillar cells**, which assist in the formation of the **inner tunnel (of Corti)**. The **stria vascularis** constitutes the outer wall of the cochlear duct. Nerve fibers lead to the **spiral ganglion** (housing pseudounipolar cells) in the **modiolus**.

b. *Membranous Labyrinth*

The **membranous labyrinth** is composed of the **utricle**, the **saccule**, and the three **semicircular canals**.

1. Utricle and Saccule

The **utricle** and **saccule** are both filled with **endolymph** and house **maculae**. Each **macula** is composed of simple **columnar epithelium** composed of two cell types, neuroepithelial **hair cells** and **supporting cells**. The free surface of the macula displays the **otolithic membrane**, housing small particles called **otoliths**.

2. Semicircular Canals

The three **semicircular canals** are oriented perpendicular to each other. The **ampulla** of each canal houses a **crista**, a structure similar to a macula, composed of neuroepithelial **hair cells** and **supporting cells**. A gelatinous **cupula** is located at the free surface of the crista, but it contains no otoliths.

Index

In this index, page numbers in *italic* designate figures; page numbers followed by the letter *t* designate tables; (*see also*) cross-references designate related topics or more detailed subtopic lists.

A

A band, 115, *117, 124–125, 126–127,* 137
Aborization, dendritic, 159
ABP. *See* Androgen-binding protein
Absorption, 297
Absorptive cells, *295*
Acceleration
   linear, 402
   rotational, 402
Accessional permanent teeth, 271
Accessory glands, male reproductive system, 381, 395–396
Accessory pancreatic duct, *318*
Accessory structures, of eyes, 402
A cells, 317, *333,* 334
Acetylcholine, 116, 139, 143, 320
Acetylcholine receptors, 143
Acetylcholinesterase, 143
Acetylcholine transferase, 143
Acid(s)
   fatty, 297
   hexuronic, 55
   hyaluronic, 51, 55, 76
   ribonucleic
      messenger, 5, *8*
      ribosomal, 5
      synthesis of, 5
      transfer, 5, *8, 9*
Acidic chyme, 291
Acidophilic cells, 207
Acidophils, 205, *214–215, 216–217,* 226, 358
Acinar glands, 50
Acini, *14–15*
   liver, 334
   mucous, *322–323,* 334
   pancreatic, *318, 324–325,* 334
   of parotid gland, *322–323*
   portal, *319*
   of Rappaport, 334
   serous, *48–49, 322–323*
      of lacrimal gland, *408–409*
      of parotid gland, 334
   of submandibular glands, 334
Acoustic nerve, *399*
Acrosomal granules, 382
ACTH. *See* Adrenocorticotropin
Actin, 115, 119
Actin filaments. *See* Microfilaments
Action potential, 143

Active site, 119
Active transport, 6, 144, *336*
Activin, 357
Activin A, 270
Acute glomerulonephritis, 341
Acute renal failure, 341
ADCC. *See* Antibody-dependent cell-mediated cytotoxicity
Addison's disease, 213
Adenocarcinoma of prostate, 385
Adenohypophysis, 205
Adenomyosis, 359
Adenylate cyclase, 211, 252, 379
ADH. *See* Antidiuretic hormone
Adherens junctions, *132–133*
Adipocytes (fat cells), *46–47, 53,* 54, *60–61, 67,* 68, *256–257, 310–311*
Adipose tissue, 54, 56, *60–61,* 68, *206*
   of breast, 377
   brown, 56
   of hypodermis, *230*
   of lymph node, *183, 192–193,* 202
   multilocular, 56
   of palate, 289
   of suprarenal gland, *220–221*
   of tongue, *280–281*
   unilocular, 56
   white, 56
Adluminal compartment, of Sertoli cells, 382, *386–387,* 395
ADP, 119
Adrenocorticotropin (ACTH), 205, 207
Adventitia
   of alimentary canal, 291
   of anal canal, 317
   of bladder, 352
   of colon, 316
   of ductus deferens, 395
   of esophagus, *300–301,* 314
   of gallbladder, 334
   of small intestine, 315
   of trachea, 265
   of ureter, *350–351,* 352
   uterine, *354,* 377
   of vagina, *372–373,* 377
Adventitial reticular cells, 100, *108–109*
Afferent arterioles, *337*
Afferent glomerular arterioles, 335, *336, 337, 342–343, 344–345,* 352
Afferent lymphatic vessels, *183,* 188, *192–193,* 202

of eye, *408–409,* 417
of ganglia, *152–153*
Glisson's, *326–327,* 334
iris, *404–405*
of kidney, *342–343,* 352
of lingual tonsils, 202
of liver, 334
of lymph node, 181–184, *183, 192–193, 196–197,* 202
major histocompatibility complex, 186
of Meissner's corpuscle, *242–243*
of muscle spindle
  inner, *129*
  outer, *129*
of palatine tonsils, *194–195,* 202
of pancreas, 334
of parathyroid gland, *208, 218–219,* 226
of parotid gland, 334
of pharyngeal tonsils, 202
of pineal body, *208,* 227
of pituitary gland, 226
of prostate gland, 396
renal, 335
of sebaceous gland, *46–47*
of spleen, *200–201,* 203
of submandibular glands, 334
of suprarenal gland, *208*
of suprarenal glands, *220–221,* 226
of testes, 395
of thymus, *183, 198–199,* 203
of thyroid gland, *218–219,* 226
Capsule cells, 140, *152–153,* 160
Carbaminohemoglobin, 252
Carbohydrates, 297
Carbonic anhydrase, 252
Carcinoma
  basal cell, 234
  squamous cell, 234
Cardia, 292
Cardiac glands, 291, 296
Cardiac muscle, 116, *118, 134–135, 136,* 180
  longitudinal section, 137
  transverse section, 137
Cardiac muscle cells, 137, *174–175*
Cardiac muscle fibers, *134–135*
Cardiac skeleton, 180
Cardiac stomach, *300–301,* 314
Caries, 271
Carotid artery, common, 179
Carrier proteins, 143
Cartilage, 71–96, *72t, 76, 96*
  calcified, *90–91,* 97
  degeneration of, 78
  elastic, 71, *72t,* 76, *82–83,* 96
  embryonic, *80–81,* 96
  fibrocartilage, 71, *72t,* 76, *82–83,* 96
  hyaline, 71, *72t,* 76, *80–81, 92,* 96, *242–243,* 247, *260–261,* 265
  of intrapulmonary bronchi, 265
  laryngeal, *254–255*
Cartilage matrix, 71, 76
Cartilage plates, *249*

elastic, 417
  hyaline, 265
Catalase, 4
Cataract, 403
Catecholamines, 211
Catenins, 35
Caveolae, 120, *132–133, 178*
Caveolated cells, 315
Cavernous spaces, 384, *392–393*
Cavernous (spongy) urethra, 396
Cavity(ies), 271
  medullary, *90–91,* 96
  nasal, 248t, *254–255,* 265, 289
  thoracic, 252
  tympanic, 397, 417
Cbfa1/Runx2, 77
CCK. *See* Cholecystokinin
CD4$^+$, 186
CD8$^+$, 186
CD4 molecule, 187
CD molecules. *See* Cluster of differentiation determinants
4CDNA, 382
Cecum, 292, 315
Cell(s), 1–29, *2, 14–15*
  A, 317, *333,* 334
  absorptive, *295*
  acidophilic, 207
  acinar, *318*
  adipose, *46–47, 256–257*
  adventitial reticular, 100, *108–109*
  amacrine, *398,* 401, 417
  androgen-producing endocrine, 379
  antigen-presenting, 184, 186, 187–188, 202
  B, 103, 317, *333,* 334
  band (stab), 100
  basal, *16–17, 38–39, 46–47, 240–241,* 245, 247, *254–255,* 265, 270, *282–283,* 379, *390–391, 392–393,* 395
  basket, *148–149*
  basophil stab, *107*
  bipolar, 139, *398,* 401, 402, 417
  B memory, 103, 187
  of Boettcher, *414–415,* 417
  bone, 76–77
  border, *414–415*
  cancellous bone, 97
  capsule, 140, *152–153,* 160
  cardiac muscle, 137, *174–175*
  caveolated, 315
  centroacinar, *318,* 320, *324–325,* 334
  chief, 207, *208, 218–219,* 226, 292, *293,* 296, *302–303, 304–305,* 314
  chondrogenic, 71, *80–81, 82–83,* 96, 97
  chromaffin, 209, 212, *222–223,* 227
  ciliated, *16–17, 42–43, 366–367, 376, 394*
  ciliated columnar, *258–259*
  of circulating blood, 203
  Clara, 250, *260–261, 262–263,* 265
  of Claudius, *414–415,* 417
  clear, *232, 244*

columnar, *306–307, 312,* 315, *370–371, 390–391, 392–393*

connective tissue, 51–54, *53,* 68–69

continuous endothelial, 266

contractile, 54

cuboidal, 226

cuboidal follicular, *360–361*

cytoplasm, 1–5

D, 317, *333,* 334

dark, *232, 244,* 246, 270, *282–283*

decalcified compact bone, 96

decidual, *372–373,* 377

dendritic, 202

dendritic reticular, 202

DNES, 292, *293, 306–307, 308–309, 310–311,* 314, 315, 316, 317

dust, 250, *251, 262–263,* 266

effector, 186

effector T, 186–187

elastic cartilage, 96

embryonic cartilage, 96

endocrine, 379

endothelial, *42–43, 53,* 68, *152–153,* 162, 165–166, 179, *192–193, 200–201,* 202, 203, *264,* 266, *344–345, 347*

enteroendocrine, *293, 295,* 320

eosinophilic stab, *111*

eosinophil stab, *107*

ependymal, 140, 159

epithelial, *14–15, 32t,* 36, *370–371, 374–375*

epithelial reticular, *184, 185, 198–199, 203*

epithelioid, *154–155*

extraglomerular mesangial, 338

fat, *46–47, 53,* 54, *60–61, 67,* 68, *256–257, 310–311*

fat-accumulating, 334

fat-storing, *319,* 320

fibrocartilage, 96

follicular, 207, *208, 218–219,* 226, 353, *354, 360–361,* 376

follicular (granulosa), 376

folliculostellate, *225*

G, 317, 321, 334

ganglia, 417

ganglion, 401

gastric gland, 314

goblet, *14–15, 16–17, 46–47,* 50, *172–173, 190–191,* 247, *256–257, 258–259,* 265, 292, *293, 295,* 296, *306–307, 308–309, 310–311,* 315, 316, 396

golgi type II, *148–149*

granule, *148–149, 150–151,* 159

granulosa, *354,* 357

granulosa lutein, *362–363, 364–365,* 376

hair, *410–411,* 418

   inner, *399,* 400, 402, *414–415,* 418

   neuroepithelial, 400, 402

   outer, *399,* 400, 402, *414–415,* 418

hematopoietic stem, *53*

of Hensen, *399, 414–415,* 417–418

horizontal, 159, *398,* 417

hyaline cartilage, 96

immature, *304–305*

of immune system, 186–188

inducible T reg, 187

intercalated, 338

intermediate, 270

intraglomerular mesangial, 335, 339

intramembranous ossification, 97

inverted, 159

Ito, *319,* 320

juxtaglomerular, *337,* 338, 340, *344–345,* 352

Kupffer, *62–63,* 317, *319,* 320, *328–329,* 334

Langerhans, *230,* 231, 245

of Leydig, 379, *388–389,* 395

light, 246, 270, *282–283*

lymphoid, *58–59,* 68, *306–307, 310–311,* 314, 315, 358, 416

M, 292, 297, 315

Martinotti, 159

mast, *14–15, 53,* 54, *58–59, 62–63, 65, 66,* 68, *172–173*

memory B, 103, 187

memory T, 186

Merkel, *230,* 231, 245

mesangial, 335, 338, 339, *344–345, 347,* 352

mesenchymal, *53,* 68, 72, 97, *278–279*

mesothelial, *53*

modified ependymal, 160

monkey, *12–13*

mucous, *42–43, 304–305, 330–331*

mucus-secreting, *304–305*

Müller, *398,* 416, 417

multipolar, *142*

multipotent hemopoietic stem, 99, 102

myeloid stem, 102

myoepithelial (basket), *46–47,* 50, 231, *232, 240–241, 244,* 246, *330–331,* 334, 358, 377

myoid, *386–387,* 395

naive T, 186

natural killer, 103, 187

natural T killer, 187

natural T reg, 187

neuroglial, *146–147, 150–151,* 159, *208,* 209, *222–223,* 227

neurovascular, 68

neutrophilic stab, *107, 111,* 113

null, 99, 102, 103, 187

olfactory, 247, *254–255,* 265

oligomucous, 292

osteogenic, *84–85*

osteoprogenitor, 72, 76, 96, 97

oxyntic, *293,* 314

oxyphil, *218–219*

paneth, 292, *293,* 296, *306–307, 308–309,* 315

parafollicular, 207, *208, 218–219,* 226

parenchymal, *48–49,* 226, 227

parietal, 292, *293,* 296, *302–303, 304–305,* 314, 352

peg, *16–17, 366–367,* 376

phalangeal

   inner, *399, 414–415*

   outer, *399, 414–415,* 418

pigment, *404–405*

Cholangioles, 334
Cholecystokinin (CCK), 292, 294t, 317, 320
Cholera, 37
Cholesterol, 1, 4, 321
Choline, 143
Chondroblasts, 53, 71, 80–81, 96
Chondrocytes, 53, 71, 74, 76, 80–81, 82–83, 96
Chondrocytic death, 97
Chondrogenic cells, 71, 80–81, 82–83, 96, 97
Chondrogenic layer, 71, 80–81, 96
Chondroitin-4-sulfate, 51, 76
Chondroitin-6-sulfate, 51, 76
Chordae tendineae, 180
Choriocapillary layer, 416
Chorionic plate, 356, 377
Chorionic sac, 377
Chorionic villi, 356, 372–373, 377
Choroid, 397, 398, 406–407, 408–409
Choroid membrane, 416
Choroid plexus, 160
Choroid plexus epithelium, 154–155
Chromaffin cells, 209, 212, 222–223, 227
Chromatin, 24–25
Chromophils, 205, 214–215
Chromophobes, 207, 214–215, 216–217, 224, 226
Chromosomes, 5, 18–19
Chronic inflammation, 54
Chyle, 297
Chylomicrons, 292, 297
Chyme, 291, 296
Cigarette smoke, 253
Cilia, 16–17, 31, 35, 38–39, 42–43, 50, 252, 254–255, 258–259, 284–285
Ciliary body, 397, 404–405, 416
Ciliary crown, 416
Ciliary epithelium, 416
Ciliary glands, 408–409
Ciliary muscles, 398
Ciliary processes, 404–405, 416
Ciliary smooth muscles, 401
Ciliated cells, 16–17, 42–43, 366–367, 376, 394
Ciliated columnar cells, 258–259
Ciliated simple columnar epithelium, 265
Cilium, 382
Circuit, pulmonary, 161, 165
Circular deoxyribonucleic acid, 1
Circulating blood, 105–106, 108–109, 112
Circulation
    closed, 188
    open, 188
Circulatory system, 161–180
Circumanal glands, 317
Circumvallate papilla, 269, 280–281, 282–283, 289
cis-Golgi network, 4
Cisternae, 26–27, 148–149
Clara cells, 250, 260–261, 262–263, 265
Classic lobule, 319, 334
Clathrin-coated endocytic vesicles, 6, 7, 8
Claudius, cells of, 414–415, 417
Clear cells, 232, 244. See also Parafollicular cells
Clear zone, 77, 94–95

Cleavage furrow, 18–19
Cleft
    intraglandular, 214–215
    synaptic, 116
Clinical considerations
    blood and hemopoiesis, 104
    cartilage and bone, 78
    circulatory system, 167
    connective tissue, 57
    digestive system, 271, 298, 321
    endocrine system, 213
    epithelium, 37
    female reproductive system, 359
    integument, 234
    lymphoid tissue, 189
    lysosomal storage diseases, 10
    male reproductive system, 385
    muscles, 120
    nervous tissue, 145
    respiratory system, 253
    special senses, 403
    urinary system, 340–341
Clitoris, 355
Clone, 186
Closed circulation, 188
Cluster of differentiation determinants (CD molecules), 103
Cluster of differentiation markers, 186, 188
CNS. See Central nervous system
Coagulation, 102, 166
Cochlea, 397, 399, 402, 412–413, 417–418
Cochlear duct, 400, 402, 410–411, 412–413, 414–415, 417–418
Cochlear nerve, 399, 400
Cochlear nerve fibers, 399, 412–413, 414–415
Codon
    signal, 6
    start, 6–9, 8
Coiled arteries, 377
Colitis, antibiotic-associated, 298
Collagen, 52, 64, 72
    dark, 52
    light, 52
    synthesis of, 54
    type I, 76
    type II, 76
    type III, 36
    type IV, 36
    type VII, 36
    type XV, 36
    type XVIII, 36
Collagen fiber bundles, 60–61, 68, 282–283, 284–285
Collagen fibers, 51, 55–56, 58–59, 60–61, 62–63, 68, 69, 82–83, 93, 96, 168–169, 170–171, 180, 220–221, 238–239, 245, 276–277, 404–405, 417
Collagen fibrils, 60–61, 64, 96
Collagenous connective tissue, 172–173, 179, 202, 226
Collagenous fiber bundles, 168–169
Collagenous fibers, 179
Collagen synthesis, 55
Collecting ducts, 336, 338, 340

Dynein, 5, 35
Dystroglycans, 36

E

Ear(s), 397–400, *399*, 402, 417–418
  external, 397, 402, 417
  inner, 397–400, 402, *410–411*, 417–418
  middle, 397, 402, 417
Ear drum. *See* Tympanic membrane
Early growth response-1, 270
Early luteal phase, *368–369*
E-cadherins, *33*, 35
Eccrine sweat glands, *46–47*, 230, 232
Edema, 57
Effector cells, 186
Effector T cells, 186–187
Efferent glomerular arterioles, 335, *336*, *337*, *342–343*, *344–345*, 352
Efferent lymphatic vessels, 188, 202
Ejaculation, 384, 385
Ejaculatory ducts, 379, *380*, 395
Elastic arteries, 162, 165, *168–169*, 179
Elastic cartilage, 71, 72*t*, 76, *82–83*, 96
Elastic cartilage plate, 417
Elastic connective tissue, *62–63*
Elastic fibers, 51, *56*, *58–59*, *62–63*, 68, 69, 76, *82–83*, 96, *168–169*, *170–171*, 179, 180, 202, 203, 252, 266, 396
Elastic lamina, *62–63*, 265
Elastic membranes, *62–63*
Elastin, 51
Elastin network, alveolar, *249*
Electrochemical domains, 55
Electron transport chain, 1
Eleidin, 233, 245
Elementary particles, 1, *3*
Embryonic cartilage, *80–81*, 96
Embryonic connective tissue, *58–59*, 68, *80–81*, *86–87*
Emphysema, 253
Enamel, of tooth, *268*, *274–275*, *278–279*, *286*, 288
Enamel knot, 270
Enamel space, *276–277*
Enamel tufts, *274–275*
Encapsulated lymphoid tissue, 184
Encapsulated organs, *182*
End foot, *126–127*
Endocardium, 161, *174–175*, 180
Endochondral ossification, 72, 74, *75*, *88–89*, *90–91*, 97
Endocrine cells, androgen-producing, 379
Endocrine glands, 32, 50, 205, *208*
Endocrine pancreas, 317, *318*, 334
Endocrine system, 205–227
Endocytic vesicles, clathrin-coated, 6, *7*, *8*
Endocytosis, 6, 233
  receptor-mediated, 1, 6, *7*
Endolymph, 402, 418
Endolymphatic duct, 402
Endolymphatic sac, 402
Endolymph-filled cochlear duct, 400

Endolysosomes, 4, 6
Endometrial cancer, 359
Endometrial changes, *356*
Endometrial glands, *370–371*
Endometrial layer, 377
Endometriosis, 359
Endometrium, *354*, 355, *356*, 357, *368–369*, 376–377
Endomysium, 115, *118*, 137
Endoneural connective tissue, *156–157*
Endoneurium, 140, *141*, *154–155*, 160
Endoplasmic reticulum, 1–4
  rough, 1, *2*, *3*, 4, *7*, *8*, *20–21*, *22–23*, *24–25*, *42–43*, 64, 67, 92, *93*, *156–157*, *258–259*, *318*, *332*
  smooth, *2*, *3*, 4, *24–25*, 297, 320
  transitional, *7*
Endosomes, 4
  early, 4, 6, *7*
  late, 4, 6, *7*
  recycling, 4, *7*
Endosteum, 72, 96, *108–109*
Endothelial cell nucleus, 179
Endothelial cells, *42–43*, 53, 68
  of arterioles, 165–166
  of blood-air barrier, *264*, 266
  of capillaries, 162, 179
  of glomerulus, *344–345*, *347*
  of lymph nodes, *192–193*
  of spleen, *200–201*, 202, 203
  of sympathetic ganglia, *152–153*
Endothelial lining, *347*
Endothelial nuclei, *134–135*
Endothelial vessels, high, 188
Endothelin, 102
Endothelin 1, 166
Endothelium
  corneal, 416
  cuboidal, 202
  penile, 396
  sinusoidal, *194–195*
  vascular, *170–171*, *172–173*, *174–175*, 179, 180
End plates, motor, *126–127*, *142*
Entactin, 36
Enteric nervous system, 139
Enteroendocrine cells. *See* Diffuse neuroendocrine system (DNES) cells
Enzyme(s), 211
  converting, 340
  hydrolytic, 4
  lysosomal, 9
  oxidative, 4
Eosinophil(s), *53*, 68, 99, 101*t*, *105–106*, *107*, 112
Eosinophilic chemotactic agent, 54
Eosinophilic metamyelocyte, *107*, *111*
Eosinophilic myelocyte, *107*, *111*
Eosinophilic stab cell, *107*, *111*
Ependymal cells, 140, 159
  modified, 160
Epicardium, 161, 180
Epidermal ridges, 229, *236–237*, 245. *See also* Dermal ridges

Genital ducts
  female, 353–355
  male, 376–377, 379, 395
Germinal centers, 181, *183, 190–191, 192–193, 194–195, 200–201,* 202
Germinal epithelium, 353, *360–361,* 376
Gingiva, *268, 276–277,* 288
  attached, *276–277*
  free, *276–277*
Gingival margin, *276–277*
Gingival sulcus, *268, 276–277*
Gingivitis, necrotizing ulcerative, 271
Gland(s), 31–36, *46–47, 48–49,* 50
  accessory, 381, 395–396
  acinar, 50
  alveolar, 50
  apocrine, 50, *230,* 377
  Bowman's, *254–255,* 265
  branched alveolar holocrine, 245
  bronchial, 265
  Brunner's, 294*t*, 296–297, *306–307,* 315
  bulbourethral, 381, 384, 396
  cardiac, 291, 296
  ceruminous, 417
  ciliary, *408–409*
  circumanal, 317
  compound, 50
  compound tubuloacinar (alveolar)
    mixed, *48–49*
    mucous, *48–49*
    serous, *48–49*
  compound tubuloalveolar, 334, 417
  Cowper's, 396
  of digestive system, 317
  eccrine, *46–47, 230,* 232
  endocrine, 32, 50, 205, *208*
  endometrial, *370–371,* 377
  esophageal cardiac, 314
  esophageal glands proper, 292, *300–301*
  exocrine, 32, 50
    multicellular, 50
    unicellular, 50
  fundic, 292, 296, *302–303, 304–305*
  gastric, 292, *293,* 296, *302–303,* 314
  of hard palate, *284–285*
  holocrine, 50
    branched alveolar, 245
  inactive, 377
  intraepithelial, *254–255, 284–285,* 338, 396
  lacrimal, 397, 402, *406–407, 408–409,* 417
  lactating, 377
  of lingual tonsils, 202
  of Littré, 338, *392–393,* 396
  mammary, *206,* 355, 358, *374–375,* 377
  meibomian, 402
  merocrine, 50
  mixed, 50
  mucosal, 381
  mucous, 50, *254–255, 256–257,* 265, *282–283,* 289, 352
  multicellular, 50
  parathyroid, 207, *208,* 213, *218–219,* 226

parotid, 317, 320, *322–323,* 334
of pharyngeal tonsils, 202
pineal, 212
pituitary, *20–21,* 205–207, *206,* 213, *214–215, 216–217, 224, 225,* 226
prostate, 379, 381, *392–393,* 396
pyloric, 296, *304–305*
salivary, *34,* 267, *269,* 288, 317, 320, *322–323, 330–331,* 334
sebaceous, *46–47, 230,* 231, *232, 238–239, 240–241,* 245, 246, *272–273,* 288, 317, *374–375,* 377, 417
seromucous, 202, 247, *254–255, 256–257,* 265
serous, 50
sublingual, 317, 320, *322–323, 330–331,* 334
submandibular, 317, 320, *322–323,* 334
submucosal, 381
suprarenal, *208,* 209, *210,* 212, 213, *220–221, 222–223,* 226–227
sweat, *40–41, 46–47, 60–61, 230,* 231, *232, 238–239, 240–241, 242–243, 244,* 245, 246, 288, 355, 377
tarsal, *408–409,* 417
thyroid, *206,* 207, *208,* 213, *218–219,* 226
tubular, 50
tubuloacinar, 50
unicellular, 50
uterine, 357, *368–369*
vestibular, 355
of von Ebner, *280–281, 282–283,* 289
Glandular portion, of smooth muscle, *130–131*
Glans penis, *380*
Glassy membrane, *232,* 245, 416
Glaucoma, 403
Glioblastoma, 145
Glisson's capsule, *326–327,* 334
Globe, of eyes, 401–402
Globular protein, *8*
Globulins, 99
Glomerular arterioles
  afferent, 335, *336, 337, 342–343, 344–345,* 352
  efferent, 335, *336, 337, 342–343, 344–345,* 352
Glomeruli, 159, 335, *342–343, 344–345, 346, 347,* 352
Glomerulonephritis, acute, 341
Glucagon, 294*t*, 317, 320
Glucocorticoids, 209
Gluconeogenesis, 320
Glycentin, 294*t*
Glycerol, 297
Glycine, 55
Glycocalyx, 296
Glycogen, 5, *136, 332, 366–367*
Glycoproteins, 51, 55, 76
Glycosaminoglycans, 55, 71
  protein-associated, 72
Glycosylation, *8,* 55
Goblet cells, *14–15, 16–17*
  of appendix, *310–311*
  of colon, *310–311,* 316
  duodenal, *172–173, 306–307*
  ileal, *46–47, 308–309*
  jejunal, *308–309*
  of large intestine, *295*
  respiratory, 247, *258–259,* 265

Herring bodies, 207, *216–217,* 226
Hexosamine, 55
Hexuronic acid, 55
Hiatal hernia, 298
High endothelial vessels, 188
Hilum, 202, 203, 335, *336*
Histamine, 162, 166
Histiocytes. *See* Macrophage
Histological organization, 50
Histophysiology, 6–10
    blood and hemopoiesis, 102–103
    cartilage and bone, 76–77
    circulatory system, 165–167
    connective tissue, 55–56
    digestive system, 270, 296–297, 320
    endocrine system, 211–212
    epithelium, 35–36
    female reproductive system, 357–358
    integument, 233
    lymphoid tissue, 186–188
    male reproductive system, 382–384
    nervous tissue, 143–144
    respiratory system, 252
    special senses, 401–402
    urinary system, 339–340
HLA. *See* Human leukocyte antigen
Hodgkin's disease, 189
Holocrine glands, 50
Hopewell-Smith, hyaline layer of, *284–285*
Horizontal cells, 159, *398,* 417
Hormonal cycle, of female reproductive system, *356*
Hormone(s), 205
    of alimentary canal, 294*t*
    anterior pituitary, 207
    antidiuretic, 207, 340
    anti-Müllerian, 382
    follicle-stimulating, 205, 353, 357, 379, 382
    gonadotropin-releasing, 357
    lactogenic, 358
    luteinizing, 205, 353, 357, 379, 382
    mechanism of action, 211
    melanocyte-stimulating, 205, 207
    nonsteroid-based, 211
    parathyroid, 207, 212
    pituitary, *206*
    steroid-based, 211
    thyroid, 211
    thyroid-stimulating, 211
    uterine response to, 357–358
Hormone-sensitive lipase, 56
Horn
    dorsal, *146–147,* 159
    ventral, *146–147,* 159
Howship's lacunae, 72, 77, *94–95,* 96, 97
Human chorionic gonadotropin (hCG), 357, 385
Human chorionic mammotropin, 357, 358
Human leukocyte antigen (HLA), 103
Humoral immune response, 187
Humorally mediated immune response, 103, 186
Huntington's chorea, 145
Huxley's layer, *232,* 245

Hyaline cartilage, 71, 72*t,* 76, *80–81, 92,* 96, *242–243, 247, 260–261,* 265
Hyaline cartilage plates, 265
Hyaline layer of Hopewell-Smith, *284–285*
Hyaline membrane disease, 253
Hyalomere, 112
Hyaluronic acid, 51, 55, 76
Hydatidiform mole, 359
Hydrolytic enzymes, 4
Hydroxyindole, 233
Hydroxylation, 55
Hydroxylysine, 55
Hydroxyproline, 55
Hyperopia, 403
Hyperparathyroidism, 213, 341
Hyperplasia, 357
Hyperthyroidism, 213
Hypertonic ultrafiltrate, 340
Hypertrophied chondrocytes, 74
Hypertrophy, 97, 357
Hypodermis, *230,* 231, *238–239,* 245
Hyponychium, 231, *242–243,* 246
Hypoosmotic, 339
Hypoosmotic ultrafiltrate, 340
Hypophyseal arteries, superior, 205
Hypophyseal portal system, 205
Hypophyseal portal veins, 205
Hypophysis. *See* Pituitary gland
Hypothalamo-hypophyseal tract, 207
Hypothalamus, *206,* 207, *214–215*
Hypotonic saliva, 320
Hypotonic ultrafiltrate, 340
H zone, 115, *122–123, 124–125,* 137

I

I bands, 115, *117, 124–125, 126–127,* 137
Icterus, 321
Igα, 187
Igβ, 187
Ileum, 292, *308–309,* 315
Iliac nodes, *182*
Immature cells, *304–305*
Immune response, 186
    cell-mediated, 103, 186
    humoral, 103, 186, 187
Immune system, cells of, 186–188
Immunoglobulin(s)
    A (IgA), 296, 320, 358
    surface, 103
Impulse
    conduction of, 165
    generation of, 165
Inactive gland, 377
Incisure, Schmidt-Lanterman, *154–155*
Inclusions, 5, *14–15*
Incus, 397, *399,* 402, 417
Inducible T reg cells, 187
Infection, lymph nodes during, 189
Infectious mononucleosis, 104
Inferior hypophyseal arteries, 205

Melatonin, 209, 212
Membrana granulosa, 353, *354, 362–363,* 376
Membrane(s), 6, *7*
   basilar, *412–413*
   Bowman's, *404–405,* 416
   choroid, 416
   Descemet's, 416
   elastic, *62–63*
   epithelial, 31
   fenestrated, *168–169,* 179
   glassy, *232,* 245, 416
   inner glassy, *240–241*
   inner nuclear, 5
   limiting
      external, *406–407, 408–409,* 416
      inner, *406–407, 408–409,* 417
   mucous, 288, *390–391,* 395
   nuclear, 5
   otolithic, 400, 402, 418
   outer nuclear, 5
   postsynaptic, 143
   presynaptic, 143
   tectorial, *399,* 400, 402, *412–413, 414–415,* 418
   tympanic, 397, 402, 417
   vestibular, *399,* 402, *412–413*
Membrane-coating granules, 229
Membrane proteins, 8, *9*
Membrane resting potential, 143
Membrane trafficking, 6, *7*
Membrane transport proteins, 6
Membranous labyrinth, 402, 418
Membranous urethra, 396
Memory cells
   B, 103, 187
   T, 186
Ménière's disease, 403
Meninges, 139, 159
Menstrual phase, 355, 357, *370–371,* 377
Menstruation, 357
Merkel cells, *230, 231,* 245
Merocrine glands, 50
Meromyosin
   heavy, 119
   light, 119
Mesangial cells, *344–345,* 347, 352
   extraglomerular, 338
   intraglomerular, 335, 339
Mesaxon
   external, *156–157*
   internal, *156–157*
Mesenchymal cells, *53,* 68, 72, 97, *278–279*
Mesenchymal connective tissue, 54, *58–59,* 68, 97
Mesoderm, *372–373*
Mesodermal epithelium, 209
Mesodermally derived muscles, 115
Mesothelia, 31
Mesothelial cells, *53*
Mesothelium
   of alimentary canal, 291
   of ovary, 353
   of spleen, 203
Mesovarium, *360–361*

Messenger, second, 211
Messenger ribonucleic acid (mRNA), 5, *8*
Messenger systems
   intracellular, 6
   second, 205
Metamyelocytes, 100
   basophilic, *107*
   eosinophilic, *107, 111*
   neutrophilic, *107, 111,* 113
Metaphase, *18–19, 354*
Metaplasia, 37
Metarterioles, 162, *164,* 165
MHC capsules. *See* Major histocompatibility complex capsules
Micelles, 297
Microfibrillar, 51
Microfibrils, 36
Microfilaments, 5
   intermediate, *132–133*
Microfold cells. *See* M cells
Microglia, 140, *150–151*
Microsomal mixed-function oxidase, 320
Microtubule(s), 5, *22–23*
   A, 35
   B, 35
Microtubule-associated proteins (MAPs), 5
Microtubule-organizing center (MTOC), 5
Microvilli, *16,* 31, 35, *42–43,* 50, 292, 296, *332,* 400
Midcortical nephrons, *342–343*
Middle circular layer
   of bladder, *350–351,* 352
   of ductus deferens, *390–391,* 395
   of myometrium, 377
   of stomach, *302–303,* 315
   of uterus, *368–369*
Middle ear, 397, 402, 417
Middle muscular layer, of vaginal wall, 355
Midluteal phase, *370–371*
Milk, 355, 358
Milk ejection reflex, 358
Mineralocorticoids, 209
Minor calyx, 338, 352
Minor mixed salivary glands, 288
Minor salivary glands, 267
Mitochondria, 1, *2, 3, 20–21, 22–23, 24–25, 28–29*
   of cardiac muscle, *136*
   of epididymis, *394*
   of epithelium, 42–43
   of fibroblasts, *64*
   of hyaline cartilage, *92*
   of liver, *332*
   of mast cells, *65*
   of myoneural junction, *126–127, 142*
   of neuron, *158*
   of primary afferent terminal, *148–149*
   of Schwann cell, *156–157*
   of skeletal muscle, *124–125*
   of smooth muscle, *132–133*
Mitosis, 5, *18–19,* 380
Mixed glands, 50
Mixed secretions, 317
Modified ependymal cells, 160

of mast cells, *65*
of Meissner's corpuscle, *242–243*
of mesenchymal cells, *58–59*
of mucus-secreting cells, *304–305*
of neuroglia, 159
of neurons, *142, 146–147, 150–151, 152–153, 158*
of oocytes, *354, 360–361*
of osteoclasts, *94–95*
of pancreas, *324–325*
paraventricular, 207
of peg cell, *366–367*
of perikaryon, 159
of pituicytes, *216–217*
of podocyte, *347*
of Purkinje cell, *148–149, 174–175*
round, *46–47*
of secretory cells, *408–409*
of sinusoidal lining cells, *200–201*
of skeletal muscle cell, *118*
of skeletal muscle cells, *122–123, 126–127,* 137
of smooth muscle cells, *130–131, 132–133,* 137, *168–169*
supraoptic, 207
of tubuloacinar glands, *48–49*
Nuel, spaces of, *414–415*
Null cells, 99, 102, 103, 187

O

Obesity, 57
Obstructive jaundice, 321
Occluding junctions, *332*
Occludins, 35
Odland bodies, 229
Odontoblast(s), *268,* 270, *278–279,* 288
Odontoblastic layer, *274–275*
Odontogenesis, *268,* 270, *278–279,* 289
Odorant, 252
Odorant-binding proteins, 252
Olfaction, mechanism of, 252
Olfactory cells, 247, *254–255,* 265
Olfactory epithelium, *254–255*
Olfactory mucosa, 247, *254–255*
Olfactory region, of nasal cavity, 265
Oligodendroglia, 140, 159
Oligodendroglioma, 145
Oligomucous cells, 292
Oligosaccharidases, 297
Oocytes, 353, *354*
primary, 353, *354, 360–361, 362–363,* 376
secondary, *354,* 376
Oogonia, 353
Oophorus, cumulus, 353, *354, 362–363,* 376
Open circulation, 188
Operators, 211
Opsin, 401
Optic disc, 401–402
Optic nerve, 397, *398,* 401
Optic nerve fiber layer, *406–407,* 417
Oral aspect, of palate, 289
Oral cavity, 267, 288, 289

Oral cavity proper, 267
Oral epithelium, *278–279*
Oral mucosa, 267
Oral region
of digestive system, 267
of tongue, 288
Ora serrata, 416
Orbicularis oculi, *408–409*
Organ(s), encapsulated, *182*
Organelles, 1, *3, 14–15*
Organization, histological, 50
Organ of Corti, *399,* 400, 402, *410–411, 412–413, 414–415,* 417
Orthochromatophilic erythroblasts, 100, *107, 110,* 113
Orthodromic spread, 143
Osmolarity, 339
Osmotic concentration gradient, 340
Osmotic pressure, colloid, 339
Osseous spiral lamina, *412–413, 414–415*
Ossicles, auditory, 397, *410–411,* 417
Ossification
endochondral, 72, 74, *75,* 88–89, *90–91,* 97
intramembranous, 72, 86–87, 97
Ossification centers, 97
epiphyseal, *88–89,* 97
primary, 97
secondary, 74, *75,* 88–89, 97
Osteoblasts, 53, 72, 76, *84–85,* 86–87, *90–91,* 93, 96, 97
Osteoclasts, 53, 72, 77, 86–87, *94–95,* 96, 97
Osteoclast-stimulating factor, 76
Osteocytes, 72, 77, *84–85,* 86–87, 96, 97, *108–109*
Osteogenesis, 72–74
Osteogenic cells, *84–85*
Osteogenic layer, of periosteum, *90–91,* 96
Osteogenic periosteum, *84–85*
Osteoid, 86–87, *90–91,* 96, 97
Osteons, 72, *73, 84–85,* 86–87, 96, 97, *284–285*
Osteopetrosis, 78
Osteopontin, 77
Osteoporosis, 78
Osteoprogenitor cells, 72, 76, 96, 97
Osterix, 77
Otoconia, 402
Otolithic membrane, 400, 402, 418
Otoliths, 402, 418
Outer capsule, *129*
Outer circular layer, 338, 352
Outer circumferential lamellae, *73,* 96
Outer enamel epithelium, *278–279*
Outer fibrous layer, of vaginal wall, 355
Outer hair cells, *399,* 400, 402, *414–415,* 418
Outer longitudinal layer
of alimentary canal, 291
of colon, *310–311,* 316
of ductus deferens, *390–391,* 395
of duodenum, *306–307*
of esophagus, 292, *300–301,* 314
of extrarenal excretory passages, 338
of ileum, *308–309*
of myometrium, 377
of oviduct, *364–365,* 376

Vestibular lip, *414–415*
Vestibular membrane, *399*, 402, *412–413*
Vestibule, *410–411*
   of ear, 402
   laryngeal, 247, *254–255*, 265
   of oral cavity, 267
Vestibulocochlear nerve, *410–411*
Villi
   anchoring, *356*
   branch, *356*
   chorionic, *356*, *372–373*, 377
   of choroid plexus, *154–155*
   duodenal, *306–307*
   of ileum, *308–309*
   primary, *356*
   secondary, *356*
   of small intestine, 292, *293*, 296, 315
   terminal, *372–373*
   tertiary, *356*
Villin, 35
Vimentin, 116, 120
Vinculin, 35
Viscera, of suprarenal gland, *210*
Visceral capillaries, *164*
Visceral layers
   of Bowman's capsule, 352
   of kidneys, 335
Visceral pleura, *249*, 252
Vision
   hyperopic, 403
   myopic, 403
Visual acuity, 401
Vitamin A, 320, 401
Vitamin deficiency, 78
Vitiligo, 234
Vitreous body, 397, *398*
Vocal folds, *254–255*, 265
Vocalis muscle, *254–255*
Volkmann's canal, 72, *73*, *84–85*, 97, *108–109*
Voltage-gated calcium channels, 143
Voltage-sensitive proteins, 119
Von Ebner's glands, *280–281*, *282–283*, 289
Von Willebrand's disease, 167
Von Willebrand's factor, 102, 166
VTC. *See* Vesicular-tubular cluster
Vulva, 355

W

Wall(s)
   nail, *242–243*, 246
   uterus, *354*
   vagina, 355
Warts (verrucae), 234
Water, absorption of, 297

White adipose tissue, 56
White blood cells (WBC). *See* Leukocytes
White bone marrow, 96
White matter
   cerebellar, *148–149*, 159
   cerebral, *150–151*, 159
   spinal cord, *146–147*, 159
   subcortical, 159
White pulp, *183*, 184, 188, *200–201*, 203
Window(s)
   oval, 397, 400, 402, 417
   round, 400, 417
Wiskott-Aldrich syndrome, 189
Woven (primary) bone, 74, 97

Y

Yellow bone marrow, 96

Z

Z band, 137
Z discs, 115, 116, *117*, *122–123*, *124–125*, *136*
Zellweger's disease, 10
Zollinger-Ellison syndrome, 298
Zona arcuata, *414–415*
Zona fasciculata, *208*, 209, 212, *220–221*, *222–223*, 227
Zona glomerulosa, *208*, 209, 212, *220–221*, 227
Zona pectinata, *414–415*
Zona pellucida, 353, *354*, *360–361*, *362–363*, 376
Zona reticularis, *208*, 209, 212, *220–221*, *222–223*, 227
Zone(s)
   basal, 77
   of calcifying cartilage, *88–89*, 97
   cell-free, *274–275*
   of cell maturation and hypertrophy, *88–89*, 97
   of cell proliferation, *88–89*, 97
   cell-rich, *274–275*
   clear, 77, *94–95*
   Golgi, *46–47*
   H, 115, *122–123*, *124–125*, 137
   marginal, 184, 188, *200–201*, 203
   of provisional ossification, 97
   of reserve cartilage, 97
   specialized, of connective tissue, 99
   transitional, 288
   vermillion, *272–273*, 288
   vesicular, 77
Zonulae adherentes, 31, *33*, 35, 50
Zonulae occludentes, 31, *33*, 35, *44–45*, 50, 382
ZO-1 proteins, 35
ZO-2 proteins, 35
ZO-3 proteins, 35
Zymogen granules, *14–15*, *48–49*, 318, *324–325*
Zymogenic cells. *See* Chief cells